Solutions Manual

to accompany Petrucci's
General Chemistry,

THIRD EDITION

Ralph H. Petrucci
California State College,
San Bernardino

Macmillan Publishing Co., Inc
New York
Collier Macmillan Publishers
London

Printed in the United States of America

Macmillan Publishing Co., Inc.
866 Third Avenue, New York, New York 10022

Collier Macmillan Canada, Inc.

ISBN: 0-02-395020-X

Printing: 2 3 4 5 6 7 8 Year: 2 3 4 5 6 7 8 9 0

TO THE STUDENT

The basic principles of chemistry are few in number yet powerful and wide ranging in their application. However, these principles are not usually mastered simply by reading about chemistry. They must be reinforced, through laboratory practice and through problem solving.

This supplement is designed to assist you in developing insight into chemical principles by offering brief solutions to the Exercises and Self-test Questions in the companion textbook: Petrucci, R. H., *General Chemistry: Principles and Modern Applications*, 3rd ed., Macmillan, New York, 1982. I offer just a few suggestions for its most effective use.

The exercises should be approached only after the text of the chapters has been studied carefully. They should be approached with pencil and paper in hand (an electronic calculator will also prove helpful); and a serious individual effort should be made to complete all the exercises (or at least a selective sampling of them). You may find it tempting to turn directly from the exercises in the textbook to the solutions offered here, but if you succumb to this temptation you will lose out on at least two counts. You will have reduced the problem solving aspect of chemistry to just some additional reading about chemistry, and you will have missed opportunities to discover by yourself alternative, and perhaps more original, solutions.

For the most part the methods used in this supplement are the same as in the textbook, although in some instances an alternative approach is suggested. Remember, any logical method based on chemical principles that produces a correct answer (and sometimes even an incorrect answer) is an acceptable solution to a problem.

Problem solving means more than just a successful manipulation of mathematical and chemical symbols in quantitative calculations. It requires also an ability to define terms clearly; to explain chemical phenomena; to represent chemical entities--atoms, ions, molecules, crystals--through names, formulas, and geometric sketches; to graph data and interpret these graphs; and so on. Try to develop your problem solving skills in this broadest sense.

Opportunities for making errors in problem solving are, unfortunately, all too numerous. You should not become discouraged as you make errors (take comfort in the fact that we all make them), but try to learn from your mistakes. First, if your answer disagrees with the one that is given only in the final digit, there is probably no error involved. The difference may stem from the method used in rounding off numbers. The method used in this supplement is to round off each intermediate result to the appropriate number of significant figures if the calculation is done in more than one step. If the calculation is done in a single step, only the final result is rounded off. Quite often an error is in a decimal point, that is, in a power of ten. In such cases you should suspect a slip-up in exponential arithmetic; your chemical reasoning may be flawless. Other times answers may disagree by a simple numerical factor, that is, the answer may be twice what it should be, or only one half, and so on. In these cases you should suspect that a simple factor was omitted or used incorrectly. In any case, if you take the time to write down all the steps in a solution and to check your work carefully, you will find yourself less likely to make errors.

Preparation of the manuscript for this book was a formidable typing task. It is a task that Idona Burrow undertook and saw through to the end, maintaining her good cheer no matter how complex some of the typing became. I am most grateful for her assistance.

San Bernardino, California

Ralph H. Petrucci

CONTENTS

Chapter 1

Matter--Its Properties and Measurement

Properties and classification of matter

1-1. An object displaying a physical property retains its basic chemical identity. Display of a chemical property is accompanied by a change in composition.

(a) Physical: The iron nail is not changed in any significant way when it is attracted to a magnet. Its basic chemical identity is unchanged.

(b) Chemical: The dark deposit on the surface of the silver indicates that the pure lustrous metal has been converted into a chemical compound, such as silver sulfide.

(c) Physical: The floating of ice on liquid water simply demonstrates the difference in a particular property of the two--density.

(d) Chemical: Large rubber molecules are broken down into smaller fragments by combining with ozone in the smog.

1-2. (a) Substance: Cane sugar is the chemical compound, sucrose, in a very high state of purity.

(b) Heterogeneous mixture: The soup is visibly heterogeneous.

(c) Homogeneous mixture: Gasoline consists of a large number of hydrocarbon liquids and special additives.

(d) Heterogeneous mixture: Although mayonnaise has a smooth uniform appearance, suspended oil droplets can be detected through a microscope.

(e) Heterogeneous mixture: Pure salt is 100% sodium chloride (NaCl). Iodized salt contains small amounts of an iodide compound as well (usually potassium iodide).

(f) Homogeneous mixture: Tap water generally contains from a few to several hundred parts per million of dissolved mineral substances.

(g) Substance: Ice is simply solid water.

1-3. (a) To obtain the elements, hydrogen and oxygen, from the compound water requires a chemical change.

(b) Seawater is a water solution containing a large quantity of dissolved substances (principally sodium chloride). Any process that separates the water from the dissolved salts is a physical change, e.g., distillation (boiling followed by condensation of the steam) or freezing (formation of ice crystals in the solution).

(c) Air is a simple physical mixture of gases--oxygen, nitrogen and traces of others. The individual gases can be separated by the physical process of liquefaction followed by distillation.

1-4. (a) Salt can be dissolved in water and the undissolved sand filtered off. The salt can be recovered by evaporating the solution to dryness.

(b) Draw a magnet through the mixture. Iron filings are attracted to the magnet and the wood is left behind.

(c) Mineral oil is both insoluble in and less dense than water. The oil can be skimmed off the water or, better still, the water can be drawn off from the bottom of the mixture through a special funnel (called a separatory funnel).

1-5. (a) Extensive: The mass of air in a balloon depends on the volume of the balloon.

(b) Intensive: Ice melts at 0°C regardless of the mass or form of the ice involved--a block of ice, a glass of crushed ice, or a field of snow.

(c) Extensive: The boiling point is an intensive property, but the length of time required to bring a sample of water to the boiling point depends on the mass of the sample.

(d) Intensive: The color of the emitted light is very distinctive. It does not depend on the size or shape of the glass tube or the amount of neon present.

Scientific method

1-6. No. The greater the number of experiments that conform to predictions based on the law, the greater the confidence in the law. However, there is no point at which the law is ever verified with certainty.

1-7. The fewer assumptions involved in formulating a theory, and the greater the range of phenomena it explains, the more acceptable the theory becomes in comparison with alternative theories.

1-8. A given set of conditions, a cause, is expected to produce a certain result, an effect. Although cause-and-effect relationships may be very difficult to establish at times ("God is subtle"), they do exist nevertheless ("but He is not malicious").

Exponential arithmetic

1-9. In each case the decimal point is moved to the left or to the right to produce a coefficient with value between 1 and 10. The exponent (power of ten) indicates the number of places that the decimal point is moved. The exponent is positive if the decimal point is shifted to the left and negative, if to the right.

(a) 7 . 5 0 0. = 7.5×10^{3}

(b) 3 . 1 7 0 0 0. = 3.17×10^{5}

(c) 8,152,000 = 8.152×10^{6}

(d) 100,000 = 1×10^{5}

(e) 0 . 0 0 6 . 2 = 6.2×10^{-3}

(f) 0 . 0 5 . 00 = 5.00×10^{-2}

(g) 0.00000038 = 3.8×10^{-7}

(h) 0.100 = 1.00×10^{-1}

(i) 3 = 3×10^{0}

1-10. The decimal point is moved to the left or to the right by the number shown in the exponent (power of ten). If the exponent is positive, the decimal point is moved to the right, and if negative, to the left. (This is just the opposite of the way in which the decimal point was shifted in Exercise 1-9, but what is involved here is the reverse of the process illustrated there.)

(a) 4.12×10^{2} = 4 . 1 2 = 412

(b) 6.65×10^{-1} = 6 . 65 = 0.665

(c) 92×10^{-3} = . 0 9 2. = 0.092

(d) 6.28×10^{5} = 6 . 2 8 0 0 0. = 628,000

(e) 4.0×10^{0} = 4.0

(f) 2.98×10^{10} = 29,800,000,000

(g) 1.93×10^{-6} = 0.00000193

(h) 830×10^{-2} = 8.30

(i) 1.235×10^{-5} = 0.00001235

1-11. Think first of how the number would be written out in decimal form. Then convert the number to the exponential form as in Exercise 1-9.

(a) 186 thousand = 186,000 = 1.86×10^{5} mi/s

(b) 5 to 6 quadrillion = 5,000,000,000,000,000 to 6,000,000,000,000,000 = 5×10^{15} to 6×10^{15} t

(c) 173 thousand trillion = 173,000,000,000,000,000 = 1.73×10^{17} W

(d) one millionth = 0.000001 = 1×10^{-6} m = 1 µm

(e) ten millionths = 10 x 0.000001 = 1×10^{-5} m = 10 µm

1-12. It is easiest first to convert each number to the exponential form and then to perform the arithmetical computations on the exponential numbers.

(a) $300 \times 6000 = 3 \times 10^{2} \times 6 \times 10^{3} = 18 \times 10^{5} = 1.8 \times 10^{6}$

(b) $42 \times 40 \times 4100 = 4.2 \times 10^{1} \times 4.0 \times 10^{1} \times 4.1 \times 10^{3} = 6.9 \times 10^{6}$

(c) $0.052 \times 0.0070 = 5.2 \times 10^{-2} \times 7.0 \times 10^{-3} = 3.6 \times 10^{-4}$

(d) $0.0040 \times 550 = 4.0 \times 10^{-3} \times 5.5 \times 10^{2} = 2.2$

(e) $4500/0.0080 = 4.5 \times 10^{3}/8.0 \times 10^{-3} = 5.6 \times 10^{5}$

(f) $$\frac{120 \times 700 \times 0.10}{0.040 \times 2.5} = \frac{1.20 \times 10^{2} \times 7 \times 10^{2} \times 1.0 \times 10^{-1}}{4.0 \times 10^{-2} \times 2.5} = 8.4 \times 10^{4}$$

1-13. In the following examples it is necessary to convert each term to a common power of ten before addition or subtraction can be performed.

(a) $0.052 + (53 \times 6.0 \times 10^{-4}) = 0.052 - 318 \times 10^{-4} = 5.2 \times 10^{-2} + 3.2 \times 10^{-2} = 8.4 \times 10^{-2}$

(b) $$\frac{20 + 380 + (1.60 \times 10^{2})}{2.8 \times 10^{-1}} = \frac{(0.20 + 3.80 + 1.60) \times 10^{2}}{2.8 \times 10^{-1}} = \frac{5.60 \times 10^{2}}{2.8 \times 10^{-1}} = 2.0 \times 10^{3}$$

(c) $$\frac{(1.2 \times 10^{-3})^{2}}{0.040 + (2.0 \times 10^{-2})} = \frac{1.4 \times 10^{-6}}{5.0 \times 10^{-2}} = 0.23 \times 10^{-4} = 2.3 \times 10^{-5}$$

(d) $$\frac{[(6.0 \times 10^{3}) + (4.4 \times 10^{4})]^{2}}{(2.2 \times 10^{3})^{2} + 160,000} = \frac{(0.60 \times 10^{4} + 4.4 \times 10^{4})^{2}}{4.8 \times 10^{6} + 0.16 \times 10^{6}} = \frac{2.5 \times 10^{9}}{5.0 \times 10^{6}} = 0.50 \times 10^{3} = 5.0 \times 10^{2}$$

Significant figures

1-14. (a) An exact number--12.

(b) The capacity of an irregularly shaped tank can only be determined by experiment and is thus subject to error.

(c) The distance between any pair of planetary bodies can only be determined through certain measured quantities. These measurements are subject to error.

(d) An exact number. Although the number of days may vary from one month to another (say from January to February), the month of January always has 31 days.

(e) The area is determined by calculation from measured dimensions; these are subject to error.

1-15. (a) Three.

(b) Two. The zero to the right of the decimal point is not significant.

(c) Five. All the digits are significant.

(d) Five. All the digits, including the two zeros, are significant.

(e) Indeterminate. The first two digits are significant; the three zeros may or may not be. The number of significant figures is between two and five.

(f) One. None of the zeros is significant. They simply locate the decimal point.

(g) Five. All digits are significant, including the three zeros.

(h) One. Of course, if the number 2 is not a measured quantity but is meant simply to signify that something is doubled, then it is an exact number.

1-16. This exercise requires use of the rules for "rounding off."

(a) 1418.2 = 1418 (b) 303.51 = 303.5 (c) 0.014045 = 0.01404

(d) 156.251 = 156.3 (e) 180,000 = 1.800×10^5 (f) 17.6050 = 17.60

(g) $1.5 \times 10^3 = 1.500 \times 10^3$

1-17. (a) $512 \times 176 = 5.12 \times 10^2 \times 1.76 \times 10^2 = 9.01 \times 10^4$

(b) $15.60 \times 10^3 \times 2.5 \times 10^5 = 39 \times 10^8 = 3.9 \times 10^9$

(c) $\dfrac{3.58 \times 10^3}{1.8 \times 10^6} = 2.0 \times 10^{-3}$

(d) 44.34 + 26.2 + 1.06 = 71.6

(e) $(1.561 \times 10^3) - (1.80 \times 10^2) + (2.02 \times 10^4) = (0.16 \times 10^4) - (0.02 \times 10^4) + (2.02 \times 10^4)$

$= 2.16 \times 10^4$

Systems of measurement

1-18. (a) no. g = $2.76\text{ kg} \times \dfrac{1000\text{ g}}{1\text{ kg}} = 2.76 \times 10^3\text{ g}$

(b) no. m = $8160\text{ mm} \times \dfrac{1\text{ m}}{1000\text{ mm}} = 8.160\text{ m}$

(c) no. kg = $368\text{ mg} \times \dfrac{1\text{ g}}{1000\text{ mg}} \times \dfrac{1\text{ kg}}{1000\text{ g}} = 3.68 \times 10^{-4}\text{ kg}$

(d) no. L = $725\text{ ml} \times \dfrac{1\text{ L}}{1000\text{ ml}} = 0.725\text{ L}$

(e) no. mm = $16.7\text{ cm} \times \dfrac{10\text{ mm}}{1\text{ cm}} = 167\text{ mm}$

(f) no. cm^3 = $0.323\text{ L} \times \dfrac{1000\text{ ml}}{1\text{ L}} \times \dfrac{1\text{ cm}^3}{1\text{ ml}} = 323\text{ cm}^3$

(g) no. mg = $2.67\text{ g} \times \dfrac{1000\text{ mg}}{1\text{ g}} = 2.67 \times 10^3\text{ mg}$

(h) no. m = $0.67\text{ km} \times \dfrac{1000\text{ m}}{1\text{ km}} = 6.7 \times 10^2\text{ m}$

1-19. (a) no. in. = $15.50\text{ ft} \times \dfrac{12\text{ in.}}{1\text{ ft}} = 186.0\text{ in.}$

(b) no. lb = $384\text{ oz} \times \dfrac{1\text{ lb}}{16\text{ oz}} = 24.0\text{ lb}$

(c) no. in. = $12.0\text{ yd} \times \dfrac{36\text{ in.}}{1\text{ yd}} = 432\text{ in.}$

(d) no. s = $1.5\text{ h} \times \dfrac{60\text{ min}}{1\text{ h}} \times \dfrac{60\text{ s}}{1\text{ min}} = 5.4 \times 10^3\text{ s}$

(e) no. yd = $1401\text{ ft} \times \dfrac{1\text{ yd}}{3\text{ ft}} = 467.0\text{ yd}$

(f) no. ft = $2.30\text{ mi} \times \dfrac{5280\text{ ft}}{1\text{ mi}} = 1.21 \times 10^4\text{ ft}$

1-20. (a) no. cm = $12\text{ in.} \times \dfrac{2.54\text{ cm}}{1\text{ in.}} = 3.0 \times 10^1\text{ cm}$

(b) $\text{no. m} = 16 \text{ ft} \times \frac{12 \text{ in.}}{1 \text{ ft}} \times \frac{1 \text{ m}}{39.37 \text{ in.}} = 4.9 \text{ m}$

(c) $\text{no. g} = 14 \text{ oz} \times \frac{1 \text{ lb}}{16 \text{ oz}} \times \frac{454 \text{ g}}{1 \text{ lb}} = 4.0 \times 10^2 \text{ g}$

(d) $\text{no. lb} = 55 \text{ kg} \times \frac{2.205 \text{ lb}}{1 \text{ kg}} = 1.2 \times 10^2 \text{ lb}$

(e) $\text{no. ft} = 22.5 \text{ m} \times \frac{39.37 \text{ in.}}{1 \text{ m}} \times \frac{1 \text{ ft}}{12 \text{ in.}} = 73.8 \text{ ft}$

(f) $\text{no. oz} = 3500 \text{ mg} \times \frac{1 \text{ g}}{1000 \text{ mg}} \times \frac{1 \text{ lb}}{454 \text{ g}} \times \frac{16 \text{ oz}}{1 \text{ lb}} = 0.12 \text{ oz}$

1-21. $\text{no. m} = 16.5 \text{ ft} \times \frac{12 \text{ in.}}{1 \text{ ft}} \times \frac{1 \text{ m}}{39.37 \text{ in.}} = 5.03 \text{ m}$

1-22. The prices must be expressed in the same units and then compared. For example, the cost of the 3-lb can in \$/kg is

$$\frac{\text{no. \$}}{\text{kg}} = \frac{\$8.86}{3 \text{ lb}} \times \frac{2.205 \text{ lb}}{1 \text{ kg}} = \$6.51/\text{kg}$$

This is cheaper than the other coffee, which is \$6.53/kg.

1-23. The quantity we are seeking has the units: s/100 m.

$$\frac{\text{no. s}}{100 \text{ m}} = \frac{9.3 \text{ s}}{100 \text{ yd}} \times \frac{1 \text{ yd}}{36 \text{ in.}} \times \frac{39.37 \text{ in.}}{1 \text{ m}} = 10.2 \text{ s}/100 \text{ m}$$

1-24. The quantity sought is no. in.; the starting point is 1 link.

$$\text{no. in.} = 1 \text{ link} \times \frac{1 \text{ chain}}{100 \text{ link}} \times \frac{1 \text{ furlong}}{10 \text{ chain}} \times \frac{1 \text{ mi}}{8 \text{ furlong}} \times \frac{5280 \text{ ft}}{1 \text{ mi}} \times \frac{12 \text{ in.}}{1 \text{ ft}} = 7.92 \text{ in.}$$

1-25. (a) $\text{no. mg} = 2 \text{ tablets} \times \frac{5.0 \text{ gr}}{1 \text{ tablet}} \times \frac{1.0 \text{ g}}{15 \text{ gr}} \times \frac{1000 \text{ mg}}{1 \text{ g}} = 6.7 \times 10^2 \text{ mg}$

(b) $\text{no. } \frac{\text{mg}}{\text{kg}} = \frac{6.7 \times 10^2 \text{ mg}}{165 \text{ lb}} \times \frac{2.20 \text{ lb}}{1 \text{ kg}} = 8.9 \frac{\text{mg}}{\text{kg}}$

1-26. $\text{no. m}^2 = 1.00 \text{ km}^2 \times \frac{10^3 \text{ m}}{1 \text{ km}} \times \frac{10^3 \text{ m}}{1 \text{ km}} = 1.00 \text{ km}^2 \times \frac{10^6 \text{ m}^2}{1 \text{ km}^2} = 1.00 \times 10^6 \text{ m}^2$

1-27. $\text{no. m}^3 = 28 \text{ in.} \times 40 \text{ in.} \times 16 \text{ in.} \times \left(\frac{1 \text{ m}}{39.37 \text{ in.}}\right)^3 = 0.29 \text{ m}^3$

1-28. (a) $\text{no. ft}^2 = 1 \text{ acre} \times \frac{1 \text{ mi}^2}{640 \text{ acre}} \times \frac{(5280)^2 \text{ ft}^2}{1 \text{ mi}^2} = 43{,}560 \text{ ft}^2$

(b) $\text{no. hm}^2 = 1 \text{ acre} \times \frac{1 \text{ mi}^2}{640 \text{ acre}} \times \frac{(5280)^2 \text{ ft}^2}{1 \text{ mi}^2} \times \frac{(12)^2 \text{ in.}^2}{1 \text{ ft}^2} \times \frac{1 \text{ m}^2}{(39.37)^2 \text{ in.}^2} \times \frac{1 \text{ hm}^2}{(100)^2 \text{ m}^2} = 0.405 \text{ hm}^2$

1-29. $\text{no. } \frac{\text{km}}{\text{h}} = 1.27 \text{ Mach} \times \frac{1130 \text{ ft/s}}{1 \text{ Mach}} \times \frac{12 \text{ in.}}{1 \text{ ft}} \times \frac{1 \text{ m}}{39.37 \text{ in.}} \times \frac{1 \text{ km}}{1000 \text{ m}} \times \frac{60 \text{ s}}{1 \text{ min}} \times \frac{60 \text{ min}}{1 \text{ h}} = 1.57 \times 10^3 \text{ km/h}$

Temperature scales

1-30. (a) $°\text{F} = (\frac{9}{5} °\text{C}) + 32 = (\frac{9}{5} \times 40) + 32 = 72 + 32 = 104°\text{F}$

(b) $°\text{C} = \frac{5}{9} (°\text{F} - 32) = \frac{5}{9} (77 - 32) = \frac{5}{9} \times 45 = 25°\text{C}$

(c) $°C = \frac{5}{9}(°F - 32) = \frac{5}{9}(1232 - 32) = \frac{5}{9} \times 1200 = 666.7°C$

(d) $°F = (\frac{9}{5}°C) + 32 = \frac{9}{5}(-176) + 32 = -317 + 32 = -285°F$

1-31. high: $°C = \frac{5}{9}(118 - 32) = \frac{5}{9}(86) = 47.8°C$

low: $°C = \frac{5}{9}(17 - 32) = \frac{5}{9}(-15) = -8.3°C$

1-32. The upper limit of the thermometer, in °F, is:

$°F = \frac{9}{5}°C + 32 = (\frac{9}{5} \times 110) + 32 = 198 + 32 = 230$

This is just below the "soft ball" stage--234 to 240°F. The thermometer cannot be used.

1-33. $°F = \frac{9}{5}°C + 32 = \frac{9}{5}(-273.15) + 32.00 = -491.67 + 32.00 = -459.67°F$

Density

1-34. $\text{density} = \frac{1892\text{ g}}{1.50\text{ L} \times \frac{1000\text{ cm}^3}{1\text{ L}}} = \frac{1892\text{ g}}{1500\text{ cm}^3} = 1.26\text{ g/cm}^3$

1-35. (a) $m = V \times d = 2.50 \times 10^2\text{ cm}^3 \times \frac{1.11\text{ g}}{1\text{ cm}^3} = 2.78 \times 10^2\text{ g}$

(b) $V = \frac{m}{d} = \frac{1.00\text{ kg} \times \frac{1000\text{ g}}{1\text{ kg}}}{1.11\text{ g/ml}} = 900.9\text{ ml} = 0.901\text{ L}$; *or*

$\text{no. L} = 1.00\text{ kg} \times \frac{1000\text{ g}}{1\text{ kg}} \times \frac{1\text{ ml}}{1.11\text{ g}} \times \frac{1\text{ L}}{1000\text{ ml}} = 0.901\text{ L}$

(c) $\text{no. lb} = 1.00\text{ gal} \times \frac{4\text{ qt}}{1\text{ gal}} \times \frac{1\text{ L}}{1.06\text{ qt}} \times \frac{1000\text{ ml}}{1\text{ L}} \times \frac{1.11\text{ g}}{1\text{ ml}} \times \frac{1\text{ kg}}{1000\text{ g}} \times \frac{2.20\text{ lb}}{1\text{ kg}} = 9.22\text{ lb}$

1-36. mass of liquid = 308.4 - 110.4 = 198.0 g

volume of liquid = 250.0 ml = 250.0 cm^3

$d = \frac{m}{V} = \frac{198.0\text{ g}}{250.0\text{ cm}^3} = 0.7920\text{ g/cm}^3$

1-37. mass of carbon tetrachloride = 245.8 - 80.3 = 165.5 g

volume of carbon tetrachloride $= 165.5\text{ g} \times \frac{1\text{ cm}^3}{1.59\text{ g}} = 104\text{ cm}^3$

volume capacity of vessel = volume of carbon tetrachloride = 104 cm^3

1-38. It is necessary to determine the mass, in grams, of each object.

(a) $\text{no. g iron} = (175\text{ cm} \times 1.0\text{ cm} \times 0.50\text{ cm}) \times \frac{7.86\text{ g iron}}{1\text{ cm}^3} = 688\text{ g iron}$

(b) $\text{no. g aluminum} = (140.0\text{ cm} \times 20.0\text{ cm} \times 0.100\text{ cm}) \times \frac{2.70\text{ g aluminum}}{1\text{ cm}^3} = 756\text{ g aluminum}$

(c) $\text{no. g water} = 1.00\text{ L} \times \frac{1000\text{ cm}^3}{1\text{ L}} \times \frac{0.998\text{ g water}}{1\text{ cm}^3} = 998\text{ g water}$

The order of increasing mass is (a) < (b) < (c).

1-39. The addition of 100 pieces of shot to water causes a volume increase of 8.8 ml - 8.4 ml = 0.4 ml. The volume per shot is 4×10^{-3} ml. The mass per shot is:

$$m = V \cdot d = 4 \times 10^{-3} \text{ ml} \times \frac{8.92 \text{ g}}{1 \text{ ml}} = 4 \times 10^{-2} \text{ g}$$

Percent composition

1-40. $\%A = \frac{6A}{50 \text{ grades}} \times 100 = 12\%A$ $\quad\%B = \frac{11B}{50 \text{ grades}} \times 100 = 22\%B$

$\%C = \frac{23C}{50 \text{ grades}} \times 100 = 46\%C$ $\quad\%D = \frac{7D}{50 \text{ grades}} \times 100 = 14\%D$

$\%F = \frac{3F}{50 \text{ grades}} \times 100 = 6\%F$

1-41. $\text{no. g phosphorus} = 5.0 \text{ lb fertilizer} \times \frac{454 \text{ g fert.}}{1 \text{ lb fert.}} \times \frac{6.8 \text{ g phosphorus}}{100 \text{ g fert.}} = 1.5 \times 10^2 \text{ g phosphorus}$

1-42. $\text{no. g ethanol} = 3.50 \text{ L soln.} \times \frac{1000 \text{ cm}^3 \text{ soln.}}{1 \text{ L soln.}} \times \frac{0.980 \text{ g soln.}}{1 \text{ cm}^3 \text{ soln.}} \times \frac{10.0 \text{ g ethanol}}{100 \text{ g soln.}} = 343 \text{ g ethanol}$

1-43. $\text{no. g sample} = 25.0 \text{ g sodium chloride} \times \frac{100 \text{ g sample}}{98.0 \text{ g sodium chloride}} = 25.5 \text{ g sample}$

1-44. $\text{no. L soln.} = 0.350 \text{ kg sodium hydroxide} \times \frac{1000 \text{ g sodium hydroxide}}{1 \text{ kg sodium hydroxide}} \times \frac{100 \text{ g soln.}}{12.0 \text{ g sodium hydroxide}} \times$

$$\frac{1 \text{ cm}^3 \text{ soln.}}{1.131 \text{ g soln.}} \times \frac{1 \text{ L soln.}}{1000 \text{ cm}^3 \text{ soln.}} = 2.58 \text{ L soln.}$$

Self-test Questions

1. (*c*) The mass 14.7 g is expressed to the nearest 0.1 g; 14.72 g to the nearest 0.01 g; 14.721 g to the nearest 0.001 g (0.001 g = 1 mg); 14.7213 g to the nearest 0.0001 g (one-tenth mg).

2. (*a*) Proceed in one of two ways. Convert all the lengths to a common unit (say, meters) and choose the largest. A simpler method is to compare the lengths two at a time. Since one meter is slightly longer than a yard (recall Figure 1-2), 4.0 m is greater than 12.0 ft: (a) > (c). The length 12 ft = 144 in.: (c) > (b) and (a) > (c) > (b). One thousandth of a kilometer is simply one meter; length (d) is much less than (a).

3. (*d*) Again there are two possibilities. One is to express all temperatures on the same scale (i.e., either °F or °C), and then choose the highest. Alternatively, temperatures (c) and (d) are above the boiling point of water (100°C = 212°F) and (a) and (b) are below. This eliminates (a) and (b). Temperature (c) is 5°F above the steam point and temperature (d) is 5°C above. Since five degrees of Celsius temperature is equivalent to nine degrees of Fahrenheit, temperature (d) must be the highest.

4. (*b*) You are expected to know the density of water: 1.00 g/cm^3. The density of the alcohol-water mixture is 0.83 g/cm^3. The density of the wood is less than 1.00 g/cm^3 (since a 10.0 cm^3 sample weighs less than 10.0 g). The density of chloroform is greater than 1.00 g/cm^3 (since a 100.0 cm^3 sample weighs more than 100.0 g). Note that no complete density calculation was required.

5. (*c*) Assign a volume to each part and select the largest. A 380-g sample of water has a volume of 380 cm^3. The volume of the chloroform is V = m/d = 600 g/1.5 g cm^{-3} = 400 cm^3. The 0.50 L of milk has a volume of 500 ml = 500 cm^3. The volume of steel is given--100 cm^3.

6. (*b*) The number 16.07 has four significant digits; 0.0140 has three (the final zero is significant); 1.070 has four significant digits; 0.016 has two. The number 200 has one, two, or three significant digits--we cannot be certain because the final zeros are used simply to locate the decimal point. The case of 0.0140 is without doubt, however.

7. (a) An element is one of a class of about 100 (actually 106) substances that cannot be reduced to simpler substances, either by physical or chemical changes. A compound is comprised of two or more elements and can be decomposed into these elements by appropriate chemical changes.

(b) The components of a heterogeneous mixture separate into physically distinct regions having different properties. In a homogeneous mixture the components are mixed uniformly--composition and properties are constant throughout the mixture.

(c) Mass is a measure of the quantity of matter in a sample. Density is the ratio of mass to volume and thus indicates the quantity of matter packed into a unit volume of a sample.

8. $(19.541 + 1.05 - 3.6) \times 651 = 17.0 \times 651 = 1.11 \times 10^4$

The sum of terms in the parenthetical expression must be stated to the nearest 0.1. The product of the three-digit numbers (17.0 and 651) must be expressed to three significant figures (1.11); the power of ten (10^4) locates the decimal point.

9. $$\text{no. lb of ethyl alcohol} = 55.0 \text{ gal} \times \frac{3.78 \text{ L}}{1 \text{ gal}} \times \frac{1000 \text{ cm}^3}{1 \text{ L}} \times \frac{0.789 \text{ g}}{1 \text{ cm}^3} \times \frac{1 \text{ lb}}{454 \text{ g}} = 361 \text{ lb ethyl alcohol}$$

total mass = 75.0 lb drum + 361 lb ethyl alcohol = 436 lb

10. SI resembles the traditional metric system in having the kilogram as the standard of mass, the meter for length, and the second for time. Also, the prefixes for multiples and submultiples of the base units are the same in the two systems, being based on factors of 10. The standards of length and time in the SI are based on universal constants rather than on one-of-a-kind standards. Also, in the SI certain units are preferred over others, for example dm^3 over L and cm^3 over ml.

Chapter 2

Development of the Atomic Theory

Law of conservation of mass

2-1. In the rusting of the iron the two principal reactants are iron and oxygen gas, but only one of these (the iron) is weighed initially. In contrast, all of the products of the reaction (the rusted iron) are recovered and weighed. Therefore the mass of the iron increases. In the burning of the match, most of the products of the reaction (carbon dioxide gas and water vapor) escape and are not weighed. All that is weighed is the unburned residue of the match; the mass of the match decreases. In both cases, however, the total mass of the products is equal to the total mass of the reactants. The law of conservation of mass does apply.

2-2. Total the masses of materials present before and after the reaction. In both cases these totals are equal.

(a) *before* = 10.00 g + 2.00 g = 12.00 g = 6.08 g + 5.92 g = *after*

(b) *before*: $10.00\text{ g} + (100.0\text{ cm}^3 \times \frac{1.148\text{ g}}{1\text{ cm}^3}) = 10.00\text{ g} + 114.8\text{ g} = 124.8\text{ g}$

after: 120.40 g + (2.22 L × 1.9769 g/L) = 120.40 g + 4.39 g = 124.79 g

Law of definite composition

2-3. (a) Determine the ratio by mass of carbon to carbon dioxide in the three cases.

$$\frac{1.00\text{ g carbon}}{3.66\text{ g carbon dioxide}} = 0.273 \qquad \frac{1.50\text{ g carbon}}{5.50\text{ g carbon dioxide}} = 0.273$$

$$\frac{1.80\text{ g carbon}}{6.60\text{ g carbon dioxide}} = 0.273$$

The constancy of these ratios establishes that carbon dioxide has a definite composition.

(b) $\%\text{ carbon} = \frac{\text{mass of carbon}}{\text{mass of carbon dioxide}} \times 100 = \frac{1.00\text{ g}}{3.66\text{ g}} \times 100 = 27.3\%$

(Also, since only the two elements carbon and oxygen are present, percent oxygen = 100 - percent carbon = 100 - 27.3 = 72.7%.)

2-4. If the law of definite composition is followed, the percentage composition of the compound must be constant. In the first experiment 1.00 g sodium → 2.54 g sodium chloride.

$\%\text{ sodium} = \frac{1.00\text{ g sodium}}{2.54\text{ g sodium chloride}} \times 100 = 39.4\%$ (% chlorine = 60.6)

In the second experiment 1.00 g chlorine → 1.65 g sodium chloride.

$\%\text{ chlorine} = \frac{1.00\text{ g chlorine}}{1.65\text{ g sodium chloride}} \times 100 = 60.6\%$ (% sodium = 39.4)

2-5. The approach is the same as in Exercise 2-4--establish the constancy of the percent composition of the compound. In the first experiment 1.50 g hydrogen → 13.41 g water.

$\%\text{ hydrogen} = \frac{1.50\text{ g hydrogen}}{13.41\text{ g water}} \times 100 = 11.2\%$ (% oxygen = 88.8)

In the second experiment, a sample of water weighing 19.66 g (17.46 g + 2.20 g) yields 2.20 g hydrogen upon electrolysis.

$\%\text{ hydrogen} = \frac{2.20\text{ g hydrogen}}{19.66\text{ g water}} \times 100 = 11.2\%$ (% oxygen = 88.8)

Dalton's atomic theory

2-6. (a) Using the rule of greatest simplicity Dalton would have assigned the formulas: AB, A_2B, AB_2.

(b) The atomic weights of the compounds would be: AB = 40 + 80 = 120; $A_2B = (2 \times 40) + 80 = 160$; $AB_2 = 40 + (2 \times 80) = 200$.

The percent A in the three compounds would be:

$$AB: \quad \% A = \frac{40 \text{ parts A}}{120 \text{ parts cpd.}} \times 100 = 33\%$$

$$A_2B: \quad \% A = \frac{(2 \times 40) \text{ parts A}}{160 \text{ parts cpd.}} \times 100 = 50\%$$

$$AB_2: \quad \% A = \frac{40 \text{ parts A}}{200 \text{ parts cpd.}} \times 100 = 20\%$$

2-7. Dalton's formulas would have indicated that the proportion of hydrogen to oxygen (both by mass and numbers of atoms) is greater in water than in hydrogen peroxide. He could have written either of two sets of formulas.

(a) water: OH hydrogen peroxide: O_2H

(b) water: OH_2 hydrogen peroxide: OH

2-8. Example 2-1 establishes the mass ratio of magnesium to magnesium oxide--0.60. That is, in 1.00 g of the oxide there is 0.60 g magnesium (and 0.40 g oxygen). The mass ratio of magnesium to oxygen is 0.60/0.40 = 1.50. Figure 2-2 pictures magnesium oxide to consist of one magnesium atom for every oxygen atom. Thus we can write

$$\frac{\text{at. wt. Mg}}{\text{at. wt. O}} = \frac{\text{at. wt. Mg}}{16.0} = 1.50 \qquad \text{at. wt. Mg} = 24.0$$

2-9. (a) HgO: Dalton always chose the formula AB if but a single compound existed.

(b) Dalton would have determined the relative atomic weights of Hg and O to be:

$$\frac{41.5 \text{ parts Hg}}{(45 - 41.5) \text{ parts O}} = \frac{41.5}{3.5} = 12$$

Since oxygen had been assigned an atomic weight of 7, that of mercury would have been 12 × 7 = 84.

(c) With an atomic weight of 16 for oxygen, Lavoisier's data yield an atomic weight for mercury of 16 × 12 = 192.

(d) The error in Dalton's atomic weight of mercury would have been due in part to experimental error, but mostly to an incorrect assumption about the formula of water, upon which the atomic weight of oxygen was based. Had he assumed the formula H_2O, he would have obtained an atomic weight of oxygen = 14 and mercury = 168.

Law of multiple proportions

2-10. Establish the ratio of g H/g C in each compound. Either Dalton's atomic weights or currently accepted values as shown below can be used for this purpose; the choice is immaterial.

$$CH_4: \frac{4 \text{ g H}}{12 \text{ g C}}; \quad C_2H_4: \frac{4 \text{ g H}}{(2 \times 12) \text{ g C}}; \quad \text{Ratio: } \frac{4/12}{4/24} = 2$$

2-11. (a) $$CO: \frac{12 \text{ g C}}{16 \text{ g O}}; \quad CO_2: \frac{12 \text{ g C}}{(2 \times 16) \text{ g O}}; \quad \text{Ratio: } \frac{12/16}{12/32} = 2$$

(b) $$Na_2O: \frac{(2 \times 23) \text{ g Na}}{16 \text{ g O}}; \quad Na_2O_2: \frac{(2 \times 23) \text{ g Na}}{(2 \times 16) \text{ g O}}; \quad \text{Ratio: } \frac{46/16}{46/32} = 2$$

(c) $$PCl_3: \frac{31 \text{ g P}}{(3 \times 35.5) \text{ g Cl}}; \quad PCl_5: \frac{31 \text{ g P}}{(5 \times 35.5) \text{ g Cl}}; \quad \text{Ratio: } \frac{31/(3 \times 35.5)}{31/(5 \times 35.5)} = \frac{5}{3}$$

2-12. The percentage gives the number of grams of each element in 100 g of compound. For example, in 100 g methane there is present 75 g carbon and 25 g hydrogen.

Methane: $\frac{75 \text{ g carbon}}{25 \text{ g hydrogen}} = 3$ Acetylene: $\frac{92.3 \text{ g carbon}}{7.7 \text{ g hydrogen}} = 12$

Ethylene: $\frac{85.7 \text{ g carbon}}{14.3 \text{ g hydrogen}} = 6$ Ethane: $\frac{80.0 \text{ g carbon}}{20.0 \text{ g hydrogen}} = 4$

Thus, the ratios of g carbon per g hydrogen in the four compounds are: 3 : 12 : 6 : 4. These are small whole numbers.

2-13. Dalton would have assigned the formulas: NO, N_2O, and NO_2. Determine the ratio, g nitrogen/ g oxygen, for each of the three compounds and compare. If these ratios can be expressed as a series of small whole numbers, the law of multiple proportions is verified. (Dalton's atomic weights are used below.)

NO: $\frac{5 \text{ g N}}{7 \text{ g O}} = 0.71$; N_2O: $\frac{(2 \times 5) \text{ g N}}{7 \text{ g O}} = 1.4$; NO_2: $\frac{5 \text{ g N}}{(2 \times 7) \text{ g O}} = 0.36$

The values, 0.7 , 1.4, 0.36, are in the ratio, 2 : 4 : 1.

2-14. For convenience let us denote one of the oxides as compound A and the other as compound B.

compound A

$$\frac{96.2 \text{ g mercury}}{3.8 \text{ g oxygen}} = \frac{25 \text{ g mercury}}{\text{g oxygen}}$$

compound B

$$\frac{92.6 \text{ g mercury}}{7.4 \text{ g oxygen}} = \frac{13 \text{ g mercury}}{\text{g oxygen}}$$

$$\text{ratio} = \frac{\frac{25 \text{ g mercury}}{\text{g oxygen}}}{\frac{13 \text{ g mercury}}{\text{g oxygen}}} \simeq 2$$

One of the oxides (A) has twice as many mercury atoms per oxygen as does the other (B). Possible formulas are Hg_2O and HgO. Note that these formulas are consistent with an atomic weight of 16 for O, 200 for Hg, and the combining ratios given here. (That is, 16 x 13 = 208 and (16 x 25)/2 = 200.)

Fundamental particles

2-15. Perhaps the most convincing proof that electrons are fundamental particles of all matter lies in the observation that (a) the properties of cathode rays are independent of the cathode material from which they are produced and (b) the e/m ratio of all cathode rays and β particles are identical.

2-16. Cathode rays are small negatively charged particles that are emitted by a cathode material (iron, platinum, and so on). Canal rays are produced through the bombardment of gaseous atoms and molecules by cathode rays (electrons). Canal rays are positively charged and much more massive than cathode rays. All cathode rays are identical in mass and charge. Canal rays have varying masses and charges (and e/m ratios).

2-17. The properties of cathode rays prove to be independent of the cathode material, residual gas in the cathode ray tube, and so on. This would have to be the case for fundamental particles of matter. Since the masses, electric charges and identities of canal ray particles depend on the experimental conditions under which they are produced, they cannot be unique particles fundamental to all matter.

2-18. Methods used to characterize electrons depended on the effects of electric and magnetic fields on these particles. Since neutrons carry no electric charge, they are unaffected by electric and magnetic fields. Altogether different approaches were required for the detection and characterization of neutrons.

Fundamental charges and charge-to-mass ratios

2-19. First determine the charges on the 10 drops. (See next page.)

Drop 1	1.28×10^{-18} C	(8)		Drop 6	3.84×10^{-18} C	(24)
Drop 2	0.64×10^{-18}	(4)		Drop 7	3.84×10^{-18}	(24)
Drop 3	0.64×10^{-18}	(4)		Drop 8	2.56×10^{-18}	(16)
Drop 4	0.32×10^{-18}	(2)		Drop 9	2.56×10^{-18}	(16)
Drop 5	5.12×10^{-18}	(32)		Drop 10	1.28×10^{-18}	(8)

These data are consistent with the value of the fundamental electronic charge given in the text (1.602×10^{-19} C). Each value is divisible by the electronic charge an integral number of times (numbers given in parentheses above). Millikan could not have inferred the fundamental electronic charge from these data. The largest common denominator of all the values listed is 3.2×10^{-19} C--twice the electronic charge.

2-20. (a) $$\text{no. electrons} = -5.5 \times 10^{-15}\ \text{C} \times \frac{1\ \text{electron}}{-1.602 \times 10^{-19}\ \text{C}} = 3.4 \times 10^{4}\ \text{electrons}$$

(b) $$\text{no. electrons} = +6.4 \times 10^{-12}\ \text{C} \times \frac{1\ \text{electron}}{-1.602 \times 10^{-19}\ \text{C}} = -4.0 \times 10^{7}\ \text{electrons}$$

2-21. (a) 0: Hydrogen atoms are electrically neutral. No net charge is associated with them, regardless of their number.

(b) The net electrical charge per fluoride ion is -1 (that is, -1.602×10^{-19} C).

$$\text{no. C} = 1.00 \times 10^{12}\ F^- \times \frac{-1.60 \times 10^{-19}\ \text{C}}{1\ F^-} = -1.60 \times 10^{-7}\ \text{C}$$

(c) The net electrical charge associated with a Ne^{2+} ion is +2 (that is, $2 \times 1.602 \times 10^{-19}$ C).

$$\text{no. C} = 1.00 \times 10^{12}\ Ne^{2+} \times \frac{3.20 \times 10^{-19}\ \text{C}}{1\ Ne^{2+}} = +3.20 \times 10^{-7}\ \text{C}$$

2-22. (a) The mass of a hydrogen atom is essentially that of a proton. Thus,

$$\frac{\text{mass H}}{\text{mass } e^-} = \frac{\text{mass p}}{\text{mass } e^-} = \frac{1.0073\ \text{amu}}{0.00055\ \text{amu}} = 1830$$

A hydrogen atom has 1830 times the mass of an electron.

(b) The highest charge-to-mass for positive rays is that of ${}^{1}_{1}H^{+}$.

$$\frac{\text{charge}}{\text{mass}} = \frac{1.602 \times 10^{-19}\ \text{C}}{1.673 \times 10^{-24}\ \text{g}} = 9.58 \times 10^{4}\ \text{C/g}$$

This ratio is considerably smaller than that for an electron: 1.759×10^{8} C/g.

2-23. We are to compare *absolute* values of e/m ratios. This means that we should treat all ratios as if they were positive quantities (even those involving negative charges). The charges are: proton, +1; electron, -1; neutron, 0; α particle, +2; ${}^{40}_{18}Ar$, 0; and ${}^{37}_{17}Cl^-$, -1. The approximate masses, expressed in amu, are: proton, 1; electron, 0.00055; neutron, 1; α particle, 4; ${}^{40}_{18}Ar$, 40; and ${}^{37}_{17}Cl^-$, 37. The order of increasing value of e/m is

	neutron	=	${}^{40}_{18}Ar$	<	${}^{37}_{17}Cl^-$	<	α particle	<	proton	<	electron
e/m =	0/1	=	0/40	<	1/37	<	2/4	<	1/1	<	1/0.00055
e/m =	0	=	0	<	0.027	<	0.50	<	1.0	<	1820

Atomic models

2-24. (a) He 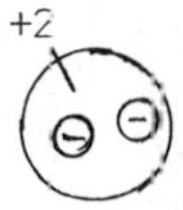 (b) O 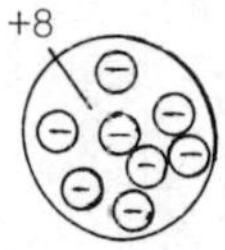 (c) N^- 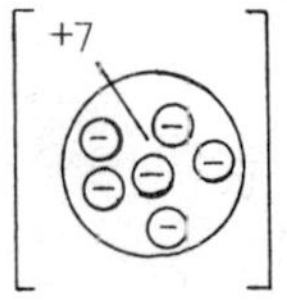 (d) F^- 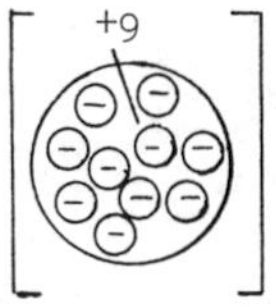

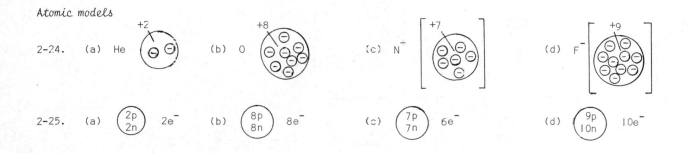

2-25. (a) (2p 2n) $2e^-$ (b) (8p 8n) $8e^-$ (c) (7p 7n) $6e^-$ (d) (9p 10n) $10e^-$

Atomic number, mass number, nuclides, and isotopes

2-26. X is the chemical symbol of an element. The numerical value of Z is the atomic number of the element X, and the numerical value of A is the mass number of a particular nuclide of the element.

2-27. The symbols $^{35}_{17}Cl$ and ^{35}Cl convey the same information; the element Cl can have but one atomic number--17. The symbols $^{35}_{17}Cl$ and $_{17}Cl$ *do not* convey the same information. Although all atoms of Cl have an atomic number of 17, the mass number is not limited to 35.

2-28.

Name	Symbol	Number protons	Number electrons	Number neutrons	Mass number
Sodium	$^{23}_{11}Na$	11	11	12	23
Potassium	^{40}K	19	19	21	40
Silicon	$^{28}_{14}Si$	14	14	14	28
Rubidium	$^{85}_{37}Rb$	37	37	48	85
Arsenic	$^{75}_{33}As$	33	33	42	75
Neon ion	$^{20}Ne^{2+}$	10	8	10	20
Bromine*	$^{80}_{35}Br$	35	35	45	80
Lead*	$^{208}_{82}Pb$	82	82	126	208

*The information given is not enough to characterize a specific nuclide; several possibilities exist.

2-29. (a) In order of increasing number of electrons: $^{22}_{10}Ne < ^{58}_{27}Co < ^{59}_{29}Cu < ^{120}_{48}Cd < ^{112}_{50}Sn < ^{122}_{52}Te$

(b) In order of increasing number of neutrons: $^{22}_{10}Ne < ^{59}_{29}Cu < ^{58}_{27}Co < ^{112}_{50}Sn < ^{122}_{52}Te < ^{120}_{48}Cd$

(c) In order of increasing mass: $^{22}_{10}Ne < ^{58}_{27}Co < ^{59}_{29}Cu < ^{112}_{50}Sn < ^{120}_{48}Cd < ^{122}_{52}Te$

2-30. Protium, deuterium, and tritium nuclei each contain but a single proton. They differ in numbers of neutrons, having 0, 1, and 2, respectively. Protium is the most abundant of the isotopes.

Atomic mass units, atomic masses

2-31. (a) Composition of $^{90}_{38}Sr$: 38 p, 38 e, 52 n = 128 fundamental particles

$$\% \text{ n} = \frac{52 \text{ n}}{128 \text{ particles}} \times 100 = 40.6\%$$

(b) $\% \text{ mass as protons} = \frac{38}{90} \times 100 = 42.2\%$

2-32. (a) $\text{no. g} = 1.00 \times 10^{12} \text{ atoms Cl-35} \times \frac{34.96885 \text{ amu}}{1 \text{ atom Cl-35}} \times \frac{1.673 \times 10^{-24} \text{ g}}{1.0073 \text{ amu}} = 5.81 \times 10^{-11} \text{ g}$

(b) $\text{no. g} = 1.00 \times 10^{12} \text{ atoms Cl-37} \times \frac{36.96590 \text{ amu}}{1 \text{ atom Cl-37}} \times \frac{1.673 \times 10^{-24} \text{ g}}{1.0073 \text{ amu}} = 6.14 \times 10^{-11} \text{ g}$

(c) $$\text{no. g} = \left(1.00 \times 10^{12} \text{ atoms Cl} \times \frac{75.53 \text{ Cl-35}}{100 \text{ atoms Cl}} \times \frac{34.96885 \text{ amu}}{1 \text{ atom Cl-35}} \times \frac{1.673 \times 10^{-24} \text{ g}}{1.0073 \text{ amu}}\right) +$$

$$\left(1.00 \times 10^{12} \text{ atoms Cl} \times \frac{24.47 \text{ Cl-37}}{100 \text{ atoms Cl}} \times \frac{36.96590 \text{ amu}}{1 \text{ atom Cl-37}} \times \frac{1.673 \times 10^{-24} \text{ g}}{1.0073 \text{ amu}}\right)$$

$$= 4.39 \times 10^{-11} \text{ g} + 1.50 \times 10^{-11} \text{ g} = 5.89 \times 10^{-11} \text{ g}$$

2-33. (a) ${}^{7}_{3}\text{Li}/{}^{12}_{6}\text{C} = 7.01601 \text{ amu}/12.00000 \text{ amu} = 0.584668$

(b) ${}^{19}_{9}\text{F}/{}^{12}_{6}\text{C} = 18.99840 \text{ amu}/12.00000 \text{ amu} = 1.583200$

(c) ${}^{84}_{36}\text{Kr}/{}^{12}_{6}\text{C} = 83.9115 \text{ amu}/12.00000 \text{ amu} = 6.99262$

Atomic weights

2-34. Masses of individual nuclides, with the exception of C-12, are nonintegral (not whole numbers). On the other hand, they do not differ from whole numbers by a great deal. (See, for example, the nuclides in Exercise 33.) These facts suggest that a mass of 63.546 for copper must be an average of the masses of two or more isotopes. Thus, we would expect that *no* individual copper atoms have a mass of 63.546.

2-35. $$\text{At. wt.} = \left\{\begin{matrix}\text{Fraction of atoms} \\ \text{that are } {}^{69}_{31}\text{Ga}\end{matrix}\right\} \times 68.9257 + \left\{\begin{matrix}\text{Fraction of atoms} \\ \text{that are } {}^{71}_{31}\text{Ga}\end{matrix}\right\} \times 70.9249$$

$$= [(0.604 \times 68.9257) + (0.396 \times 70.9249)] = 41.6 + 28.1 = 69.7$$

2-36. $$\text{At. wt.} = (0.9927 \times 238.05) + (0.0072 \times 235.04) + (0.00006 \times 234.04)$$
$$= 236.3 + 1.7 + 0.01 = 238.0$$

2-37. (a) Li-7 is the more abundant. This is so because the atomic weight of the naturally occurring element is much closer to 7 than to 6.

(b) Because the atomic weight of 6.941 is about nine-tenths of the way along the interval between the masses of the two isotopes (6.01513 and 7.01601 amu), we should expect about 9 parts Li-7 to 1 part Li-6.

(c) Let x = fraction of atoms that are Li-7 and $(1 - x)$ = fraction of Li-6. Express the experimentally determined atomic weight in terms of these fractions and the masses of the individual nuclides, as in Exercises 2-35 and 2-36. Solve for x.

$$\text{At. wt.} = x(7.01601) + (1 - x)\cdot(6.01513) = 6.941$$
$$7.016x + 6.015 - 6.015x = 6.941$$
$$1.001x = 0.926; \; x = 0.925; \; 1 - x = 0.075$$

Abundances of the isotopes: 92.5% ${}^{7}_{3}\text{Li}$ and 7.5% ${}^{6}_{3}\text{Li}$

2-38. Let x = fraction of atoms that are N-15. Proceed as in Exercise 2-37. The atomic weight of naturally occurring nitrogen is 14.0067.

$$\text{At. wt.} = x(15.0001) + (1 - x)\cdot(14.0031) = 14.0067$$
$$15.0001x + 14.0031 - 14.0031x = 14.0067$$
$$0.997x = 0.0036; \quad x = 0.0036; \quad \%\,^{15}_{7}\text{N} = 0.36$$

Mass spectrometry

2-39. Mass of $^{16}_{8}O$ = 1.3329 × (mass of $^{12}_{6}C$) = 1.3329 × 12.00000 amu = 15.995 amu

Mass of $^{22}_{10}Ne$ = 1.3749 × 15.995 amu = 21.992 amu

Mass of $^{40}_{18}Ar$ = 1.8172 × 21.992 amu = 39.964 amu

2-40. (a) Six different molecules of HCl are possible: $^{1}H^{35}Cl$, $^{2}H^{35}Cl$, $^{3}H^{35}Cl$, $^{1}H^{37}Cl$, $^{2}H^{37}Cl$, and $^{3}H^{37}Cl$.

(b) The mass numbers of the nuclei listed in (a) are 36, 37, 38, 38, 39 and 40, respectively.

(c) By far the most abundant of the hydrogen isotopes is H-1. The more abundant of the two chlorine isotopes is Cl-35. As a result the most abundant of the HCl molecules is $^{1}H^{35}Cl$, and the second most abundant, $^{1}H^{37}Cl$.

(d)

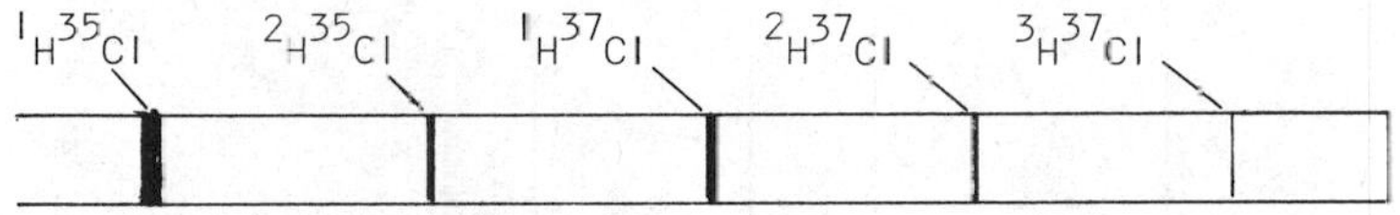

The line due to $^{3}H^{35}Cl$ is covered by the much stronger one for $^{1}H^{37}Cl$. The faintest of the five lines is that of $^{3}H^{37}Cl$.

Self-test Questions

1. (*d*) The existence of isotopes disproves statement (*a*). The existence of radioactivity establishes that not all atoms are indivisible and indestructible. Oxygen is now known to have an atomic weight of 16, not 7.

2. (*b*) Cathode rays are fundamental particles of negative electrical charge--electrons. So too are β particles. Cathode rays are not electromagnetic radiation, and their properties are independent of their source.

3. (*a*) The other responses can be eliminated in terms of earlier discoveries. For example, Thomson established that electrons are fundamental particles of all matter, and Millikan, that all electrons have the same charge.

4. (*c*) $^{32}_{16}S$ has 16 electrons; $^{35}_{17}Cl^{-}$ has 18; $^{34}_{16}S^{+}$ has 15; and $^{35}_{16}S^{2-}$ has 18. An argon atom has 18 electrons but the ion, $^{40}_{18}Ar^{2+}$ has 16 electrons.

5. (*b*) 12.01115 amu is the atomic weight of naturally occurring carbon and is established by an appropriate averaging of the masses of the isotopes of carbon. These isotopes are C-12, C-13 and C-14 and their masses are given in (*a*), (*c*), and (*d*).

6. (*d*) Since the isotope $^{113}_{49}In$ has a mass of 112.9043 amu and the atomic weight of In is 114.82 amu, the second isotope must have a mass greater than 114.82 amu. Of the possibilities listed, only $^{115}_{49}In$ meets this requirement.

7. When the strip of magnesium is burned in open air, the original mass is that of the pure metal and the final mass is that of the magnesium oxide formed by its combustion. Since the oxygen gas consumed in the reaction (derived from the atmosphere) is not included in the original mass, an increase in mass of the strip is observed. In the case of the photoflash bulb, the oxygen gas that is to be consumed in the reaction *is* weighed along with the strip of metal initially. Thus there is no change in mass.

8. The redefinition of atomic weights described here would cause them all to be increased by the ratio: 84.00000/83.9115. In this way the atomic weight of ${}^{84}_{36}Kr$ would become $83.9115 \times \frac{84.00000}{83.9115} = 84.00000$ as desired.

The corresponding change for carbon-12 would be $12.00000 \times \frac{84.00000}{83.9115} = 12.0127$

9. $$e/m = \frac{-1.602 \times 10^{-19}\ C}{36.966\ amu \times \frac{1.673 \times 10^{-24}\ g}{1.0073\ amu}} = -2.609 \times 10^{3}\ C/g$$

10. The atomic weight is expressed in terms of the masses of the two isotopes and their relative abundances. (Note that the abundance of ${}^{109}_{47}Ag$ must be 48.18%; there are only two isotopes to consider.)

$107.87 = (0.5182 \times 106.9) + 0.4818x$

$x = \frac{107.87 - 55.40}{0.4818} = 108.9$ Mass of ${}^{109}_{47}Ag$ = 108.9 amu

Chapter 3

Stoichiometry I: Elements and Compounds

Terminology

3-1. (a) One mole of hydrogen atoms consists of 6.02×10^{23} H atoms and weighs 1.008 g. One mole of hydrogen molecules consists of 6.02×10^{23} H_2 molecules and weighs 2.016 g.

(b) A formula unit is the smallest collection of atoms from which the formula of a compound can be established. A molecule is the smallest collection of atoms that can exist as a separate identifiable unit. In some cases the molecule and formula unit are identical; in some, the molecule consists of a number of formula units. For ionic compounds in the solid state there are no identifiable molecules.

(c) The empirical formula is the formula established from the formula unit of a compound. The molecular formula is the formula based on a molecule of compound. In some cases the molecular formula is the same as the empirical formula. In others, the molecular formula is a "multiple" of the empirical formula.

(d) A cation is a positive ion formed by the loss of an electron(s) by one or a group of atoms. An anion is a negative ion produced when one or a group of atoms gains an electron(s).

(e) A binary compound is made up of two elements; a ternary compound consists of three elements.

(f) A qualitative analysis reveals what elements or compounds are present in a sample of matter. In a quantitative analysis the actual quantities of elements and/or compounds in a sample are determined.

Avogadro's number and the mole

3-2. (a) $\text{no. Fe atoms} = 2.50 \text{ mol Fe} \times \frac{6.02 \times 10^{23} \text{ Fe atoms}}{1 \text{ mol Fe}} = 1.50 \times 10^{24} \text{ Fe atoms}$

(b) $\text{no. Ar atoms} = 0.015 \text{ mol Ar} \times \frac{6.02 \times 10^{23} \text{ Ar atoms}}{1 \text{ mol Ar}} = 9.0 \times 10^{21} \text{ Ar atoms}$

(c) $\text{no. Pu atoms} = 4.0 \times 10^{-10} \text{ mol Pu} \times \frac{6.02 \times 10^{23} \text{ Pu atoms}}{1 \text{ mol Pu}} = 2.4 \times 10^{14} \text{ Pu atoms}$

3-3. (a) $\text{no. S atoms} = 4.5 \text{ mol S} \times \frac{6.02 \times 10^{23} \text{ S atoms}}{1 \text{ mol S}} = 2.7 \times 10^{24} \text{ S atoms}$

(b) $\text{no. S atoms} = 2.8 \text{ mol } S_8 \times \frac{8 \text{ mol S}}{1 \text{ mol } S_8} \times \frac{6.02 \times 10^{23} \text{ S atoms}}{1 \text{ mol S}} = 1.3 \times 10^{25} \text{ S atoms}$

(c) $\text{no. S atoms} = 5.0 \times 10^{-5} \text{ mol } H_2S \times \frac{1 \text{ mol S}}{1 \text{ mol } H_2S} \times \frac{6.02 \times 10^{23} \text{ S atoms}}{1 \text{ mol S}} = 3.0 \times 10^{19} \text{ S atoms}$

(d) $\text{no. S atoms} = 1.40 \text{ mol } CS_2 \times \frac{2 \text{ mol S}}{1 \text{ mol } CS_2} \times \frac{6.02 \times 10^{23} \text{ S atoms}}{1 \text{ mol S}} = 1.69 \times 10^{24} \text{ S atoms}$

3-4. (a) no. mol C = $2.48 \times 10^{25}\ C_2H_5OH$ molecules $\times \frac{1\ \text{mol}\ C_2H_5OH}{6.02 \times 10^{23}\ C_2H_5OH\ \text{molecules}} \times \frac{2\ \text{mol C}}{1\ \text{mol}\ C_2H_5OH}$ = 82.4 mol C

(b) no. mol H = $2.48 \times 10^{25}\ C_2H_5OH$ molecules $\times \frac{1\ \text{mol}\ C_2H_5OH}{6.02 \times 10^{23}\ C_2H_5OH\ \text{molecules}} \times \frac{6\ \text{mol H}}{1\ \text{mol}\ C_2H_5OH}$ = 247 mol H

(c) no. mol O = $2.48 \times 10^{25}\ C_2H_5OH$ molecules $\times \frac{1\ \text{mol}\ C_2H_5OH}{6.02 \times 10^{23}\ C_2H_5OH\ \text{molecules}} \times \frac{1\ \text{mol O}}{1\ \text{mol}\ C_2H_5OH}$ = 41.2 mol O

3-5. (a) no. Mg atoms = 125 g Mg $\times \frac{1\ \text{mol Mg}}{24.3\ \text{g Mg}} \times \frac{6.02 \times 10^{23}\ \text{Mg atoms}}{1\ \text{mol Mg}} = 3.10 \times 10^{24}$ Mg atoms

(b) no. g O_2 = 3.75 mol $O_2 \times \frac{32.0\ \text{g}\ O_2}{1\ \text{mol}\ O_2}$ = 120 g O_2

(c) no. kg Fe = 3.25×10^{28} Fe atoms $\times \frac{1\ \text{mol Fe}}{6.02 \times 10^{23}\ \text{Fe atoms}} \times \frac{55.85\ \text{g Fe}}{1\ \text{mol Fe}} \times \frac{1\ \text{kg Fe}}{1000\ \text{g Fe}} = 3.02 \times 10^3$ kg Fe

(d) no. cm^3 Na = 1 mol Na $\times \frac{23.0\ \text{g Na}}{1\ \text{mol Na}} \times \frac{1\ \text{cm}^3\ \text{Na}}{0.971\ \text{g Na}} = 23.7\ \text{cm}^3$ Na

(e) no. ^{81}Br atoms = 75.0 cm^3 $Br_2 \times \frac{3.12\ \text{g}\ Br_2}{1\ \text{cm}^3\ Br_2} \times \frac{1\ \text{mol Br}}{79.9\ \text{g}\ Br_2} \times \frac{6.02 \times 10^{23}\ \text{Br atoms}}{1\ \text{mol Br}}$

$\times \frac{49.46\ ^{81}\text{Br atoms}}{100\ \text{Br atoms}} = 8.72 \times 10^{23}\ ^{81}$Br atoms

3-6. (a) There are three ions in a formula unit of Cs_2S, two Cs^+ and one S^{2-}. Thus, regardless of the sample size, one-third of all the ions in Cs_2S are S^{2-}: 1/3 = 0.33.

(b) We need to determine the formula weight of Cs_2S and then determine the fraction of this that is contributed by S^{2-}.

Fraction S, by mass = $\frac{\text{mass 1 mol S}}{\text{mass of 1 mol}\ Cs_2S} = \frac{32.1\ \text{g S}}{[(2 \times 133) + 32.1]\ \text{g}\ Cs_2S} = \frac{32.1}{298} = 0.108$

3-7. Determine the number of grams of tin, lead and bismuth in the sample, and then add together these three masses.

no. g Sn = 1.00×10^{25} atoms $\times \frac{2\ \text{Sn atoms}}{10\ \text{atoms}} \times \frac{1\ \text{mol Sn}}{6.02 \times 10^{23}\ \text{Sn atoms}} \times \frac{118.7\ \text{g Sn}}{1\ \text{mol Sn}}$ = 394 g Sn

no. g Pb = 1.00×10^{25} atoms $\times \frac{5\ \text{Pb atoms}}{10\ \text{atoms}} \times \frac{1\ \text{mol Pb}}{6.02 \times 10^{23}\ \text{Pb atoms}} \times \frac{207.2\ \text{g Pb}}{1\ \text{mol Pb}}$ = 1720 g Pb

no. g Bi = 1.00×10^{25} atoms $\times \frac{3\ \text{Bi atoms}}{10\ \text{atoms}} \times \frac{1\ \text{mol Bi}}{6.02 \times 10^{23}\ \text{Bi atoms}} \times \frac{209.0\ \text{g Bi}}{1\ \text{mol Bi}}$ = 1040 g Bi

Total mass = 394 g Sn + 1720 g Pb + 1040 g Bi = 3.15×10^3 g

3-8. no. Ag atoms = 1.40 oz $\times \frac{1\ \text{lb}}{16\ \text{oz}} \times \frac{454\ \text{g}}{1\ \text{lb}} \times \frac{92.5\ \text{g Ag}}{100\ \text{g}} \times \frac{1\ \text{mol Ag}}{108\ \text{g Ag}}$

$\times \frac{6.02 \times 10^{23}\ \text{Ag atoms}}{1\ \text{mol Ag}} = 2.05 \times 10^{23}$ Ag atoms

3-9. Determine the number of Cl^- associated with the $MgCl_2$, the number with KCl, and then the total number.

$$\text{no. } Cl^- \text{ ions} = 450 \text{ g mixture} \times \frac{35.0 \text{ g } MgCl_2}{100 \text{ g mixture}} \times \frac{1 \text{ mol } MgCl_2}{95.2 \text{ g } MgCl_2} \times \frac{2 \text{ mol } Cl^-}{1 \text{ mol } MgCl_2}$$

$$\times \frac{6.02 \times 10^{23} \text{ } Cl^- \text{ ions}}{1 \text{ mol } Cl^-} = 1.99 \times 10^{24} \text{ } Cl^- \text{ ions}$$

$$\text{no. } Cl^- \text{ ions} = 450 \text{ g mixture} \times \frac{65.0 \text{ g KCl}}{100 \text{ g mixture}} \times \frac{1 \text{ mol KCl}}{74.6 \text{ g KCl}} \times \frac{1 \text{ mol } Cl^-}{1 \text{ mol KCl}}$$

$$\times \frac{6.02 \times 10^{23} \text{ } Cl^- \text{ ions}}{1 \text{ mol } Cl^-} = 2.36 \times 10^{24} \text{ } Cl^- \text{ ions}$$

Total number of Cl^- ions $= 1.99 \times 10^{24} + 2.36 \times 10^{24} = 4.35 \times 10^{24}$ Cl^- ions

3-10. $$\text{no. Pb atoms} = 500 \text{ cm}^3 \times \frac{1 \text{ m}^3}{(100)^3 \text{ cm}^3} \times \frac{3.01 \times 10^{-6} \text{g Pb}}{1 \text{ m}^3} \times \frac{1 \text{ mol Pb}}{207.2 \text{ g Pb}}$$

$$\times \frac{6.02 \times 10^{23} \text{ Pb atoms}}{1 \text{ mol Pb}} = 4.37 \times 10^{12} \text{ Pb atoms}$$

3-11. (a) $$\text{no. mol } S_8 = 4.15 \text{ mm}^3 \times \frac{1 \text{ cm}^3}{(10)^3 \text{ mm}^3} \times \frac{2.07 \text{ g}}{1 \text{ cm}^3} \times \frac{1 \text{ mol } S_8}{(8 \times 32.06)\text{g}} = 3.35 \times 10^{-5} \text{ mol } S_8$$

(b) $$\text{no. S atoms} = 3.35 \times 10^{-5} \text{ mol } S_8 \times \frac{8 \text{ mol S}}{1 \text{ mol } S_8} \times \frac{6.02 \times 10^{23} \text{ S atoms}}{1 \text{ mol S}} = 1.61 \times 10^{20} \text{ S atoms}$$

3-12. (a) $$\text{no. } CHCl_3 \text{ molecules} = 250 \text{ g water} \times \frac{1 \text{ g } CHCl_3}{1 \times 10^9 \text{ g water}} \times \frac{1 \text{ mol } CHCl_3}{119 \text{ g } CHCl_3}$$

$$\times \frac{6.02 \times 10^{23} \text{ } CHCl_3 \text{ molecules}}{1 \text{ mol } CHCl_3} = 1.26 \times 10^{15} \text{ } CHCl_3 \text{ molecules}$$

(b) $$\text{no. g } CHCl_3 = 250 \text{ g water} \times \frac{1 \text{ g } CHCl_3}{1 \times 10^9 \text{ g water}} = 2.50 \times 10^{-7} \text{ g } CHCl_3$$

This mass of $CHCl_3$ is much below the limit of detectability by an ordinary analytical balance.

Chemical formulas

3-13. (a) Incorrect: In CO the proportions of C to O, by mass, is 12:16. These same proportions will be found in $C_6H_{12}O_6$ (because there are six O atoms for every six C atoms). However, their percentages, by mass, cannot be the same in $C_6H_{12}O_6$ as in CO because of the introduction of the third element--hydrogen.

(b) Correct: In both $C_6H_{12}O_6$ and H_2O the ratio, by *number*, of H to O atoms is 2:1.

(c) Correct: The mass of 6 mol O is 96 g, compared to 72 g for 6 mol C and 12 g for 12 mol H. Since oxygen contributes most to the total mass of the compound, it is present in the highest percentage.

(d) Incorrect: Carbon and oxygen are present in the same proportions by number, 6:6 = 1:1. Because the masses of C and O differ, the mass ratio cannot be 1:1.

3-14. (a) mol. wt. $C_5H_{11}NO_2S = (5 \times 12.0) + (11 \times 1.01) + 14.0 + (2 \times 16.0) + 32.1$

$$= 60.0 + 11.1 + 14.0 + 32.0 + 32.1 = 149.2$$

(b) $$\text{no. atoms C} = 100 \text{ g cpd.} \times \frac{1 \text{ mol cpd.}}{149 \text{ g cpd.}} \times \frac{5 \text{ mol C}}{1 \text{ mol cpd.}} \times \frac{6.02 \times 10^{23} \text{ atoms C}}{1 \text{ mol C}} = 2.02 \times 10^{24} \text{ atoms C}$$

3-15. (a) Number of atoms in a formula unit = 7 C + 3 N + 5 H + 6 O = 21

(b) There are six O atoms and three N atoms in a formula unit, so their ratio in the compound is 6:3 or 2:1.

(c) The ratio of hydrogen to carbon is set up below, first in numbers of atoms and then by mass.

$$\text{Ratio of H:C} = \frac{5 \text{ mol H}}{7 \text{ mol C}} = \frac{5 \text{ mol H} \times \dfrac{1.01 \text{ g H}}{1 \text{ mol H}}}{7 \text{ mol C} \times \dfrac{12.0 \text{ g C}}{1 \text{ mol C}}} = \frac{5.05 \text{ g H}}{84.0 \text{ g C}} = 0.060 \text{ g H/g C}$$

(d) One mole of TNT contains: $7 \times 12 = 84$ g C; $3 \times 14 = 42$ g N; $5 \times 1 = 5$ g H; $6 \times 16 = 96$ g O. The element present in the greatest proportion, by mass, is oxygen.

Percent composition of compounds

3-16. mol. wt. $= (18 \times 12.01) + (21 \times 1.008) + 14.01 + (3 \times 16.00) = 299.4$ g/mol

$$\% \text{ C} = \frac{(18 \times 12.01) \text{g C}}{299.4 \text{ cpd.}} \times 100 = 72.2\%$$

$$\% \text{ H} = \frac{(21 \times 1.008) \text{g H}}{299.4 \text{ cpd.}} \times 100 = 7.1\%$$

$$\% \text{ N} = \frac{14.01 \text{ g N}}{299.4 \text{ g cpd.}} \times 100 = 4.7\%$$

$$\% \text{ O} = \frac{(3 \times 16.00) \text{g O}}{299.4 \text{ g cpd.}} \times 100 = 16.0\%$$

3-17. Each of the compounds contains one sulfur atom per formula unit. The one that has the smallest formula weight must have the highest % S, that is, the smaller the denominator in the quantity,

$\% \text{ S} = \dfrac{32.1 \text{ g S}}{? \text{ g cpd.}} \times 100$, the greater the % S. Of the compounds listed Li_2S has the smallest formula weight and the greatest percent S.

3-18. The formula weights of the compounds are: $CO(NH_2)_2 = 60$; $NH_4NO_3 = 80$; $HNC(NH_2)_2 = 59$. Urea and NH_4NO_3 have two N atoms per formula unit; guanidine has three. This, together with the fact that it has the smallest formula weight of the three, means that guanidine has the highest percent nitrogen. Alternatively, determine the percent N in each compound and compare the results.

3-19. $$\text{no. lb } (NH_4)_2SO_4 = 1.0 \text{ lb N} \times \frac{454 \text{ g N}}{1 \text{ lb N}} \times \frac{1 \text{ mol N}}{14.0 \text{ g N}} \times \frac{1 \text{ mol } (NH_4)_2SO_4}{2 \text{ mol N}}$$

$$\times \frac{132 \text{ g } (NH_4)_2SO_4}{1 \text{ mol } (NH_4)_2SO_4} \times \frac{1 \text{ lb } (NH_4)_2SO_4}{454 \text{ g } (NH_4)_2SO_4} = 4.7 \text{ lb } (NH_4)_2SO_4$$

Note that in addition to the usual cancellation of units the term "454" also cancels. A still simpler approach expresses the relative proportion of N in $(NH_4)_2SO_4$ in pounds rather than grams.

$$\text{no. lb } (NH_4)_2SO_4 = 1.0 \text{ lb N} \times \frac{132 \text{ lb } (NH_4)_2SO_4}{(2 \times 14.0) \text{ lb N}} = 4.7 \text{ lb } (NH_4)_2SO_4$$

Chemical formulas from percent composition

3-20. A compound having 38.8% Cl and 61.2% O has the following numbers of moles of each element in 100 g of compound:

$$\text{no. mol Cl} = 38.8 \text{ g Cl} \times \frac{1 \text{ mol Cl}}{35.5 \text{ g Cl}} = 1.09 \text{ mol Cl}$$

$$\text{no. mol O} = 61.2 \text{ g O} \times \frac{1 \text{ mol O}}{16.0 \text{ g O}} = 3.82 \text{ mol O}$$

The empirical formula of the compound is $Cl_{1.09}O_{3.82} = Cl_{\frac{1.09}{1.09}}O_{\frac{3.82}{1.09}} = ClO_{3.50} = Cl_2O_7$

3-21. $$\text{no. mol B} = 78.5 \text{ g B} \times \frac{1 \text{ mol B}}{10.8 \text{ g B}} = 7.27 \text{ mol B}$$

$$\text{no. mol H} = 21.5 \text{ g H} \times \frac{1 \text{ mol H}}{1.01 \text{ g H}} = 21.3 \text{ mol H}$$

The empirical formula is $B_{7.27}H_{21.3} = BH_3$

The formula weight based on the above empirical formula is 13.8. This is just one half of the experimentally determined molecular weight of 27.5. The true molecular formula is B_2H_6.

3-22. Based on 100.0 g of caffeine we can write

$$\text{no. mol C} = 49.5 \text{ g C} \times \frac{1 \text{ mol C}}{12.0 \text{ g C}} = 4.12 \text{ mol C}$$

$$\text{no. mol H} = 5.2 \text{ g H} \times \frac{1 \text{ mol H}}{1.01 \text{ g H}} = 5.15 \text{ mol H}$$

$$\text{no. mol N} = 28.8 \text{ g N} \times \frac{1 \text{ mol N}}{14.0 \text{ g N}} = 2.06 \text{ mol N}$$

$$\text{no. mol O} = 16.5 \text{ g O} \times \frac{1 \text{ mol O}}{16.0 \text{ g O}} = 1.03 \text{ mol O}$$

The empirical formula is $C_{4.12}H_{5.15}N_{2.06}O_{1.03} = C_{\frac{4.12}{1.03}}H_{\frac{5.15}{1.03}}N_{\frac{2.06}{1.03}}O_{\frac{1.03}{1.03}} = C_4H_5N_2O$

formula weight = (4 × 12.0) + (5 × 1.01) + (2 × 14.0) + 16.0 = 97.0

molecular weight = 194.2 = 2 × formula weight

molecular formula = 2 x empirical formula = $C_8H_{10}N_4O_2$

3-23. The first oxide: $\text{no. mol Co} = 78.6 \text{ g Co} \times \frac{1 \text{ mol Co}}{58.9 \text{ g Co}} = 1.33$

$$\text{no. mol O} = 21.4 \text{ g O} \times \frac{1 \text{ mol O}}{16.0 \text{ g O}} = 1.34$$

Formula: CoO
Name: cobalt(II) oxide

The second oxide: $\text{no. mol Co} = 71.1 \text{ g Co} \times \frac{1 \text{ mol Co}}{58.9 \text{ g Co}} = 1.21$

$$\text{no. mol O} = 28.9 \text{ g O} \times \frac{1 \text{ mol O}}{16.0 \text{ g O}} = 1.81$$

$Co_{\frac{1.21}{1.21}}O_{\frac{1.81}{1.21}} = CoO_{1.50} = Co_2O_3$ (Formula)
Name: cobalt(III) oxide

3-24. Several approaches are possible here, although the simplest is to determine the percent Cl in each of the possible compounds--C_6H_5Cl, $C_6H_4Cl_2$, $C_6H_3Cl_3$, and so on--and find the one with about 48.2% Cl.

$$C_6H_5Cl: \quad \%Cl = \frac{35.5 \text{ g Cl}}{113 \text{ g } C_6H_5Cl} \times 100 = 31.4\% \qquad C_6H_4Cl_2: \quad \%Cl = \frac{(2 \times 35.5)\text{g Cl}}{147 \text{ g } C_6H_4Cl_2} \times 100 = 48.3\%$$

We need proceed no further. The compound in question is $C_6H_4Cl_2$.

Nomenclature

3-25. (a) KI = potassium iodide

(b) $CaCl_2$ = calcium chloride

(c) $Mg(NO_3)_2$ = magnesium nitrate

(d) K_2CrO_4 = potassium chromate

(e) Cs_2SO_4 = cesium sulfate

(f) Cr_2O_3 = chromium(III) oxide

(g) $FeSO_4$ = iron(II) sulfate

(h) ZnS = zinc sulfide

(i) $Ca(HCO_3)_2$ = calcium hydrogen carbonate (calcium bicarbonate)

(j) KCN = potassium cyanide

(k) K_2HPO_4 = potassium hydrogen phosphate

(l) NH_4I = ammonium iodide

(m) $Cu(OH)_2$ = copper(II) hydroxide

3-26. SnF_2, stannous fluoride

$SnCl_4$, stannic chloride

PbO, lead(II) oxide

$Pb(C_2H_3O_2)_4$, lead(IV) acetate

$CoSO_4$, cobalt(II) sulfate

$Co_2(SO_4)_3$, cobalt(III) sulfate

KIO_3, potassium iodate

KIO_4, potassium periodate

AuCl, aurous chloride

$AuCl_3$, auric chloride

3-27. (a) ICl = iodine (mono)chloride

(b) ICl_3 = iodine trichloride

(c) ClF_3 = chlorine trifluoride

(d) BrF_5 = bromine pentafluoride

3-28. (a) calcium oxide = CaO

(b) strontium fluoride = SrF_2

(c) aluminum sulfate = $Al_2(SO_4)_3$

(d) ammonium chromate = $(NH_4)_2CrO_4$

(e) magnesium hydroxide = $Mg(OH)_2$

(f) potassium carbonate = K_2CO_3

(g) zinc acetate = $Zn(C_2H_3O_2)_2$

(h) mercury(II) nitrate = $Hg(NO_3)_2$

(i) iron(III) oxide = Fe_2O_3

(j) chromium(II) chloride = $CrCl_2$

(k) lithium sulfide = Li_2S

(l) calcium dihydrogen phosphate = $Ca(H_2PO_4)_2$

(m) magnesium perchlorate = $Mg(ClO_4)_2$

(n) potassium hydrogen sulfate = $KHSO_4$

3-29. (a) chlorine dioxide = ClO_2 (b) silicon tetrafluoride = SiF_4

(c) tricarbon disulfide = C_3S_2 (d) diboron tetrabromide = B_2Br_4

Hydrates

3-30. Formula weight = 65.4 + 32.1 + (4 × 16.0) + (7 × 18.0) = 287.5

$$\%H_2O = \frac{(7 \times 18.0)\text{g } H_2O}{287.5 \text{ g hydrate}} \times 100 = 43.8\%$$

3-31. The hydrate with the greatest % H_2O will be the one with the highest ratio of mass of water to that of the anhydrous compound.

(a) $\frac{5\ H_2O}{CuSO_4} = \frac{5 \times 18.0}{160} = \frac{90}{160}$ (b) $\frac{18\ H_2O}{Cr_2(SO_4)_3} = \frac{18 \times 18.0}{392} = \frac{324}{392}$

(c) $\frac{6\ H_2O}{MgCl_2} = \frac{6 \times 18.0}{95.2} = \frac{108}{95.2}$ (d) $\frac{2\ H_2O}{LiC_2H_3O_2} = \frac{2 \times 18.0}{66.0} = \frac{36.0}{66.0}$

The correct answer is (c). Only in $MgCl_2 \cdot 6H_2O$ does the mass of water exceed that of the anhydrous compound. $MgCl_2 \cdot 6H_2O$ has the highest % H_2O.

3-32. In 5.018 g of hydrate there is 2.449 g $MgSO_4$ and 5.018 - 2.449 = 2.569 g H_2O. On a molar basis,

$$\text{no. mol } MgSO_4 = 2.449 \text{ g } MgSO_4 \times \frac{1 \text{ mol } MgSO_4}{120.4 \text{ g } MgSO_4} = 0.0203 \text{ mol } MgSO_4$$

$$\text{no. mol } H_2O = 2.569 \text{ g } H_2O \times \frac{1 \text{ mol } H_2O}{18.02 \text{ g } H_2O} = 0.143 \text{ mol } H_2O$$

$$\text{Formula: } (MgSO_4)_{0.0203}(H_2O)_{0.143} = (MgSO_4)_{\frac{0.0203}{0.0203}}(H_2O)_{\frac{0.143}{0.0203}} = (MgSO_4)(H_2O)_7 = MgSO_4 \cdot 7H_2O$$

3-33.

$$\text{no. g } Na_2SO_4 \cdot 10\ H_2O = 1.00 \text{ g } Na_2SO_4 \times \frac{1 \text{ mol } Na_2SO_4}{142 \text{ g } Na_2SO_4} \times \frac{1 \text{ mol } Na_2SO_4 \cdot 10\ H_2O}{1 \text{ mol } Na_2SO_4}$$

$$\times \frac{322 \text{ g } Na_2SO_4 \cdot 10\ H_2O}{1 \text{ mol } Na_2SO_4 \cdot 10\ H_2O} = 2.27 \text{ g } Na_2SO_4 \cdot 10\ H_2O$$

The increase in mass is 2.27 g - 1.00 g = 1.27 g.

3-34. Proceed in the usual manner. That is, determine the number of moles of each component in 100.0 g of compound. Treat the H_2O as a single component.

$$\text{no. mol Cu} = 20.3 \text{ g Cu} \times \frac{1 \text{ mol Cu}}{63.5 \text{ g Cu}} = 0.320 \text{ mol Cu}$$

$$\text{no. mol Si} = 8.95 \text{ g Si} \times \frac{1 \text{ mol Si}}{28.1 \text{ g Si}} = 0.319 \text{ mol Si}$$

$$\text{no. mol F} = 36.3 \text{ g F} \times \frac{1 \text{ mol F}}{19.0 \text{ g F}} = 1.91 \text{ mol F}$$

$$\text{no. mol } H_2O = 34.5 \text{ g } H_2O \times \frac{1 \text{ mol } H_2O}{18.0 \text{ g } H_2O} = 1.92 \text{ mol } H_2O$$

$$\text{Empirical formula} = Cu_{0.320}Si_{0.319}F_{1.91}(H_2O)_{1.92} = Cu_{\frac{0.320}{0.319}}Si_{\frac{0.319}{0.319}}F_{\frac{1.91}{0.319}}(H_2O)_{\frac{1.92}{0.319}} = CuSiF_6 \cdot 6H_2O$$

3-35. (a) First determine the number of grams of C in the CO_2 and grams of H in the H_2O. These elements are derived from the hydrocarbon.

$$\text{no. g C} = 0.5184 \text{ g } CO_2 \times \frac{1 \text{ mol } CO_2}{44.01 \text{ g } CO_2} \times \frac{1 \text{ mol C}}{1 \text{ mol } CO_2} \times \frac{12.01 \text{ g C}}{1 \text{ mol C}} = 0.1415 \text{ g C}$$

$$\text{no. g H} = 0.0849 \text{ g } H_2O \times \frac{1 \text{ mol } H_2O}{18.0 \text{ g } H_2O} \times \frac{2 \text{ mol H}}{1 \text{ mol } H_2O} \times \frac{1.01 \text{ g H}}{1 \text{ mol H}} = 0.00953 \text{ g H}$$

The percent composition of the hydrocarbon is

$$\%C = \frac{0.1415 \text{ g C}}{0.1510 \text{ g cpd.}} \times 100 = 93.71\% \qquad \%H = \frac{0.00953 \text{ g H}}{0.1510 \text{ g cpd.}} \times 100 = 6.31\%$$

(b) In 100 grams of the compound there is 93.71 g C and 6.31 g H.

$$\text{no. mol C} = 93.71 \text{ g C} \times \frac{1 \text{ mol C}}{12.01 \text{ g C}} = 7.80 \text{ mol C}$$

$$\text{no. mol H} = 6.31 \text{ g H} \times \frac{1 \text{ mol H}}{1.01 \text{ g H}} = 6.25 \text{ mol H}$$

The empirical formula is $C_{7.80}H_{6.25} = C_{\frac{7.80}{6.25}}H_{\frac{6.25}{6.25}} = C_{1.25}H = C_5H_4$

(c) Since the formula weight based on the empirical formula is 64, just one half of the molecular weight, the molecular formula must be $C_{10}H_8$.

3-36. From the combustion data we determine the percent composition of *n*-butanol. The method is the same as that of the preceding exercise, except that three conversion factors are converted into a single one.

$$\text{no. g C} = 1.0904 \text{ g } CO_2 \times \frac{12.01 \text{ g C}}{44.01 \text{ g } CO_2} = 0.2976 \text{ g C}$$

$$\text{no. g H} = 0.5580 \text{ g } H_2O \times \frac{(2 \times 1.008)\text{g H}}{18.02 \text{ g } H_2O} = 0.06243 \text{ g H}$$

$$\%C = \frac{0.2976 \text{ g C}}{0.4590 \text{ g cpd.}} \times 100 = 64.84\% \text{ C} \qquad \%H = \frac{0.06243 \text{ g H}}{0.4590 \text{ g cpd.}} \times 100 = 13.60\% \text{ H}$$

$$\%O = 100.00 - \%C - \%H = 100.00 - 64.84\% - 13.60\% = 21.56\% \text{ O}$$

In 100.0 g compound,

$$\text{no. mol C} = 64.84 \text{ g C} \times \frac{1 \text{ mol C}}{12.01 \text{ g C}} = 5.40 \text{ mol C} \qquad \text{no. mol H} = 13.60 \text{ g H} \times \frac{1 \text{ mol H}}{1.008 \text{ g H}} = 13.5 \text{ mol H}$$

$$\text{no. mol O} = 21.56 \text{ g O} \times \frac{1 \text{ mol O}}{16.0 \text{ g O}} = 1.35 \text{ mol O}$$

Empirical formula $= C_{5.40}H_{13.5}O_{1.35} = C_{\frac{5.40}{1.35}}H_{\frac{13.5}{1.35}}O_{\frac{1.35}{1.35}} = C_4H_{10}O$

3-37. The percent composition of the compound is determined as in the preceding exercise:

$$\text{no. g C} = 0.305 \text{ g } CO_2 \times \frac{12.0 \text{ g C}}{44.0 \text{ g } CO_2} = 0.0832 \text{ g C} \qquad \text{no. g H} = 0.249 \text{ g } H_2O \times \frac{(2 \times 1.01)\text{g H}}{18.0 \text{ g } H_2O} = 0.0279 \text{ g H}$$

$$\%C = \frac{0.0832 \text{ g C}}{0.208 \text{ g cpd.}} \times 100 = 40.0\% \qquad \%H = \frac{0.0279 \text{ g H}}{0.208 \text{ g cpd.}} \times 100 = 13.4\%$$

%N can be obtained by difference: 100.0 - 40.0 - 13.4 = 46.6, or directly: $\%N = \frac{0.163 \text{ g N}}{0.350 \text{ g cpd.}} \times 100 = 46.6\%$

Based on 100 g of dimethylhydrazine we may write:

$$\text{no. mol C} = 40.0 \text{ g C} \times \frac{1 \text{ mol C}}{12.0 \text{ g C}} = 3.33 \text{ mol C} \qquad \text{no. mol H} = 13.4 \text{ g H} \times \frac{1 \text{ mol H}}{1.01 \text{ g H}} = 13.3 \text{ mol H}$$

$$\text{no. mol N} = 46.6 \text{ g N} \times \frac{1 \text{ mol N}}{14.0 \text{ g N}} = 3.33 \text{ mol N}$$

The empirical formula is CH_4N.

3-38. The compound has the formula C_xH_y. Calculate the number of grams of CO_2 and grams of H_2O derived from a given mass of the compound, say 1.00 g. These quantities will be expressed in terms of x and y. The ratio of g CO_2 to H_2O must be 1.955:1. Find values of x and y consistent with this ratio.

$$\text{no. g } CO_2 = 1.00 \text{ g } C_xH_y \times \frac{(12x)\text{g C}}{(12x + 1y)\text{g } C_xH_y} \times \frac{44 \text{ g } CO_2}{12 \text{ g C}} = \frac{44x}{12x + y}$$

$$\text{no. g } H_2O = 1.00 \text{ g } C_xH_y \times \frac{(1y)\text{g H}}{(12x + 1y)\text{g } C_xH_y} \times \frac{18 \text{ g } H_2O}{2 \text{ g H}} = \frac{9y}{12x + y}$$

$$\frac{\text{no. g } CO_2}{\text{no. g } H_2O} = \frac{\frac{44x}{12x + y}}{\frac{9y}{12x + y}} = \frac{44x}{9y} = 1.955; \quad \frac{x}{y} = \frac{9}{44} \times 1.955 = 0.40 = \frac{4}{10} = \frac{2}{5}$$

The ratio of carbon atoms (x) to hydrogen atoms (y) in the hydrocarbon is 2:5. The empirical formula is C_2H_5.

Precipitation Analysis

3-39. $\text{no. g AgI} = 0.1565 \text{ g KI} \times \frac{1 \text{ mol KI}}{166.0 \text{ g KI}} \times \frac{1 \text{ mol I}^-}{1 \text{ mol KI}} \times \frac{1 \text{ mol AgI}}{1 \text{ mol I}^-} \times \frac{234.8 \text{ g AgI}}{1 \text{ mol AgI}} = 0.2214 \text{ g AgI}$

3-40. Determine the number of grams of tin in 0.215 g SnO_2, grams of lead in 0.101 g $PbSO_4$, and grams of zinc in 0.216 g $Zn_2P_2O_7$. Once these masses are determined the percent composition, by mass, follows easily.

$$\text{no. g Sn} = 0.215 \text{ g } SnO_2 \times \frac{118.7 \text{ g Sn}}{150.7 \text{ g } SnO_2} = 0.169 \text{ g Sn}$$

$$\text{no. g Pb} = 0.101 \text{ g } PbSO_4 \times \frac{207.2 \text{ g Pb}}{303.3 \text{ g } PbSO_4} = 0.0690 \text{ g Pb}$$

$$\text{no. g Zn} = 0.216 \text{ g } Zn_2P_2O_7 \times \frac{(2 \times 65.4)\text{g Zn}}{305 \text{ g } Zn_2P_2O_7} = 0.0926 \text{ g Zn}$$

$$\%\text{Sn} = \frac{0.169 \text{ g Sn}}{1.502 \text{ g brass}} \times 100 = 11.3; \quad \%\text{Pb} = 4.6; \quad \%\text{Zn} = 6.2; \quad \%\text{Cu} = 77.9$$

3-41. Determine the no. mol SO_4^{2-} in the zinc sulfate sample.

$$\text{no. mol } SO_4^{2-} = 0.9335 \text{ g } BaSO_4 \times \frac{1 \text{ mol } BaSO_4}{233.4 \text{ g } BaSO_4} \times \frac{1 \text{ mol } SO_4^{2-}}{1 \text{ mol } BaSO_4} = 4.000 \times 10^{-3} \text{ mol } SO_4^{2-}$$

$$\text{no. mol } Zn^{2+} = \text{no. mol } SO_4^{2-} = \text{no. mol } ZnSO_4 = 4.000 \times 10^{-3} \text{ mol } ZnSO_4$$

$$\text{no. g } ZnSO_4 = 4.000 \times 10^{-3} \text{ mol } ZnSO_4 \times \frac{161.4 \text{ g } ZnSO_4}{1 \text{ mol } ZnSO_4} = 0.6456 \text{ g } ZnSO_4$$

$$\text{no. g } H_2O = 1.150 \text{ g sample} - 0.6456 \text{ g } ZnSO_4 = 0.504 \text{ g } H_2O$$

$$\text{no. mol } H_2O = 0.504 \text{ g } H_2O \times \frac{1 \text{ mol } H_2O}{18.0 \text{ g } H_2O} = 0.0280 = 28.0 \times 10^{-3} \text{ mol } H_2O$$

The mol ratio, $H_2O:ZnSO_4$ = 7:1. The formula of the hydrate is $ZnSO_4 \cdot 7H_2O$.

Atomic weight determinations

3-42. The two compounds can be represented as XCl_y and XCl_z, where y and z are integral (whole) numbers.

$$XCl_y: \quad \%Cl = \frac{y(35.5)}{137} \times 100 = 77.5 \qquad y = \frac{77.5 \times 137}{35.5 \times 100} = 3$$

XCl_3 has a molecular weight of X + 3(35.5) = 137. The atomic weight of X = 137 - 3(35.5) = 137 - 106.5 = 30.5. X is phosphorus.

$$XCl_z: \quad \%Cl = \frac{z(35.5)}{208} \times 100 = 85.1 \qquad z = \frac{85.1 \times 208}{35.5 \times 100} = 5$$

XCl_5 has a molecular weight of X + 5(35.5) = 208. The atomic weight of X = 208 - 5(35.5) = 208 - 177.5 = 30.5. X is phosphorus.

3-43. Proceed as outlined in Example 3-16 of the textbook.

$$\text{no. g } SO_4 \text{ in the } BaSO_4 = 0.2528 \text{ g } BaSO_4 \times \frac{1 \text{ mol } BaSO_4}{233.4 \text{ g } BaSO_4} \times \frac{1 \text{ mol } SO_4}{1 \text{ mol } BaSO_4} \times \frac{96.06 \text{ g } SO_4}{1 \text{ mol } SO_4} = 0.1040 \text{ g } SO_4$$

The number of g SO_4 in the MSO_4 is also 0.1040.
The number g M in MSO_4 = 0.1304 g MSO_4 - 0.1040 g SO_4 = 0.0264 g M.
In the compound MSO_4 there is 0.0264 g M for every 0.1040 g SO_4, leading to the conversion factor: 0.0264 g M/0.1040 g SO_4. Use this factor to determine the number of g M associated with one mole (96.06 g) of SO_4. This will be the atomic weight of M, since there is one mole of M for every mole of SO_4 in the compound.

$$\text{no. g M} = 1 \text{ mol } SO_4 \times \frac{96.06 \text{ g } SO_4}{1 \text{ mol } SO_4} \times \frac{0.0264 \text{ g M}}{0.1040 \text{ g } SO_4} = 24.4$$

3-44. This solution varies slightly from the preceding exercise. The primary difference is in the last step.

$$\text{no. g } SO_4 \text{ in the } BaSO_4 = 1.239 \text{ g } BaSO_4 \times \frac{96.06 \text{ g } SO_4}{233.4 \text{ g } BaSO_4} = 0.5099 \text{ g } SO_4$$

$$\text{no. g M in } M_2(SO_4)_3 = 0.605 \text{ g } M_2(SO_4)_3 - 0.510 \text{ g } SO_4 = 0.095 \text{ g M}$$

Ratio of g M/g SO_4 = 0.095 g M/0.510 g SO_4

Each mole of the compound contains 2 mol M and 3 mol SO_4; per mol M there is 1.5 mol SO_4. We need to determine the number of g M associated with 1.5 mol SO_4; this is the atomic weight.

$$\text{no. g M} = 1.5 \text{ mol } SO_4 \times \frac{96.06 \text{ g } SO_4}{1 \text{ mol } SO_4} \times \frac{0.095 \text{ g M}}{0.510 \text{ g } SO_4} = 27$$

3-45. Set up an equation in the usual conversion-factor format, to show how many grams of MS can be obtained from the given mass of M_2O_3. Of course, the number of grams of MS is not unknown; it is 0.457. What is unknown is the atomic weight of the metal M; call this x and solve for x.

$$\text{no. g MS} = 0.415 \text{ g } M_2O_3 \times \frac{1 \text{ mol } M_2O_3}{[2x + (3 \times 16.0)] \text{g } M_2O_3} \times \frac{2 \text{ mol M}}{1 \text{ mol } M_2O_3} \times \frac{1 \text{ mol MS}}{1 \text{ mol M}} \times \frac{(x + 32.1) \text{g MS}}{1 \text{ mol MS}} = 0.457 \text{ g MS}$$

$$\frac{0.415 \times 2 \times (x + 32.1)}{2x + 48.0} = 0.457 \qquad 0.830x + 26.6 = 0.914x + 21.9$$

$$0.084x = 4.7 \qquad x = 56$$

Self-test Questions

1. (*c*) One mole of F_2 weighs 38.0 g and contains 6.02×10^{23} F_2 molecules. In 6.02×10^{23} F_2 molecules there are $2 \times 6.02 \times 10^{23} = 1.20 \times 10^{24}$ F atoms. The answer (d) is one of those "foolish" errors always to be avoided. Avogadro's number is a number of atoms, molecules, etc.; it is not a number of grams.

2. (*b*) If a formula is divisible by an integer, the formula must be a molecular formula. Divide the subscripts of N_2O_4 by two and obtain NO_2. The other formulas are not divisible by integers.

3. (*d*) This result can be obtained by eliminating the first three choices and then proving that the fourth is correct. The compound contains 17 atoms per formula unit, but $17 \times 6.02 \times 10^{23}$ atoms per mole. The compound contains equal numbers of C and H atoms; but since the C atom is so much more massive than H, the percentages by mass are not equal. Again, there are twice as many O atoms as N atoms; but since an O atom is heavier than an N atom, the % O by mass is more than twice the % N. Each N atom contributes 14 units to the mass of the compound; each H atom 1 unit; and every 7 H atoms, 7 units. Since the mass contribution of N is almost exactly twice that of H, the % N, by mass, will be twice % H.

4. (*a*) We could simply calculate the number of N atoms in each sample and choose the largest. It is simpler, however, to work in moles. For example, 17 g NH_3 = 1 mol NH_3 = 1 mol N, but 1 mol N_2 = 2 mol N; therefore (d) > (b). The mol. wt. of N_2O = 44. In 50.0 g N_2O there is more than 1 mol N_2O, and, therefore, more than 2 mol N; (a) > (d). The mol. wt. of C_6H_5N = 91. A 150-cm^3 sample will weigh less than 150 g (because the density is less than 1.00 g/cm^3), contain less than 2 mol of C_6H_5N, and less than 2 mol N.

5. (*c*) The contribution of 3 F atoms to the formula weight of XF_3 is $3 \times 19.0 = 57.0$. This represents 65% of the mass of the compound. $(57/x) \times 100 = 65$. $x = 5700/65 = 88$. The compound XF_3 has a formula weight of 88. The at. wt. of X = 88 − 57 = 31. An alternative method is to assume each of the four possible values for the at. wt. of X, determine the formula weight, and then the % F. Choose the value of X that yields 65% F.

6. $$\text{no. cm}^3\ CHBr_3 = 3.40 \times 10^{24} \text{ molecules } CHBr_3 \times \frac{1 \text{ mol } CHBr_3}{6.02 \times 10^{23} \text{ molecules } CHBr_3} \times \frac{253\ CHBr_3}{1 \text{ mol } CHBr_3} \times \frac{1 \text{ cm}^3\ CHBr_3}{2.89 \text{ g } CHBr_3} = 494 \text{ cm}^3$$

7. (a) CaI_2 = calcium iodide
   (b) $Fe_2(SO_4)_3$ = iron(III) sulfate
   (c) SO_3 = sulfur trioxide
   (d) BrF_5 = bromine pentafluoride
   (e) NH_4CN = ammonium cyanide
   (f) $Ca(ClO_2)_2$ = calcium chlorite
   (g) $LiHCO_3$ = lithium hydrogen carbonate

8. (a) $$\%Cu = \frac{(2 \times 63.55)}{(2 \times 63.55) + 12.01 + (5 \times 16.00) + (2 \times 1.008)} \times 100 = \frac{127}{221} \times 100 = 57.5\%\ Cu$$

   (b) $$\text{no. g CuO} = 1000 \text{ g } CuCO_3 \cdot Cu(OH)_2 \times \frac{1 \text{ mol } CuCO_3 \cdot Cu(OH)_2}{221 \text{ g } CuCO_3 \cdot Cu(OH)_2} \times \frac{2 \text{ mol Cu}}{1 \text{ mol } CuCO_3 \cdot Cu(OH)_2} \times \frac{1 \text{ mol CuO}}{1 \text{ mol Cu}} \times \frac{79.6 \text{ g CuO}}{1 \text{ mol CuO}} = 720 \text{ g CuO}$$

9. In the usual fashion, based on a 100.0 g sample,

no. mol N = 25.9 g N × $\frac{1 \text{ mol N}}{14.0 \text{ g N}}$ = 1.85 mol N

no. mol O = 74.1 g O × $\frac{1 \text{ mol O}}{16.0 \text{ g O}}$ = 4.63 mol O

Empirical formula $= N_{\frac{1.85}{1.85}}O_{\frac{4.63}{1.85}} = NO_{2.50} = N_2O_5$

10. If the hydrate contains almost exactly 50% H_2O, by mass, then the contribution of H_2O to the formula weight must be almost exactly the same as that of Na_2SO_3 (sodium sulfite). The formula weight of Na_2SO_3 = 126. A contribution of 126 would also be made by 126/18 = 7 molecules of H_2O. The hydrate formula is $Na_2SO_3 \cdot 7H_2O$.

Chapter 4

Stoichiometry II: Chemical Reactions

Evidence for chemical reactions

4-1. (a) No reaction. The ions present in the clear colorless solution after mixing are the same ones as present originally.

(b) The formation of a precipitate is visual evidence of a chemical reaction. The precipitate is radium sulfate, $RaSO_4$. (Radium is a radioactive element.) The balanced chemical equation is

$RaCl_2(aq) + Na_2SO_4(aq) \longrightarrow 2\ NaCl(aq) + RaSO_4(s)$

In the net ionic form, all that appears is the combination of Ra^{2+} ion (from $RaCl_2$) and SO_4^{2-} ion (from Na_2SO_4). $Ra^{2+}(aq) + SO_4^{2-}(aq) \longrightarrow RaSO_4(s)$

(c) Determine the formula of the oxide of iron with 72.3% Fe and 27.7% O. In 100 g of the oxide,

$$\text{no. mol Fe} = 72.3\ \text{g Fe} \times \frac{1\ \text{mol Fe}}{55.85\ \text{g Fe}} = 1.29\ \text{mol Fe}$$

$$\text{no. mol O} = 27.1\ \text{g O} \times \frac{1\ \text{mol O}}{16.0\ \text{g O}} = 1.69\ \text{mol O}$$

$$Fe_{1.29}O_{1.69} = Fe_{\frac{1.29}{1.29}}O_{\frac{1.69}{1.29}} = FeO_{1.31} = Fe_3O_{(3 \times 1.31)} = Fe_3O_4$$

$3\ Fe_2O_3 + H_2 \longrightarrow 2\ Fe_3O_4 + H_2O$

4-2. (a) $2\ Mg(s) + O_2(g) \longrightarrow 2\ MgO(s)$

(b) $S(s) + O_2(g) \longrightarrow SO_2(g)$

(c) $CH_4(g) + 2\ O_2(g) \longrightarrow CO_2(g) + 2\ H_2O(l)$

(d) $Ag_2SO_4(aq) + BaI_2(aq) \longrightarrow BaSO_4(s) + 2\ AgI(s)$

or $2\ Ag^+ + SO_4^{2-} + Ba^{2+} + 2\ I^- \longrightarrow BaSO_4(s) + 2\ AgI(s)$

4-3. (a) $H_2O(g) + C(s) \longrightarrow CO(g) + H_2(g)$

(b) $2\ Al(s) + 3\ Cu^{2+}(aq) \longrightarrow 2\ Al^{3+}(aq) + 3\ Cu(s)$

(c) $ZnS(s) + 2\ H^+(aq) \longrightarrow Zn^{2+}(aq) + H_2S(g)$

(d) $2\ Cl_2(g) + 2\ H_2O(g) \longrightarrow 4\ HCl(g) + O_2(g)$

4-4. (a) $Na_2SO_4(s) + 2\ C(s) \longrightarrow Na_2S(s) + 2\ CO_2(g)$

(b) $Cl_2(aq) + H_2O(l) \longrightarrow HCl(aq) + HOCl(aq)$

(c) $PCl_3(l) + 3\ H_2O(l) \longrightarrow H_3PO_3(aq) + 3\ HCl(aq)$

(d) $6\ P_2H_4(l) \longrightarrow 8\ PH_3(g) + P_4(g)$

(e) $3\ PbO(s) + 2\ NH_3(g) \longrightarrow 3\ Pb(s) + N_2(g) + 3\ H_2O(l)$

(f) $3\ NO_2(g) + H_2O(l) \longrightarrow 2\ HNO_3(aq) + NO(g)$

(g) $6\ S_2Cl_2 + 16\ NH_3 \longrightarrow N_4S_4 + 12\ NH_4Cl + S_8$

(h) $Mg_3N_2 + 6\ H_2O \longrightarrow 3\ Mg(OH)_2 + 2\ NH_3$

(i) $SO_2Cl_2 + 8\ HI \longrightarrow H_2S + 2\ H_2O + 2\ HCl + 4\ I_2$

(j) $S_8 + 12\ NaOH \longrightarrow 4\ Na_2S + 2\ Na_2S_2O_3 + 6\ H_2O$

4-5. (a) $Zn(s) + 2\ Ag^+(aq) \longrightarrow Zn^{2+}(aq) + 2\ Ag(s)$

(b) $Mn^{2+}(aq) + H_2S(g) \longrightarrow MnS(s) + 2\ H^+(aq)$

(c) $2\ Al(s) + 6\ H^+(aq) \longrightarrow 2\ Al^{3+}(aq) + 3\ H_2(g)$

(d) $S_2O_3^{\ 2-}(aq) + 2\ H^+(aq) \longrightarrow H_2O(l) + S(s) + SO_2(g)$

(e) $MnO_2(s) + 4\ H^+(aq) + 2\ Cl^-(aq) \longrightarrow Mn^{2+}(aq) + 2\ H_2O(l) + Cl_2(g)$

4-6. (a) $C_5H_{12} + 8\ O_2 \longrightarrow 5\ CO_2 + 6\ H_2O$

(b) $2\ C_6H_6 + 15\ O_2 \longrightarrow 12\ CO_2 + 6\ H_2O$

(c) $C_6H_{12}O_6 + 6\ O_2 \longrightarrow 6\ CO_2 + 6\ H_2O$

(d) $2\ C_2H_6O_2 + 5\ O_2 \longrightarrow 4\ CO_2 + 6\ H_2O$

(e) $2\ C_3H_7OH + 9\ O_2 \longrightarrow 6\ CO_2 + 8\ H_2O$

Stoichiometry of chemical reations

4-7. $\text{no. mol } Cl_2 = 4.4 \text{ mol Fe} \times \frac{3 \text{ mol } Cl_2}{2 \text{ mol Fe}} = 6.6 \text{ mol } Cl_2$

4-8. $\text{no. mol } Cl_2 = 4.50 \text{ mol } PCl_3 \times \frac{6 \text{ mol } Cl_2}{4 \text{ mol } PCl_3} = 6.75 \text{ mol } Cl_2$

$\text{no. mol } P_4 = 4.50 \text{ mol } PCl_3 \times \frac{1 \text{ mol } P_4}{4 \text{ mol } PCl_3} = 1.12 \text{ mol } P_4$

4-9. (a) $\text{no. mol } H_2 = 125 \text{ g } CaH_2 \times \frac{1 \text{ mol } CaH_2}{42.1 \text{ g } CaH_2} \times \frac{2 \text{ mol } H_2}{1 \text{ mol } CaH_2} = 5.94 \text{ mol } H_2$

(b) $\text{no. g } H_2O = 125 \text{ g } CaH_2 \times \frac{1 \text{ mol } CaH_2}{42.1 \text{ g } CaH_2} \times \frac{2 \text{ mol } H_2O}{1 \text{ mol } CaH_2} \times \frac{18.0 \text{ g } H_2O}{1 \text{ mol } H_2O} = 107 \text{ g } H_2O$

(c) $\text{no. g } CaH_2 = 1.00 \times 10^{24} \text{ molecules } H_2 \times \frac{1 \text{ mol } H_2}{6.02 \times 10^{23} \text{ molecules } H_2} \times \frac{1 \text{ mol } CaH_2}{2 \text{ mol } H_2}$

$\times \frac{42.1 \text{ g } CaH_2}{1 \text{ mol } CaH_2} = 35.0 \text{ g } CaH_2$

4-10. (a) $\text{no. mol } O_2 = 10.0 \text{ g } KClO_3 \times \frac{1 \text{ mol } KClO_3}{123 \text{ g } KClO_3} \times \frac{3 \text{ mol } O_2}{2 \text{ mol } KClO_3} = 0.122 \text{ mol } O_2$

(b) $\text{no. molecules } O_2 = 0.122 \text{ mol } O_2 \times \frac{6.02 \times 10^{23} \text{ molecules } O_2}{1 \text{ mol } O_2} = 7.34 \times 10^{22} \text{ molecules } O_2$

(c) $\text{no. g KCl} = 10.0 \text{ g } KClO_3 \times \frac{1 \text{ mol } KClO_3}{123 \text{ g } KClO_3} \times \frac{2 \text{ mol KCl}}{2 \text{ mol } KClO_3} \times \frac{74.6 \text{ g KCl}}{1 \text{ mol KCl}} = 6.07 \text{ g KCl}$

4-11. $\text{no. g } CO_2 = 12.0 \text{ g sample} \times \frac{52.5 \text{ g } Na_2CO_3}{100 \text{ g sample}} \times \frac{1 \text{ mol } Na_2CO_3}{106 \text{ g } Na_2CO_3} \times \frac{1 \text{ mol } CO_2}{1 \text{ mol } Na_2CO_3} \times \frac{44.0 \text{ g } CO_2}{1 \text{ mol } CO_2} = 2.62 \text{ g } CO_2$

4-12. The key to this problem is to determine how much *pure* Fe_2O_3 is required to produce 453 kg Fe; the quantity will be less than 752 kg. The percent Fe_2O_3 in the ore is determined in the usual way.

$$\text{no. kg } Fe_2O_3 = 453 \text{ kg Fe} \times \frac{1000 \text{ g Fe}}{1 \text{ kg Fe}} \times \frac{1 \text{ mol Fe}}{55.8 \text{ g Fe}} \times \frac{1 \text{ mol } Fe_2O_3}{2 \text{ mol Fe}} \times \frac{160 \text{ g } Fe_2O_3}{1 \text{ mol } Fe_2O_3}$$

$$\times \frac{1 \text{ kg } Fe_2O_3}{1000 \text{ g } Fe_2O_3} = 649 \text{ kg } Fe_2O_3$$

$$\%Fe_2O_3 = \frac{649 \text{ kg } Fe_2O_3}{752 \text{ kg ore}} \times 100 = 86.3\%$$

Rather than to convert from kg Fe to g Fe and, later, from g Fe_2O_3 to kg Fe_2O_3, consider the concept of a *kilomole*:

1 kmol Fe = 55.8 kg Fe   1 kmol Fe_2O_3 = 160 kg Fe_2O_3

$$\text{no. kg } Fe_2O_3 = 453 \text{ kg Fe} \times \frac{1 \text{ kmol Fe}}{55.8 \text{ kg Fe}} \times \frac{1 \text{ kmol } Fe_2O_3}{2 \text{ kmol Fe}} \times \frac{160 \text{ kg } Fe_2O_3}{1 \text{ kmol } Fe_2O_3} = 649 \text{ kg } Fe_2O_3$$

4-13. First write a balanced equation for the reaction, and then proceed as in Exercise 4-12. That is, determine the mass of *pure* Ag_2O required to produce 0.104 g O_2.

$$2\, Ag_2O(s) \longrightarrow 4\, Ag(s) + O_2(g)$$

$$\text{no. g } Ag_2O = 0.104 \text{ g } O_2 \times \frac{1 \text{ mol } O_2}{32.0 \text{ g } O_2} \times \frac{2 \text{ mol } Ag_2O}{1 \text{ mol } O_2} \times \frac{232 \text{ g } Ag_2O}{1 \text{ mol } Ag_2O} = 1.51 \text{ g } Ag_2O$$

$$\%\, Ag_2O = \frac{1.51 \text{ g } Ag_2O}{1.60 \text{ g sample}} \times 100 = 94.4\%$$

4-14. $\text{no. g } H_2 = (4.0 \text{ in.} \times 3.0 \text{ in.} \times 0.025 \text{ in.}) \times \frac{(2.54)^3 \text{ cm}^3}{(1)^3 \text{ in.}^3} \times \frac{2.70 \text{ g Al}}{1 \text{ cm}^3} \times \frac{1 \text{ mol Al}}{27.0 \text{ g Al}}$

$$\times \frac{3 \text{ mol } H_2}{2 \text{ mol Al}} \times \frac{2.02 \text{ g } H_2}{1 \text{ mol } H_2} = 1.49 \text{ g } H_2$$

4-15. $\text{no. ml} = 7.50 \text{ g KI} \times \frac{1 \text{ mol KI}}{166 \text{ g KI}} \times \frac{2 \text{ mol } KMnO_4}{10 \text{ mol KI}} \times \frac{158 \text{ g } KMnO_4}{1 \text{ mol } KMnO_4} \times \frac{1}{15.8 \text{ g } KMnO_4} \times \frac{1000 \text{ ml}}{1 \text{ L}} = 90.4 \text{ ml}$

Molar concentration

4-16. (a) $\frac{1.50 \text{ mol } C_2H_5OH}{4.80 \text{ L}} = 0.312 \text{ M } C_2H_5OH$

(b) $$\frac{12.5 \text{ g } CH_3OH \times \frac{1 \text{ mol } CH_3OH}{32.0 \text{ g } CH_3OH}}{50.0 \text{ ml} \times \frac{1 \text{ L}}{1000 \text{ ml}}} = 7.81 \text{ M } CH_3OH$$

(c) $$\frac{10.0 \text{ ml } C_3H_8O_3 \times \frac{1.26 \text{ g } C_3H_8O_3}{1.00 \text{ ml } C_3H_8O_3} \times \frac{1 \text{ mol } C_3H_8O_3}{92.1 \text{ g } C_3H_8O_3}}{0.250 \text{ L}} = 0.547 \text{ M } C_3H_8O_3$$

(d) $$\frac{125 \text{ g sample} \times \frac{98.6 \text{ g } CO(NH_2)_2}{100 \text{ g sample}} \times \frac{1 \text{ mol } CO(NH_2)_2}{60.1 \text{ g } CO(NH_2)_2}}{0.500 \text{ L}} = 4.10 \text{ M } CO(NH_2)_2$$

(e) $$\frac{15.0 \text{ mg } (C_2H_5)_2O \times \frac{1.00 \text{ g } (C_2H_5)_2O}{1000 \text{ mg } (C_2H_5)_2O} \times \frac{1 \text{ mol } (C_2H_5)_2O}{74.1 \text{ g } (C_2H_5)_2O}}{3.00 \text{ gal} \times \frac{3.78 \text{ L}}{1 \text{ gal}}} = 1.79 \times 10^{-5} \text{ M } (C_2H_5)_2O$$

4-17. (a) $\text{no. mol KCl} = 1.50 \times 10^2 \text{ L} \times \frac{0.275 \text{ mol KCl}}{\text{L}} = 41.2 \text{ mol KCl}$

(b) $\text{no. g } Na_2SO_4 = 0.325 \text{ L} \times \frac{0.115 \text{ mol } Na_2SO_4}{\text{L}} \times \frac{142 \text{ g } Na_2SO_4}{1 \text{ mol } Na_2SO_4} = 5.31 \text{ g } Na_2SO_4$

(c) $\text{no. cm}^3 \; CH_3OH = 2.50 \text{ L} \times \frac{0.150 \text{ mol } CH_3OH}{\text{L}} \times \frac{32.0 \text{ g } CH_3OH}{1 \text{ mol } CH_3OH} \times \frac{1 \text{ cm}^3 \; CH_3OH}{0.792 \text{ g } CH_3OH} = 15.2 \text{ cm}^3 \; CH_3OH$

(d) $\text{no. gal } C_2H_5OH = 55.0 \text{ gal} \times \frac{3.78 \text{ L}}{1 \text{ gal}} \times \frac{2.10 \text{ mol } C_2H_5OH}{\text{L}} \times \frac{46.1 \text{ g } C_2H_5OH}{1 \text{ mol } C_2H_5OH} \times \frac{1 \text{ cm}^3 \; C_2H_5OH}{0.789 \text{ g } C_2H_5OH}$

$\times \frac{1 \text{ L } C_2H_5OH}{1000 \text{ cm}^3 \; C_2H_5OH} \times \frac{1 \text{ gal } C_2H_5OH}{3.78 \text{ L } C_2H_5OH} = 6.75 \text{ gal } C_2H_5OH$

4-18. Determine the total number of moles of sucrose and divide by the total solution volume, in liters.

$\text{no. mol } C_{12}H_{22}O_{11} = 0.385 \text{ L} \times \frac{1.50 \text{ mol } C_{12}H_{22}O_{11}}{\text{L}} = 0.578 \text{ mol } C_{12}H_{22}O_{11}$

$\text{no. mol } C_{12}H_{22}O_{11} = 0.615 \text{ L} \times \frac{1.25 \text{ mol } C_{12}H_{22}O_{11}}{\text{L}} = 0.769 \text{ mol } C_{12}H_{22}O_{11}$

$\text{total mol } C_{12}H_{22}O_{11} = 0.578 + 0.769 = 1.347 \text{ mol } C_{12}H_{22}O_{11}$

$\text{final molarity} = \frac{1.347 \text{ mol } C_{12}H_{22}O_{11}}{(0.385 + 0.615) \text{ L}} = 1.35 \text{ M } C_{12}H_{22}O_{11}$

4-19. The mass of pure HCl required in the solution is determined in the usual way. But this mass must then be converted to mass of concentrated acid, by using the *reciprocal* of the percent composition (100/36.0), and then to volume of concentrated acid, by using the *reciprocal* of the density (1.00/1.26).

$\text{no. ml conc. acid} = 15.0 \text{ L soln.} \times \frac{0.500 \text{ mol HCl}}{1 \text{ L soln.}} \times \frac{36.5 \text{ g HCl}}{1 \text{ mol HCl}} \times \frac{100 \text{ g conc. acid}}{36.0 \text{ g HCl}}$

$\times \frac{1 \text{ ml conc. acid}}{1.26 \text{ g conc. acid}} = 604 \text{ ml conc. acid}$

4-20. The amount of solute in the final, diluted solution is calculated first.

$\text{no. mol KOH} = 2.00 \text{ L} \times \frac{0.278 \text{ mol KOH}}{\text{L}} = 0.556 \text{ mol KOH}$

Now determine the volume of 1.000 M KOH required to contain this same amount of solute.

$$\text{no. L} = 0.556 \text{ mol KOH} \times \frac{1 \text{ L}}{1.000 \text{ mol KOH}} = 0.556 \text{ L} = 556 \text{ ml}$$

4-21. Determine the no mol $MgSO_4$ in the original solution.

$$\text{no. mol } MgSO_4 = 0.0700 \text{ L} \times \frac{0.485 \text{ mol } MgSO_4}{\text{L}} = 0.0340 \text{ mol } MgSO_4$$

This much solute remains in 45.0 ml of solution, leading to a molar concentration of

$$\frac{0.0340 \text{ mol } MgSO_4}{0.0450 \text{ L}} = 0.756 \text{ M } MgSO_4$$

An alternative method is to solve equation (4.10) for M_{final}.

$$M_{final} = M_{orig.} \times \frac{V_{orig.}}{V_{final}} = 0.485 \text{ M} \times \frac{0.0700 \text{ L}}{0.0450 \text{ L}} = 0.754 \text{ M } MgSO_4$$

Chemical reactions in solutions

4-22. The no. mol NaOH consumed in the titration can be calculated first.

$$\text{no. mol NaOH} = 0.02500 \text{ L} \times \frac{0.1252 \text{ mol } HNO_3}{\text{L}} \times \frac{1 \text{ mol NaOH}}{1 \text{ mol } HNO_3} = 3.130 \times 10^{-3} \text{ mol NaOH}$$

Now determine the volume of 0.1060 M NaOH containing this much NaOH.

$$\text{no. ml} = 3.130 \times 10^{-3} \text{ mol NaOH} \times \frac{1 \text{ L}}{0.1060 \text{ mol NaOH}} \times \frac{1000 \text{ ml}}{1 \text{ L}} = 29.53 \text{ ml}$$

4-23. (a) $\text{no. g } Ca(OH)_2 = 0.325 \text{ L} \times \frac{0.410 \text{ mol HCl}}{\text{L}} \times \frac{1 \text{ mol } Ca(OH)_2}{2 \text{ mol HCl}} \times \frac{74.1 \text{ g } Ca(OH)_2}{1 \text{ mol } Ca(OH)_2} = 4.94 \text{ g } Ca(OH)_2$

(b) $\text{no. kg } Ca(OH)_2 = 152 \text{ L soln.} \times \frac{1000 \text{ cm}^3 \text{ soln.}}{1 \text{ L soln.}} \times \frac{1.15 \text{ g soln.}}{1 \text{ cm}^3 \text{ soln.}} \times \frac{30.12 \text{ g HCl}}{100 \text{ g soln.}}$

$$\times \frac{1 \text{ mol HCl}}{36.5 \text{ g HCl}} \times \frac{1 \text{ mol } Ca(OH)_2}{2 \text{ mol HCl}} \times \frac{74.1 \text{ g } Ca(OH)_2}{1 \text{ mol } Ca(OH)_2} \times \frac{1 \text{ kg } Ca(OH)_2}{1000 \text{ g } Ca(OH)_2} = 53.4 \text{ kg } Ca(OH)_2$$

4-24. (a) The number of moles of NH_3 present in the 5.00 ml sample is

$$\text{no. mol } NH_3 = 31.20 \text{ ml acid} \times \frac{1 \text{ L acid}}{1000 \text{ ml acid}} \times \frac{1.000 \text{ mol HCl}}{1 \text{ L acid}} \times \frac{1 \text{ mol } NH_3}{1 \text{ mol HCl}} = 0.0312 \text{ mol } NH_3$$

$$\text{Molarity of } NH_3 = \frac{0.0312 \text{ mol } NH_3}{0.00500 \text{ L}} = 6.24 \text{ M } NH_3$$

(b) $\frac{\text{no. g } NH_3}{\text{L}} = \frac{6.24 \text{ mol } NH_3}{1 \text{ L}} \times \frac{17.0 \text{ g } NH_3}{1 \text{ mol } NH_3} = \frac{106 \text{ g } NH_3}{\text{L}}$

The mass of one liter of solution is: $m = d \cdot v$.

$\text{no. g} = 0.96 \text{ g/ml} \times 1000 \text{ ml} = 960 \text{ g}$ $\qquad \% NH_3 = \frac{106 \text{ g } NH_3}{960 \text{ g soln.}} \times 100 = 11.0\%$

4-25. (a) $\text{no. mol HCl} = 20 \text{ L} \times \frac{0.25 \text{ mol HCl}}{\text{L}} = 5.0 \text{ mol HCl}$

The volume of concentrated HCl(aq) to produce 5.0 mol HCl is calculated next.

$$\text{no. ml conc. acid} = 5.0 \text{ mol HCl} \times \frac{36.5 \text{ g HCl}}{1 \text{ mol HCl}} \times \frac{100 \text{ g conc. acid}}{38 \text{ g HCl}} \times \frac{1 \text{ ml conc. acid}}{1.19 \text{ g conc. acid}} = 404 \text{ ml conc. acid}$$

(b) $$\text{no. mol HCl} = 0.03010 \text{ L} \times \frac{0.2000 \text{ mol NaOH}}{\text{L}} \times \frac{1 \text{ mol HCl}}{1 \text{ mol NaOH}} = 6.020 \times 10^{-3} \text{ mol HCl}$$

$$\text{molarity} = \frac{6.020 \times 10^{-3} \text{ mol HCl}}{0.02500 \text{ L}} = 0.2408 \text{ M HCl}$$

(c) Measurements required to produce the diluted acid from concentrated HCl(aq) cannot be made with sufficient precision to yield four significant figures in the calculated molarity. That is, the 404 ml of concentrated acid cannot easily be measured to within 0.1 ml and the 20 L final solution volume cannot easily be measured to the nearest 10 ml. Equally important is the fact that the percent composition of the acid is usually not known to the nearest 0.01%, nor can we be assured that its concentration does not change during storage. Titration, on the other hand, easily yields four significant figures for solution concentrations.

4-26. From the titration data first determine the mass of Fe in the ore sample.

$$\text{no. g Fe} = 0.03610 \text{ L} \times \frac{0.0410 \text{ mol } K_2Cr_2O_7}{\text{L}} \times \frac{6 \text{ mol Fe}}{1 \text{ mol } K_2Cr_2O_7} \times \frac{55.85 \text{ g Fe}}{1 \text{ mol Fe}} = 0.496 \text{ g Fe}$$

$$\%\text{Fe} = \frac{0.496 \text{ g Fe}}{0.8515 \text{ g ore}} \times 100 = 58.3\% \text{ Fe}$$

4-27. The quantity to determine first is the number of moles of HCl that must be reacted to change the concentration in the manner desired.

Initial solution

$$\text{no. mol HCl} = 0.500 \text{ L} \times \frac{1.012 \text{ mol HCl}}{1 \text{ L}} = 0.506 \text{ mol HCl}$$

Final solution

$$\text{no. mol HCl} = 0.500 \text{ L} \times \frac{1.000 \text{ mol HCl}}{1 \text{ L}} = 0.500 \text{ mol HCl}$$

The amount of HCl to be reacted is 0.506 - 0.500 = 0.006 mol HCl. The quantity of magnesium required for the reaction may now be calculated.

$$\text{no. mg Mg} = 0.006 \text{ mol HCl} \times \frac{1 \text{ mol Mg}}{2 \text{ mol HCl}} \times \frac{24 \text{ g Mg}}{1 \text{ mol Mg}} \times \frac{1000 \text{ mg Mg}}{1 \text{ g Mg}} = 72 \text{ mg Mg}$$

Determining the limiting reagent

4-28. The reaction of interest is: $3\ CS_2 + 6\ NaOH \longrightarrow 2\ Na_2CS_3 + Na_2CO_3 + 3\ H_2O$

(a) The CS_2 is the excess reactant because only 0.50 mol CS_2 is consumed along with 1.00 mol NaOH, whereas 1.00 mol of each is available originally.

$$\text{no. mol } CS_2 \text{ consumed} = 1.00 \text{ mol NaOH} \times \frac{3 \text{ mol } CS_2}{6 \text{ mol NaOH}} = 0.50 \text{ mol } CS_2$$

The amounts of the products must be related either to the 1.00 mol NaOH or to the 0.50 mol CS_2 consumed.

$$\text{no. mol } Na_2CS_3 = 1.00 \text{ mol NaOH} \times \frac{2 \text{ mol } Na_2CS_3}{6 \text{ mol NaOH}} = 0.33 \text{ mol } Na_2CS_3$$

$$\text{no. mol } Na_2CO_3 = 1.00 \text{ mol NaOH} \times \frac{1 \text{ mol } Na_2CO_3}{6 \text{ mol NaOH}} = 0.17 \text{ mol } Na_2CO_3$$

$$\text{no. mol } H_2O = 1.00 \text{ mol NaOH} \times \frac{3 \text{ mol } H_2O}{6 \text{ mol NaOH}} = 0.50 \text{ mol } H_2O$$

(b) First determine the limiting reagent. For example, calculate the number of mol CS_2 in 100.0 cm^3 of the liquid.

$$\text{no. mol } CS_2 = 100.0 \text{ cm}^3\ CS_2 \times \frac{1.26 \text{ g } CS_2}{1 \text{ cm}^3\ CS_2} \times \frac{1 \text{ mol } CS_2}{76.1 \text{ g } CS_2} = 1.66 \text{ mol } CS_2$$

Now compare this to the available NaOH: $\text{no. mol } CS_2 = 3.50 \text{ mol NaOH} \times \frac{3 \text{ mol } CS_2}{6 \text{ mol NaOH}} = 1.75 \text{ mol } CS_2$

To react with all of the NaOH, 1.75 mol CS_2 is required. However, only 1.66 mol CS_2 is available. CS_2 is the limiting reagent.

$$\text{no. g } Na_2CS_3 = 1.66 \text{ mol } CS_2 \times \frac{2 \text{ mol } Na_2CS_3}{3 \text{ mol } CS_2} \times \frac{154 \text{ g } Na_2CS_3}{1 \text{ mol } Na_2CS_3} = 170 \text{ g } Na_2CS_3$$

4-29. First, write a balanced equation for the reaction: $2\ NH_4Cl + Ca(OH)_2 \longrightarrow CaCl_2 + 2\ H_2O + 2\ NH_3(g)$
Next, determine the no. mol of each reactant.

$$\text{no. mol } NH_4Cl = 15.0 \text{ g } NH_4Cl \times \frac{1 \text{ mol } NH_4Cl}{53.5 \text{ g } NH_4Cl} = 0.280 \text{ mol } NH_4Cl$$

$$\text{no. mol } Ca(OH)_2 = 15.0 \text{ g } Ca(OH)_2 \times \frac{1 \text{ mol } Ca(OH)_2}{74.1 \text{ g } Ca(OH)_2} = 0.202 \text{ mol } Ca(OH)_2$$

From the balanced equation we see that 2 mol NH_4Cl is consumed for every mol $Ca(OH)_2$ that reacts. However, the amount of NH_4Cl available is less than twice the amount of $Ca(OH)_2$. NH_4Cl is the limiting reagent.

$$\text{no. g } NH_3 = 0.280 \text{ mol } NH_4Cl \times \frac{2 \text{ mol } NH_3}{2 \text{ mol } NH_4Cl} \times \frac{17.0 \text{ g } NH_3}{1 \text{ mol } NH_3} = 4.76 \text{ g } NH_3$$

4-30. (a) $2\ H_2 + O_2 \longrightarrow 2\ H_2O$

(b) First it must be determined which reactant is consumed and which is in excess. For example, determine the number of grams of H_2 required to react completely with all of the available O_2.

$$\text{no. g } H_2 = 36.40 \text{ g } O_2 \times \frac{1 \text{ mol } O_2}{32.00 \text{ g } O_2} \times \frac{2 \text{ mol } H_2}{1 \text{ mol } O_2} \times \frac{2.016 \text{ g } H_2}{1 \text{ mol } H_2} = 4.586 \text{ g } H_2$$

no. g H_2 available = 4.800. Therefore, excess H_2 remains and all of the O_2 is consumed.

$$\text{no. g } H_2O \text{ produced} = 36.40 \text{ g } O_2 \times \frac{1 \text{ mol } O_2}{32.00 \text{ g } O_2} \times \frac{2 \text{ mol } H_2O}{1 \text{ mol } O_2} \times \frac{18.02 \text{ g } H_2O}{1 \text{ mol } H_2O} = 41.00 \text{ g } H_2O$$

no. g H_2 left = 4.800 g H_2 available − 4.586 g H_2 consumed = 0.214 g H_2

no. g O_2 left = 0

(c) Original mass = 36.40 g O_2 + 4.800 g H_2 = 41.20 g total

Final mass = 41.00 g H_2O + 0.214 g H_2 + 0.00 g O_2 = 41.21 g total

Within the limits of experimental error, the law of conservation of mass is verified.

4-31. Again it is necessary to express the amount of each reactant in number of moles. Percentage composition and density enter into these calculations as conversion factors.

$$\text{no. mol } K_2Cr_2O_7 = 61.3 \text{ g sample} \times \frac{96 \text{ g } K_2Cr_2O_7}{100 \text{ g sample}} \times \frac{1 \text{ mol } K_2Cr_2O_7}{294 \text{ g } K_2Cr_2O_7} = 0.20 \text{ mol } K_2Cr_2O_7$$

$$\text{no. mol HCl} = 320 \text{ ml acid} \times \frac{1.15 \text{ g acid}}{1 \text{ ml acid}} \times \frac{30 \text{ g HCl}}{100 \text{ g acid}} \times \frac{1 \text{ mol HCl}}{36.5 \text{ g HCl}} = 3.0 \text{ mol HCl}$$

Inspection of the balanced chemical equation reveals that 14 mol HCl are consumed for every mol $K_2Cr_2O_7$. To react with the 0.20 mol $K_2Cr_2O_7$, 2.8 mol HCl is required. More than this amount of HCl is available. It is the reactant in excess; $K_2Cr_2O_7$ is the limiting reagent.

$$\text{no. g } Cl_2 = 0.20 \text{ mol } K_2Cr_2O_7 \times \frac{3 \text{ mol } Cl_2}{1 \text{ mol } K_2Cr_2O_7} \times \frac{70.9 \text{ g } Cl_2}{1 \text{ mol } Cl_2} = 43 \text{ g } Cl_2$$

Simultaneous reactions

4-32. Determine the number of moles of HCl required to dissolve each portion of the sample. Add these two amounts together and convert the total number of moles to a mass in grams.

$$\text{no. mol HCl} = 140.0 \text{ g sample} \times \frac{26.0 \text{ g } MgCO_3}{100 \text{ g sample}} \times \frac{1 \text{ mol } MgCO_3}{84.3 \text{ g } MgCO_3} \times \frac{2 \text{ mol HCl}}{1 \text{ mol } MgCO_3} = 0.864 \text{ mol HCl}$$

$$\text{no. mol HCl} = 140.0 \text{ g sample} \times \frac{74.0 \text{ g } Mg(OH)_2}{100 \text{ g sample}} \times \frac{1 \text{ mol } Mg(OH)_2}{58.3 \text{ g } Mg(OH)_2} \times \frac{2 \text{ mol HCl}}{1 \text{ mol } Mg(OH)_2} = 3.55 \text{ mol HCl}$$

$$\text{no. g HCl} = (0.86 + 3.55) \text{ mol HCl} \times \frac{36.5 \text{ g HCl}}{1 \text{ mol HCl}} = 161 \text{ g HCl}$$

4-33. The procedure here is similar to that of Exercise 4-32, except that an equation must be written for each combustion reaction.

$$C_3H_8 + 5\ O_2 \longrightarrow 3\ CO_2 + 4\ H_2O \qquad 2\ C_4H_{10} + 13\ O_2 \longrightarrow 8\ CO_2 + 10\ H_2O$$

$$\text{no. mol } CO_2 = 225 \text{ g mixture} \times \frac{68.2 \text{ g } C_3H_8}{100 \text{ g mixture}} \times \frac{1 \text{ mol } C_3H_8}{44.1 \text{ g } C_3H_8} \times \frac{3 \text{ mol } CO_2}{1 \text{ mol } C_3H_8} = 10.4 \text{ mol } CO_2$$

$$\text{no. mol } CO_2 = 225 \text{ g mixture} \times \frac{31.8 \text{ g } C_4H_{10}}{100 \text{ g mixture}} \times \frac{1 \text{ mol } C_4H_{10}}{58.1 \text{ g } C_4H_{10}} \times \frac{8 \text{ mol } CO_2}{2 \text{ mol } C_4H_{10}} = 4.93 \text{ mol } CO_2$$

$$\text{total no. mol } CO_2 = 10.4 + 4.9 = 15.3 \text{ mol } CO_2$$

4-34. Again, we begin by writing balanced equations for the reactions.

$$2\ CH_3OH + 3\ O_2 \longrightarrow 2\ CO_2 + 4\ H_2O \qquad C_2H_5OH + 3\ O_2 \longrightarrow 2\ CO_2 + 3\ H_2O$$

The simplest approach is to calculate the number of grams of CO_2 that would be obtained by burning 0.220 g of a pure alcohol. If one of the results corresponds to the observed mass of CO_2--0.352 g--then the liquid is a pure alcohol. If neither of the results yields 0.352 g CO_2, the liquid must be a mixture.

If pure CH_3OH

$$\text{no. g } CO_2 = 0.220 \text{ g } CH_3OH \times \frac{1 \text{ mol } CH_3OH}{32.0 \text{ g } CH_3OH} \times \frac{2 \text{ mol } CO_2}{2 \text{ mol } CH_3OH} \times \frac{44.0 \text{ g } CO_2}{1 \text{ mol } CO_2} = 0.302 \text{ g } CO_2$$

If pure C_2H_5OH

$$\text{no. g } CO_2 = 0.220 \text{ g } C_2H_5OH \times \frac{1 \text{ mol } C_2H_5OH}{46.1 \text{ g } C_2H_5OH} \times \frac{2 \text{ mol } CO_2}{1 \text{ mol } C_2H_5OH} \times \frac{44.0 \text{ g } CO_2}{1 \text{ mol } CO_2} = 0.420 \text{ g } CO_2$$

Since neither of the results is 0.352 g CO_2, the liquid must be a mixture. (Can you determine the percent composition of this mixture?)

Consecutive reactions

4-35. $$\text{no. mol } Cl_2 = 15.0 \text{ mol } CCl_2F_2 \times \frac{1 \text{ mol } CCl_4}{1 \text{ mol } CCl_2F_2} \times \frac{4 \text{ mol } Cl_2}{1 \text{ mol } CCl_4} = 60.0 \text{ mol } Cl_2$$

4-36. In addition to the equation given for the precipitation of $BaCO_3$, we need an equation to represent the combustion of C_6H_6.

$$2\ C_6H_6 + 15\ O_2 \longrightarrow 12\ CO_2 + 6\ H_2O \qquad CO_2 + Ba(OH)_2(aq) \longrightarrow BaCO_3(s) + H_2O$$

Factors from these equations are used together with volume and density data to achieve the following series of conversions:

$$\text{ml } C_6H_6 \rightarrow \text{g } C_6H_6 \rightarrow \text{mol } C_6H_6 \rightarrow \text{mol } CO_2 \rightarrow \text{mol } BaCO_3 \rightarrow \text{g } BaCO_3 .$$

$$\text{no. g } BaCO_3 = 5.00 \text{ ml } C_6H_6 \times \frac{0.879 \text{ g } C_6H_6}{1 \text{ ml } C_6H_6} \times \frac{1 \text{ mol } C_6H_6}{78.1 \text{ g } C_6H_6} \times \frac{12 \text{ mol } CO_2}{2 \text{ mol } C_6H_6} \times \frac{1 \text{ mol } BaCO_3}{1 \text{ mol } CO_2}$$

$$\times \frac{197 \text{ g } BaCO_3}{1 \text{ mol } BaCO_3} = 66.5 \text{ g } BaCO_3$$

4-37. Factors from three equations are required, starting with I_2 in the final step and working backwards to $AgNO_3$ in the first step.

$$\text{no. g } AgNO_3 = 1.00 \text{ g } I_2 \times \frac{1 \text{ mol } I_2}{254 \text{ g } I_2} \times \frac{2 \text{ mol } FeI_2}{2 \text{ mol } I_2} \times \frac{2 \text{ mol } AgI}{1 \text{ mol } FeI_2} \times \frac{1 \text{ mol } AgNO_3}{1 \text{ mol } AgI} \times \frac{170 \text{ g } AgNO_3}{1 \text{ mol } AgNO_3} = 1.34 \text{ g } AgNO_3$$

4-38. First, all equations must be balanced.

$$Fe + Br_2 \longrightarrow FeBr_2 \qquad 3\ FeBr_2 + Br_2 \longrightarrow Fe_3Br_8$$

$$Fe_3Br_8 + 4\ Na_2CO_3 \longrightarrow 8\ NaBr + 4\ CO_2 + Fe_3O_4$$

$$\text{no. kg Fe} = 1.00 \times 10^3 \text{ kg NaBr} \times \frac{1000 \text{ g NaBr}}{1 \text{ kg NaBr}} \times \frac{1 \text{ mol NaBr}}{103 \text{ g NaBr}} \times \frac{1 \text{ mol } Fe_3Br_8}{8 \text{ mol NaBr}} \times \frac{3 \text{ mol } FeBr_2}{1 \text{ mol } Fe_3Br_8}$$

$$\times \frac{1 \text{ mol Fe}}{1 \text{ mol } FeBr_2} \times \frac{55.85 \text{ g Fe}}{1 \text{ mol Fe}} \times \frac{1 \text{ kg Fe}}{1000 \text{ g Fe}} = 203 \text{ kg Fe}$$

Theoretical, actual, and percent yield

4-39. First, we must determine which of the two reactants, nitrobenzene or triethylene glycol, is the limiting reagent. Next, we must determine the quantity of azobenzene that should theoretically be produced in the reaction. The ratio of the actual yield to this calculated yield (multiplied by 100) gives the percent yield.

$$\text{no. mol nitrobenzene} = 0.10 \text{ L} \times \frac{1000 \text{ ml}}{1 \text{ L}} \times \frac{1.20 \text{ g}}{1 \text{ ml}} \times \frac{1 \text{ mol } C_6H_5NO_2}{123 \text{ g } C_6H_5NO_2} = 0.98 \text{ mol } C_6H_5NO_2$$

$$\text{no. mol } C_6H_{14}O_4 = 0.30 \text{ L} \times \frac{1000 \text{ ml}}{1 \text{ L}} \times \frac{1.12 \text{ g}}{1 \text{ ml}} \times \frac{1 \text{ mol } C_6H_{14}O_4}{150 \text{ g } C_6H_{14}O_4} = 2.24 \text{ mol } C_6H_{14}O_4$$

The reaction requires twice the number of moles of $C_6H_{14}O_4$ as $C_6H_5NO_2$; more than this is available. $C_6H_5NO_2$ is the limiting reagent.

$$\text{no. g } (C_6H_5N)_2 = 0.98 \text{ mol } C_6H_5NO_2 \times \frac{1 \text{ mol } (C_6H_5N)_2}{2 \text{ mol } C_6H_5NO_2} \times \frac{182 \text{ g } (C_6H_5N)_2}{1 \text{ mol } (C_6H_5N)_2} = 89 \text{ g } (C_6H_5N)_2 \text{ (theoretical yield)}$$

$$\%\text{yield} = \frac{\text{actual yield}}{\text{theoretical yield}} \times 100 = \frac{55 \text{ g}}{89 \text{ g}} \times 100 = 62\%$$

4-40. Since the yield is only 70% of theoretical, we need to determine the quantity of acetic acid required to produce, not 50.0, but 50.0/0.70 = 71.4 g acetyl chloride. In the set up on the next page the factor that produces this conversion is: 100 g theoretical/70 g actual. The other factors are obtained and used in the customary way. It is necessary to balance the equation before proceeding.

Balanced equation: $3\ C_2H_4O_2 + PCl_3 \longrightarrow 3\ C_2H_3OCl + H_3PO_3$

$$\text{no. g acetic acid} = 50.0\text{ g actual } C_2H_3OCl \times \frac{100\text{ g theoretical } C_2H_3OCl}{70\text{ g actual } C_2H_3OCl} \times \frac{1\text{ mol } C_2H_3OCl}{78.5\text{ g } C_2H_3OCl}$$

$$\times \frac{3\text{ mol } C_2H_4O_2}{3\text{ mol } C_2H_3OCl} \times \frac{60.1\text{ g } C_2H_4O_2}{1\text{ mol } C_2H_4O_2} \times \frac{100\text{ g acetic acid}}{97\text{ g } C_2H_4O_2} = 56\text{ g acetic acid}$$

4-41. For simplicity the factors required to convert from theoretical to actual yield in each step are introduced simply as "0.98".

$$\text{no. g Cu} = 1.00\text{ g Cu} \times \frac{1\text{ mol Cu}}{63.5\text{ g Cu}} \times \frac{1\text{ mol } Cu(NO_3)_2}{1\text{ mol Cu}} \times (0.98) \times \frac{1\text{ mol } CuCO_3}{1\text{ mol } Cu(NO_3)_2} \times (0.98)$$

$$\times \frac{1\text{ mol } CuSO_4}{1\text{ mol } CuCO_3} \times (0.98) \times \frac{1\text{ mol Cu}}{1\text{ mol } CuSO_4} \times (0.98) \times \frac{63.5\text{ g Cu}}{1\text{ mol Cu}} = 0.92\text{ g Cu}$$

Industrial chemistry

4-42. $$\text{no. L acid} = 1.00 \times 10^3\text{ kg NaCl} \times \frac{1000\text{ g NaCl}}{1\text{ kg NaCl}} \times \frac{1\text{ mol NaCl}}{58.5\text{ g NaCl}} \times \frac{1\text{ mol } H_2SO_4}{2\text{ mol NaCl}} \times \frac{98.1\text{ g } H_2SO_4}{1\text{ mol } H_2SO_4}$$

$$\times \frac{100\text{ g acid}}{80\text{ g } H_2SO_4} \times \frac{1\text{ cm}^3\text{ acid}}{1.73\text{ g acid}} \times \frac{1\text{ L acid}}{1000\text{ cm}^3\text{ acid}} = 6.1 \times 10^2\text{ L acid}$$

4-43. Let us make all comparisons on a mole basis, and let us begin by calculating the number of mol Cl_2 in 1.00 kg Cl_2

$$\text{no. mol } Cl_2 = 1.00\text{ kg } Cl_2 \times \frac{1000\text{ g } Cl_2}{1\text{ kg } Cl_2} \times \frac{1\text{ mol } Cl_2}{70.9\text{ g } Cl_2} = 14.1\text{ mol } Cl_2$$

14.1 mol Cl_2 yields 14.1 mol NaOCl, which in turn yields 14.1 mol NH_2Cl, and finally, 14.1 mol N_2H_4. Whatever excess NH_3 remains in the reaction mixture from the second reaction becomes part of the NH_3 required in the third reaction. Determine the amount of NH_3 required to maintain a 30:1 mol ratio in the third reaction.

$$\text{no. mol } NH_3 \text{ required} = 14.1\text{ mol } NH_2Cl \times \frac{30\text{ mol } NH_3}{1\text{ mol } NH_2Cl} = 423\text{ mol } NH_3$$

The amount of NH_3 consumed in the third reaction is

$$\text{no. mol } NH_3 = 14.1\text{ mol } NH_2Cl \times \frac{1\text{ mol } NH_3}{1\text{ mol } NH_2Cl} = 14.1\text{ mol } NH_3$$

The quantity of recoverable NH_3 is

$$\text{no. kg } NH_3 = (423 - 14)\text{ mol } NH_3 \times \frac{17.0\text{ g } NH_3}{1\text{ mol } NH_3} \times \frac{1\text{ kg } NH_3}{1000\text{ g } NH_3} = 6.95\text{ kg } NH_3$$

4-44. (a) $2\ CH_2CHCH_3 + 2\ NH_3 + 3\ O_2 \longrightarrow 2\ CH_2CHCN + 6\ H_2O$

(b) First calculate the theoretical yield

$$\text{no. lb } CH_2CHCN = 1.00\text{ lb } CH_2CHCH_3 \times \frac{454\text{ g } CH_2CHCH_3}{1\text{ lb } CH_2CHCH_3} \times \frac{1\text{ mol } CH_2CHCH_3}{42.1\text{ g } CH_2CHCH_3} \times \frac{2\text{ mol } CH_2CHCN}{2\text{ mol } CH_2CHCH_3}$$

$$\times \frac{53.1\text{ g } CH_2CHCN}{1\text{ mol } CH_2CHCN} \times \frac{1\text{ lb } CH_2CHCN}{454\text{ g } CH_2CHCN} = 1.26\text{ lb } CH_2CHCN$$

$$\%\text{yield: } \frac{0.73\text{ lb (actual)}}{1.26\text{ lb (theoretical)}} \times 100 = 58\%$$

(c) $\text{no. lb } NH_3 = 2000 \text{ lb } CH_2CHCN \times \frac{454 \text{ g } CH_2CHCN}{1 \text{ lb } CH_2CHCN} \times \frac{1 \text{ mol } CH_2CHCN}{53.1 \text{ g } CH_2CHCN} \times \frac{2 \text{ mol } NH_3}{2 \text{ mol } CH_2CHCN} \times \frac{17.0 \text{ g } NH_3}{1 \text{ mol } NH_3}$

$$\times \frac{1 \text{ lb } NH_3}{454 \text{ g } NH_3} \times \frac{100 \text{ lb } NH_3 \text{ (actual)}}{58 \text{ lb } NH_3 \text{ (theoretical)}} = 1100 \text{ lb } NH_3$$

Self-test Questions

1. (*c*) The relationships from the balanced equation are that 2 mol $H_2S \Leftrightarrow$ 1 mol $SO_2 \Leftrightarrow$ 3 mol S $\Leftrightarrow$ 2 mol H_2O. Since 2 mol $H_2S \Leftrightarrow$ 2 mol H_2O is the same as 1 mol $H_2S \Leftrightarrow$ 1 mol H_2O, the correct answer is (c).

2. (*d*) Because of the relationship 1 mol $CaCN_2 \Leftrightarrow$ 3 mol H_2O, the limiting reagent must be H_2O. Now consider the relationship between NH_3 and H_2O: 2 mol $NH_3 \Leftrightarrow$ 3 mol H_2O. This yields the conversion factor, 2 mol NH_3/3 mol H_2O. From 1 mol H_2O one obtains 0.67 mol NH_3.

3. (*a*) The combining ratio of O_2 to NH_3 is 5 mol O_2/4 mol NH_3. In a mixture of 1.0 mol each of NH_3 and O_2, there is not enough O_2 available to react with all of the NH_3 (1.25 mol O_2 would be required). O_2 is entirely consumed in the reaction; NH_3 is in excess. Statement (b) is incorrect because 4.0 mol NH_3 and 5 mol O_2 would be required to produce 4 mol NO. Statement (c) is incorrect because to produce 1.50 mol H_2O would require that 1.00 mol NH_3 be consumed, but NH_3 is not the limiting reagent.

4. (*a*) To increase the concentration of KCl from 0.40 M to 0.50 M requires either that solute be added or water evaporated. Statement (b), involving the addition of water, must be incorrect. In 100 ml of 0.40 M KCl there is 0.04 mol KCl, and in 100 ml of 0.50 M KCl, 0.05 mol KCl. The increase in concentration would require 0.01 mol KCl = 0.75 g KCl. Statement (a)--0.75 g KCl--is correct, and (c)--0.10 mol KCl--incorrect. Evaporating 10 ml water would produce an increase in concentration to (100/90) x 0.40 = 0.44 M.

5. (*b*) To complete the titration of 10.00 ml 0.0500 M NaOH requires 0.0100 L x 0.0500 mol NaOH/L x 1 mol H_2SO_4/2 mol NaOH = 2.5×10^{-4} mol H_2SO_4. The number of mol H_2SO_4 in the four solutions given are (a) 5.0×10^{-4}; (b) 2.5×10^{-4}; (c) 1.0×10^{-3}; (d) 1.0×10^{-3}.

6. (*c*) From 2.0 mol CCl_4 the theoretical yield of CCl_2F_2 is 2.0 mol. [Statements (a) and (b) are incorrect.] Furthermore, the theoretical yield is independent of how much HF is present in excess. [Statement (d) is in error.] The percent yield of the reaction is (1.70/2.00) x 100 = 85%.

7. (a) $Hg(NO_3)_2(s) \longrightarrow Hg(l) + 2\ NO_2(g) + O_2(g)$

   (b) $Na_2CO_3(aq) + 2\ HCl(aq) \longrightarrow 2\ NaCl(aq) + H_2O + CO_2(g)$

   (c) The percent composition data must be used to establish the formula of benzoic acid. Then an equation can be written.

   In 100.0 g benzoic acid:

   $$\text{no. mol C} = 68.8 \text{ g C} \times \frac{1 \text{ mol C}}{12.0 \text{ g C}} = 5.73 \text{ mol C}$$

   $$\text{no. mol H} = 4.95 \text{ g H} \times \frac{1 \text{ mol H}}{1.01 \text{ g H}} = 4.90 \text{ mol H}$$

   $$\text{no. mol O} = 26.2 \text{ g O} \times \frac{1 \text{ mol O}}{16.0 \text{ g O}} = 1.64 \text{ mol O}$$

   empirical formula: $C_{5.73}H_{4.90}O_{1.64} = C_{\frac{5.73}{1.64}}H_{\frac{4.90}{1.64}}O_{\frac{1.64}{1.64}} = C_{3.5}H_3O = C_7H_6O_2$

   combustion reaction: $2\ C_7H_6O_2 + 15\ O_2 \longrightarrow 14\ CO_2 + 6\ H_2O$

8. Consider the following two-step procedure. Determine the no. mol $Ba(OH)_2$ required for the titration, and then the volume of solution containing this much $Ba(OH)_2$.

$$\text{no. mol } Ba(OH)_2 = 0.01000 \text{ L} \times \frac{0.0526 \text{ mol } HNO_3}{\text{L}} \times \frac{1 \text{ mol } Ba(OH)_2}{2 \text{ mol } HNO_3} = 2.63 \times 10^{-4} \text{ mol } Ba(OH)_2$$

$$\text{no. ml soln.} = 2.63 \times 10^{-4} \text{ mol } Ba(OH)_2 \times \frac{1 \text{ L soln.}}{0.0102 \text{ mol } Ba(OH)_2} \times \frac{1000 \text{ ml soln.}}{1 \text{ L soln.}} = 25.8 \text{ ml soln.}$$

9. The product of the first two terms in the following setup represents the no. mol NaOH that is to be produced in the reaction.

$$\text{no. g Na} = 0.125 \text{ L} \times \frac{0.250 \text{ mol NaOH}}{\text{L}} \times \frac{2 \text{ mol Na}}{2 \text{ mol NaOH}} \times \frac{23.0 \text{ g Na}}{1 \text{ mol Na}} = 0.719 \text{ g Na}$$

10. A less-than-100% yield of desired product in synthesis reactions is almost always the case. This is because of side reactions yielding products other than the desired one (by-products) and because of the loss of material in various steps of the process. Almost by definition, a chemical reaction used in analyzing a compound must have a 100% yield. If an unknown quantity of product is lost in the reaction, errors enter into the analytical results. For this reason only certain carefully selected reactions can be used in analytical chemistry.

Pressure and its measurement

5-1. Refer to expression (5.3) in the textbook to formulate appropriate conversion factors.

(a) $\text{no. atm} = 738\ \text{mmHg} \times \frac{1\ \text{atm}}{760\ \text{mm Hg}} = 0.971\ \text{atm}$

(b) $\text{no. atm} = 3.12\ \text{kg/cm}^2 \times \frac{1\ \text{atm}}{1.033\ \text{kg/cm}^2} = 3.02\ \text{atm}$

(c) $\text{no. atm} = 70\ \text{psi} \times \frac{1\ \text{atm}}{14.7\ \text{psi}} = 4.8\ \text{atm}$

(d) $\text{no. atm} = 992\ \text{mb} \times \frac{1\ \text{atm}}{1013.25\ \text{mb}} = 0.979\ \text{atm}$

(e) $\text{no. atm} = 1.67 \times 10^5\ \text{N/m}^2 \times \frac{1\ \text{atm}}{101{,}325\ \text{N/m}^2} = 1.65\ \text{atm}$

5-2. The key to each of the following answers is that normal atmospheric pressure will support a column of mercury 76 cm high. If the glass tube is less than 76 cm in height, it will be filled completely. If the tube is greater than 76 cm in height, it will be filled only to a level of 76 cm.

(a) 10 cm (b) 20 cm (c) 76 cm (d) 76 cm

5-3. (a) $\text{no. mmHg} = 1.52\ \text{atm} \times \frac{760\ \text{mmHg}}{1\ \text{atm}} = 1.16 \times 10^3\ \text{mmHg} = 116\ \text{cm Hg}$

(b) Use the expression $g \times h_{glyc.} \times d_{glyc.} = g \times h_{CCl_4} \times d_{CCl_4}$ and solve for $h_{glyc.}$

Note that the term g can be cancelled out.

$$h_{glyc.} = \frac{h_{CCl_4} \times d_{CCl_4}}{d_{glyc.}} = 2.40\ \text{m} \times \frac{1.59\ \text{g/cm}^3}{1.26\ \text{g/cm}^3} = 3.03\ \text{m}$$

(c) Here we must use equation (5.2), substituting $g = 9.80\ \text{m s}^{-2}$ and expressing density in kg/m^3. A pressure of $1.10 \times 10^4\ \text{N/m}^2$ is the same as $1.10 \times 10^4\ \text{kg m}^{-1}\ \text{s}^{-2}$ (i.e., as described in Appendix B, $1\ \text{N} = 1\ \text{kg m s}^{-2}$).

$$P = 1.10 \times 10^4\ \text{kg m}^{-1}\ \text{s}^{-2} = 9.80\ \text{m s}^{-2} \times h \times \frac{0.879\ \text{g}}{\text{cm}^3} \times \frac{1\ \text{kg}}{1000\ \text{g}} \times \frac{(100)^3\ \text{cm}^3}{1\ \text{m}^3}$$

$$h = \frac{1.10 \times 10^4\ \text{kg m}^{-1}\ \text{s}^{-2}}{9.80\ \text{m s}^{-2} \times 879\ \text{kg m}^{-3}} = 1.28\ \text{m}$$

An alternative approach is to convert the pressure of $1.10 \times 10^4\ \text{N/m}^2$ to is equivalent in atm--0.109 atm. Next, express this pressure in mmHg--82.5 mmHg. Finally, use the method of Example 5-1 to determine the height of a benzene column equivalent to this mercury column: 82.5 × (13.6/0.879) = 1280 mmHg = 1.28 m.

(d) The most direct approach is probably the alternative method outlined in part (c). The pressure, in cm Hg, corresponding to a pressure of 10.0 psi is

$$\text{no. cm Hg} = 10.0\ \text{psi} \times \frac{760\ \text{mmHg}}{14.7\ \text{psi}} \times \frac{1\ \text{cm Hg}}{10\ \text{mmHg}} = 51.7\ \text{cm Hg}$$

Then use the method of Example 5-1 to solve for $d_{unk.}$ (the density of the unknown liquid).

$$g \times h_{Hg} \times d_{Hg} = g \times h_{unk.} \times d_{unk.}$$

$$d_{unk.} = \frac{51.7 \text{ cm} \times 13.6 \text{ g/cm}^3}{15.0 \text{ ft} \times \frac{12 \text{ in.}}{1 \text{ ft}} \times \frac{2.54 \text{ cm}}{1 \text{ in.}}} = 1.54 \text{ g/cm}^3$$

5-4. This condition corresponds to that pictured in Figure 5-4b, that is, $P_{gas} > P_{bar}$.

$\Delta P = 385 - 195 = 190$ mmHg.

$P_{gas} = P_{bar} + \Delta P = 752 \text{ mmHg} + 190 \text{ mmHg} = 942 \text{ mmHg}$

$$P_{gas} \text{ (in atm)} = 942 \text{ mmHg} \times \frac{1 \text{ atm}}{760 \text{ mmHg}} = 1.24 \text{ atm}$$

5-5. The difference between barometric pressure and that of the gas corresponds to 2.4 cm of water. Since the water level is higher inside the container than outside, $P_{bar} > P_{gas}$.

$$h_{Hg} = \frac{h_{H_2O} \times d_{H_2O}}{d_{Hg}} = \frac{2.4 \text{ cm} \times 1.00 \text{ g/cm}^3}{13.6 \text{ g/cm}^3} = 0.18 \text{ cm} = 1.8 \text{ mmHg}$$

$P_{gas} = P_{bar} + \Delta P = 748.7 \text{ mmHg} - 1.8 \text{ mmHg} = 746.9 \text{ mmHg}$

Boyle's law

5-6. In each case, $P_fV_f = P_iV_i$. Use the three values given and solve for the fourth. Check to see that the answer corresponds to that required by a "commonsense" approach.

(a) $$V_f = \frac{P_iV_i}{P_f} = \frac{748 \text{ mmHg} \times 14.4 \text{ L}}{615 \text{ mmHg}} = 17.5 \text{ L}$$

A decrease in gas pressure should produce an *increase* in gas volume.

(b) $$V_f = \frac{P_iV_i}{P_f} = \frac{748 \text{ mmHg} \times 14.4 \text{ L}}{1.72 \text{ atm} \times \frac{760 \text{ mmHg}}{1 \text{ atm}}} = 8.24 \text{ L}$$

An increase in pressure is expected to produce a *decrease* in gas volume.

5-7. Here the Boyle's law equation is solved for P_f. Since the gas is expanded, we expect the pressure to decrease, i.e., $P_f < P_i$.

$$P_f = \frac{P_iV_i}{V_f} = \frac{755 \text{ mmHg} \times 235 \text{ cm}^3}{345 \text{ cm}^3} = 514 \text{ mmHg}$$

Charles' law

5-8. Substitute three known values and solve for the fourth (V_f) in the Charles' law expression. Check to see that volume changes in the expected manner, i.e., in (a) $V_f > V_i$ and in (b) $V_f < V_i$.

(a) $$\frac{V_i}{T_i} = \frac{V_f}{T_f} \qquad V_f = V_i \times \frac{T_f}{T_i} = 125 \text{ cm}^3 \times \frac{(273 + 60)\text{K}}{(273 + 30)\text{K}} = 137 \text{ cm}^3$$

(b) $$V_f = V_i \times \frac{T_f}{T_i} = 125 \text{ cm}^3 \times \frac{(273 + 0)\text{K}}{(273 + 30)\text{K}} = 113 \text{ cm}^3$$

5-9. Here Charles' law must be solved for T_f.

$$T_f = T_i \times \frac{V_f}{V_i} = (273 + 23)K \times \frac{115\ cm^3}{90.0\ cm^3} = 378\ K\ (= 105°C)$$

Since the gas volume is to increase the gas temperature must also *increase.*

Additional applications of the simple gas laws

5-10. (a) Boyle's law is required. $V_f = V_i \times \frac{P_i}{P_f} = V_i \times \frac{3.0\ atm}{1.0\ atm} = 3.0\ V_i$

(b) Charles' law is required. $V_f = V_i \times \frac{T_f}{T_i} = V_i \times \frac{100\ K}{400\ K} = V_i/4$

(c) The easiest approach is probably the "commonsense" one. What ratios of pressures and temperatures, when multiplied by the initial volume, cause this volume to change in the manner predicted by Boyle's and Charles' laws?

$$V_f = V_i \times \frac{300\ K}{200\ K} \times \frac{2\ atm}{3\ atm} = V_i$$

The increase in volume produced by raising the gas temperature is exactly offset by the decrease in volume caused by an increase in pressure.

5-11. The amount of gas and volume are held constant. How must the gas temperature be changed if the pressure is to be reduced from 825 mmHg to 1.00 atm? The temperature must be *lowered* (see also, Example 5-8 in the textbook). Thus, by the "commonsense" approach

$$T_f = T_i \times \text{ratio of pressures} = 298\ K \times \frac{760\ mmHg}{825\ mmHg} = 275\ K$$

5-12. The pressure and volume of the gas are to be held constant. Raising the temperature of a fixed amount of gas in a fixed volume would cause the gas pressure to increase. If the gas volume and pressure are to be held constant, some gas must be allowed to escape, that is, the amount of gas must be less at the higher temperature. Let us use a "commonsense" approach to relate the amount of gas and temperature (with pressure and volume held constant).

final amount = initial amount × ratio of temperatures

$$\text{final amount} = 10.00\ g \times \frac{(0 + 273)K}{(157 + 273)K} = 6.35\ g$$

quantity of gas to be released = 10.00 - 6.35 = 3.65 g

An alternative approach is to use the ideal gas equation.

For the initial gas: $n_i = \frac{P_iV_i}{RT_i}$ and $n_iT_i = \frac{P_iV_i}{R}$

For the final gas: $n_f = \frac{P_fV_f}{RT_f}$ and $n_fT_f = \frac{P_fV_f}{R}$

The pressure and volume of the gas remain constant. This means that PV/R is a constant, and $n_f = n_i(T_i/T_f)$. The number of moles of gas is equal simply to the mass of gas, m, divided by the molecular weight of the gas, (MW). (The molecular weight of the gas is a constant.)

$$\frac{m_f}{MW} = \frac{m_i}{MW} \times \frac{T_i}{T_f} \qquad m_f = m_i \times \frac{T_i}{T_f} = 10.00\ g \times \frac{273\ K}{(273 + 157)K} = 6.35\ g$$

The quantity of gas that must be released is 10.00 - 6.35 = 3.65 g.

Ideal gas equation

5-13. The data needed for the ideal gas equation are:

$$n = 35.2 \text{ g } N_2 \times \frac{1 \text{ mol } N_2}{28.0 \text{ g } N_2} = 1.26 \text{ mol } N_2$$

$$P = 741 \text{ mmHg} \times \frac{1 \text{ atm}}{760 \text{ mmHg}} = 0.975 \text{ atm}$$

$$T = 35 + 273 = 308 \text{ K}$$

$$V = \frac{nRT}{P} = \frac{1.26 \text{ mol} \times 0.0821 \text{ L atm mol}^{-1} \text{ K}^{-1} \times 308 \text{ K}}{0.975 \text{ atm}} = 32.7 \text{ L}$$

5-14. In this example let us make the necessary conversions within the ideal gas equation.

$$P = \frac{nRT}{V} = \frac{(52.0/32.0)\text{mol} \times 0.0821 \text{ L atm mol}^{-1} \text{ K}^{-1} \times 298 \text{ K}}{10.0 \text{ L}} = 3.98 \text{ atm}$$

5-15. Use the initial P-V-T data to determine the number of moles of gas. Then, calculate the volume occupied by this amount of gas at the new temperature and pressure.

$$n = \frac{PV}{RT} = \frac{(738/760)\text{atm} \times 3.52 \text{ L}}{0.0821 \text{ L atm mol}^{-1} \text{ K}^{-1} \times 303.2 \text{ K}} = 0.137 \text{ mol gas}$$

$$V = \frac{nRT}{P} = \frac{0.137 \text{ mol} \times 0.0821 \text{ L atm mol}^{-1} \text{ K}^{-1} \times 298.2 \text{ K}}{(758/760)\text{atm}} = 3.36 \text{ L}$$

5-16. Calculate the no. g N_2 in 25.0 L at 10°C and 1.75 atm.

$$n = \frac{PV}{RT} = \frac{1.75 \text{ atm} \times 25.0 \text{ L}}{0.0821 \text{ L atm mol}^{-1} \text{ K}^{-1} \times 283 \text{ K}} = 1.88 \text{ mol}$$

$$\text{no g } N_2 = 1.88 \text{ mol } N_2 \times \frac{28.0 \text{ g } N_2}{1 \text{ mol } N_2} = 52.6 \text{ g } N_2$$

The quantity of $N_2(g)$ that must be released is 128 g N_2 - 52.6 g N_2 = 75 g N_2

5-17. Solve the ideal gas equation for T.

$$T = \frac{PV}{nR} = \frac{375 \text{ atm} \times 4.5 \text{ L}}{(725/20.2)\text{mol} \times 0.0821 \text{ L atm mol}^{-1} \text{ K}^{-1}} = 5.7 \times 10^2 \text{ K}$$

5-18. First determine the no. mol He in 1.00 ft^3 He(g) at STP.

$$V = 1.00 \text{ ft}^3 \times \frac{(12)^3 \text{ in.}^3}{1 \text{ ft}^3} \times \frac{(2.54)^3 \text{ cm}^3}{1 \text{ in.}^3} \times \frac{1 \text{ L}}{1000 \text{ cm}^3} = 28.3 \text{ L}$$

$$n = \frac{PV}{RT} = \frac{1.00 \text{ atm} \times 28.3 \text{ L}}{0.0821 \text{ L atm mol}^{-1} \text{ K}^{-1} \times 273 \text{ K}} = 1.26 \text{ mol He}$$

Now, calculate the pressure of 1.26 mol He(g) in 75.0 L at -20°C.

$$P = \frac{nRT}{V} = \frac{1.26 \text{ mol} \times 0.0821 \text{ L atm mol}^{-1} \text{ K}^{-1} \times 253 \text{ K}}{75.0 \text{ L}} = 0.349 \text{ atm}$$

Molecular weight determination

5-19. Substitute the given data into equation (5.11),

$$(MW) = \frac{mRT}{PV} = \frac{0.341\ g \times 0.0821\ L\ atm\ mol^{-1}\ K^{-1} \times (273.2 + 98.7)K}{(743/760)atm \times 0.355\ L} = 30.0\ g/mol$$

5-20. $$(MW) = \frac{0.185\ g \times 0.0821\ L\ atm\ mol^{-1}\ K^{-1} \times 299\ K}{(743/760)atm \times 0.110\ L} = 42.2\ g/mol$$

Because carbon has an atomic weight of 12, there cannot be more than three C atoms in a molecule (3 x 12 = 36). For example, a compound with the formula C_3H_6 would have a molecular weight of about 42.

5-21. Determine the mol. wt. of the compound, as in the preceding example.

$$(MW) = \frac{2.650\ g \times 0.08206\ L\ atm\ mol^{-1}\ K^{-1} \times 297.5\ K}{(742.3/760.0)atm \times 0.428\ L} = 155\ g/mol$$

Now determine the empirical formula of a compound with the given percent composition. This requires the method introduced in Chapter 3. For example, in a 100.0 g sample

$$\text{no. mol C} = 15.5\ g\ C \times \frac{1\ mol\ C}{12.0\ g\ C} = 1.29\ mol\ C \qquad \text{no. mol Cl} = 23.0\ g\ Cl \times \frac{1\ mol\ Cl}{35.5\ g\ Cl} = 0.648\ mol\ Cl$$

$$\text{no. mol F} = 61.5\ g\ F \times \frac{1\ mol\ F}{19.0\ g\ F} = 3.24\ mol\ F$$

$$\text{Empirical formula: } C_{\frac{1.29}{0.648}}Cl_{\frac{0.648}{0.648}}F_{\frac{3.24}{0.648}} = C_2ClF_5$$

Formula weight = (2 x 12.0) + 35.5 + (5 x 19.0) = 154.5 = molecular weight

The molecular formula of the compound is C_2ClF_5.

Gas densities

5-22. Use equation (5.12) with the data given.

$$\frac{m}{V} = \frac{(MW)P}{RT} = \frac{44.0\ g\ mol^{-1} \times (744/760)atm}{0.0821\ L\ atm\ mol^{-1}\ K^{-1} \times 303.5\ K} = 1.73\ g/L$$

5-23. Solve equation (5.12) for (MW).

$$(MW) = \frac{mRT}{PV} = \frac{2.64\ g \times 0.0821\ L\ atm\ mol^{-1}\ K^{-1} \times (310 + 273)K}{(775/760)atm \times 1.00\ L} = 124\ g/mol$$

Since the atomic weight of P = 31.0, a molecular weight of 124 g/mol corresponds to a molecular formula of P_4.

Cannizzaro's method

5-24.

Substance	Mol. wt. (relative to H=1)	X (%, by mass)	Relative mass of X per molecule
Hydrogen	2	--	--
Nitryl fluoride	65.01	49.4	32.1
Nitrosyl fluoride	49.01	32.7	16.0
Thionyl fluoride	86.07	18.6	16.0
Sulfuryl fluoride	102.07	31.4	32.0

The atomic weight of X is the smallest of the relative masses per molecule: 16. The element is oxygen.

65.01 × .494 = 32.1

5-25. We can first determine the no. mol $SO_2(g)$. Then we can calculate the volume occupied by this gas under the given conditions.

$$\text{no. mol } SO_2 = 1.0 \times 10^6 \text{ lb coal} \times \frac{454 \text{ g coal}}{1 \text{ lb coal}} \times \frac{2.18 \text{ g S}}{100 \text{ g coal}} \times \frac{1 \text{ mol S}}{32.1 \text{ g S}} \times \frac{1 \text{ mol } SO_2}{1 \text{ mol S}} = 3.1 \times 10^5 \text{ mol } SO_2$$

$$V = \frac{nRT}{P} = \frac{3.1 \times 10^5 \text{ mol} \times 0.0821 \text{ L atm mol}^{-1} \text{ K}^{-1} \times 298 \text{ K}}{(754/760)\text{atm}} = 7.6 \times 10^6 \text{ L}$$

5-26. As in Exercise 5-25, first determine the no. mol CO_2 and then the volume of CO_2.

$$\text{no. mol } CO_2 = 1.00 \text{ kg NaOH} \times \frac{1000 \text{ g NaOH}}{1 \text{ kg NaOH}} \times \frac{1 \text{ mol NaOH}}{40.0 \text{ g NaOH}} \times \frac{1 \text{ mol } CO_2}{2 \text{ mol NaOH}} = 12.5 \text{ mol } CO_2$$

$$V = \frac{nRT}{P} = \frac{12.5 \text{ mol} \times 0.0821 \text{ L atm mol}^{-1} \text{ K}^{-1} \times 299 \text{ K}}{(755/760)\text{atm}} = 309 \text{ L}$$

5-27. Use the ideal gas equation to calculate no. mol O_2.

$$n = \frac{PV}{RT} = \frac{(741/760)\text{atm} \times 0.0902 \text{ L}}{0.0821 \text{ L atm mol}^{-1} \text{ K}^{-1} \times 296 \text{ K}} = 3.62 \times 10^{-3} \text{ mol}$$

Next, calculate the mass of $KClO_3$ that must be decomposed to have produced this much O_2.

$$\text{no. g } KClO_3 = 3.62 \times 10^{-3} \text{ mol } O_2 \times \frac{2 \text{ mol } KClO_3}{3 \text{ mol } O_2} \times \frac{123 \text{ g } KClO_3}{1 \text{ mol } KClO_3} = 0.297 \text{ g } KClO_3$$

$$\text{Finally, } \%KClO_3 = \frac{0.297 \text{ g } KClO_3}{2.15 \text{ g sample}} \times 100 = 13.8\% \text{ } KClO_3$$

5-28. (a) Because all gases are measured at the same temperature and pressure (STP), we can write

$$\text{no. L } H_2(g) = 4.0 \times 10^3 \text{ L } N_2(g) \times \frac{3 \text{ L } H_2(g)}{1 \text{ L } N_2(g)} = 1.2 \times 10^4 \text{ L } H_2(g)$$

(b) Although not at STP, the gases are still at identical temperatures and pressures.

$$\text{no. L } NH_3(g) = 185 \text{ L } H_2(g) \times \frac{2 \text{ mol } NH_3(g)}{3 \text{ mol } H_2(g)} = 123 \text{ L } NH_3(g)$$

(c) The gas temperatures and pressures are not the same for the two gases. We must first determine the no. mol H_2 in 185 L at 525°C and 515 atm.

$$n = \frac{PV}{RT} = \frac{515 \text{ atm} \times 185 \text{ L}}{0.0821 \text{ L atm mol}^{-1} \text{ K}^{-1} \times 798 \text{ K}} = 1.45 \times 10^3 \text{ mol } H_2$$

$$\text{no. mol } NH_3 = 1.45 \times 10^3 \text{ mol } H_2 \times \frac{2 \text{ mol } NH_3}{3 \text{ mol } H_2} = 967 \text{ mol } NH_3$$

Now calculate the volume of this amount of NH_3 at STP

$$\text{no. L } NH_3 = 967 \text{ mol } NH_3 \times \frac{22.4 \text{ L } NH_3}{1 \text{ mol } NH_3} = 2.17 \times 10^4 \text{ L } NH_3$$

5-29. First calculate the number of moles of each gas.

$$H_2S: \quad n = \frac{PV}{RT} = \frac{(735/760)\text{atm} \times 1.50 \text{ L}}{0.0821 \text{ L atm mol}^{-1} \text{ K}^{-1} \times (273 + 23)\text{K}} = 5.97 \times 10^{-2} \text{ mol } H_2S$$

$$O_2: \quad n = \frac{PV}{RT} = \frac{(750/760)\text{atm} \times 4.45 \text{ L}}{0.0821 \text{ L atm mol}^{-1} \text{ K}^{-1} \times (273 + 26)\text{K}} = 1.79 \times 10^{-1} \text{ mol } O_2$$

(a) It is necessary to determine the limiting reactant. Consider the number of moles of O_2 required to react with all the H_2S. (O_2 is the reactant in excess.)

$$\text{no. mol } O_2 = 5.97 \times 10^{-2} \text{ mol } H_2S \times \frac{3 \text{ mol } O_2}{2 \text{ mol } H_2S} = 8.96 \times 10^{-2} \text{ mol } O_2$$

$$\text{no. mol } SO_2 = 5.97 \times 10^{-2} \text{ mol } H_2S \times \frac{2 \text{ mol } SO_2}{2 \text{ mol } H_2S} = 5.97 \times 10^{-2} \text{ mol } SO_2$$

(b) no. mol $SO_2(g) = 5.97 \times 10^{-2}$ no mol $H_2O(g)$ = no mol $SO_2(g) = 5.97 \times 10^{-2}$

$$\text{Excess no. mol } O_2(g) = 17.9 \times 10^{-2} - 8.96 \times 10^{-2} = 8.9 \times 10^{-2}$$

$$\text{Total no. mol gas} = 5.97 \times 10^{-2} + 5.97 \times 10^{-2} + 8.9 \times 10^{-2} = 2.08 \times 10^{-1}$$

$$V = \frac{nRT}{P} = \frac{0.208 \text{ mol} \times 0.0821 \text{ L atm mol}^{-1} \text{ K}^{-1} \times 393 \text{ K}}{(748/760)\text{atm}} = 6.82 \text{ L}$$

Mixtures of gases

5-30. First, determine the total number of moles of gas.

$$\text{no. mol gas} = \left(15.0 \text{ g} \times \frac{1 \text{ mol Ne}}{20.2 \text{ g Ne}}\right) + \left(30.1 \text{ g Ar} \times \frac{1 \text{ mol Ar}}{40.0 \text{ g Ar}}\right) = 1.50 \text{ mol gas}$$

$$V = \frac{nRT}{P} = \frac{1.50 \text{ mol} \times 0.0821 \text{ L atm mol}^{-1} \text{ K}^{-1} \times 318 \text{ K}}{10.0 \text{ atm}} = 3.92 \text{ L}$$

5-31. We need to determine three molar quantities--the no. mol N_2, the total no. mol gas in the mixture, and their difference.

$$\text{no. mol } N_2 = \frac{PV}{RT} = \frac{20.0 \text{ atm} \times 55.0 \text{ L}}{0.0821 \text{ L atm mol}^{-1} \text{ K}^{-1} \times 296 \text{ K}} = 45.3 \text{ mol } N_2$$

$$\text{no. mol gas} = \frac{PV}{RT} = \frac{75.0 \text{ atm} \times 55.0 \text{ L}}{0.0821 \text{ L atm mol}^{-1} \text{ K}^{-1} \times 296 \text{ K}} = 170 \text{ mol gas}$$

$$\text{no. g Ne} = (170 - 45)\text{mol Ne} \times \frac{20.2 \text{ g Ne}}{1 \text{ mol Ne}} = 2.52 \times 10^3 \text{ g Ne}$$

5-32. Again we must determine the amount of each gas and add these amounts together to obtain the total no. mol gas. In addition, the final gas volume is the sum of the volumes of the two containers.

$$n_{H_2} = \frac{PV}{RT} = \frac{(765/760)\text{atm} \times 1.50 \text{ L}}{0.0821 \text{ L atm mol}^{-1} \text{ K}^{-1} \times 298 \text{ K}} = 0.0617 \text{ mol } H_2$$

$$n_{He} = \frac{PV}{RT} = \frac{(742/760)\text{atm} \times 2.52 \text{ L}}{0.0821 \text{ L atm mol}^{-1} \text{ K}^{-1} \times 298 \text{ K}} = 0.101 \text{ mol He}$$

$$P_{tot.} = \frac{n_{tot.}RT}{V_{tot.}} = \frac{(0.101 + 0.062)\text{mol} \times 0.0821 \text{ L atm mol}^{-1} \text{ K}^{-1} \times 298 \text{ K}}{(1.50 + 2.52)\text{L}} = 0.992 \text{ atm} = 754 \text{ mmHg}$$

5-33. In order for the gas volume to double at STP, the number of moles of gas must be doubled. This doubling of gas volume is produced by adding 10.0 g H_2 = 5.0 mol H_2. Thus there must have been 5.0 mol gas present initially. Of this gas, 4.0 g H_2 = 2.0 mol was hydrogen. The remainder must have been He: 5.0 mol total − 2.0 mol H_2 = 3.0 mol He.

$$\text{no. g He} = 3.0 \text{ mol He} \times \frac{4.0 \text{ g He}}{1 \text{ mol He}} = 12 \text{ g He}$$

5-34. (a) Calculate the no. mol $N_2O(g)$ produced in the reaction. Then determine the partial pressure of this gas.

$$\text{no mol } N_2O = 0.800 \text{ g } NH_4NO_3 \times \frac{1 \text{ mol } NH_4NO_3}{80.0 \text{ g } NH_4NO_3} \times \frac{1 \text{ mol } N_2O}{1 \text{ mol } NH_4NO_3} = 0.0100 \text{ mol } N_2O$$

$$P = \frac{nRT}{V} = \frac{0.0100 \text{ mol} \times 0.0821 \text{ L atm mol}^{-1} \text{ K}^{-1} \times 523 \text{ K}}{1.50 \text{ L}} = 0.286 \text{ atm (217 mmHg)}$$

(b) The total gas pressure is the sum of the partial pressures of $N_2O(g)$ and $H_2O(g)$. Because 2 mol $H_2O(g)$ is produced for every mol N_2O, and because in a constant volume at a fixed temperature, gas pressure is proportional to the amount of gas, $P_{H_2O} = 2 \times P_{N_2O}$ $= 2 \times 0.286 \text{ atm} = 0.572 \text{ atm}$.

$$P_{tot.} = P_{N_2O} + P_{H_2O} = 0.286 \text{ atm} + 0.572 \text{ atm} = 0.858 \text{ atm (652 mmHg)}$$

5-35. (a) Proceed in the same fashion as in Example 5-18 of the textbook.

$$\text{apparent mol. wt.} = \left(0.751 \text{ mol } N_2 \times \frac{28.0 \text{ g } N_2}{1 \text{ mol } N_2}\right) + \left(0.152 \text{ mol } O_2 \times \frac{32.0 \text{ g } O_2}{1 \text{ mol } O_2}\right)$$

$$+ \left(0.038 \text{ mol } CO_2 \times \frac{44.0 \text{ g } CO_2}{1 \text{ mol } CO_2}\right) + \left(0.059 \text{ mol } H_2O \times \frac{18.0 \text{ g } H_2O}{1 \text{ mol } H_2O}\right) = 28.6 \text{ g/mol}$$

(b) From equation (5.12) we see that at a given T and P gas density is directly proportional to mol. wt.. Since the apparent mol. wt. of expired air (28.6) is less than that of normal air (29.0), its density is also less.

(c) Here we use equation (5.16). Assume a total pressure of 1.00 atm for expired air and for normal air.

$$\text{expired air:} \quad P_{CO_2} = \frac{V_{CO_2}}{V_{tot.}} \times P_{tot.} = 0.038 \times 1.00 \text{ atm} = 0.038 \text{ atm}$$

$$\text{normal air:} \quad P_{CO_2} = \frac{V_{CO_2}}{V_{tot.}} \times P_{tot.} = 0.0003 \times 1.00 \text{ atm} = 0.0003 \text{ atm}$$

ratio of partial pressures of CO_2, expired air/ordinary air = 0.038 atm/0.0003 atm $\simeq$ 130

Collection of gases over water

5-36. To determine the no. mol $H_2(g)$ use information from the balanced equation.

$$\text{no. mol } H_2 = 2.65 \text{ g Al} \times \frac{1 \text{ mol Al}}{27.0 \text{ g Al}} \times \frac{3 \text{ mol } H_2}{2 \text{ mol Al}} = 0.147 \text{ mol } H_2$$

The partial pressure of this $H_2(g)$ is $P_{gas} = P_{bar} - P_{H_2O} = 746 - 25.2 = 721$ mmHg

Finally, use the ideal gas equation.

$$V = \frac{nRT}{P} = \frac{0.147 \text{ mol} \times 0.0821 \text{ L atm mol}^{-1} \text{ K}^{-1} \times 299 \text{ K}}{(721/760)\text{atm}} = 3.80 \text{ L}$$

5-37. The partial pressure of $O_2(g)$ is $P_{bar} - P_{H_2O} = 752 - 19.8 = 732$ mmHg. Now use equation (5.11) to calculate the mass of oxygen.

$$m = \frac{(MW)PV}{RT} = \frac{32.0\ g\ mol^{-1} \times (732/760)atm \times 0.0848\ L}{0.0821\ L\ atm\ mol^{-1}\ K^{-1} \times 295\ K} = 0.108\ g\ O_2$$

5-38. Originally, P_{Ar} = 755 mmHg; but after saturation of the gas with water vapor, $P_{Ar} + P_{H_2O} = P_{bar}$ = 755 mmHg. Thus, in the final gas mixture, P_{Ar} = 755 - 25.2 = 730 mmHg. In effect, the pressure of the original 146 cm^3 Ar has been allowed to decrease from 755 mmHg to 730 mmHg. The volume of the Ar (and hence of the gaseous mixture) must be

$$V = 146\ cm^3 \times \text{ratio of pressures} = 146\ cm^3 \times \frac{755\ mmHg}{730\ mmHg} = 151\ cm^3$$

5-39. Barometric pressure is given by $P_{O_2} + P_{H_2O} = (P_{O_2} + 23.8)$mmHg. To determine P_{O_2} use data in the ideal gas equation written in the form of equation (5.11).

$$P_{O_2} = \frac{mRT}{(MW)V} = \frac{1.58\ g \times 0.0821\ L\ atm\ mol^{-1}\ K^{-1} \times 298\ K}{32.0\ g\ mol^{-1} \times 1.28\ L} = 0.944\ atm = 717\ mmHg$$

$$P_{bar} = (717 + 23.8)mmHg = 741\ mmHg$$

Kinetic molecular theory

5-40. Molecules of different gases compared at the same T and P have equal kinetic energies, and the average kinetic energy of gas molecules is $\overline{\varepsilon_k} = \frac{1}{2} \cdot m \cdot \overline{u^2}$. The molecules of different gases will have equal speeds, u, only if their masses, m, are equal. Compared at the same T and P, lighter molecules have greater speeds and more massive molecules, lower speeds.

5-41. The expressions referred to in this exercise are:

$$PV = \frac{2}{3} \cdot n' \cdot \overline{\varepsilon_k} \qquad (5.19)$$

$$\overline{\varepsilon_k} = \frac{3}{2} \cdot \frac{R}{N} \cdot T = \frac{3}{2} \cdot kT \qquad (5.21)$$

Boyle's Law

Equation (5.21) establishes the proportionality between absolute temperature and the average kinetic energy of molecules ($\overline{\varepsilon_k}$). When temperature is held constant, $\overline{\varepsilon_k}$ = constant. If the amount of gas is also held constant, n' = constant. This results in the following form of equation (5.19):

$$PV = \frac{2}{3} n' \overline{\varepsilon_k} = \text{constant}$$

This is the same expression as Boyle's law, equation (5.4).

Charles' law

Equation (5.19) can be rearranged to the form

$$V = \frac{2}{3} \cdot \frac{n'}{P} \cdot \overline{\varepsilon_k}$$

and this combined with equation (5.21) to yield

$$V = \text{constant} \cdot \frac{n'}{P} \cdot T$$

If the amount of gas and the gas pressure are held constant, then volume is seen to be proportional to absolute temperature; this is the same as equation (5.6)--Charles' law: V = constant • T.

5-42. (a) at 273 K: $u_{rms} = \sqrt{\frac{3 \times R \times T}{(MW)}} = \sqrt{\frac{3 \times R \times 273}{(MW)}} = 1.84 \times 10^3$ m/s

at T: $u_{rms} = 3.68 \times 10^3\ m/s = 2 \times 1.84 \times 10^3\ m/s = 2\sqrt{\frac{3 \times R \times 273}{(MW)}}$

$$= \sqrt{4} \times \sqrt{\frac{3 \times R \times 273}{(MW)}} = \sqrt{\frac{4 \times 3 \times R \times 273}{(MW)}} = \sqrt{\frac{3 \times R \times (4 \times 273)}{(MW)}}$$

The temperature T = (4 × 273) = 1092 K

(b) Two approaches are possible here. One is a direct substitution into equation (5.22), as in Example 5-20 of the textbook. The other follows the lines of the derivation of equation (5.24).

$$\frac{(u_{rms})_{N_2}}{(u_{rms})_{H_2}} = \sqrt{\frac{3\ RT/(MW)_{N_2}}{3\ RT/(MW)_{H_2}}} = \sqrt{\frac{(MW)_{H_2}}{(MW)_{N_2}}} = \sqrt{\frac{2.016}{28.01}} = 0.268$$

$$(u_{rms})_{N_2} = 0.268 \times (u_{rms})_{H_2} = 0.268 \times 1.84 \times 10^3\ \text{m/s} = 493\ \text{m/s}$$

5-43. Here a direct application of equation (5.22) is required, rather than just a comparison to another gas. Use the method of Example 5-20 in the textbook.

$$(u_{rms})_{Cl_2} = \sqrt{\frac{3\ RT}{(MW)}} = \sqrt{\frac{3 \times 8.314\ \text{kg m}^2\ \text{s}^{-2}\ \text{mol}^{-1}\ \text{K}^{-1} \times 298\ \text{K}}{0.0709\ \text{kg mol}^{-1}}} = 324\ \text{m/s}$$

5-44. $$\bar{u} = \frac{(9.8 + 9.0 + 8.3 + 6.5 + 3.7 + 1.8) \times 10^3\ \text{m/s}}{6} = 6.5 \times 10^3\ \text{m/s}$$

$$u_{rms} = \sqrt{\frac{[(9.8)^2 + (9.0)^2 + (8.3)^2 + (6.5)^2 + (3.7)^2 + (1.8)^2] \times 10^6\ \text{m}^2\ \text{s}^{-2}}{6}} = 7.1 \times 10^3\ \text{m/s}$$

Effusion of gases

5-45. Use equation (5.24) to set up the desired ratios of rates of diffusion, as follows:

$$\frac{\text{rate } H_2}{\text{rate } O_2} = \sqrt{\frac{\text{mol. wt. } O_2}{\text{mol. wt. } H_2}} = \sqrt{\frac{32.0}{2.02}} = 4.0 \qquad \frac{\text{rate } H_2}{\text{rate } D_2} = \sqrt{\frac{\text{mol. wt. } D_2}{\text{mol. wt. } H_2}} = \sqrt{\frac{4.0}{2.0}} = 1.4$$

$$\frac{\text{rate } ^{235}UF_6}{\text{rate } ^{238}UF_6} = \sqrt{\frac{\text{mol. wt. } ^{238}UF_6}{\text{mol. wt. } ^{235}UF_6}} = \sqrt{\frac{352}{349}} = 1.004$$

5-46. Following Example 5-21 of the textbook,

$$\frac{\text{effusion time for unknown}}{\text{effusion time for } N_2(g)} = \frac{55\ \text{s}}{38\ \text{s}} = \sqrt{\frac{(MW)_{unknown}}{(MW)_{N_2}}} = \sqrt{\frac{(MW)_{unk.}}{28.0}}$$

$$\frac{(MW)_{unk.}}{28.0} = \left(\frac{55}{38}\right)^2 = 2.1 \qquad (MW)_{unk.} = 28.0 \times 2.1 = 59$$

Nonideal gases

5-47. The problem simply calls for determining PV/RT for each gas. The value obtained should be n, the number of moles of gas. If the experimentally determined value of n is equal or very nearly equal to the number of moles of gas given, the gas is ideal. If not, the gas is nonideal.

(a) 1.00 mol CO_2 (actual)

$$n = \frac{PV}{RT} = \frac{19.7\ \text{atm} \times 1.20\ \text{L}}{0.0821\ \text{L atm mol}^{-1}\ \text{K}^{-1} \times (273 + 40)\ \text{K}} = 0.920\ \text{mol (exptl.)}$$

The gas is nonideal.

(b) 0.113 g Ar = 2.83×10^{-3} mol Ar (actual)

$$n = \frac{PV}{RT} = \frac{5.05 \times 10^{-2}\ \text{atm} \times 1.25\ \text{L}}{0.0821\ \text{L atm mol}^{-1}\ \text{K}^{-1} \times 273\ \text{K}} = 2.82 \times 10^{-3}\ \text{mol (exptl.)}$$

The gas is ideal.

(c) $1.00\ g\ H_2 = 0.495\ mol\ H_2$ (actual)

$$n = \frac{PV}{RT} = \frac{200\ atm \times 0.06306\ L}{0.0821\ L\ atm\ mol^{-1}\ K^{-1} \times 273\ K} = 0.563\ mol\ (exptl.)$$

The gas is nonideal.

5-48. (a) $$P = \frac{nRT}{V} = \frac{1.00\ mol \times 0.0821\ L\ atm\ mol^{-1}\ K^{-1} \times (273 + 30)\ K}{0.855\ L} = 29.1\ atm$$

(b) $(P + a/V^2)(V - b) = RT$ (for one mole of gas)

$$P = \frac{RT}{V-b} - \frac{a}{V^2} = \frac{0.0821\ L\ atm\ mol^{-1}\ K^{-1} \times 303\ K}{(0.855 - 0.043)\ L\ mol^{-1}} - \frac{3.61\ L^2\ atm\ mol^{-2}}{(0.855)^2\ L^2\ mol^{-2}}$$

$P = 30.6\ atm - 4.9\ atm = 25.7\ atm$

(c) The two values differ by about 3.4 atm. The pressure calculated by the van der Waals equation is lower than that calculated by the ideal gas equation, because the van der Waals equation accounts for forces of attraction between molecules (intermolecular forces). These forces cause gas molecules to strike a container wall with less force than if the gas were ideal. The real gas pressure is expected to be less than the calculated ideal gas pressure.

Self-test Questions

1\. (*b*) The pressure corresponding to 10.0 g H_2 at STP is standard pressure--1.00 atm. Each of the other pressures is less than 1.00 atm. That is, in (a) 75.0 cm Hg is less than standard (76.0 cm Hg). In (c), a column of air 10 mi high does not extend to the full height of the atmosphere; it would exert less than 1 atm pressure. In (d), since 60.0 cm Hg exerts less than 1 atm pressure, so too must 60.0 cm CCl_4--a liquid much less dense than Hg.

2\. (*a*) A temperature of 100°C = 373 K. Thus, the gas temperature is *lowered* from 373 K to 200 K. The gas volume must *decrease* . Only answer (a) represents a decrease in volume.

3\. (*c*) Since $P_{O_2} = P_{bar} - P_{H_2O} = 751 - 21 = 730$ mmHg, items (a) and (b) must be incorrect. A pressure of 730 mmHg is less than atmospheric (760 mmHg). Item (d) must be wrong; and, by a process of elimination, item (c) must be correct.

4\. (*a*) The gases cannot have equal volumes or equal effusion rates because their amounts differ, as do their molecular weights. When different gases are compared at the same temperature, their average molecular kinetic energies are equal. Their average molecular speeds in this case would be equal only if their molecular weights were equal (and for H_2 and He they are not).

5\. (*b*) Because of its lower molecular weight we should expect $H_2(g)$ to effuse more rapidly than $SO_2(g)$. In the gas that *remains* the proportion of SO_2 increases with time and that of H_2 decreases. This means that the partial pressure of SO_2 will exceed that of H_2 (they were equal originally).

6\. (*d*) Use the molar volume at STP--22.4 L/mol--to make comparisons. In 2.24 L $O_2(g)$ at STP, there is 0.10 mol O_2. If the pressure is to be 2.00 atm, the amount of gas must be doubled--to 0.20 mol. The amount of oxygen present is 1.60/32.0 = 0.05 mol; 0.15 mol gas must be added. Adding another 1.60 g O_2 represents only an additional 0.05 mol; item (a) is incorrect. Item (b) is incorrect because it speaks of *releasing* $O_2(g)$. Item (c) refers to 2.00 g He; but this is 0.50 mol He. By the process of elimination, item (d) is correct. But also, 0.60/4.00 = 0.15 mol He, and this is the amount of gas that we indicated must be added.

7\. This problem can be solved in several ways. One method involves determining the total number of moles of gas.

$$\text{no. mol } H_2 = 2.24\ L\ H_2(STP) \times \frac{1\ mol\ H_2}{22.4\ L\ H_2(STP)} = 0.10\ mol\ H_2$$

total no. mol gas = 0.10 mol H_2 + 0.10 mol He = 0.20 mol

Now use the ideal gas equation, with n = 0.20 mol; P = 1 atm; and T = 373 K.

$$V = \frac{nRT}{P} = \frac{0.20 \text{ mol} \times 0.0821 \text{ L atm mol}^{-1} \text{ K}^{-1} \times 373 \text{ K}}{1 \text{ atm}} = 6.1 \text{ L}$$

8. (a) The pressure exerted by a liquid column depends only on the height of the column and the density of the liquid. P = ghd. In the derivation of this equation, (5.2 in the textbook), the cross-sectional area of the liquid column, A, does appear. Moreover, the cross-sectional area of a barometer tube does depend on the diameter. However, because the term A appears both in the numerator and denominator, it cancels out.

(b) For an open-end manometer, $P_{gas} = P_{bar} + \Delta P$. If $P_{gas} < P_{bar}$, ΔP is negative. Moreover, if P_{gas} is very small, this means that the magnitudes of P_{bar} and ΔP will be almost equal. A small difference between two large numbers cannot be measured very accurately, e.g., 751.3 - 751.2 = 0.1 mmHg. In this case each mercury column must be measured to four significant figures to obtain a result that is good only to one significant figure. To measure very high pressures with an open-end manometer would require the open-end arm to be very long--much higher than 1 m.

9. Because the gases are not measured at the same T and P, comparisons must be on a mole basis.

$$\text{no. mol CO} = 30.0 \text{ L(STP)} \times \frac{1 \text{ mol CO}}{22.4 \text{ L(STP)}} = 1.34 \text{ mol CO}$$

$$\text{no. mol } H_2 = 1.34 \text{ mol CO} \times \frac{7 \text{ mol } H_2}{3 \text{ mol CO}} = 3.13 \text{ mol } H_2$$

$$V = \frac{nRT}{P} = \frac{3.13 \text{ mol} \times 0.0821 \text{ L atm mol}^{-1} \text{ K}^{-1} \times 295 \text{ K}}{(745/760) \text{atm}} = 77.3 \text{ L } H_2(g)$$

10. Suppose that we base the calculation on 100.0 g of the gaseous mixture.

$$n_{O_2} = 50.0 \text{ g } O_2 \times \frac{1 \text{ mol } O_2}{32.0 \text{ g } O_2} = 1.56 \text{ mol } O_2$$

$$n_{N_2} = 25.0 \text{ g } N_2 \times \frac{1 \text{ mol } N_2}{28.0 \text{ g } N_2} = 0.893 \text{ mol } N_2$$

$$n_{Cl_2} = 25.0 \text{ g } Cl_2 \times \frac{1 \text{ mol } Cl_2}{70.9 \text{ g } Cl_2} = 0.353 \text{ mol } Cl_2$$

$$n_{tot.} = 1.56 \text{ mol } O_2 + 0.893 \text{ mol } N_2 + 0.353 \text{ mol } Cl_2 = 2.81 \text{ mol gas}$$

Now use the expression $\frac{P_{Cl_2}}{P_{tot.}} = \frac{n_{Cl_2}}{n_{tot.}}$

$$P_{Cl_2} = \frac{0.353}{2.81} \times 1.00 = 0.126 \text{ atm}$$

Chapter 6

Thermochemistry

Specific heat

6-1. $\text{no. cal} = 415 \text{ g } CHCl_3 \times \frac{0.23 \text{ cal}}{\text{g } CHCl_3 \text{ °C}} \times (51.0 - 21.4)\text{°C} = 2.8 \times 10^3 \text{ cal}$

6-2. (a) $\text{no. cal} = 612 \text{ g} \times \frac{0.4 \text{ J}}{\text{g °C}} \times (20 - 515)\text{°C} = -1.2 \times 10^5 \text{ J}$

(b) The heat given off by the burner is absorbed by a mass of water, *m*.

$$\text{no. J} = 1.2 \times 10^5 \text{ J} = m \times \frac{4.184 \text{ J}}{\text{g } H_2O \text{ °C}} \times (100 - 20)\text{°C}$$

$$m = \frac{1.2 \times 10^5}{4.184 \times (100 - 20)} \text{ g } H_2O = 3.6 \times 10^2 \text{ g } H_2O$$

6-3. $q_{zinc} = -q_{water}$

$$150.0 \text{ g Zn} \times \text{sp. ht.} \times (39.0 - 100.0)\text{°C} = -[50.0 \text{ g water} \times \frac{1.00 \text{ cal}}{\text{g water °C}} \times (39.0 - 22.0)\text{°C}]$$

$$\text{sp. ht.} = \frac{-50.0 \times 17.0 \text{ cal}}{150.0 \text{ g Zn} \times (-61.0)\text{°C}} = \frac{0.0929 \text{ cal}}{\text{g Zn °C}}$$

6-4. From the data given we are able to calculate both the heat lost by Mg and gained by water. These quantities can then be compared.

$$q_{Mg} = 70.0 \text{ g Mg} \times \frac{1.04 \text{ J}}{\text{g Mg °C}} \times (47.2 - 99.8)\text{°C} = -3830 \text{ J}$$

$$q_{water} = 50.0 \text{ g water} \times \frac{4.184 \text{ J}}{\text{g water °C}} \times (47.2 - 30.0)\text{°C} = 3600 \text{ J}$$

According to the law of conservation of energy we should expect $q_{Mg} + q_{water} = 0$. In this case however, -3830 J + 3600 J = -230 J. There appears to be a net loss of 230 J. The "problem" here is not with the failure of the law of conservation of energy but failure to account for all of the heat lost by the Mg. For example, some might go toward vaporizing a small quantity of water (see Chapter 11) and some may simply be given off from the magnesium-water mixture to the surroundings.

6-5. Since $q_{Cu} = -q_{glyc.}$, we may write

$$74.8 \text{ g Cu} \times \frac{0.393 \text{ J}}{\text{g Cu °C}} \times (31.1 - 143.2)\text{°C} = -[165 \text{ cm}^3 \times \frac{1.26 \text{ g glyc.}}{\text{cm}^3} \times \text{sp. ht.} \times (31.1 - 24.8)\text{°C}]$$

$$\text{sp. ht.} = \frac{74.8 \times 0.393 \times (31.1 - 143.2) \text{ J}}{-165 \times 1.26 \text{ g glyc.} \times (31.1 - 24.8)\text{°C}} = \frac{2.5 \text{ J}}{\text{g glyc. °C}}$$

$$\text{molar heat capacity} = \frac{2.5 \text{ J}}{\text{g glyc. °C}} \times \frac{92.1 \text{ g glyc.}}{1 \text{ mol glyc.}} = \frac{2.3 \times 10^2 \text{ J}}{\text{mol glyc. °C}}$$

6-6. Again, the basic expression required is $q_{brass} + q_{water} = 0$, or $q_{brass} = -q_{water}$. In this case, however, the unknown is the final temperature, *t*.

$$\left(7.00 \text{ mm} \times \frac{1.00 \text{ cm}}{10.00 \text{ mm}}\right)^3 \times \frac{8.40 \text{ g brass}}{\text{cm}^3} \times \frac{0.385 \text{ J}}{\text{g brass °C}} \times (t - 85.6)\text{°C}$$

$$= -[15.0 \text{ g water} \times \frac{4.184 \text{ J}}{\text{g water °C}} \times (t - 25.2)\text{°C}]$$

$1.11\,t - 95.0 = -62.8\,t + 1582$ $\quad\quad 63.9\,t = 1677 \quad\quad t = 26.2 \text{ °C}$

First law of thermodynamics

6-7. In each of the following cases the required equation is $\Delta E = q - w$. The sign conventions for q and w are those introduced in the textbook. In case (c) a conversion from cal to J is also required.

(a) $\Delta E = (+50 \text{ J}) - (+50 \text{ J}) = 0$ (b) $\Delta E = (+100 \text{ cal}) - (+75 \text{ cal}) = +25 \text{ cal}$

(c) $\Delta E = (+150 \text{ cal} \times 4.184 \text{ J/cal}) - (+675 \text{ J}) = -47 \text{ J}$

(d) $\Delta E = (-20 \text{ J}) - (-415 \text{ J}) = +395 \text{ J}$ (e) $\Delta E = (0) - (+125 \text{ J}) = -125 \text{ J}$

6-8. (a) Yes: Work must always be performed by a gas when it expands against an external pressure.

(b) Yes: The energy required for the work of expansion is absorbed from the surroundings.

(c) The temperature of the gas remains constant. This is what is meant by an *isothermal* process.

6-9. The water at the top of the waterfall has more potential energy than that at the bottom. When the water falls, this potential energy is transformed into heat, which raises the water temperature.

Heats of reaction

6-10. The first law of thermodynamics is $\Delta E = q - w$. This equation can be rearranged to $q = \Delta E + w$. This expression describes the heat of a reaction, regardless of how the reaction is carried out. Thus expression (c) is the most general. Expressions (a) and (d) are limited to describing the heat of a reaction at constant volume and (b) and (e), to a heat of reaction at constant pressure.

6-11. (a) $\text{no. kJ} = \dfrac{-350 \text{ kJ}}{\text{mol}} \times \dfrac{1 \text{ mol}}{56.1 \text{ g CaO}} = -6.24 \text{ kJ/g CaO}$

(b) $\text{no. kJ} = 50.0 \text{ kg Ca(OH)}_2 \times \dfrac{1000 \text{ g Ca(OH)}_2}{1 \text{ kg Ca(OH)}_2} \times \dfrac{1 \text{ mol Ca(OH)}_2}{74.1 \text{ g Ca(OH)}_2} \times \dfrac{-350 \text{ kJ}}{1 \text{ mol Ca(OH)}_2} = -2.36 \times 10^5 \text{ kJ}$

(c) First calculate the quantity of $Ca(OH)_2$ produced and water consumed in the slaking of the lime.

$$\text{no. g Ca(OH)}_2 = 10.0 \text{ g CaO} \times \frac{1 \text{ mol CaO}}{56.1 \text{ g CaO}} \times \frac{1 \text{ mol Ca(OH)}_2}{1 \text{ mol CaO}} \times \frac{74.1 \text{ g Ca(OH)}_2}{1 \text{ mol Ca(OH)}_2} = 13.2 \text{ g Ca(OH)}_2$$

$$\text{no. g H}_2\text{O} = 10.0 \text{ g CaO} \times \frac{1 \text{ mol CaO}}{56.1 \text{ g CaO}} \times \frac{1 \text{ mol H}_2\text{O}}{1 \text{ mol CaO}} \times \frac{18.0 \text{ g H}_2\text{O}}{1 \text{ mol H}_2\text{O}} = 3.21 \text{ g H}_2\text{O}$$

The mixture that results from the reaction is 13.2 g $Ca(OH)_2$ and (100.0 - 3.2) = 96.8 g H_2O. Let us next determine the quantity of heat required to raise the temperature of this mixture from 25°C to 100°C.

$$\text{no. J} = [13.2 \text{ g Ca(OH)}_2 \times \frac{1.09 \text{ J}}{\text{g Ca(OH)}_2 \text{ °C}} \times (100 - 25)\text{°C}] + [96.8 \text{ g H}_2\text{O} \times \frac{4.184 \text{ J}}{\text{g H}_2\text{O °C}} \times (100 - 25)\text{°C}]$$

$$= 1.08 \times 10^3 \text{ J} + 3.04 \times 10^4 \text{ J} = 3.15 \times 10^4 \text{ J}$$

Now we can compare this quantity of heat with that liberated in the slaking of 10.0 g CaO.

$$\text{no. J} = 10.0 \text{ g CaO} \times \frac{1 \text{ mol CaO}}{56.1 \text{ g CaO}} \times \frac{-350 \text{ kJ}}{1 \text{ mol CaO}} \times \frac{1000 \text{ J}}{1 \text{ kJ}} = -6.24 \times 10^4 \text{ J}$$

More than enough heat is released in the slaking of the quicklime to bring the reaction mixture to the boiling point.

6-12. (a) Consider this two-step approach. First determine the quantity of heat released in the combustion reaction.

$$\text{no. kJ} = 1.50 \times 10^3 \text{ g CH}_4 \times \frac{1 \text{ mol CH}_4}{16.0 \text{ g CH}_4} \times \frac{-890 \text{ kJ}}{1 \text{ mol CH}_4} = -8.34 \times 10^4 \text{ kJ}$$

Now calculate the mass of water that could be heated.

$$\text{no. kJ} = m_{H_2O} \times \frac{4.184\ \text{J}}{\text{g } H_2O\ °\text{C}} \times (48.2 - 22.5)°\text{C} = 8.34 \times 10^4\ \text{kJ} \times \frac{1000\ \text{J}}{1\ \text{kJ}}$$

$$m_{H_2O} = \frac{8.34 \times 10^7}{4.184 \times (48.2 - 22.5)}\ \text{g } H_2O = 7.76 \times 10^5\ \text{g } H_2O$$

Finally, assuming a density of $H_2O = 1.00\ \text{g/cm}^3$

$$\text{no. L } H_2O = 7.76 \times 10^5\ \text{g } H_2O \times \frac{1\ \text{cm}^3\ H_2O}{1.00\ \text{g } H_2O} \times \frac{1\ \text{L } H_2O}{1000\ \text{cm}^3\ H_2O} = 776\ \text{L } H_2O$$

(b) $$\text{no. mol } CH_4 = -1.00 \times 10^6\ \text{kJ} \times \frac{1\ \text{mol } CH_4}{-890\ \text{kJ}} = 1.12 \times 10^3\ \text{mol } CH_4$$

Now use the ideal gas equation to solve for V.

$$V = \frac{nRT}{P} = \frac{1.12 \times 10^3\ \text{mol} \times 0.0821\ \text{L atm mol}^{-1}\ \text{K}^{-1} \times 295.7\ \text{K}}{(748/760)\text{atm}} = 2.76 \times 10^4\ \text{L}$$

6-13. Use the ideal gas equation to calculate the total number of moles of gas.

$$n = \frac{PV}{RT} = \frac{(738/760)\text{atm} \times 150.0\ \text{L}}{0.0821\ \text{L atm mol}^{-1}\ \text{K}^{-1} \times 296\ \text{K}} = 5.99\ \text{mol gas}$$

Now determine the quantity of heat liberated by the combustion of each gas and add these quantities together.

$$\text{no. kJ} = 5.99\ \text{mol gas} \times \frac{83.0\ \text{mol } CH_4}{100\ \text{mol gas}} \times \frac{-890\ \text{kJ}}{1\ \text{mol } CH_4} = -4.42 \times 10^3\ \text{kJ}$$

$$\text{no. kJ} = 5.99\ \text{mol gas} \times \frac{11.2\ \text{mol } C_2H_6}{100\ \text{mol gas}} \times \frac{-1559\ \text{kJ}}{1\ \text{mol } C_2H_6} = -1.05 \times 10^3\ \text{kJ}$$

$$\text{no. kJ} = 5.99\ \text{mol gas} \times \frac{5.8\ \text{mol } C_3H_8}{100\ \text{mol gas}} \times \frac{-2219\ \text{kJ}}{1\ \text{mol } C_3H_8} = -0.77 \times 10^3\ \text{kJ}$$

$$\text{total heat} = -4.42 \times 10^3 - 1.05 \times 10^3 - 0.77 \times 10^3 = -6.24 \times 10^3\ \text{kJ}$$

6-14. (a) $q_{KOH} + q_{water} = 0$ and $q_{KOH} = -q_{water}$

$$q_{water} = 45.0\ \text{g } H_2O \times \frac{4.184\ \text{J}}{\text{g } H_2O\ °\text{C}} \times (24.9 - 24.1)°\text{C} = 1.5 \times 10^2\ \text{J}$$

$$q_{KOH} = \frac{-1.5 \times 10^2\ \text{J}}{0.150\ \text{g KOH}} \times \frac{56.1\ \text{g KOH}}{1\ \text{mol KOH}} = -5.6 \times 10^4\ \text{J/mol KOH} = -56\ \text{kJ/mol KOH}$$

(b) The precision could be increased to three significant figures by using a large enough sample of KOH to produce a temperature increase in the water of more than 10°C.

6-15. $$\text{no. mol NaOH} = 250\ \text{ml} \times \frac{1\ \text{L}}{1000\ \text{ml}} \times \frac{6\ \text{mol NaOH}}{1\ \text{L}} = 1.5\ \text{mol NaOH}$$

$$\text{no. cal} = 1.5\ \text{mol NaOH} \times \frac{-10\ \text{kcal}}{1\ \text{mol NaOH}} \times \frac{1000\ \text{cal}}{1\ \text{kcal}} = -15{,}000\ \text{cal}$$

Assume that the NaOH solution weighs 250 g and has a specific heat capacity of about 1.00 cal/g °C.

$$15{,}000\ \text{cal} = 250\ \text{g} \times \frac{1.00\ \text{cal}}{\text{g } °\text{C}} \times \Delta t \qquad \Delta t = \frac{15{,}000}{250} = 60°\text{C}$$

Since the original temperature was 21°C, the final temperature should be about 81°C.

6-16. (a) $\Delta\bar{E} = \dfrac{-33.41 \text{ kJ}}{\text{g } C_3H_7OH} \times \dfrac{60.10 \; C_3H_7OH}{1 \text{ mol } C_3H_7OH} = -2008 \text{ kJ/mol } C_3H_7OH$

(b) Use the expression $\Delta H(\text{in kJ}) = \Delta E(\text{in kJ}) + 2.48\ \Delta n_g$

$\Delta\bar{H} = -2008 + 2.48 \times (3 - 9/2) = -2008 - 3.72 = -2012 \text{ kJ/mol } C_3H_7OH$

6-17. The expression: $\Delta H(\text{in kJ}) = \Delta E(\text{in kJ}) + 2.48\ \Delta n_g$ must be applied in each case.

(a) $\Delta H = \Delta E + 2.48 \times (2 - 1) = \Delta E + 2.48$

$\Delta H > \Delta E$, since a positive quantity (+2.48) is added to ΔE to obtain ΔH.

(b) $\Delta H = \Delta E + 2.48(1 - 3 - 7) = \Delta E - (9 \times 2.48)$ $\quad \Delta H < \Delta E$

(c) $C_4H_7OH(l) + 11/2\ O_2(g) \longrightarrow 4\ CO_2(g) + 4\ H_2O(l)$

$\Delta H = \Delta E + 2.48(4 - 11/2) = \Delta E - (1.5 \times 2.48)$ $\quad \Delta H < \Delta E$

(d) $NH_4NO_3(s) \longrightarrow 2\ H_2O(l) + N_2O(g)$

$\Delta H = \Delta E + 2.48(1) = \Delta E + 2.48$ $\quad \Delta H > \Delta E$

Bomb calorimetry

6-18. The heat absorbed by the water in the calorimeter is

$\text{no. J} = 1155 \text{ g } H_2O \times \dfrac{4.184 \text{ J}}{\text{g } H_2O\ °C} \times 3.68°C = 1.78 \times 10^4 \text{ J}$

The heat absorbed by the rest of the calorimeter assembly is

$2.09 \times 10^4 \text{ J} - 1.78 \times 10^4 \text{ J} = 0.31 \times 10^4 \text{ J} = 3.1 \times 10^3 \text{ J}$

The heat capacity of the bomb is $\dfrac{3.1 \times 10^3 \text{ J}}{3.68°C} = 8.4 \times 10^2 \text{ J/°C}$

6-19. In the basic equation for bomb calorimetry, the unknown is Δt. $q_V = -(q_{water} + q_{bomb})$

$$0.242 \text{ g } C_{10}H_8 \times \frac{-4.02 \times 10^4 \text{ J}}{\text{g } C_{10}H_8} = -\left\{1025 \text{ g } H_2O \times \frac{4.184 \text{ J}}{\text{g } H_2O\ °C} \times \Delta t\right\} - \left\{\frac{802 \text{ J}}{°C} \times \Delta t\right\}$$

$-9.73 \times 10^3 = -4.29 \times 10^3\ \Delta t - 802\ \Delta t$ $\qquad \Delta t = \dfrac{9.73 \times 10^3}{(4.29 \times 10^3)+(0.802 \times 10^3)} = 1.91°C$

6-20. (a) $q_V = -(q_{water} + q_{bomb}) = -\left\{[980.0 \text{ g water} \times \dfrac{4.184 \text{ J}}{\text{g water } °C} \times (28.33 - 24.92)°C]\right.$

$\left. + [\dfrac{785 \text{ J}}{°C} \times (28.33 - 24.92)°C]\right\} = -\left\{1.40 \times 10^4 \text{ J} + 2.68 \times 10^3 \text{ J}\right\} = -1.67 \times 10^4 \text{ J}$

$\text{Heat of combustion} = \dfrac{-1.67 \times 10^4 \text{ J}}{1.010 \text{ g } C_{12}H_{12}O_{11}} \times \dfrac{342 \text{ g } C_{12}H_{12}O_{11}}{1 \text{ mol } C_{12}H_{12}O_{11}} \times \dfrac{1 \text{ kJ}}{1000 \text{ J}} = -5.65 \times 10^3 \text{ kJ/mol } C_{12}H_{22}O_{11}$

(b) $C_{12}H_{22}O_{11}(s) + 12\ O_2(g) \longrightarrow 12\ CO_2(g) + 11\ H_2O(l)$

(c) The value obtained in part (a) is q_V, and therefore ΔE for the reaction.

$\Delta H = \Delta E + 2.48\ \Delta n_g$; but since $\Delta n_g = 0$ for this reaction,

$\Delta H = \Delta E = -5.65 \times 10^3 \text{ kJ/mol } C_{12}H_{22}O_{11}$.

(d) The heat of combustion of one teaspoon (4.8 g) of sucrose is

$$\text{no kcal} = \frac{-5.65 \times 10^3 \text{ kJ}}{\text{mol } C_{12}H_{22}O_{11}} \times \frac{1 \text{ mol } C_{12}H_{22}O_{11}}{342.3 \text{ g } C_{12}H_{22}O_{11}} \times \frac{1 \text{ kcal}}{4.184 \text{ kJ}} \times 4.8 \text{ g } C_{12}H_{22}O_{11} = -19 \text{ kcal} = -19 \text{ Calories}$$

6-21. From the data for the first experiment we can calculate the heat capacity of the bomb.

$$q_v = -(q_{water} + q_{bomb})$$

$$1.148 \text{ g } C_7H_6O_s \times \frac{-26.42 \text{ kJ}}{\text{g } C_7H_6O_2} = -\left\{1215 \text{ g water} \times \frac{4.184 \text{ J}}{\text{g water °C}} \times \frac{1 \text{ kJ}}{1000 \text{ J}} \times (30.26 - 25.12)\text{°C}\right\}$$

$$- \left\{\text{ht. cap. bomb} \times (30.26 - 25.12)\text{°C}\right\}$$

$$-30.33 \text{ kJ} = -26.13 \text{ kJ} - (\text{ht. cap. bomb} \times 5.14\text{°C})$$

$$\text{ht. cap. bomb} = \frac{-(30.33 - 26.13)\text{kJ}}{-5.14\text{°C}} \times \frac{1000 \text{ J}}{1 \text{ kJ}} = 817 \text{ J/°C}$$

Next, determine the heat of combustion per g coal.

$$q_v = -(q_{water} + q_{bomb})$$

$$q_v = -\left\{1187 \text{ g } H_2O \times \frac{4.184 \text{ J}}{\text{g } H_2O \text{ °C}} \times (29.71 - 24.98)\text{°C}\right\} - \left\{\frac{817 \text{ J}}{\text{°C}} \times (29.71 - 24.98)\text{°C}\right\}$$

$$= -2.35 \times 10^4 \text{ J} - 3.86 \times 10^3 \text{ J} = -2.74 \times 10^4 \text{ J} = -27.4 \text{ kJ}$$

$$\text{Heat of combustion of the coal} = \frac{-27.4 \text{ kJ}}{0.895 \text{ g coal}} = -30.6 \text{ kJ/g coal}$$

Finally, the required quantity of coal is calculated through the setup

$$\text{no. m ton coal} = -1.00 \times 10^9 \text{ kJ} \times \frac{1 \text{ g coa}}{-30.6 \text{ kJ}} \times \frac{1 \text{ kg coal}}{1000 \text{ g coal}} \times \frac{1 \text{ m ton coal}}{1000 \text{ kg coal}} = 32.7 \text{ m ton coal}$$

6-22. If there is no water in the calorimeter, all the heat liberated in the combustion reaction is absorbed by the bomb: $q_v = -q_{bomb}$. In Example 6-5 $q_v = -26.42$ kJ

$$-26.42 \text{ kJ} = -(\text{ht. cap. bomb} \times \Delta t)$$

$$-26.42 \text{ kJ} \times \frac{1000 \text{ J}}{1 \text{ kJ}} = -7.9 \times 10^2 \text{ J/°C} \times \Delta t$$

$$\Delta t = \frac{26.42 \times 1000}{7.9 \times 10^2} \text{°C} = 33\text{°C}$$

The temperature will increase to about 33°C above room temperature.

Functions of state

6-23. Our interest in enthalpy (H) always centers on enthalpy *change* (ΔH). Because enthalpy is a function of state, the difference in enthalpy between two states has a unique value, regardless of the actual enthalpy values in the two states. Thus, it is not necessary to know absolute values of enthalpy at all.

6-24. Because diamond and graphite are different solids, all properties of state, such as enthalpy, must be different for the two. The final state of the combustion--CO_2(g) and H_2O(l)--is the same in the two cases, but the initial states are different. As a result, the enthalpy changes (ΔH) for the two combustion processes must be different. (As a matter of fact, this difference proves to be slight; the heat of combustion of diamond is about 2 kJ/mol greater than of graphite.)

6-25. The heats of reaction must be different because the initial states are different; the spring is relaxed in one case and compressed in the other. The dissolving of the compressed spring should liberate slightly more heat than the relaxed spring. The difference would correspond to the work done on the spring to compress it initially.

6-26. Combine the two equations given in the textbook in this manner:

$NO(g) \longrightarrow 1/2\ N_2(g) + 1/2\ O_2(g)$	$\Delta\overline{H} = -90.37$ kJ/mol
$1/2\ N_2(g) + O_2(g) \longrightarrow NO_2(g)$	$\Delta\overline{H} = +33.85$ kJ/mol
$NO(g) + 1/2\ O_2(g) \longrightarrow NO_2(g)$	$\Delta\overline{H} = -56.52$ kJ/mol

6-27. First, let us write equations for the three combustion reactions.

$C_4H_6(g) + 11/2\ O_2(g) \longrightarrow 4\ CO_2(g) + 3\ H_2O(l)$	$\Delta\overline{H} = -2543.5$ kJ/mol
$C_4H_{10}(g) + 13/2\ O_2(g) \longrightarrow 4\ CO_2(g) + 5\ H_2O(l)$	$\Delta\overline{H} = -2878.6$ kJ/mol
$H_2(g) + 1/2\ O_2(g) \longrightarrow H_2O(l)$	$\Delta\overline{H} = -285.85$ kJ/mol

Now we must combine these to yield as a net equation:

$C_4H_6(g) + 2\ H_2(g) \longrightarrow C_4H_{10}(g)$ $\qquad \Delta\overline{H} = ?$

This is accomplished as follows:

$C_4H_6(g) + \cancel{11/2\ O_2(g)} \longrightarrow \cancel{4\ CO_2(g)} + \cancel{3\ H_2O(l)}$	$\Delta\overline{H} = -2543.5$ kJ/mol
$2\ H_2(g) + \cancel{O_2(g)} \longrightarrow \cancel{2\ H_2O(l)}$	$\Delta\overline{H} = 2 \times (-285.85)$ kJ/mol
$\cancel{4\ CO_2(g)} + \cancel{5\ H_2O(l)} \longrightarrow \cancel{13/2\ O_2(g)} + C_4H_{10}(g)$	$\Delta\overline{H} = -(-2878.6)$ kJ/mol
$C_4H_6(g) + 2\ H_2(g) \longrightarrow C_4H_{10}(g)$	$\Delta\overline{H} = -2543.5 - (2 \times 285.85) + 2878.6$ $= -236.6$ kJ/mol

6-28. Combine the data listed in the following way:

$CO(g) + \cancel{1/2\ O_2(g)} \longrightarrow CO_2(g)$	$\Delta\overline{H} = -282.97$ kJ/mol
$2\ H_2(g) + \cancel{O_2(g)} \longrightarrow 2\ H_2O(l)$	$\Delta\overline{H} = 2 \times (-285.85)$ kJ/mol
$\cancel{3\ C\ (graphite)} + 6\ H_2(g) \longrightarrow 3\ CH_4(g)$	$\Delta\overline{H} = 3 \times (-74.85)$ kJ/mol
$3\ CO(g) \longrightarrow \cancel{3\ C\ (graphite)} + \cancel{3/2\ O_2(g)}$	$\Delta\overline{H} = -3 \times (-110.54)$ kJ/mol

$4\ CO(g) + 8\ H_2(g) \longrightarrow 3\ CH_4(g) + CO_2(g) + 2\ H_2O(l)$

$\Delta\overline{H} = -282.97 - (2 \times 285.85) - (3 \times 74.85) + (3 \times 110.54)$ kJ/mol $= -747.6$ kJ/mol

6-29. Here the required combination of equations is:

$CO(g) \longrightarrow \cancel{C\ (graphite)} + \cancel{1/2\ O_2(g)}$	$\Delta\overline{H} = -\ (-110.54)$ kJ/mol
$2\ H_2(g) + \cancel{O_2(g)} \longrightarrow \cancel{2\ H_2O(l)}$	$\Delta\overline{H} = 2 \times (-285.85)$ kJ/mol
$\cancel{CO_2(g)} + \cancel{2\ H_2O(l)} \longrightarrow \cancel{3/2\ O_2(g)} + CH_3OH(l)$	$\Delta\overline{H} = -\ (-726.6)$ kJ/mol
$\cancel{C\ (graphite)} + \cancel{O_2(g)} \longrightarrow \cancel{CO_2(g)}$	$\Delta\overline{H} = -393.51$ kJ/mol

$CO(g) + 2\ H_2(g) \longrightarrow CH_3OH(l)$

$$\Delta\overline{H} = \left\{ 110.54 - (2 \times 285.85) + 726.6 - 393.51 \right\} \text{kJ/mol} = -128.1 \text{ kJ/mol}$$

6-30. Equations (6.20), (6.21) and (6.24) must be combined in the following manner to yield the desired net equation:

$$2 \times (6.20): \quad 2\,C(s) + 2\,H_2O(g) \longrightarrow 2\,\cancel{CO(g)} + 2\,\cancel{H_2(g)}$$

$$(6.24): \quad \cancel{CO(g)} + 3\,\cancel{H_2(g)} \longrightarrow CH_4(g) + \cancel{H_2O(g)}$$

$$(6.21): \quad \cancel{CO(g)} + \cancel{H_2O(g)} \longrightarrow CO_2(g) + \cancel{H_2(g)}$$

$$2\,C(s) + 2\,H_2O(g) \longrightarrow CH_4(g) + CO_2(g)$$

Enthalpies (heats) of formation

6-31. For the reaction $2\,Cl_2(g) + 2\,H_2O(l) \longrightarrow 4\,HCl(g) + O_2(g)$

$$\Delta\overline{H}^\circ_{rx} = 4\,\Delta\overline{H}^\circ_f[HCl(g)] - 2\,\Delta\overline{H}^\circ_f[H_2O(l)] = 4 \times (-92.30\text{ kJ/mol}) - 2 \times (-285.85\text{ kJ/mol}) = +202.5\text{ kJ/mol}$$

6-32. First write a balanced equation for the reaction. Then use heat of formation data in equation (6.19) to calculate $\Delta\overline{H}^\circ_{rx}$.

$$H_2S(g) + 3/2\,O_2(g) \longrightarrow SO_2(g) + H_2O(l) \qquad \Delta\overline{H}^\circ_{rx} = ?$$

$$\Delta\overline{H}^\circ_{rx} = \Delta\overline{H}^\circ_f[SO_2(g)] + \Delta\overline{H}^\circ_f[H_2O(l)] - \Delta\overline{H}^\circ_f[H_2S(g)] = -296.90\text{ kJ/mol} - 285.85\text{ kJ/mol} - (-20.17\text{ kJ/mol})$$

$$= -562.58\text{ kJ/mol}$$

6-33. Equation (6.19) is written with data given in the exercise and in Table 6-2. The heat of formation of $CCl_4(g)$ appears as an unknown in this equation.

$$CH_4(g) + 4\,Cl_2(g) \longrightarrow CCl_4(g) + 4\,HCl(g) \qquad \Delta\overline{H}^\circ = -402\text{ kJ/mol}$$

$$\Delta\overline{H}^\circ_{rx} = -402\text{ kJ/mol} = \Delta\overline{H}^\circ_f[CCl_4(g)] + 4\,\Delta\overline{H}^\circ_f[HCl(g)] - \Delta\overline{H}^\circ_f[CH_4(g)]$$

$$-402\text{ kJ/mol} = \Delta\overline{H}^\circ_f[CCl_4(g)] + 4 \times (-92.30\text{ kJ/mol}) - (-74.85\text{ kJ/mol})$$

$$\Delta\overline{H}^\circ_f[CCl_4(g)] = -402\text{ kJ/mol} + 369.2\text{ kJ/mol} - 74.85\text{ kJ/mol} = -108\text{ kJ/mol}$$

6-34. $2\,C(s) + 2\,H_2O(g) \longrightarrow CH_4(g) + CO_2(g)$

$$\Delta\overline{H}^\circ_{rx} = \Delta\overline{H}^\circ_f[CH_4(g)] + \Delta\overline{H}^\circ_f[CO_2(g)] - 2\,\Delta\overline{H}^\circ_f[H_2O(g)] = -74.85\text{ kJ/mol} - 393.51\text{ kJ/mol} - 2 \times (-241.84\text{ kJ/mol})$$

$$= +15.32\text{ kJ/mol}$$

6-35. Express the desired reaction as the sum of the following two:

$$C_2H_4(g) + 3\,O_2(g) \longrightarrow 2\,CO_2(g) + 2\,H_2O(l) \qquad \Delta\overline{H}^\circ = -1410.8\text{ kJ/mol}$$

$$2\,H_2O(l) \longrightarrow 2\,H_2O(g) \qquad \Delta\overline{H}^\circ = 2\,\Delta\overline{H}^\circ_f[H_2O(g)] - 2\,\Delta\overline{H}^\circ_f[H_2O(l)]$$

$$= 2 \times (-241.84) - 2 \times (-285.85)$$

$$= 88.02\text{ kJ/mol}$$

$$C_2H_4(g) + 3\,O_2(g) \longrightarrow 2\,CO_2(g) + 2\,H_2O(g) \qquad \Delta\overline{H}^\circ = -1322.8\text{ kJ/mol}$$

Consider that if the reaction first occurred to produce $H_2O(l)$, some of the liberated heat would have to be reabsorbed to vaporize the water. This would make $\Delta\overline{H}^\circ$ smaller (less negative) when $H_2O(g)$ is produced than when $H_2O(l)$ is formed, as the above calculation shows.

6-36. Equation (6.19) can be used twice, first to establish $\Delta\bar{H}_f^\circ[C_5H_{12}(l)]$ and then to calculate $\Delta\bar{H}_{rx}^\circ$ for the given reaction.

$$C_5H_{12} + 8\ O_2(g) \longrightarrow 5\ CO_2(g) + 6\ H_2O(l) \qquad \Delta\bar{H}^\circ = -3534\ \text{kJ/mol}$$

$$\Delta\bar{H}_{rx}^\circ = -3534\ \text{kJ/mol} = 5\ \Delta\bar{H}_f^\circ[CO_2(g)] + 6\ \Delta\bar{H}_f^\circ[H_2O(l)] - \Delta\bar{H}_f^\circ[C_5H_{12}(l)]$$

$$-3534\ \text{kJ/mol} = 5 \times (-393.51\ \text{kJ/mol}) + 6 \times (-285.85\ \text{kJ/mol}) - \Delta\bar{H}_f^\circ[C_5H_{12}(l)]$$

$$\Delta\bar{H}_f^\circ[C_5H_{12}(l)] = -1967.55 - 1715.10 + 3534 = -149\ \text{kJ/mol}$$

$$5\ CO(g) + 11\ H_2(g) \longrightarrow C_5H_{12}(l) + 5\ H_2O(l)$$

$$\Delta\bar{H}_{rx}^\circ = \Delta\bar{H}_f^\circ[C_5H_{12}(l)] + 5\ \Delta\bar{H}_f^\circ[H_2O(l)] - 5\ \Delta\bar{H}_f^\circ[CO(g)]$$

$$= -149\ \text{kJ/mol} + 5 \times (-285.85\ \text{kJ/mol}) - 5 \times (-110.54\ \text{kJ/mol}) = -1026\ \text{kJ/mol}$$

6-37. (a) First, determine $\Delta\bar{H}^\circ$ for the reaction $CaCO_3(s) \longrightarrow CaO(s) + CO_2(g)$

$$\Delta\bar{H}_{rx}^\circ = \Delta\bar{H}_f^\circ[CaO(s)] + \Delta\bar{H}_f^\circ[CO_2(g)] - \Delta\bar{H}_f^\circ[CaCO_3(s)]$$

$$= -635.5\ \text{kJ/mol} - 393.51\ \text{kJ/mol} - (-1207.1\ \text{kJ/mol}) = +178.1\ \text{kJ/mol}$$

$$\text{no. kJ} = 1000\ \text{kg}\ CaCO_3 \times \frac{1000\ \text{g}\ CaCO_3}{1\ \text{kg}\ CaCO_3} \times \frac{1\ \text{mol}\ CaCO_3}{100\ \text{g}\ CaCO_3} \times \frac{178.1\ \text{kJ}}{1\ \text{mol}\ CaCO_3} = 1.78 \times 10^6\ \text{kJ}$$

(b) Now, determine $\Delta\bar{H}^\circ$ for the reaction $CH_4(g) + 2\ O_2(g) \longrightarrow CO_2(g) + 2\ H_2O(l)$

$$\Delta\bar{H}_{rx}^\circ = \Delta\bar{H}_f^\circ[CO_2(g)] + 2\ \Delta\bar{H}_f^\circ[H_2O(l) - \Delta\bar{H}_f^\circ[CH_4(g)]$$

$$= -393.51\ \text{kJ/mol} + 2 \times (-285.85\ \text{kJ/mol}) - (-74.85\ \text{kJ/mol}) = -890.36\ \text{kJ/mol}$$

$$\text{no. mol}\ CH_4(g) = 1.78 \times 10^6\ \text{kJ} \times \frac{1\ \text{mol}\ CH_4}{890.36\ \text{kJ}} = 2.00 \times 10^3$$

$$V = \frac{nRT}{P} = \frac{2.00 \times 10^3 \times 0.0821\ \text{L atm mol}^{-1}\ \text{K}^{-1} \times 297.7\ \text{K}}{(752/760)\text{atm}} = 4.94 \times 10^4\ \text{L}$$

6-38. (a) The enthalpy of formation of a substance depends on the state in which the substance is found (i.e., enthalpy is a function of state). Pure $H_2SO_4(l)$ and H_2SO_4 in aqueous solutions of differing molar concentrations all represent different conditions or states for a substance. As a result there are different values of $\Delta\bar{H}_f$.

(b) All of the heats of formation are negative, more negative the more dilute the solution. Whether dilute $H_2SO_4(aq)$ solution is prepared by mixing pure $H_2SO_4(l)$ with water or by adding water to a more concentrated solution, $\Delta H = q_p < 0$. Thus the dilution processes are exothermic. Heat of dilution is absorbed by the water (surroundings) in which dilution occurs; the solution temperature rises.

(c) Express the dilution process as follows:

$$H_2SO_4(l) + aq \longrightarrow H_2SO_4(0.02\ M)$$

$$\Delta\bar{H} = \Delta\bar{H}_f[H_2SO_4(0.02M)] - \Delta\bar{H}_f[H_2SO_4(l)] = -897\ \text{kJ/mol} - (-814\ \text{kJ/mol}) = -83\ \text{kJ/mol}$$

The amount of H_2SO_4 involved in the dilution is that contained in 250 ml 0.02 M H_2SO_4

$$\text{no. mol}\ H_2SO_4 = 0.250\ \text{L} \times \frac{0.02\ \text{mol}\ H_2SO_4}{\text{L}} = 0.005\ \text{mol}\ H_2SO_4$$

$$\text{no. J} = 0.005 \text{ mol } H_2SO_4 \times \frac{-83 \text{ kJ}}{\text{mol } H_2SO_4} \times \frac{1000 \text{ J}}{1 \text{ kJ}} = -415 \text{ J}$$

The heat gained by the solution is +415 J, and

$$\text{no. g } H_2O \times \text{sp. ht. } H_2O \times \Delta t = 415 \text{ J} \qquad 250 \text{ g } H_2O \times \frac{4.184 \text{ J}}{\text{g } H_2O \text{ °C}} \times \Delta t = 415 \text{ J}$$

$\Delta t = 0.4°C$

The solution temperature increases by 0.4°C.

6-39, Determine the heat of combustion of the pure gases CH_4 and C_2H_6. Then calculate the mole percent of each gas in the mixture. Volume and mole percents are identical (recall equation 5.16). The molar heat of combustion of $CH_4(g)$ calculated in Exercise 6-37 is -890.36 kJ/mol.

$$C_2H_6(g) + 7/2\ O_2(g) \longrightarrow 2\ CO_2(g) + 3\ H_2O(l)$$

$$\Delta\overline{H}° = 2\ \Delta\overline{H}^\circ_f[CO_2(g)] + 3\ \Delta\overline{H}^\circ_f[H_2O(l)] - \Delta\overline{H}^\circ_f[C_2H_6(g)]$$

$$= 2 \times (-393.51 \text{ kJ/mol}) + 3 \times (-285.85 \text{ kJ/mol}) - (-84.68 \text{ kJ/mol})$$

$$= -787.02 \text{ kJ/mol} - 857.55 \text{ kJ/mol} + 84.68 \text{ kJ/mol}$$

$$= -1559.89 \text{ kJ/mol}$$

In 1.00 L of gas at STP there is a total of 1.00/22.4 = 0.0446 mol gas. If we let the no. mol $CH_4(g) = x$ and no. mol $C_2H_6(g) = y$, $x + y = 0.0446$ and

$$\left(x \text{ mol } CH_4 \times \frac{-890.36 \text{ kJ}}{\text{mol } CH_4}\right) + \left(y \text{ mol } C_2H_6 \times \frac{-1559.89 \text{ kJ}}{\text{mol } C_2H_6}\right) = -43.6 \text{ kJ}$$

or

$$-890.36\ x - 1559.89\ y = -43.6$$

Substitute $y = 0.0446 - x$ to obtain

$$-890.36\ x - 1559.89(0.0446 - x) = -43.6$$

$$-890.36\ x - 69.6 + 1559.89\ x = -43.6$$

$$669.53\ x = 69.6 - 43.6 = 26.0$$

$$x = 0.0388 \qquad y = 0.0446 - 0.0388 = 0.0058$$

Mole percents (volume percents)

$$\%CH_4: \frac{0.0388 \text{ mol}}{0.0446 \text{ mol}} \times 100 = 87.0\% \qquad \%C_2H_6 = \frac{0.0058 \text{ mol}}{0.0446 \text{ mol}} \times 100 = 13.0\%$$

6-40. Estimate $\Delta\overline{H}^\circ_f[C_7H_{16}(l)]$ from data given in Appendix D and the rule stated in the exercise. That is,

	$C_3H_8(g)$	$C_4H_{10}(g)$	$C_5H_{12}(g)$	$C_6H_{14}(g)$	$C_7H_{16}(g)$
$\Delta\overline{H}^\circ_f$, kJ/mol	-103.85	-125	-146	-167	-188

For the reaction $C_7H_{16}(g) + 11\ O_2(g) \longrightarrow 7\ CO_2(g) + 8\ H_2O(l)$

$$\Delta\overline{H}° = 7\ \Delta\overline{H}^\circ_f[CO_2(g)] + 8\ \Delta\overline{H}^\circ_f[H_2O(l)] - \Delta\overline{H}^\circ_f[C_7H_{16}(g)]$$

$$= 7 \times (-393.51 \text{ kJ/mol}) + 8 \times (-285.85 \text{ kJ/mol}) - (-188 \text{ kJ/mol})$$

$$= -2754.57 \text{ kJ/mol} - 2286.80 \text{ kJ/mol} + 188 \text{ kJ/mol}$$

$$= -4.85 \times 10^3 \text{ kJ/mol}$$

Self-test Questions

1. (*c*) Item (a) is the definition of a calorie, not a kilocalorie. To raise the temperature of 1.00 L water by 1°C requires 1 kcal; by 10°C, 10 kcal--item (b) is incorrect. When the temperature of 100 cm^3 water (100 g water) is lowered by 10°C, 1 kcal of heat is released. Item (d) is incorrect because 1 kcal = 1.0×10^3 cal, not 1.0×10^6 cal.

2. (*b*) Use the expression $\Delta E = q - w$, with $\Delta E = +100$ J and $q = -100$ J. Under these conditions $w = q - \Delta E = -100\text{ J} - 100\text{ J} = -200$ J. The surroundings must do 200 J of work on the system.

3. (*a*) Solve the expression $\Delta E = q - w$ for q. $q = \Delta E + w$. This is the most general equation for a heat of reaction. Item (b) has the wrong sign, and items (c) and (d) refer only to the special conditions of constant volume and constant pressure, respectively.

4. (*d*) In this reaction 2 mol gaseous reactants yield 2 mol gaseous product--$\Delta n_g = 0$. Since $\Delta H = \Delta E + 2.48\Delta n_g$, if $\Delta n_g = 0$, $\Delta H = \Delta E$.

5. (*c*) The reaction given is the *reverse* of the reaction for the formation of NH_3 (ΔH = 46 kJ) and it is doubled (ΔH = +92 kJ).

6. (*d*) For the given reaction, $\Delta\overline{H}° = -3534$ kJ/mol

$$= 5\ \Delta\overline{H}^°_f[CO_2(g)] + 6\ \Delta\overline{H}^°_f[H_2O(l)] - \Delta\overline{H}^°_f[C_5H_{12}(l)]$$

$$\Delta\overline{H}^°_f[C_5H_{12}(l)] = 5\ \Delta\overline{H}^°_f[CO_2(g)] + 6\ \Delta\overline{H}^°_f[H_2O(l)] + 3534$$

$$\Delta\overline{H}^°_f[C_5H_{12}(l)] = 5 \times (-394) + 6 \times (-286) + 3534$$

7. (a) Specific heat is the quantity of heat required to change the temperature of one gram of substance by one degree C. Molar heat capacity refers to the quantity of heat required to change the temperature of one mole of substance to the same extent.

   (b) An endothermic reaction absorbs heat from its surroundings, and an exothermic reaction gives off heat to the surroundings.

   (c) ΔH for a reaction is the heat of reaction at constant pressure, and ΔE is the heat of reaction at constant volume. Also, $\Delta H = \Delta E + P\Delta V$ (at constant pressure).

   (d) The heat of formation of $C_4H_{10}(g)$ refers to the enthalpy change in the reaction where C_4H_{10} is formed from the most stable form of its elements at 1 atm pressure:

$$4\ C\ (\text{graphite}) + 5\ H_2(g) \longrightarrow C_4H_{10}(g)$$

   The heat of combustion is ΔH for the combustion reaction:

$$2\ C_4H_{10}(g) + 13\ O_2(g) \longrightarrow 8\ CO_2(g) + 10\ H_2O(l)$$

8. Use the expression $q_{iron} = -q_{water}$, solve for Δt and then the initial temperature of the iron.

$$1500\text{ g Fe} \times \frac{0.59\text{ J}}{\text{g Fe °C}} \times \Delta t = -\left\{755\text{ g water} \times \frac{4.184\text{ J}}{\text{g water °C}} \times (38.6 - 21.3)\text{°C}\right\}$$

$$\Delta t = \frac{-755 \times 4.184 \times 17.3}{1500 \times 0.59}\text{ °C} = -62\text{°C}$$

$$\Delta t = t_f - t_i = 38.6\text{°C} - t_i = -62\text{°C} \qquad t_i = 101\text{°C}$$

9. (a) $C_6H_5OH(s) + 7\ O_2(g) \longrightarrow 6\ CO_2(g) + 3\ H_2O(l)$

   (b) $$\Delta\overline{E} = \frac{-32.55\text{ kJ}}{\text{g } C_6H_5OH} \times \frac{94.11\text{ g } C_6H_5OH}{1\text{ mol } C_6H_5OH} = -3063\text{ kJ/mol } C_6H_5OH$$

   (c) $\Delta\overline{H} = \Delta\overline{E} + 2.48\ n_g = -3063\text{ kJ/mol} + 2.48 \times (6 - 7) = -3065$ kJ/mol

10. From the reaction $CO(g) + Cl_2(g) \longrightarrow COCl_2(g)$ $\quad \Delta\overline{H} = -108$ kJ/mol, we can write

$\Delta\overline{H} = \Delta\overline{H}^\circ_f[COCl_2(g)] - \Delta\overline{H}^\circ_f[CO(g)] = -108$ kJ/mol

But we need a value of $\Delta\overline{H}^\circ_f[CO(g)]$, which we obtain from

$$C\ (graphite) + O_2(g) \longrightarrow CO_2(g) \qquad \Delta\overline{H}^\circ = -393.51\ kJ/mol$$

$$CO_2(g) \longrightarrow CO(g) + 1/2\ O_2(g) \qquad \Delta\overline{H}^\circ = -(-282.97) = +282.97\ kJ/mol$$

$$C\ (graphite) + 1/2\ O_2(g) \longrightarrow CO(g) \qquad \Delta\overline{H}^\circ_f = -393.51 + 282.97 = -110.54\ kJ/mol$$

$\Delta\overline{H}^\circ_f[COCl_2(g)] = -108$ kJ/mol $+ (-110.54$ kJ/mol$) = -219$ kJ/mol

Chapter 7

Electrons in Atoms

Electromagnetic radiation

7-1. (a) $\text{no. nm} = 3000\ \text{Å} \times \dfrac{1 \times 10^{-10}\ \text{m}}{1\ \text{Å}} \times \dfrac{1\ \text{nm}}{1 \times 10^{-9}\ \text{m}} = 300\ \text{nm}$

(b) $\text{no. cm} = 1.56\ \mu\text{m} \times \dfrac{1 \times 10^{-6}\ \text{m}}{1\ \mu\text{m}} \times \dfrac{100\ \text{cm}}{1\ \text{m}} = 1.56 \times 10^{-4}\ \text{cm}$

(c) $\text{no. nm} = 3.6\ \text{cm} \times \dfrac{1\ \text{m}}{100\ \text{cm}} \times \dfrac{1\ \text{nm}}{1 \times 10^{-9}\ \text{m}} = 3.6 \times 10^{7}\ \text{nm}$

(d) $\text{no. Å} = 2.18\ \mu\text{m} \times \dfrac{1 \times 10^{-6}\ \text{m}}{1\ \mu\text{m}} \times \dfrac{1\ \text{Å}}{1 \times 10^{-10}\ \text{m}} = 2.18 \times 10^{4}\ \text{Å}$

(e) $\text{no. m} = 0.62\ \mu\text{m} \times \dfrac{1 \times 10^{-6}\ \text{m}}{1\ \mu\text{m}} = 6.2 \times 10^{-7}\ \text{m}$

(f) $\text{no. m} = 470\ \text{nm} \times \dfrac{1 \times 10^{-9}\ \text{m}}{1\ \text{nm}} = 4.70 \times 10^{-7}\ \text{m}$

7-2. In each case use the expression $\lambda = c/\nu$, with $c = 3.00 \times 10^{8}$ m/s.

(a) $\lambda = \dfrac{3.00 \times 10^{8}\ \text{m/s}}{1.00 \times 10^{14}\ \text{s}^{-1}} = 3.00 \times 10^{-6}\ \text{m}$

(b) $\lambda = \dfrac{3.00 \times 10^{8}\ \text{m/s}}{8.6 \times 10^{12}\ \text{s}^{-1}} = 3.5 \times 10^{-5}\ \text{m}$

(c) $\lambda = \dfrac{3.00 \times 10^{8}\ \text{m/s}}{2.0 \times 10^{9}\ \text{s}^{-1}} = 1.5 \times 10^{-1}\ \text{m}$

7-3. Here, use the expression $\nu = c/\lambda$, with $c = 3.00 \times 10^{8}$ m/s.

(a) $\nu = \dfrac{3.00 \times 10^{8}\ \text{m/s}}{1.8 \times 10^{-3}\ \text{cm} \times \dfrac{1\ \text{m}}{100\ \text{cm}}} = 1.7 \times 10^{13}\ \text{s}^{-1}$

(b) $\nu = \dfrac{3.00 \times 10^{8}\ \text{m/s}}{12.6\ \mu\text{m} \times \dfrac{1 \times 10^{-6}\ \text{m}}{1\ \mu\text{m}}} = 2.38 \times 10^{13}\ \text{s}^{-1}$

(c) $\nu = \dfrac{3.00 \times 10^{8}\ \text{m/s}}{480\ \text{Å} \times \dfrac{1 \times 10^{-10}\ \text{m}}{1\ \text{Å}}} = 6.25 \times 10^{15}\ \text{s}^{-1}$

(d) $\nu = \dfrac{3.00 \times 10^{8}\ \text{m/s}}{305\ \text{nm} \times \dfrac{1 \times 10^{-9}\ \text{m}}{1\ \text{nm}}} = 9.84 \times 10^{14}\ \text{s}^{-1}$

7-4. The number of periods per sec is simply the number of vibrations per sec, that is, the frequency of the radiation.

$\nu = 9.192631770 \times 10^{9}\ \text{s}^{-1}$.

$$\lambda = \frac{c}{\nu} = \frac{2.997925 \times 10^{8}\ \text{m s}^{-1}}{9.192631770 \times 10^{9}\ \text{s}^{-1}} = 3.261226 \times 10^{-2}\ \text{m} = 3.261226\ \text{cm}$$

Because of the extreme precision with which the frequency is stated--10 significant figures--the most precise expression for the speed of light (see inside back cover) can be used, yielding a result to seven significant figures.

7-5. (a) Correct: The wavelength of the radiation in question is 285.2 nm. This is a shorter wavelength than 315 nm. From the relationship, $c = \nu \cdot \lambda$, we see that the shorter the wavelength, the greater the frequency.

(b) Incorrect: The visible region of the spectrum ranges from about 380 to 760 nm (see Figure 7-3).

(c) Incorrect: All forms of electromagnetic radiation have the same speed in vacuum.

(d) Correct: The radiation in question, 285.2 nm, is in the ultraviolet range of the spectrum. X rays have shorter wavelengths than ultraviolet light.

7-6. $$\text{no min} = 93 \times 10^{6}\ \text{mi} \times \frac{5280\ \text{ft}}{1\ \text{mi}} \times \frac{12\ \text{in.}}{1\ \text{ft}} \times \frac{1\ \text{m}}{39.37\ \text{in.}} \times \frac{1\ \text{s}}{3.00 \times 10^{8}\ \text{m}} \times \frac{1\ \text{min}}{60\ \text{s}} = 8.3\ \text{min}$$

Atomic spectra

7-7. The longest wavelength component corresponds to a value of n = 3. The other three lines correspond to values of n = 4, n = 5, and n = 6. Use the form of the Balmer equation given in equation (7.2).

longest wavelength line: $n = 3$

$$\lambda(\text{in Å}) = 3645.6\left(\frac{n^2}{n^2 - 4}\right) = 3645.6\left(\frac{9}{9-4}\right) = 6562\ \text{Å}\ (=656.2\ \text{nm})$$

$n = 4$

$$\lambda = 3645.6\left(\frac{16}{16-4}\right) = 4861\ \text{Å}\ (=486.1\ \text{nm})$$

$n = 5$

$$\lambda = 3645.6\left(\frac{25}{25-4}\right) = 4340\ \text{Å}\ (=434.0\ \text{nm})$$

$n = 6$

$$\lambda = 3645.6\left(\frac{36}{36-4}\right) = 4101\ \text{Å}\ (=410.1\ \text{nm})$$

7-8. The longest wavelength for a line in the Balmer series is obtained for $n = 3$. In Exercise 7 this was calculated to be 656.2 nm. The spectral line at 1880 nm is of still longer wavelength. This line cannot be in the Balmer series.

7-9. By referring to Exercise 7, we see that the wavelengths corresponding to the spectral lines get shorter as n becomes larger. The shortest wavelength will be for $n = \infty$.

$$\lambda(\text{in Å}) = 3645.6\left(\frac{n^2}{n^2 - 4}\right) = 3645.6\left(\frac{\infty^2}{\infty^2 - 4}\right) = 3645.6\ \text{Å}\ (=364.56\ \text{nm})$$

Quantum theory

7-10. (a) energy per photon $= E = h\nu = 6.626 \times 10^{-34}\ \text{J s}^{-1} \times 1.15 \times 10^{15}\ \text{s}^{-1} = 7.62 \times 10^{-19}\ \text{J}$

(b) energy per mol photons $= \frac{7.62 \times 10^{-19}\ \text{J}}{\text{photon}} \times \frac{6.02 \times 10^{23}\ \text{photon}}{1\ \text{mol}} = 4.59 \times 10^{5}\ \text{J/mol} = 459\ \text{kJ/mol}$

7-11. Convert from the energy content of 100 kcal/mol to a value in J/photon. Following this, apply the Planck equation, $E = h\nu$, solving for ν. Finally, determine the corresponding wavelength with the expression $c = \nu\lambda$

$$\text{no. J/photon} = \frac{100 \text{ kcal}}{1 \text{ mol}} \times \frac{4.184 \text{ kJ}}{1 \text{ kcal}} \times \frac{1000 \text{ J}}{1 \text{ kJ}} \times \frac{1 \text{ mol}}{6.02 \times 10^{23} \text{ photon}} = 6.95 \times 10^{-19} \text{ J/photon}$$

$$\nu = \frac{E}{h} = \frac{6.95 \times 10^{-19} \text{ J}}{6.626 \times 10^{-34} \text{ J s}} = 1.05 \times 10^{15} \text{ s}^{-1} \qquad \lambda = c/\nu = \frac{3.00 \times 10^{8} \text{ m/s}}{1.05 \times 10^{15} \text{ s}^{-1}} = 2.86 \times 10^{-7} \text{m} = 286 \text{ nm}$$

Light of this wavelength is in the ultraviolet region of the electromagnetic spectrum.

7-12. Convert the wavelength limits $\lambda = 390$ nm and $\lambda = 770$ nm to frequency limits through the expression $c = \nu\lambda$. Then calculate the energies with Planck's equation, $E = h\nu$.

Short wavelength limit

$$\nu = c/\lambda = \frac{3.00 \times 10^{8} \text{ m/s}}{390 \text{ nm} \times \frac{1 \times 10^{-9} \text{ m}}{1 \text{ nm}}} = 7.69 \times 10^{14} \text{ s}^{-1} \qquad E = h\nu = 6.626 \times 10^{-34} \text{ J s} \times 7.69 \times 10^{14} \text{ s}^{-1} = 5.10 \times 10^{-19} \text{ J/photon}$$

Long wavelength limit

$$\nu = \frac{3.00 \times 10^{8} \text{ m/s}}{770 \text{ nm} \times \frac{1 \times 10^{-9} \text{ m}}{1 \text{ nm}}} = 3.90 \times 10^{14} \text{ s}^{-1} \qquad E = h\nu = 6.626 \times 10^{-34} \text{ J s} \times 3.90 \times 10^{14} \text{ s}^{-1} = 2.58 \times 10^{-19} \text{ J/photon}$$

The photoelectric effect

7-13. (a) The energy per photon corresponding to a frequency of 1.3×10^{15} s^{-1} is

$$E = h\nu = 6.626 \times 10^{-34} \text{ J s} \times 1.3 \times 10^{15} \text{ s}^{-1} = 8.6 \times 10^{-19} \text{ J}$$

(b) Refer to Exercise 7-12 for the energy limits corresponding to visible light: 2.58×10^{-19} to 5.10×10^{-19} J/photon. The energy calculated in part (a) is greater than 5.10×10^{-19}. The photoelectric effect will not be displayed by platinum with visible light, and certainly not with infrared (which is still less energetic than visible light). Somewhere within the ultraviolet range, platinum will display the photoeletric effect (corresponding to $E = 8.6 \times 10^{-19}$ J; $\nu = 1.3 \times 10^{15}$ s^{-1}; and $\lambda = 231$ nm).

7-14. (a) First express the work function in J/photon.

$$\frac{\text{no. J}}{\text{photon}} = \frac{435 \text{ kJ}}{\text{mol photons}} \times \frac{1 \text{ mol photons}}{6.02 \times 10^{23} \text{ photons}} \times \frac{1000 \text{ J}}{1 \text{ kJ}} = 7.23 \times 10^{-19} \text{ J/photon}$$

Next determine the threshold frequency with the relationship $E = h\nu$.

$$\nu = \frac{E}{h} = \frac{7.23 \times 10^{-19} \text{ J}}{6.626 \times 10^{-34} \text{ J s}} = 1.09 \times 10^{15} \text{ s}^{-1}$$

(b) $$\text{Wavelength} = \lambda = c/\nu = \frac{3.00 \times 10^{8} \text{ m/s}}{1.09 \times 10^{15} \text{ s}^{-1}} = 2.75 \times 10^{-7} \text{ m} = 275 \text{ nm}$$

(c) Refer to Figure 7-3 for the wavelength limits of visible light. The wavelength, 275 nm, is below this limit, i.e., in the ultraviolet. Mercury does not display the photoelectric effect with visible light.

7-15. In the photoelectric effect a single photon transfers all its energy to a single electron. Any energy in excess of that required to just secure the release of an electron appears as excess kinetic energy of the ejected electron. A single photon cannot transfer its energy to two different electrons, nor can two different photons cooperatively transfer their energy to a single electron.

7-16. (a) Radius of a Bohr orbit, $r = a_o n^2$ (where a_o = 0.53 Å = 0.053 nm).

For the orbit, n = 5, r = 0.053 nm × $(5)^2$ = 1.3 nm

(b) Energy corresponding to *n* = 5 (use equation 7.5):

$$E = \frac{-B}{n^2} = \frac{-2.179 \times 10^{-18}\ J}{(5)^2} = -8.716 \times 10^{-20}\ J$$

7-17. (a) The distance between the Bohr orbits n = 1 and n = 3 is $r_3 - r_1$, where $r_3 = a_o(3)^2$ and $r_1 = a_o(1)^2$.

$$r_3 - r_1 = a_o[(3)^2 - (1)^2] = 8\ a_o = 8 \times 0.053\ nm = 0.42\ nm$$

(b) Similarly, the difference in energy ΔE is $E_3 - E_1$, where $E_3 = -B/(3)^2$ and $E_1 = -B/(1)^2$.

$$\Delta E = \frac{-B}{9} - (-B) = \frac{8B}{9} = \frac{8 \times 2.179 \times 10^{-18}\ J}{9} = 1.937 \times 10^{-18}\ J$$

7-18. (a) Calculate the energies corresponding to an electron in the Bohr orbit n = 5 and n = 4. Then determine the difference in energy ΔE, which is also equal to hν.

$$E_4 = \frac{-B}{(4)^2} = \frac{-B}{16} \qquad E_5 = \frac{-B}{(5)^2} = \frac{-B}{25}$$

$$\Delta E = E_4 - E_5 = \frac{-B}{16} - (\frac{-B}{25}) = \frac{-B}{16} + \frac{B}{25} = -0.0625\ B + 0.0400\ B$$

ΔE = -0.0225 B (The negative sign signifies the energy is emitted.)

$$\nu = \frac{\Delta E}{h} = \frac{0.0225 \times 2.179 \times 10^{-18}\ J}{6.626 \times 10^{-34}\ J\ s} = 7.40 \times 10^{13}\ s^{-1}$$

(b) $$\lambda = c/\nu = \frac{3.00 \times 10^8\ m/s}{7.40 \times 10^{13}\ s^{-1}} = 4.05 \times 10^{-6}\ m = 4.05\ \mu m = 4.05 \times 10^{-4}\ cm$$

(c) Radiation of this wavelength is in the infrared.

7-19. Energy must be absorbed if an electron is to be moved from one orbit to another of higher quantum number. This would be the case for (a), (b), and (c), but not for (d), where energy is released ($n = \infty \rightarrow n = 1$). For (a), (b), and (c) determine the energy difference between quantum levels in terms of B, and then compare these differences.

(a) $$\Delta E = \frac{-B}{(2)^2} - \frac{-B}{(1)^2} = B - \frac{B}{4} = 3\ B/4$$

(b) $$\Delta E = \frac{-B}{(4)^2} - \frac{-B}{(2)^2} = \frac{B}{4} - \frac{B}{16} = 3\ B/16$$

(c) $$\Delta E = \frac{-B}{(6)^2} - \frac{-B}{(3)^2} = \frac{B}{9} - \frac{B}{36} = 3\ B/36$$

The greatest energy requirement is for case (a)--an electronic transition from n = 1 to n = 2 (recall also, Figure 7-13).

7-20. (a) For He^+: $$E_1 = \frac{-(2)^2 \times 2.179 \times 10^{-18}\ J}{(1)^2} = -8.716 \times 10^{-18}\ J$$

(b) For Li^{2+}: $E_3 = \dfrac{-(3)^2 \times 2.179 \times 10^{-18}\ J}{(3)^2} = -2.179 \times 10^{-18}\ J$

7-21. Lines in the Balmer series correspond to transitions of an electron from a higher level to the level, n = 2. The higher the level from which the electron drops, the shorter the wavelength of the emitted light. Converging lines in the violet region of the Balmer series correspond to transitions from the converging series of energy levels in the energy-level diagram. The more closely spaced these upper energy levels, the more closely spaced the spectral lines.

The uncertainty principle

7-22. The radius of a Bohr orbit is exact ($r = a_o \cdot n^2$); this means a precise statement of the location of the electron. The dynamic properties of an electron, such as velocity, are assumed to have their precise classical values. Thus the Bohr model permits a precise statement of both the position and momentum of an electron. This is in violation of the Heisenberg uncertainty principle.

7-23. Einstein believed strongly in the law of cause and effect. He felt that the need to use probability and chance ("the playing of dice") in a description of atomic structure resulted because a suitable theory had not been developed to permit accurate predictions. He believed that such a theory could be developed, whereas Heisenberg and Bohr argued that it was an inherent law of nature that uncertainty must always exist in the behavior of subatomic particles.

7-24. The quantity $h/2\pi$ has a numerical value of $6.626 \times 10^{-34}/2\pi = 1 \times 10^{-34}$. Expressed in kg, the mass of an automobile is about 1×10^3. If the position of an automobile were known to the nearest 0.001 m, and its velocity to the nearest 0.001 m/sec, we would surely say that its behavior was precisely known. Yet, under these conditions, $\Delta x \cdot \Delta p = \Delta x \cdot m \cdot \Delta v = 1 \times 10^{-3} \times 1 \times 10^3 \times 1 \times 10^{-3} = 1 \times 10^{-3}$, which is far in excess of 1×10^{-34}. The velocity and position of an automobile could be defined with astonishing precision and still the Heisenberg uncertainty limit would not be reached.

7-25. Start with the statement: $\Delta x \cdot \Delta p > h/2\pi$, where $\Delta p = m\Delta v$. Thus, $\Delta x > h/2\pi \cdot m\Delta v$. Δx is the uncertainty in position of the proton. Convert the unit J to kg $m^2\ s^{-2}$. The uncertainty in velocity of the proton is 1% of 0.1 c = 0.001 c = 3.00×10^5 m/s.

$$\Delta x = \frac{6.626 \times 10^{-34}\ \text{kg m}^2\ \text{s}^{-2}\ \text{s}}{2\pi \times 1.67 \times 10^{-24}\ \text{g} \times \dfrac{1\ \text{kg}}{1000\ \text{g}} \times 3.00 \times 10^5\ \text{m/s}} = 2.1 \times 10^{-13}\ \text{m}$$

Wave-particle duality

7-26. The de Broglie equation, $\lambda = h/mv$, must be solved for v. The wavelength, λ, must be expressed in m (1nm = 1×10^{-9} m). The joule = 1 kg $m^2\ s^{-2}$.

$$v = \frac{h}{m\lambda} = \frac{6.626 \times 10^{-34}\ \text{kg m}^2\ \text{s}^{-2}}{9.110 \times 10^{-28}\ \text{g} \times \dfrac{1\ \text{kg}}{1000\ \text{g}} \times 1 \times 10^{-9}\ \text{m}} = 7.27 \times 10^5\ \text{m/s}$$

Wave mechanics

7-27.

	Bohr Theory	*Wave Mechanics*
(a)	The electron may be found only in one of a fixed set of closed circular orbits.	The electron may be found anywhere outside the nucleus, but there are certain regions in which the highest probabilities exist; these are called orbitals.
(b)	The electron orbit is a planar figure--a circle.	Electron orbitals correspond to three-dimensional regions--spherical shells, dumbbell-shaped regions, and so on.
(c)	The position and velocity of the electron can be described with a high degree of certainty.	Certainty is replaced by probability in describing the position and velocity of the electron.

The principal similarity is that the radii of the Bohr orbits do correspond to the distances from the nucleus at which there is a high probability of finding an electron.

7-28. For any *single* point the probability of finding an electron in a $1s$ orbital is greatest at the nucleus of the atom. At greater distances from the nucleus, however, there are many points equivalent to one another. Although the probability at any one of these points is considerably less than at the nucleus, the total probability is based on the sum of the probabilities at equivalent points. Thus, the region of greatest probability becomes a spherical shell at some distance from the nucleus, in fact, having a radius equal to the first Bohr orbit.

Quantum numbers and electron orbitals

7-29. Whether the spin quantum number, m_s, is $+1/2$ or $-1/2$ does not depend on the values of the other quantum numbers. The magnetic quantum number, m_l cannot exceed the value of the orbital quantum number, l. Therefore, if $m_l = 2$, $l \neq 1$. Neither can $l = 0$. The only allowable value of $l = 2$. The correct answer is (d).

7-30.

principal shell	N															
n =	4	4	4	4	4	4	4	4	4	4	4	4	4	4	4	4
l =	0	1	1	1	2	2	2	2	2	3	3	3	3	3	3	3
m_l =	0	-1	0	+1	-2	-1	0	+1	+2	-3	-2	-1	0	+1	+2	+3
orbital designation:	$4s$	$4p$	$4p$	$4p$	$4d$	$4d$	$4d$	$4d$	$4d$	$4f$	$4f$	$4f$	$4f$	$4f$	$4f$	$4f$
number of orbitals in subshell:	1		3				5						7			
total number of orbitals:								16								

7-31. Apply the statements describing the relationships among quantum numbers given in Section 7-8 of the textbook in each of the following cases:

(a) All the required relationships are met by the combination, $n = 2$, $l = 1$, $m_l = 0$. This is an allowable set.

(b) This set is not allowable; l cannot be equal to n. Thus, if $n = 2$, $l = 1$ or $l = 0$.

(c) This is an allowable set. All the rules are obeyed.

(d) This is also an allowable set.

(e) This set is not allowable. If $l = 0$, m_l must also be equal to zero.

(f) This set is not allowable. The value of l (3) is not permitted to exceed that of n (2).

7-32. (a) $l = 1$ specifies a p orbital; $n = 2$, the second principal shell. The orbital is a $2p$ orbital

(b) $l = 0$ specifies an s orbital; $n = 4$, the fourth principal shell. The orbital is a $4s$ orbital.

(c) $l = 2$ specifies a d orbital; $n = 5$, the fifth principal shell. The orbital is a $5d$ orbital.

7-33. The l quantum number designations establish the orbital type (s, p, d, f) and the n quantum numbers, the principal electronic shell in which the orbital is found. $3s$: $n = 3$, $l = 0$; $4p$: $n = 4$, $l = 1$; $5d$: $n = 5$, $l = 2$.

7-34. For each orbital type establish the value of l. The number of possibilities for m_l and, therefore, the number of possible orbitals of the given type is $2l + 1$.

(a) $2s$: $l = 0$, $2l + 1 = 1$; there is one $2s$ orbital.

(b) $3f$: f orbitals require that $l = 3$, but $l \neq 3$ if $n = 3$. There can be no $3f$ orbitals.

(c) $4p$: $l = 1$, $2l + 1 = 3$; there are three $4p$ orbitals.

(d) $5d$: $l = 2$, $2l + 1 = 5$; there are five $5d$ orbitals.

7-35. For an electron with $n = 4$ and $m_l = -2$,

(a) Correct: The electron is in the fourth principal shell.

(b) Correct: The electron *may* be associated with a $4d$ orbital. It will if $l = 2$. However, if $l = 3$ and $m_l = -2$, this will correspond to a $4f$ orbital.

(c) Incorrect: The m_l quantum numbers associated with p orbitals are -1, 0, and +1.

(d) Incorrect: The spin quantum number does not depend on the values of n and m_l. That is, m_s may be either +1/2 or -1/2.

Electron configurations

7-36. Use either expression (7.13) or Figure 7-23 to arrange the listed orbitals in the following order of increasing energy: $3p < 3d < 4p < 5s < 6s < 6p < 5f$

7-37. Probably the most direct approach is to convert each set of quantum numbers to an orbital designation, and then arrange the orbitals in accordance with expression (7.13) and Figure 7-23.

(a) $4s$; (b) $3p$; (c) $3d$; (d) $3d$; (e) $3s$

order of increasing energy: $3s < 3p < 4s < 3d = 3d$
(e)< (b)< (a)< (c)= (d)

7-38. Various possibilities exist for relating these electron configurations to the elements possessing them. One approach is to total the number of electrons and to identify the element through its atomic number.

(a) 5 electrons = boron, B

(b) Ar has 18 electrons + 5 electrons = 23 electrons = vanadium, V

(c) 14 electrons = silicon, Si

7-39. When the blanks are filled in, the listing should appear as follows:

(a) Na (Z = 11) $1s^2\ 2s^2\ 2p^6\ 3s^1$

(b) P (Z = 15) $1s^2\ 2s^2\ 2p^6\ 3s^2\ 3p^3$

(c) Zr (Z = 40) [Kr] $4d^2\ 5s^2$. 38 electrons are accounted for in the portion of the electron configuration that is shown. Two $4d$ electrons are required to complete the configuration.

(d) Te (Z = 52) [Kr] $4d^{10}\ 5s^2\ 5p^4$. Before the $5p$ subshell can receive electrons, the $4d$ subshell must contain 10 electrons.

(e) I (Z = 53) [Kr] $4d^{10}\ 5s^2\ 5p^5$. As in case (d) the $4d$ and $5s$ subshells must be complete before filling of the $5p$ begins.

(f) Bi (Z = 83) [Xe] $4f^{14}\ 5d^{10}\ 6s^2\ 6p^3$. Before electrons can enter the $6p$ subshell, the $4f$ must fill (with 14 electrons), the $5d$ (10 electrons), and the $6s$ (2 electrons). This accounts for 54 + 14 + 10 + 2 = 80 electrons. Three electrons must be assigned to the $6p$ subshell.

7-40. (a) Incorrect: The two electrons in the $3s$ orbital must have opposing spins. The situation shown violates the Pauli exclusion principle.

(b) Incorrect: The $3s$ orbital must fill before electrons enter the $3p$ subshell.

(c) Correct.

(d) Incorrect: The diagram shown violates Hund's rule. The $3p$ orbitals must be singly occupied before electrons begin to pair up.

7-41. (a) The electron configuration of S is $1s^2\ 2s^2\ 2p^6\ 3c^2\ 3p^4$. The arrangement of the four $3p$ electrons among the three $3p$ orbitals is to have an electron pair in one orbital and unpaired electrons in the other two. There are *two* unpaired electrons in a sulfur atom.

(b) The $3d$ subshell begins to fill after the $4s$, that is, with element Z = 21 (Sc). Since Cl has Z = 17, the Cl atom has no $3d$ electrons.

(c) The $4p$ subshell fills after the $3d$, following Zn (Z = 30), which has the electron configuration [Ar] $3d^{10}\ 4s^2$. Ge has the atomic number, 32. Its electron configuration is [Ar] $3d^{10}\ 4s^2\ 4p^2$. There are *two* $4p$ electrons in an atom of Ge.

(d) The third electronic shell is completely filled in an atom of Rb ($3s^2\ 3p^6\ 3d^{10}$). Therefore, the atom has *two* $3s$ electrons.

(e) The element Pb (Z = 82) follows the inner transition series of elements in which the $4f$ subshell is filled. That is, the electron configuration of Pb is [Xe] $4f^{14}\ 5d^{10}\ 5s^2\ 5p^2$. A Pb atom has 14 $4f$ electrons.

7-42. (a) The normal configuration for four electrons would be $1s^2\ 2s^2$. One of the $2s$ electrons has been promoted to an empty $2p$ orbital in the configuration shown.

(b) The element in question has Z = 16 (sulfur); its normal electron configuration is [Ne] $3s^2\ 3p^4$. The configuration shown involves the promotion of two $3p$ electrons to $3d$ orbitals.

(c) Although the $4s$ orbital may have only a single electron for some atoms with a partially filled $3d$ subshell, once the $3d$ subshell is closed (with 10 electrons) the $4s$ must also be closed (with 2 electrons) before the filling of the $4p$ begins. The configuration shown involves the promotion of a $4s$ electron to a $4p$ orbital.

7-43. (a) We must assign 55 electrons into the usual orbitals but increase the capacity of each orbtial to three electrons, that is, $1s^3$, $2s^3$, and so on.

$1s^3\ 2s^3\ 2p^9\ 3s^3\ 3p^9\ 3d^{15}\ 4s^3\ 4p^9\ 5s^1$

(b) The effect of permitting l = n is that of adding a p orbital to the first shell, d to the second, f to the third, and so on. Under these conditions the order of filling might be:

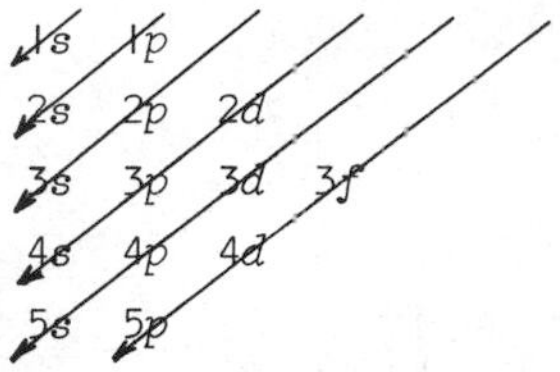

We must assign 55 electrons according to the order suggested above and observe all the normal rules of electron configurations while doing so.

$1s^2\ 1p^6\ 2s^2\ 2p^6\ 2d^{10}\ 3s^2\ 3p^6\ 3d^{10}\ 3f^1\ 4s^2\ 4p^6\ 5s^2$

Self-test Questions

1. (*b*) Convert all wavelengths to a common unit, e.g., meters, and choose the shortest.

(a) 735 nm × (1 × 10^{-9} m/1 nm) = 7.35 × 10^{-7} m

(b) 6.3 × 10^{-5} cm × (1 × 10^{-2} m/1 cm) = 6.3 × 10^{-7} m

(c) 1.05 μm × (1 × 10^{-6} m/1 μm) = 1.05 × 10^{-6} m

(d) 3.5 × 10^{-6} m

2. (*a*) The shorter the wavelength the higher the frequency of electromagnetic radiation. Radiation of 200 nm wavelength must have a higher frequency than 400-nm radiation. Item (b) is incorrect because 200-nm radiation is in the ultraviolet region; (c) is incorrect because the speed of light in vacuum is independent of wavelength; (c) is incorrect because 100-nm radiation has a greater frequency, and therefore a higher energy content, than 200-nm radiation.

3. (*d*) An electron cannot have its l quantum number equal to its n quantum number. If $n = 2$, l can only be equal to 1 or 0, not 2. The set of quantum numbers $n = 2$, $l = 2$, $m_l = 0$ is not allowed.

4. (*b*) Electrons in *d* orbitals have $l = 2$ and $m_l = -2, -1, 0, +1,$ or $+2$. (a) is incorrect; (b) is an acceptable answer; (c) is incorrect because +1/2 and −1/2 describe the m_s quantum number, not m_l; (d) is incorrect because m_l cannot be greater than 2.

5. (*d*) The electron configuration of Cl is $1s^2\ 2s^2\ 2p^6\ 3s^2\ 3p^5$. The number of 2*p* electrons is *six*. (Do not confuse the 2*p* electrons with the 3*p* electrons, of which there are five.)

6. (*c*) Because scandium has an odd atomic number (Z = 21) there must be at least one unpaired electron. The electron configuration of Ca (Z = 20) has all electrons unpaired, $1s^2\ 2s^2\ 2p^6\ 3s^2\ 3p^6\ 4s^2$. The additional electron in building up Sc from Ca goes into a 3*d* orbital, unpaired.

7. Use the Planck equation E = hν to determine the energy per photon. Then convert to a mole basis.

$$E = h\nu = 6.626 \times 10^{-34}\ \text{J s} \times 4.00 \times 10^{14}\ \text{s}^{-1} = 2.65 \times 10^{19}\ \text{J/photon}$$

$$\text{kJ/mol} = \frac{2.65 \times 10^{-19}\ \text{J}}{\text{photon}} \times \frac{6.02 \times 10^{23}\ \text{photons}}{1\ \text{mol}} \times \frac{1\ \text{kJ}}{1000\ \text{J}} = 1.60 \times 10^{2}\ \text{kJ/mol}$$

8. The line at the shorter wavelength, 589.0 nm, has a higher frequency and higher energy content than the longer wavelength line. To obtain the *difference* in energy between the two, determine the frequencies for these lines and then use the Planck equation.

589.0 nm line

$$\nu = c/\lambda = \frac{3.00 \times 10^{8}\ \text{m/s}}{589.0 \times 10^{-9}\ \text{m}}$$

589.6 nm line

$$\nu = \frac{3.00 \times 10^{8}\ \text{m/s}}{589.6 \times 10^{-9}\ \text{m}}$$

$$\Delta E = (h\nu)_1 - (h\nu)_2 = 6.626 \times 10^{-34}\ \text{J s} \times 3.00 \times 10^{8}\ \text{m/s} \times \left(\frac{1}{589.0 \times 10^{-9}} - \frac{1}{589.6 \times 10^{-9}}\right)\ \text{m}^{-1}$$

$$\Delta E = 6.626 \times 10^{-34} \times 3.00 \times 10^{8} \times (1.698 \times 10^{6} - 1.696 \times 10^{6})\ \text{J}$$

$$\Delta E = 4 \times 10^{-22}\ \text{J}$$

9. Find the frequency corresponding to 434 nm; substitute this into the equation given; and solve for n.

$$\nu = c/\lambda = 3.00 \times 10^{8}\ \text{m s}^{-1}/434 \times 10^{-9}\ \text{m} = 6.91 \times 10^{14}\ \text{s}^{-1}$$

$$6.91 \times 10^{14}\ \text{s}^{-1} = 3.2881 \times 10^{15}\ \text{s}^{-1}\left(\frac{1}{2^2} - \frac{1}{n^2}\right)$$

$$\left(\frac{1}{4} - \frac{1}{n^2}\right) = 6.91 \times 10^{14}/3.2881 \times 10^{15} = 0.210$$

$$0.250 - \frac{1}{n^2} = 0.210 \qquad \frac{1}{n^2} = 0.250 - 0.210 = 0.040 \qquad n^2 = \frac{1}{0.040} \qquad n^2 = 25 \qquad n = 5$$

10. (a) Se: $1s^2\ 2s^2\ 2p^6\ 3s^2\ 3p^6\ 3d^{10}\ 4s^2\ 4p^4$

(b) I: [Kr]

	4*d*					5*s*	5*p*		
[Kr]	↑↓	↑↓	↑↓	↑↓	↑↓	↑↓	↑↓	↑↓	↓

Chapter 8

Atomic Properties and the Periodic Table

The periodic law

8-1. Use Figure 8-1 to estimate the atomic volume of Fr (Z = 87)-- say 85 cm^3/mol.

$$d = \frac{\text{no. g}}{cm^3} = \frac{\text{at. wt.}}{\text{at. vol.}} = \frac{223\ g/mol}{85\ cm^3/mol} = 2.6\ g/cm^3$$

8-2. Determine the atomic volumes of elements similar to Z=114 (Group IVA) from Figure 8-1: Ge, 15 cm^3/mol; Sn, 18 cm^3/mol; Pb, 19 cm^3/mol. From this trend we would expect the atomic volume of Z = 114 to be about 20 cm^3/mol. The expected density is

$$d = \frac{\text{at. wt.}}{\text{at. vol.}} = \frac{298\ g/mol}{20\ cm^3/mol} = 15\ g/cm^3$$

8-3. Assign atomic numbers to each of the listed elements and plot melting points against atomic numbers. The melting points are seen to rise to a maximum with the Group IVA element, drop to comparatively low values in Groups VIA and VIIA, and reach a minimum for Group 0 (noble gases). Because no data are given for transition elements, generalizations encompassing the entire range of atomic numbers cannot be made.

The periodic table

8-4. To produce additional elements within the body of the periodic table would require adding protons in *fractions*, but this would be contrary to all experience--atomic numbers must be integers. Since all the integral atomic numbers from 1 to 106 have been assigned to known elements, there appears to be no possibility of discovering new elements with atomic numbers less than 106.

8-5. The expected atomic number of the noble gas following radon is 86 + 32 = 118, and of the alkali metal following francium, 87 + 32 = 119. Both of these elements would have atomic weights of about 310.

8-6. (a) There can be but one element at the "intersection" of the fifth period and the column, IIIA. The element is indium, In.

(b) An element similar to sulfur would be in Group VIA of the periodic table, such as oxygen and selenium. *Most* elements are unlike sulfur, for instance the metals in Groups IA and IIA and all of the transition elements.

(c) The most active metal in any period is the first member of the period, the alkali metal (Group IA). The most active metal in the sixth period is cesium, Cs.

(d) The fifth period runs from rubidium (Z = 37) to xenon (Z = 54). The element within this period that also falls in the halogen family (Group VIIA) is iodine (Z = 53).

(e) The element with Z = 18 is the noble gas, argon. Xe (Z = 54) and Rn (Z = 86) both have an atomic number greater than 50 and properties similar to argon.

8-7. These are the inversions found in the periodic table: Ar-K, Co-Ni, Te-I. The periodic table is based on electron configurations, and these in turn are related to *atomic numbers*. Therefore, the arrangement of elements in the periodic table must be by increasing atomic number, even if in a few cases this results in an inverse order by atomic weight.

8-8. The length of a period is determined by the number of elements that intervene before a similar electron configuration is attained. Thus, following Li ($1s^2\ 2s^1$) the next element with one electron in an *s* orbital of the outer shell is Na ($1s^2\ 2s^2\ 2p^6\ 3s^1$). The length of the second period is 8. K ($1s^2\ 2s^2\ 2p^6\ 3s^2\ 3p^6\ 4s^1$) is also eight elements removed from its earlier family member, Na; the third period is eight members long. But before the 5*s* orbital acquires an electron, the filling of 4*s*, 3*d*, and 4*p* must occur. This requires 18 electrons; the fourth period is 18 members long, and so is the fifth. In the sixth period the orbitals that must be filled are 6*s*, 4*f*, 5*d*, and 6*p*, making the period 32 members long.

8-9. To accomodate all the known elements within the body of the periodic table would require a width of 32 elements, corresponding to the filling of 6*s*, 4*f*, 5*d*, and 6*p* orbitals in the sixth period and 7*s*, 5*f*, 6*d*, and 7*p*, in the seventh.

H																															He
Li	Be																									B	C	N	O	F	Ne
Na	Mg																									Al	Si	P	S	Cl	Ar
K	Ca	Sc															Ti	V	Cr	Mn	Fe	Co	Ni	Cu	Zn	Ga	Ge	As	Se	Br	Kr
Rb	Sr	Y															Zr	Nb	Mo	Tc	Ru	Rh	Pd	Ag	Cd	In	Sn	Sb	Te	I	Xe
Cs	Ba	La	Ce	Pr	Nd	Pm	Sm	Eu	Gd	Tb	Dy	Ho	Er	Tm	Yb	Lu	Hf	Ta	W	Re	Os	Ir	Pt	Au	Hg	Tl	Pb	Bi	Po	At	Rn
Fr	Ra	Ac	Th	Pa	U	Np	Pu	Am	Cm	Bk	Cf	Es	Fm	Md	No	Lr	Ku	Ha													

8-10. 0: An atom with an outer-shell electron configuration, $ns^2\ np^6$, is a noble gas. The noble gases are in Group 0.

IVA: This atom has 4 outer-shell electrons ($4s^2\ 4p^2$); it is in Group IVA. (The element is Ge.)

IA: Atoms of this element have a single outer-shell electron. The element is the alkali metal, sodium.

IB: Although this element has a single electron in the *s* orbital of an outer shell--the next-to-outermost shell is not that of a noble gas. The element is not in Group IA. Instead, this is an element that follows a transition series (in which the 3*d* subshell fills). The element is copper (Z = 29).

VIB: The 4*f* subshell is filled, but the 5*d* is not. This element is in the third transition series. Its atomic number is 74, placing it in the same group as Mo (Z = 42) and Cr (Z = 24).

8-11. (a) Ga (Z = 31) is in Group IIIA, following the first transition series (filling of the 3*d* subshell). These facts can be combined to write $1s^2\ 2s^2\ 2p^6\ 3s^2\ 3p^6\ 3d^{10}\ 4s^2\ 4p^1$.

(b) Y (Z = 39) is in Group IIIB. It is the first member of the second transition series (filling of the 4*d* subshell) and directly follows a member of Group IIA (Sr).
$1s^2\ 2s^2\ 2p^6\ 3s^2\ 3p^6\ 3d^{10}\ 4s^2\ 4p^6\ 4d^1\ 5s^2$

(c) Sn (Z = 50) is in Group IVA, following the second transition series. Since it is in the fifth period, its outer-shell configuration is $5s^2\ 5p^2$.
$1s^2\ 2s^2\ 2p^6\ 3s^2\ 3p^6\ 3d^{10}\ 4s^2\ 4p^6\ 4d^{10}\ 5s^2\ 5p^2$

(d) Ag (Z = 47) is in the fifth period, Group IB, and immediately following the second transition series. These facts lead to the electron configuration $1s^2\ 2s^2\ 2p^6\ 3s^2\ 3p^6\ 3d^{10}\ 4s^2\ 4p^6\ 4d^{10} 5s^1$

8-12. (a) The elements in question have atomic numbers 89, 104, and 105.

(b) One of these elements, Ac, comes before the inner transition series in which 5*f* orbitals are filled. Its electron configuration is expected to resemble that of La, which is in the period preceding it. The other two elements, Z = 104 and Z = 105, follow the actinide series. Their 5*f* orbitals are filled. The differentiating electrons in these atoms are expected to go into 6*d* orbitals, and the elements are expected to resemble Hf and Ta.

8-13. (a) 3: There are three outer-shell electrons in a Ga atom (Group IIIA).

(b) 6: Tungsten is in the sixth period of elements; its atoms contain electrons in six principal electronic shells.

(c) 5: These are the five elements of Group VIA--O, S, Se, Te, Po.

(d) 3: Arsenic is in periodic Group VA and in the fourth period. Its outer-shell electron configuration is $4s^2\ 4p^3$. The two $4s$ electrons are paired, and the three $4p$ orbitals are singly occupied by unpaired electrons.

(e) 24: The sixth period (from Ba to Xe) includes an inner transition series of 14 elements, in which the $4f$ subshell fills, and a regular transition series of 10 elements, in which the $5d$ subshell fills.

8-14. (a) 1: All atoms in Group IA have a single s electron in the outermost shell, and for K, which is in the fourth period of elements, this shell is n = 4.

(b) 5: I is in the portion of the periodic table characterized by the filling of the $5p$ subshell. This subshell is filled with Xe and one electron away from being filled with I (that is, $5p^5$).

(c) 10: Zn occurs at the end of the first transition series, where the filling of the $3d$ subshell occurs.

(d) 6: The *second* electronic shell of the sulfur atom is closed ($2s^2\ 2p^6$). Vacancies occur in p orbitals of the *third* shell ($3s^2\ 3p^4$).

(e) 14: Pb is a representative element in Group IVA of the sixth period. Both the $4f$ and $5d$ subshells are filled before this point.

(f) 8: The best approach here is to use the atomic number of Ni (Z = 28) to establish the total number of electrons to be assigned, and the fact Ni is a transition element with two electrons in the $4s$ orbital. The complete electron configuration for Ni is: $1s^2\ 2s^2\ 2p^6\ 3s^2\ 3p^6\ 3d^8\ 4s^2$. There are *eight* $3d$ electrons.

8-15. In each of the following cases start with the electron configuration of the neutral atom and modify this configuration by adding or removing the appropriate number of electrons. Only s and p orbitals are involved in these particular ionization processes.

(a) Rb^+: $1s^2\ 2s^2\ 2p^6\ 3s^2\ 3p^6\ 3d^{10}\ 4s^2\ 4p^6$ or [Kr]

(b) Br^-: $1s^2\ 2s^2\ 2p^6\ 3s^2\ 3p^6\ 3d^{10}\ 4s^2\ 4p^6$ or [Kr]

(c) O^{2-}: $1s^2\ 2s^2\ 2p^6$ or [Ne]

(d) Ba^{2+}: $1s^2\ 2s^2\ 2p^6\ 3s^2\ 3p^6\ 3d^{10}\ 4s^2\ 4p^6\ 4d^{10}\ 5s^2\ 5p^6$ or [Xe]

(e) Zn^{2+}: $1s^2\ 2s^2\ 2p^6\ 3s^2\ 3p^6\ 3d^{10}$ or [Ar] $3d^{10}$

(f) Ag^+: $1s^2\ 2s^2\ 2p^6\ 3s^2\ 3p^6\ 3d^{10}\ 4s^2\ 4p^6\ 4d^{10}$ or [Kr] $4d^{10}$

(g) Bi^{3+}: $1s^2\ 2s^2\ 2p^6\ 3s^2\ 3p^6\ 3d^{10}\ 4s^2\ 4p^6\ 4d^{10}\ 4f^{14}\ 5s^2\ 5p^6\ 5d^{10}\ 6s^2$ or [Xe] $4f^{14}\ 5d^{10}\ 6s^2$

8-16. (a) Starting with the electron configuration of Xe (Z = 54), for Pb (Z = 82) we may write

Pb: [Xe] $4f^{14}\ 5d^{10}\ 6s^2\ 6p^2$

(b) By applying the rules for electron configurations from Chapter 7, we might write for element, Z = 114

Z = 114: [Xe] $4f^{14}\ 5d^{10}\ 6s^2\ 6p^6\ 7s^2\ 5f^{14}\ 6d^{10}\ 7p^2$

or

Z = 114: [Rn] $5f^{14}\ 6d^{10}\ 7s^2\ 7p^2$

Note the similarity of this electron configuration to that for Pb.

Atomic sizes

8-17. The basic reason why the sizes of atoms do not increase uniformly with atomic number stems from the electronic shell structure of atoms. If electrons are added to the same outermost shell while protons are added to the nucleus, the increased nucleus charge results in a greater attraction for outer-shell electrons and a decrease in size (moving from left to right across a period in the periodic table). If electrons enter an inner electronic shell (transition elements) there is little effect on atomic size in moving from one atom to the next. If an electron enters a new electronic shell (as in moving from a noble gas atom to an alkali metal atom), there is a large increase in size.

8-18. (a) The smallest atoms are located at the top of the periodic groups. The smallest atom in Group IIIA is boron (B).

(b) All of the atoms except Po are in the fifth period; Po is in the sixth. Within a period, atoms decrease in size from left to right. Of the elements listed, Te is farthest to the right. Po is in the same group as Te, but farther toward the bottom. Te should be the smallest of the atoms listed.

8-19. We should expect the hydrogen ion, H^+, to be the smallest of atomic species, since it consists of a lone proton. Certainly H^+ should be smaller than He, which has one shell with two electrons. The hydride ion, H^-, should be larger than the He atom. Although H^- and He both have two electrons ($1s^2$), in H^- there is only one proton to offset the negative charge; in He there are two protons. Repulsion between the electrons is more significant in H^- than in He, resulting in a larger atomic size.

8-20. The basic principle in the following arrangement of atomic sizes is that if the number of protons exceeds the number of electrons (positive ion) the atomic size is smaller than in the corresponding neutral species (in this case, the noble gas, Kr). If the number of electrons exceeds the number of protons (negative ion), the atomic size is larger. Our comparisons then must be based on the noble gas Kr.

$Y^{3+} < Sr^{2+} < Rb^+ < Kr < Br^- < Se^{2-}$

8-21. Consider Li^+ and Y. Li^+ is in the second period and Y is in the fifth. We expect a large decrease in size when an Li atom becomes an Li^+ ion. With respect to their atomic sizes $Li^+ < Y$. Now consider Se and Br. The neutral atoms should be similar in size, but there is a large increase in size when Br is converted to Br^- (i.e., comparing the covalent and ionic radii of Br). Therefore, with respect to their atomic sizes, $Se < Br^-$. Based on the relationship of atomic size to position in a period of elements, we should expect Se < Y. The expected order of increasing size is $Li^+ < Se < Y < Br^-$. A further check on this prediction is possible by referring to Figures 8-5 and 8-7.

Ionization energies, electron affinities

8-22. I_2 measures the energy required to move an electron away from a species that acquires a +2 charge; I_1, from a species that acquires a +1 charge. For any given element $I_2 > I_1$.

8-23. The first electron lost by a Na atom is a $3s$ electron. The same is true for Mg. However, because of its larger size, this $3s$ electron is extracted more easily from Na than from Mg. That is, I_1 (Na) < I_1 (Mg). The second electron lost by a Mg atom is also a $3s$ electron, whereas that lost by Na must now come from the extremely stable Ne core ($2s^2\ 2p^6$). As a result, I_2 (Na) > I_2 (Mg).

8-24. In each case the ionization energy is that required to remove an electron from an especially stable electron configuration, that of the noble gas Ne, $1s^2\ 2s^2\ 2p^6$. With Ne the electron is moved away from a unipositive ion, Ne^+; the required energy is I_1 (Ne). With sodium, removal of the electron converts Na^+ to Na^{2+}. To move an electron away from a dipositive ion requires more energy than from a unipositive ion. Thus, I_2 (Na) > I_1 (Ne).

8-25. The energy requirement to convert Mg to Mg^+ is I_1 = 7.6 eV, and to convert Mg^+ to Mg^{2+}, I_2 = 15.0 eV (see Table 8-5). The total requirement, per atom, is 22.6 eV.

$$\text{no. J} = 22.6\ \text{eV/atom} \times \frac{96.49\ \text{kJ/mol}}{1\ \text{eV/atom}} \times 3.50 \times 10^{-5}\ \text{mol} \times \frac{1000\ \text{J}}{1\ \text{kJ}} = 76.3\ \text{J}$$

8-26. Refer to Table 8-5 and add together the individual ionization energies, $I_1 + I_2 + \ldots I_7$.

total energy = 13.0 + 23.8 + 39.6 + 53.5 + 67.8 + 97.0 + 114.2 = 408.9 eV

8-27. The energy per atom associated with the process Cl(g) + e^- ⟶ Cl^-(g) is the electron affinity, -3.7 eV.

$$\text{no. kJ} = -3.7\ \text{eV/atom} \times \frac{96.49\ \text{kJ/mol}}{1\ \text{eV/atom}} \times \frac{\text{mol Cl}}{35.5\ \text{g Cl}} \times 1.00\ \text{g Cl} = -10\ \text{kJ}$$

8-28. The ionization energy for an H atom (from Figure 7-13) is $E_\infty - E_1 = 0 - \frac{-B}{(1)^2} = +2.179 \times 10^{-18}$ J

$$\text{no. eV/atom} = \frac{2.179 \times 10^{-18}\ \text{J}}{\text{atom}} \times \frac{6.02 \times 10^{23}\ \text{atom}}{1\ \text{mol}} \times \frac{1\ \text{kJ}}{1000\ \text{J}} \times \frac{1\ \text{eV/atom}}{96.49\ \text{kJ/mol}} = 13.6\ \text{eV/atom}$$

8-29. In general ionization energies *increase* from left to right in a period of elements and *decrease* from top to bottom in a group. If we apply these observations to the elements listed, we obtain for the order of increasing first ionization energy: Cs < Sr < As < S < F.

Electronegativities, metals and nonmetals

8-30. *Se*: The electronegativity of Se must be less than that of S (2.58), greater than that of As (2.18), and less than that of Br (2.96). Furthermore, we might expect the increase in electronegativity between As and Se to be similar to that between P and S (0.4). All of these facts suggest an electronegativity for Se of about 2.5.

Te: The electronegativity of Te should be somewhat less than that just estimated for Se (2.5), and less than that of I (2.66). Considering again that the electronegativity difference between a group VA and VIA element is about 0.4, we conclude that the electronegativity of Te should be about 2.4.

Ge and Sn: The electronegativity of Ge should be intermediate to those of Ga (1.81) and As (2.18), and that of Sn should be intermediate to those of In (1.78) and Sb (2.05). Furthermore, the electronegativity of Ge should be slightly greater than that of Sn. These facts lead to the estimates: Ge, 2.0; Sn, 1.9.

8-31. All the transition elements are metallic. We would not expect them to be as metallic as the Group IA or IIA metals, but we might expect them to be about as metallic as the elements toward the bottom of Groups IIIA, IVA, and VA. A reasonable estimate might be between 1.2 and 2.0.

8-32. The atoms to be compared in this exercise are Bi, S, Ba, As and Mg.

(a) The choice of the most metallic element of the set is limited to Ba and Mg, both members of group IIA. Between the two we should choose *Ba*, because it is a larger atom than Mg. (The larger atoms are found at the bottom of a group.)

(b) As and Bi are in Group VA. S is in Group VIA and is closer to the top of its group than are As and Bi. Both of these factors suggest that *S* is the most nonmetallic element in the set.

(c) We have identified Mg and Ba as being clear-cut metals and S, a nonmetal. Of the remaining two--As and Bi--As is somewhat more nonmetallic and Bi, more metallic. Thus, if we arrange the elements in increasing order of electronegativity, we should expect *Bi* to occupy the middle position.

electronegativities: Ba < Mg < Bi < As < S

8-33. Of the elements listed, Sc, Fe, Rb, and Ca are metals; Te is a metalloid; and Br, O, and F are nonmetals. The decreasing metallic character of the metals is Rb > Ca > Sc > Fe. The increasing nonmetallic character of the nonmetals is Te < Br < O < F. The overall order of decreasing metallic character, then, is Rb > Ca > Sc > Fe > Te > Br > O > F.

8-34. We need to compare Table 8-6 (selected electronegativities) with Figure 8-8 (ionization energies as a function of atomic number). The most active metals, those with electronegativities of about 1 or less, all have low ionization energies--$I_1 < 5$ eV. I_1 is a good criterion for these elements. The highest ionization energies are those of the noble gases, but these are not the most nonmetallic elements. Ionization energy as a measure of nonmetallic character does not work for them. The most nonmetallic elements according to electronegativity data--the smaller members of Groups VIA and VIIA--do have high ionization energies ($I_1 > 12$ eV). There is a reasonably good correlation between ionization energy and nonmetallic character for them. The greatest shortcoming of ionization energy as a criterion of metallic/nonmetallic character is with those elements that lie in the "middle". For example, Zn, which is a fairly active metal has $I_1 \approx 9$ eV (see Figure 8-8), whereas Si, which is a metalloid, has $I_1 = 8.2$ eV (see Table 8-5).

Magnetic properties

8-35. Three of the species listed have the electron configuration of a noble gas and thus all electrons are paired. The three are F^- ($1s^2\ 2s^2\ 2p^6$); Ca^{2+} ($1s^2\ 2s^2\ 2p^6\ 3s^2\ 3p^6$); and S^{2-} ($1s^2\ 2s^2\ 2p^6\ 3s^2\ 3p^6$) By a process of elimination we are led to conclude that Fe^{2+} has unpaired electrons. But we can also arrive at this conclusion through the electron configuration. Fe^{2+} $1s^2\ 2s^2\ 2p^6\ 3s^2\ 3p^6\ 3d^6$

If the $3d$ electrons enter orbitals singly before pairing up, we conclude that there are *four* unpaired electrons (six electrons distributed among five $3d$ orbitals).

8-36. *diamagnetic:* K^+, Zn^{2+}, Sn^{2+}

K^+ is isoelectronic with Ar. Zn^{2+} has the electron configuration [Ar] $3d^{10}$, with all $3d$ electrons paired. Sn^{2+} has the electron configuration [Kr] $4d^{10}\ 5s^2$, again with all electrons paired.

paramagnetic: Cr^{3+}, Co^{3+}

The atomic number of Cr is 24. Cr^{3+} has 21 electrons; at least one of these must be unpaired. (Actually, the electron configuration of Cr^{3+} is [Ar] $3d^3$, with three unpaired electrons.) In Co^{3+} there are 24 electrons in the electron configuration [Ar] $3d^6$. When these six $3d$ electrons are distributed among five $3d$ orbitals, *four* of the electrons are left unpaired.

8-37. V^{3+}: $1s^2\ 2s^2\ 2p^6\ 3s^2\ 3p^6\ 3d^2$. The two $3d$ electrons are unpaired.

Cu^{2+}: $1s^2\ 2s^2\ 2p^6\ 3s^2\ 3p^6\ 3d^9$. Of the nine $3d$ electrons there are four pairs and a single unpaired electron in the remaining $3d$ orbital.

Cr^{3+}: $1s^2\ 2s^2\ 2p^6\ 3s^2\ 3p^6\ 3d^3$. The three $3d$ electrons are all unpaired.

8-38. All atoms with an odd atomic number must be paramagnetic, for there is no way to pair up all the electrons in an odd-numbered set. However, it does not follow that all atoms with an even atomic number are diamagnetic. The electrons would all be paired if they entered orbitals in pairs, but Hund's rule states that the tendency is for orbitals to be singly occupied where possible. As an illustration consider oxygen. It has an even atomic number (8) and two unpaired electrons.

	$1s$	$2s$	$2p$
O	[↓↑]	[↓↑]	[↓↑ | ↓ | ↓]

Predictions based on periodic relationships

8-39. Dobereiner's method works only when the numbers of intervening elements between the first pair and the second pair of elements in the triad are the same. For example, in (a) this separation is 8 elements: Li (Z = 3), Na (Z = 11), and K (Z = 19); but in (c) the first pair--C (Z = 6) and Si (Z = 14)--are separated by 8 elements and the second pair--Si (Z = 14) and Ge (Z = 32)--by 18 elements.

(a) $\text{at. wt. Na (est.)} = \dfrac{\text{at. wt. Li + at. wt. K}}{2} = \dfrac{6.94 + 39.10}{2} = 23.02$ actual: 22.99

(b) $\text{at. wt. Br (est.)} = \dfrac{\text{at. wt. Cl + at. wt. I}}{2} = \dfrac{35.45 + 126.90}{2} = 81.18$ actual: 79.90

(c) $\text{at. wt. Si (est.)} = \dfrac{\text{at. wt. C + at. wt. Ge}}{2} = \dfrac{12.0 + 72.59}{2} = 42.30$ actual: 28.09

(d) $\text{at. wt. Sb (est.)} = \dfrac{\text{at. wt. As + at. wt. Bi}}{2} = \dfrac{74.92 + 208.98}{2} = 141.95$ actual: 121.75

(e) $\text{at. wt. Ga (est.)} = \dfrac{\text{at. wt. B + at. wt. Tl}}{2} = \dfrac{10.81 + 204.37}{2} = 107.59$ actual: 69.72

8-40. Assuming a regular relationship within each group of substances, we might estimate boiling points of about -60°C for SnH_4 and about -100°C for H_2O. The true boiling points are -52°C for SnH_4 and 100°C for H_2O. The estimation is quite good for SnH_4 but greatly in error for H_2O.

8-41. (a) Since Figure 8-1 is based on atomic numbers we must use the atomic number of Ga in this estimation. Its atomic number is 31 and its atomic volume is approximately 12 cm^3/mol. But let us use Mendeleev's estimate of the atomic weight of Ga--68.

$$\text{estimated density} = \frac{68\ \text{g/mol}}{12\ \text{cm}^3/\text{mol}} = 5.7\ \text{g/cm}^3$$

(b) Because Ga is expected to resemble Al, we would predict the formula R_2O_3 (see Table 8-1), i.e., Ga_2O_3.

$$\%\text{Ga} = \frac{(2 \times 68)\text{g Ga}}{[(2 \times 68) + (3 \times 16)]\text{g } Ga_2O_3} \times 100 = 74\%\ \text{Ga}\ \&\ 26\%\ \text{O}$$

8-42. (a) *$Sr(NO_3)_2$:* Sr is similar to Ca. Ca exists as Ca^{2+} in CaO. The nitrate ion must be NO_3^- (based on KNO_3).

(b) *$BaBr_2$:* Ba is similar to Ca. We expect it to form the ion Ba^{2+}. It combines with Br^- to form $BaBr_2$.

(c) *Ag_2O:* Based on their sulfates, we expect Ag to resemble Na, i.e. to form the ion Ag^+. Combined with O^{2-}, Ag^+ yields the compound Ag_2O.

(d) *Cu_2Te:* Te should resemble O and form the ion Te^{2-} (analogous to O^{2-}). The copper ion in the compound is Cu^+.

(e) *$Al_2(SO_4)_3$:* From the several examples given we deduce that the appropriate ionic charges are Al^{3+} and SO_4^{2-}.

(f) *Ga_2O_3:* Ga, like B, is in Group IIIA, suggesting the ion, Ga^{3+}. Combined with O^{2-} this results in Ga_2O_3.

(g) *Li_3N:* Similar to the other alkali metals, Li forms compounds containing the ion, Li^+. Nitrogen, in group VA, has the capacity to form the nitride ion, N^{3-}.

8-43. One H atom has a combining capacity for one Cl atom, and vice versa. An oxygen atom has a combining capacity for two H atoms. Since C has a combining capacity for 4 Cl atoms, we might expect it also to have the capacity to combine with 4 H atoms or 2 O atoms. The compounds CH_4 and CO_2 do indeed exist, but so does CO. CO appears to be the inconsistent formula in the set. (Note that because of the similarity of Si and C we should also expect CO_2 because of the existence of SiO_2.)

8-44. (a) $Mg(s) + 2\ HCl(aq) \longrightarrow MgCl_2(aq) + H_2(g)$

(b) $2\ Cs(s) + 2\ H_2O(l) \longrightarrow 2\ CsOH(aq) + H_2(g)$

(c) $Be(s) + H_2O(l) \longrightarrow$ no reaction

Be is a light member of Group IIA, not one of the heavier members.

(d) $2\ Na(s) + 2\ HI(aq) \longrightarrow 2\ NaI(aq) + H_2(g)$

Because I and Cl are both in Group VIIA, we should expect HI(aq) to resemble HCl(aq).

(e) $Si(s) + HCl(aq) \longrightarrow$ insufficient information. From the observations given in the exercise, we cannot conclude what happens when a Group IVA element is brought into contact with HCl(aq).

(f) $Ba(s) + 2\ H_2O(l) \longrightarrow Ba(OH)_2(aq) + H_2(g)$

8-45. (a) Metals with low ionization energies are the ones expected to exhibit the photoelectric effect with visible light--Cs, Rb, and K, for example. Metals with higher ionization energies would not be expected to, for example, Fe, Cu, Zn.

(b) We should expect the highest density to correspond to the heaviest atoms. This is an effect not likely to be overcome by the factor of increased atomic radius when comparing elements in the sixth and seventh periods. The expectation is for Rn to be the most dense noble gas.

(c) Use Figure 8-8 to estimate the value of I_1 for the element with Z = 100; the value obtained is about 5 eV/atom.

(d) Refer to the series of melting points for Group IA elements in Section 8-2. The estimate for Fr would be about 25°C.

(e) Use Figure 8-1 to determine the atomic volume of the element with Z = 88. This value is about 38 cm^3/mol.

$$\text{density} = \frac{\text{at. wt.}}{\text{at. vol.}} = \frac{226\ \text{g/mol}}{38\ \text{cm}^3/\text{mol}} \simeq 6\ \text{g/cm}^3$$

(f) Refer to Table 8-6. The electronegativity of Te should be about 2.4. That of Po should be somewhat lower (since Po is below Te in Group VIA), say about 2.0.

Self-test Questions

1. (*b*) The element in question is in Group IVA of the periodic table (it is Sn). As such, it resembles Pb, which is also in Group IVA. The element does not bear a particular resemblance to Se [eliminating (c) as an answer], nor is it a transition element [eliminating (d)].

2. (*c*) Arsenic is in Group VA. An atom with five 4*p* electrons would be in Group VIIA. Atoms with the 4*d* subshell filled are found in the fifth period, but As is in the fourth period. All atoms following Ar have six 3*p* electrons; this includes As. No atom may have three electrons in an *s* subshell.

3. (*d*) The species listed are isoelectronic. All have the electron configuration of Ar. The positive ions are smaller than Ar, and the negative ion, Cl^- is larger.

4. (*b*) We can eliminate the two metals, Cs and Li, which have low ionization energies, and compare the two nonmetals. The more nonmetallic of the two, and therefore the more difficult to ionize, is Cl.

5. (*c*) The most metallic of the four elements is the one found farthest to the left and farthest down in the periodic table. This element will have the lowest first ionization energy; it is K.

6. (*b*) The outer-shell electron configuration of I is $5s^2\ 5p^5$. The $5s$ electrons are paired, as are four of the $5p$ electrons. The remaining $5p$ electron is unpaired.

7. All the questions can be answered by reference to a periodic table.

(a) There are 34 protons in $^{79}_{34}Se$.

(b) The number of neutrons is 79 - 34 = 45.

(c) The third principal shell is filled with 18 electrons in Se. That is, the electron configuration is [Ar] $3d^{10}\ 4s^2\ 4p^4$.

(d) There are *two* electrons in the $2s$ orbital of all atoms starting with Be.

(e) From the electron configuration written in (c), we see that there are *four* $4p$ electrons.

(f) The number of electrons in the shell of highest principal quantum number corresponds to the group numeral for a representative element. Se is in Group VIA. It has *six* outer shell electrons.

8. The element with the highest electronegativity must be a nonmetal. There are two nonmetals in the listing: Br and As. Bromine is the more nonmetallic of the two (being in Group VIIA).

9. (a) C: The element at the top of a group has the smallest atoms.

(b) Rb: The alkali metal that opens a period of elements has the largest atomic radius in the period.

(c) At: The members at the bottom of a group are more metallic (less nonmetallic) than those higher in the group; they have lower electronegativities.

10. (a) The theoretical basis of the periodic table is to bring together in vertical columns elements with similar electron configurations. Electronic shells have differing capacities for electrons, and the subshells fill in a particular order. Because of this, the number of elements that must intervene before an element similar to a previous one is encountered is not constant, being 2 in one case, 8 in two cases, and 18 and 32 in others.

(b) The modern periodic table arranges elements according to increasing atomic number. In a few cases the order by atomic weight is not the same as by atomic number, for example Ar (Z = 18) has a higher atomic weight than K (Z = 19).

Chapter 9

Chemical Bonding I: Basic Concepts

Lewis theory

9-1.

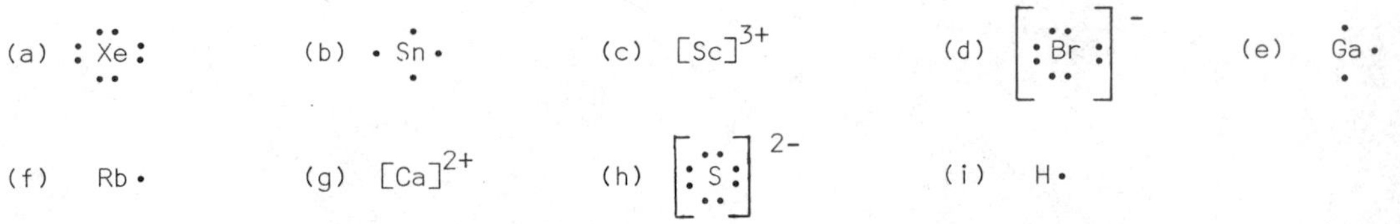

9-2. The Lewis structure of an ionic compound is written to emphasize that electrons are *transferred* from metal to nonmetal atoms. This is done by indicating net ionic charges on the Lewis symbols. The principal requirement of the Lewis structure of a covalent bond is that the *sharing* of an electron pair(s) be represented. For most covalent compounds and many ionic compounds the electron configurations of the bonded atoms become those of a noble gas, but there are important exceptions to this idea.

Ionic bonding

9-3.

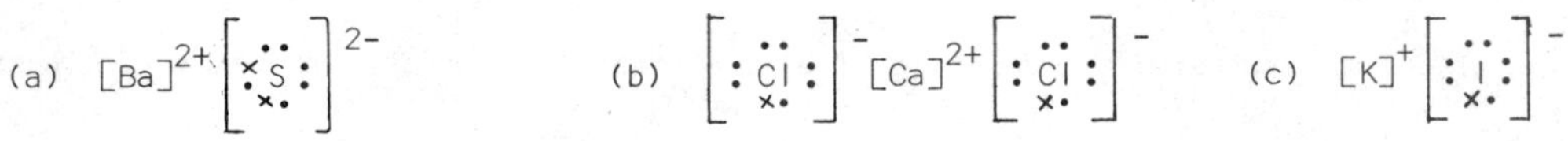

9-4.

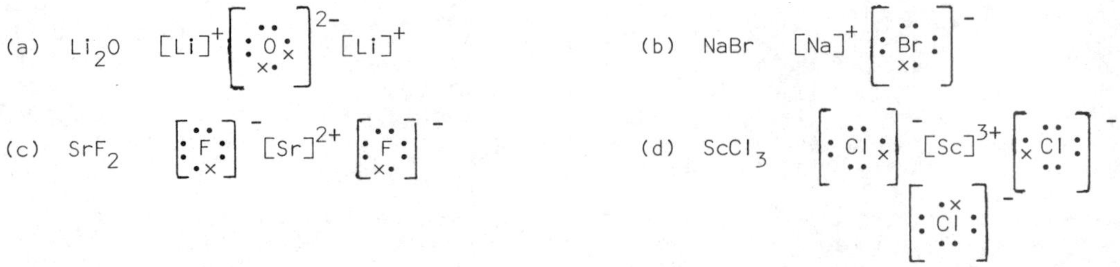

9-5. The nonmetals are representative elements whose atoms lack one (Group VIIA), two (Group VIA) or, occasionally, three (N in Group VA) electrons from having the electron configurations of noble gases. When the nonmetals gain these small numbers of electrons, they form anions with noble gas electron configurations. Among metals, which tend to lose electrons to form cations, noble gas electron configurations are achieved only for those metals with one, two, or possibly three electrons beyond a noble gas core. But there are many metals (e.g., transition elements) for which the underlying core is not that of a noble gas (see Table 9-1).

9-6. Solid NaCl consists of an array of positive (Na^+) and negative (Cl^-) ions. There are no identifiable small groups of ions that exist separate from others--there are no entities that could be called molecules. In *gaseous* NaCl discrete ion pairs (such as the one pictured in Figure 9-2) can exist. These might be referred to as molecules.

Lewis structures

9-7. Several of these terms are described in the section, "Some New Terms". What is intended here is a description of terms in relation to Lewis structures.

(a) Valence electrons are the outer-shell electrons of an atom, represented by dots in a Lewis structure.

(b) An octet refers to eight electrons in the outer shell of an atom (represented as eight dots surrounding a chemical symbol in a Lewis structure).

(c) Unshared electron pairs or nonbonding electron pairs are identified as belonging exclusively to one atom in a Lewis structure.

(d) Multiple bonds result from the sharing of more than one pair of electrons between two atoms (shown in Lewis structures as double (=) and triple (≡) bonds).

(e) A coordinate covalent bond is one in which all the electrons being shared are identified as coming from a single atom in the bonded pair of atoms.

(f) Resonance describes a condition in which more than a single plausible Lewis structure can be written for a species.

(g) An odd electron species is one in which the total number of valence electrons is an odd number, which means that not all electrons in the Lewis structure can be paired.

(h) An expanded octet results whenever more than eight valence electrons (e.g., 10 or 12) are represented in a Lewis structure.

9-8.   (a) RbCl, rubidium chloride, f. wt. = 120.92, (ionic): $[Rb]^+$ $\begin{bmatrix} \ddot{\underset{\cdot\cdot}{\overset{\cdot\cdot}{Cl}}} \end{bmatrix}^-$

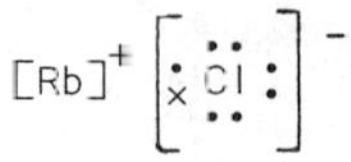

(b) H_2Se, hydrogen selenide, f. wt. = 80.98, (covalent):   H —Se̤:
                                                                              |
                                                                              H

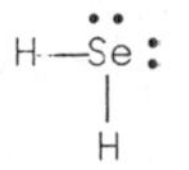

(c) BCl_3, boron trichloride, f. wt. = 117.17, (covalent):   :Cl—B—Cl:
                                                                              |
                                                                            :Cl:

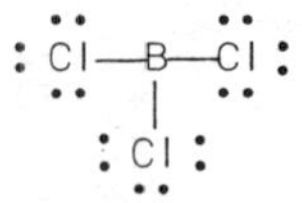

(d) Cs_2S, cesium sulfide, f. wt. = 297.88, (ionic): $[Cs]^+$ $\begin{bmatrix} :\overset{\cdot\cdot}{\underset{\cdot\cdot}{S}}\times \end{bmatrix}^{2-}$ $[Cs]^+$

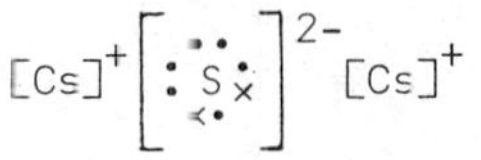

(e) SrO, strontium oxide, f. wt. = 103.62, (ionic): $[Sr]^{2+}$ $\begin{bmatrix} \overset{\cdot\cdot}{\underset{\times}{O}}: \end{bmatrix}^{2-}$

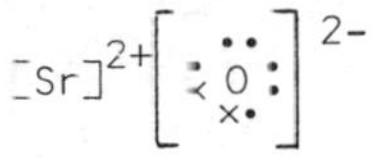

(f) OF_2, oxygen fluoride, f. wt. = 54.00, (covalent):   :O—F:
                                                                              |
                                                                            :F:

9-9.   (a) :Br—Br: (b) :I—Cl: (c) :O—F: (d) :I—N—I:
                                                              | |
                                                            :F: :I:

(e)   H—Te:
         |
         I:

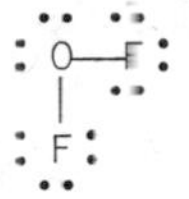

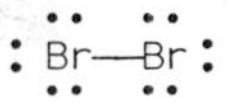

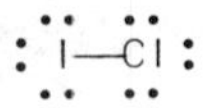

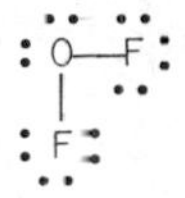

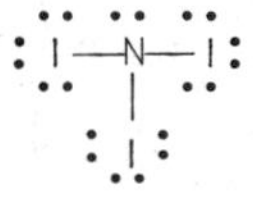

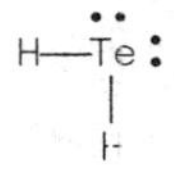

9-10.   (a) A plausible Lewis structure can be written by starting with the Lewis symbols of the individual atoms, combining them, and shifting electrons into the carbon-oxygen bond until the basic requirements for a Lewis structure are met--octets, all electrons paired, etc.

(b) The approach here is similar to (a). The Lewis structure shows two carbon-sulfur double bonds.

$$:\overset{\cdot\cdot}{S}\cdot \ + \ \cdot \overset{\cdot}{C}\cdot \ + \ \cdot\overset{\cdot\cdot}{S}: \ \longrightarrow \ :\overset{\cdot\cdot}{S}:\overset{\curvearrowleft}{C}:\overset{\curvearrowright}{S}: \ \longrightarrow \ :\overset{\cdot\cdot}{S} = C = \overset{\cdot\cdot}{S}:$$

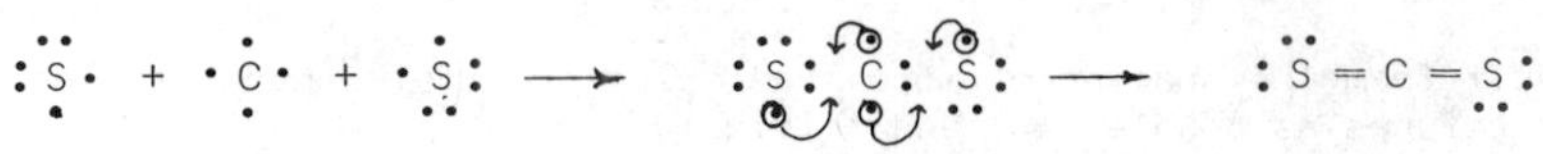

(c) The best approach here, perhaps, is to start with Lewis symbols that are different from those normally written for O atoms.

$$:\overset{\cdot\cdot}{O} \ + \ :\overset{\cdot\cdot}{O} \ + \ :\overset{\cdot\cdot}{O} \ \longrightarrow \ :\overset{\cdot\cdot}{O} - \overset{\cdot\cdot}{O} - \overset{\cdot\cdot}{O}$$

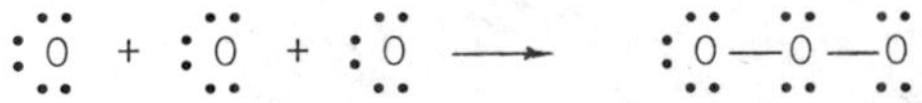

The deficiency of the Lewis structure above is that of having only 6 electrons in the outer shell of the O atom on the right. This can be corrected by shifting an electron pair into an oxygen-oxygen bond. Two equally plausible structures are shown. The true structure is a resonance hybrid of the two.

$$:\overset{\cdot\cdot}{O} = \overset{\cdot\cdot}{O} - \overset{\cdot\cdot}{O}: \ \leftrightarrow \ :\overset{\cdot\cdot}{O} - \overset{\cdot\cdot}{O} = \overset{\cdot\cdot}{O}:$$

(d)

$$H\cdot \ + \ \cdot \overset{\cdot}{\underset{\cdot}{C}}\cdot \ + \ \cdot\overset{\cdot\cdot}{O}: \ \longrightarrow \ H:\overset{}{\underset{H}{C}}:\overset{\curvearrowleft\curvearrowright}{O}: \ \longrightarrow \ H - \overset{}{\underset{H}{C}} = \overset{\cdot\cdot}{O}:$$

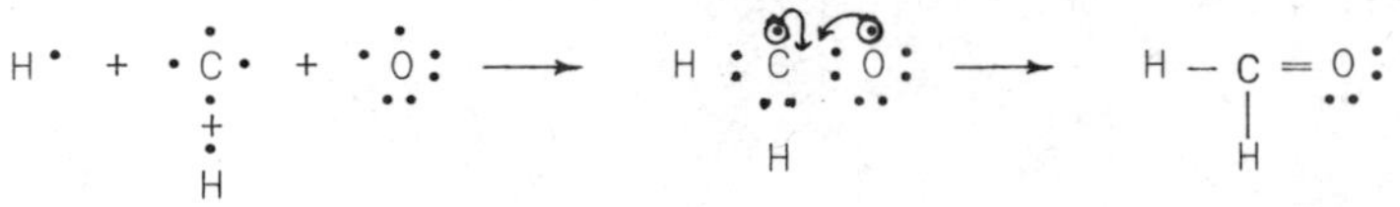

9-11. (a) An H atom cannot form more than one covalent bond. Also, N does not have a complete octet. Replace the structure by

$$H - \overset{\cdot\cdot}{\underset{|}{N}} - \overset{\cdot\cdot}{O} - H$$
$$H$$

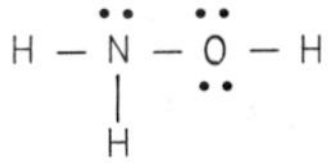

(b) There is one electron too many in this structure. ClO_2 is an odd-electron molecule with a total of 19 valence electrons. A plausible structure is

$$:\overset{\cdot\cdot}{O} - \overset{\cdot\cdot}{Cl} - \overset{\cdot\cdot}{O}\cdot$$

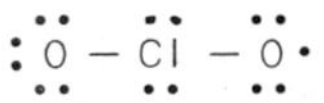

(c) One Br atom is shown to have 10 valence electrons. A more plausible structure uses only single covalent bonds.

$$:\overset{\cdot\cdot}{Br} - \overset{\cdot\cdot}{\underset{|}{P}} - \overset{\cdot\cdot}{Br}:$$
$$:\overset{}{\underset{\cdot\cdot}{Br}}:$$

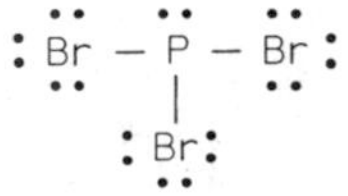

(d) Calcium oxide should be represented as an ionic compound, not covalent.

$$[Ca]^{2+} \ \left[:\overset{\cdot\cdot}{\underset{\cdot\cdot}{O}}:\right]^{2-}$$

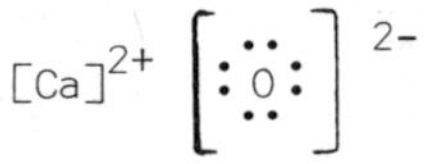

(e) The C atom is shown with only six valence electrons, two of which are unpaired. The C atom can be given an octet, with all electrons paired, by showing a carbon-to-nitrogen triple bond.

$$[:C \equiv N:]^{-}$$

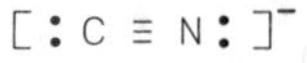

(f) The C atom is shown with only six valence electrons instead of eight. Move a pair of electrons from the S atom to create a carbon-to-sulfur double bond.

$$[:\overset{\cdot\cdot}{S} = C = \overset{\cdot\cdot}{N}:]^{-}$$

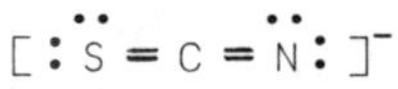

(g) The compound OCl_2, since it consists of two nonmetals, should be covalent, not ionic.

$$:\overset{\cdot\cdot}{Cl} - \overset{\cdot\cdot}{O} - \overset{\cdot\cdot}{Cl}:$$

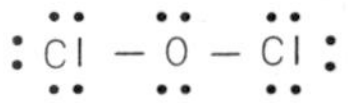

9-12. In the species H_3, one H atom would have to be bonded to two others simultaneously. This would place four electrons in the valence shell (n = 1) of that H atom, an impossibility. The species HHe would require three electrons in the outer shell of the He atom, H•He, but this shell (n = 1) can accomodate only two. In the species He_2 there would be four electrons in the outer shell of one of the atoms (He:He); this, too, is an impossibility. The structure H_3O would require 9 electrons in the outer-most shell of the O atom, still another impossibility.

Formal charge

9-13. (a) No formal charges. Each I atom is assigned 7 valence electrons in the Lewis structure and would also have 7 valence electrons as an isolated atom.

(b) The O atom in the sulfur-to-oxygen double bond has no formal charge. The other O atom has a formal charge of -1 (seven electrons assigned in the Lewis structure compared to six in the isolated atom). The S atom has a formal charge of +1 (five electrons are assigned to it in the Lewis structure).

(c) There are no formal charges. Each atom is assigned six electrons in the Lewis structure and would have this same number as an isolated atom.

(d) There are no formal charges. The numbers of electrons are four for C, six for O, and seven for Cl.

(e) The O atom at the right side of the structure is assigned seven electrons (compared to its normal six). This results in a formal charge of -1--equal to the charge on the ion. The other two atoms have no formal charge.

(f) The O atom joined to the N atom by a double bond has no formal charge. The other O atom is assigned seven electrons; it has a formal charge of -1. The N atom, assigned four electrons, has a formal charge of +1.

(g) There are no formal charges in this structure. The F atoms are each assigned seven electrons and the S and O atoms, six.

9-14. Write Lewis structures for each of the possibilities listed. Choose as the most plausible the one that best meets the requirements stated in the text.

(a) 

The structure on the left has no formal charges. In the structure on the right the O atom has a formal charge of +1 and the N atom, -1. The structure on the left is the more plausible.

(b) 

The structure on the left has no formal charges. For the structure on the right, formal charges are -2 for C, +2 for the central S atom, and 0 for the S atom on the right. The structure on the left is the more plausible. Note that other structures can be written that have the same skeleton as the one on the right and no formal charges. But in these cases some of the basic principles for writing Lewis structures are violated. For example

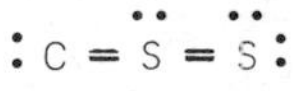

Note that this structure has an incomplete octet for C and an expanded octet for the central S atom.

(c) 

The structure on the left has formal charges on N(-1) and O(+1). The structure on the right has no formal charges. The structure on the right is the more plausible.

(d)

(I)

$:N \equiv N - \overset{\cdot\cdot}{\underset{\cdot\cdot}{O}}:$

(III)

$:N \equiv \overset{\cdot\cdot}{O} - \overset{\cdot\cdot}{N}:$

(II)

$\overset{\cdot\cdot}{:N} = N = \overset{\cdot\cdot}{O}:$

(IV)

$\overset{\cdot\cdot}{:N} = \overset{\cdot\cdot}{O} = \overset{\cdot\cdot}{N}:$

Four structures are represented above--two with the skeleton structures NNO and two with NON. Structure I has formal charges of +1 on the central N and -1 on the O atom. Structure II has a formal charge of +1 on the central N atom and -1 on the other N atom. Structure III has a formal charge of +2 on the central O atom and -2 on the N atom at the right. In structure IV the central O atom has a formal charge of +2 and each N atom, -1. Structures I and II, having N as the central atom, seem more plausible than structures III and IV, in which O is the central atom. The magnitudes of the formal charges are minimized in I and II. Structure I is perhaps most plausible of all because it places the negative formal charge on the most electronegative atom--O.

Polyatomic ions

9-15. Consider the Lewis symbol of a sulfur atom to be not the normal $:\overset{\cdot\cdot}{S}\cdot$, but $:\overset{\cdot\cdot}{S}:$; that of S^{2-} is $[:\overset{\cdot\cdot}{S}:]^{2-}$. The number of valence electrons for an S atom is 6, and for an S^{2-} ion, 8. Thus, in the Lewis structure of S_2^{2-} 14 electrons must be assigned; in S_3^{2-}, 20; S_4^{2-}, 26; S_5^{2-}, 32.

(a) $S_2^{2-} = [:\overset{\cdot\cdot}{\underset{\cdot\cdot}{S}}:\overset{\cdot\cdot}{\underset{\cdot\cdot}{S}}:]^{2-}$

(b) $S_3^{2-} = [:\overset{\cdot\cdot}{\underset{\cdot\cdot}{S}}:\overset{\cdot\cdot}{\underset{\cdot\cdot}{S}}:\overset{\cdot\cdot}{\underset{\cdot\cdot}{S}}:]^{2-}$

(c) $S_4^{2-} = [:\overset{\cdot\cdot}{\underset{\cdot\cdot}{S}}:\overset{\cdot\cdot}{\underset{\cdot\cdot}{S}}:\overset{\cdot\cdot}{\underset{\cdot\cdot}{S}}:\overset{\cdot\cdot}{\underset{\cdot\cdot}{S}}:]^{2-}$

(d) $S_5^{2-} = [:\overset{\cdot\cdot}{\underset{\cdot\cdot}{S}}:\overset{\cdot\cdot}{\underset{\cdot\cdot}{S}}:\overset{\cdot\cdot}{\underset{\cdot\cdot}{S}}:\overset{\cdot\cdot}{\underset{\cdot\cdot}{S}}:\overset{\cdot\cdot}{\underset{\cdot\cdot}{S}}:]^{2-}$

9-16. (a) $\overset{\cdot\cdot}{\underset{\cdot\cdot}{O}} + :\overset{\cdot\cdot}{Br}: + \overset{\cdot\cdot}{\underset{\cdot\cdot}{O}}: \longrightarrow :\overset{\cdot\cdot}{\underset{\cdot\cdot}{O}}:Br:\overset{\cdot\cdot}{\underset{\cdot\cdot}{O}}: \longrightarrow \left[:\overset{\cdot\cdot}{\underset{\cdot\cdot}{O}} - Br - \overset{\cdot\cdot}{\underset{\cdot\cdot}{O}}: \right]^-$

with the lower O and e⁻ arrow

(b) $:\overset{\cdot\cdot}{\underset{\cdot\cdot}{O}} + :\overset{\cdot\cdot}{Cl}: \longrightarrow \left[:\overset{\cdot\cdot}{\underset{\cdot\cdot}{O}} - \overset{\cdot\cdot}{\underset{\cdot\cdot}{Cl}}: \right]^-$

with upper O and e⁻ arrow, +

(c) $:\overset{\cdot\cdot}{O}\cdot + \cdot \overset{\cdot}{N}\cdot + \cdot\overset{\cdot\cdot}{O}: \longrightarrow :\overset{\cdot\cdot}{\underset{}{O}}:N:\overset{\cdot\cdot}{\underset{}{O}}: \longrightarrow \left[:\overset{\cdot\cdot}{O} = \overset{\cdot\cdot}{N} - \overset{\cdot\cdot}{\underset{\cdot\cdot}{O}}: \right]^-$ or $\left[:\overset{\cdot\cdot}{\underset{\cdot\cdot}{O}} - \overset{\cdot\cdot}{N} = \overset{\cdot\cdot}{O}: \right]^-$

9-17. (a) $\left[\begin{matrix} H \\ \overset{\cdot\cdot}{} \\ H:N:H \\ \overset{\cdot\cdot}{} \\ H \end{matrix} \right]^+ \quad \left[:\overset{\cdot\cdot}{\underset{\cdot\cdot}{I}}: \right]^-$

(b) $[Na]^+ \quad \left[:\overset{\cdot\cdot}{\underset{\cdot\cdot}{O}}:H \right]^-$

(c) $H - \overset{\cdot\cdot}{\underset{\cdot\cdot}{O}} - \overset{\cdot\cdot}{\underset{\cdot\cdot}{Cl}}:$

(d) $[Ca]^{2+}$

$\left[:\overset{\cdot\cdot}{\underset{\cdot\cdot}{O}} - Cl - \overset{\cdot\cdot}{\underset{\cdot\cdot}{O}}: \right]^-$

$\left[:\overset{\cdot\cdot}{\underset{\cdot\cdot}{O}} - Cl - \overset{\cdot\cdot}{\underset{\cdot\cdot}{O}}: \right]^-$

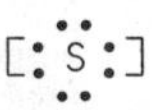

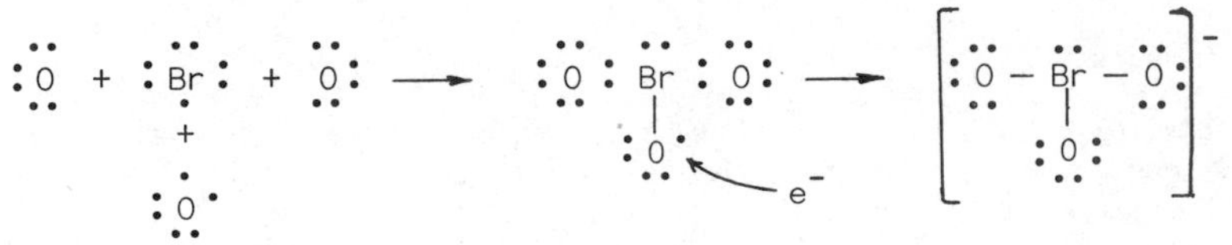

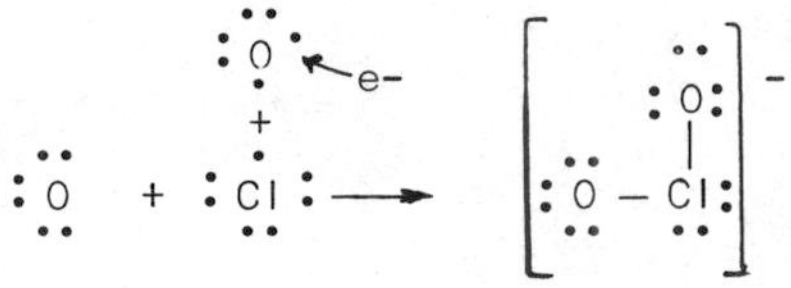

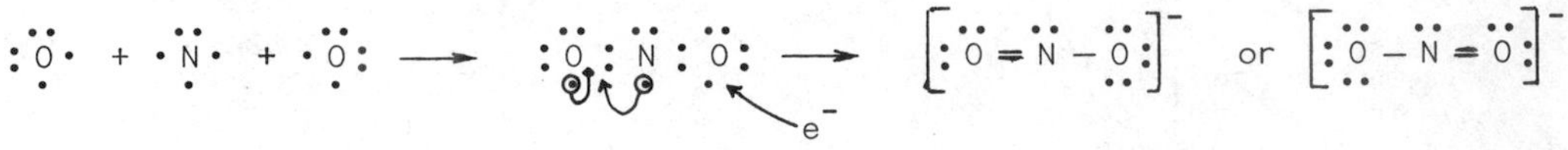

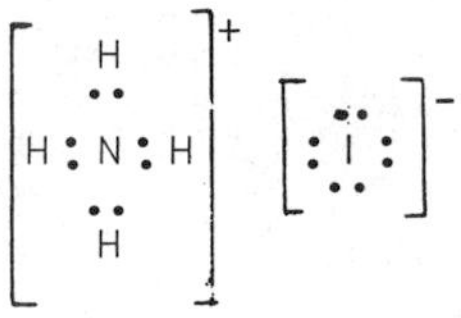

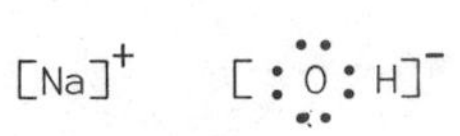

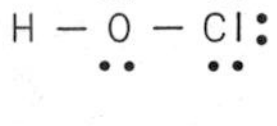

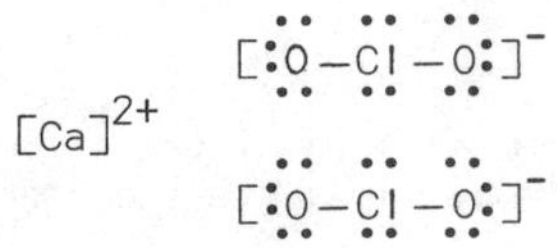

9-18.   In the Lewis structure of SO_3 there are 24 valence-shell electrons to be depicted.   The three O atoms are bonded to a central S atom.

$$:O\cdot \;+\; :\overset{+}{\underset{..}{S}}: \;+\; \overset{..}{\underset{..}{O}}: \;\longrightarrow\; :\overset{\overset{\textstyle :O:}{|}}{\underset{..}{O}}-S-\overset{..}{O}:$$

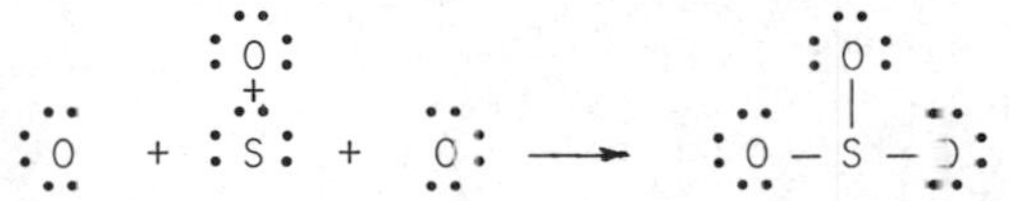

The difficulty with the structure written above is that the S atom lacks an octet.   This can be remedied by shifting an electron pair into one of the S — O bonds.   There are three ways of doing so.

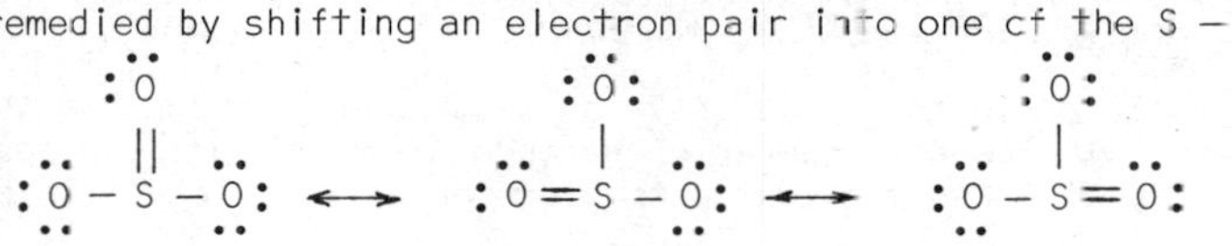

$$:\overset{\overset{\textstyle :O}{\|}}{\underset{..}{O}}-S-\overset{..}{\underset{..}{O}}: \;\longleftrightarrow\; :\overset{\overset{\textstyle :O:}{|}}{O}=S-\overset{..}{\underset{..}{O}}: \;\longleftrightarrow\; :\overset{\overset{\textstyle :O:}{|}}{\underset{..}{O}}-S=\overset{..}{O}:$$

9-19. $:\overset{..}{O}\cdot \;+\; \cdot\overset{..}{N}\cdot \;+\; \cdot\overset{..}{O}: \;\longrightarrow\; :\overset{..}{\underset{..}{O}}: \;N\; :\overset{..}{\underset{..}{O}}: \;\longrightarrow\; [:\overset{..}{O}=N-\overset{..}{\underset{..}{O}}:]^{-}$ or $[:\overset{..}{\underset{..}{O}}-N=\overset{..}{O}:]^{-}$

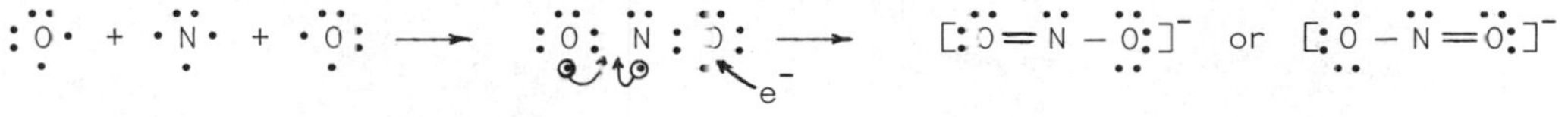

9-20.   Two equally plausible Lewis structures for ozone are illustrated below.   The true structure is a resonance hybrid with equal contributions from the following.

$$:\overset{..}{\underset{..}{O}}-O=\overset{..}{O}: \;\longleftrightarrow\; :\overset{..}{O}=O-\overset{..}{\underset{..}{O}}:$$

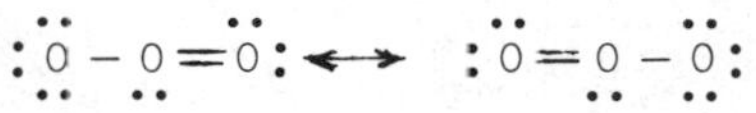

9-21.   Examine each of the structures to determine the extent to which rules on writing Lewis structures and assigning formal charges are followed.   Then comment on the plausibility of each structure.

   (a) $:N \equiv N - \overset{..}{\underset{..}{O}}:$

       All of the ordinary rules for Lewis structures are obeyed.   The central N atom has a formal charge of +1 and the O atom, -1.   This assignment is reasonable considering the electronegativities of N and O.   The structure is a plausible one.

   (b) $:\overset{..}{N}=N=\overset{..}{O}:$

       Here the central N atom has a formal charge of +1 and the other N atom, -1.   This structure may be a contributor to the resonance hybrid of N_2O, but it would seem somewhat less plausible than structure (a).   The negative formal charge is not found on the most electronegative element (O).

   (c) $:\overset{..}{\underset{..}{N}}-N \equiv O:$

       In this structure all atoms carry a formal charge: +1 for the central N atom; +1 for the O atom; and -2 for the second N atom.   This structure is least plausible of the three in that it involves a high formal charge (-2) on one atom, and the most electronegative atom (O) acquires a *positive* formal charge.

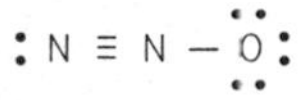

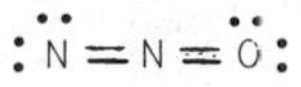

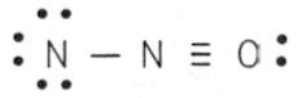

Experimental evidence that would help to establish the relative importance of structures (a) and (b) would be bond strengths and distances.   This would indicate whether the nitrogen-to-nitrogen bond is essentially double or triple, and the nitrogen-to-oxygen bond, single or double.

Odd-electron species

9-22.   The total number of valence electrons is 11 (five from N and six from O).   These will appear as five pairs and one unpaired electron.   A plausible structure is

   $\cdot N = \overset{..}{\underset{..}{O}}:$

This structure has no formal charges. Another structure, which seems less plausible because it involves formal charges and places a positive formal charge on the more electronegative atom (O), is

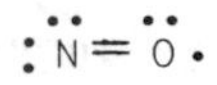

9-23. The dimer, N_2O_4, is diamagnetic. All electrons are paired.

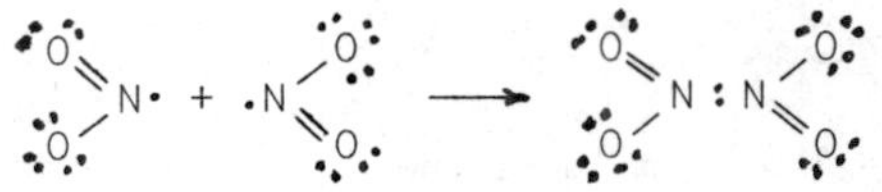

9-24. Species which contain odd numbers of valence electrons must have at least one unpaired electron; they must be paramagnetic. Most species with an even number of valence electrons are diamagnetic, but some are paramagnetic; for these we must write the Lewis structure and predict magnetic properties from this structure.

(a) OH^-; 8 valence electrons; $[:\ddot{\underset{..}{O}}:H]^-$; diamagnetic.

(b) OH; 7 valence electrons; paramagnetic.

(c) NO_3; 23 valence electrons; paramagnetic.

(d) SO_3; 24 valence electrons; see structures in the solution to Exercise 9-18; diamagnetic.

(e) SO_3^{2-}; 26 valence electrons; 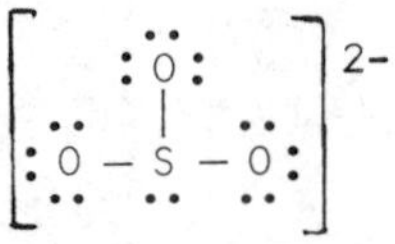 ; diamagnetic. (There is some double-bond character in SO_3^{2-} but this fact is not apparent from the simple Lewis structure.)

(f) HO_2; 13 valence electrons; paramagnetic.

Expanded octets

9-25. A valence-shell octet is based on the filling of *s* and *p* orbitals. The use of an expanded octet depends on the availability of *d* orbitals in the central atom. Third-period elements have such orbitals available (3 *d*) but second-period elements do not (no 2*d*). Since As and Se do have *d* orbitals available they should resemble P and S more nearly than they do N and O.

9-26. (a) The central Br atom must accomodate 10 electrons in its valence shell to form five Br—F bonds.

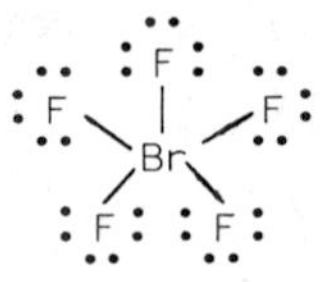

(b) A Lewis structure for PF_3 can be written without the need of an expanded octet.

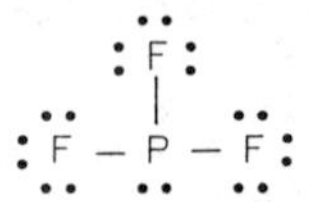

(c) Because an I atom has seven valence electrons, in order to form three I—Cl bonds the I atom must accomodate 10 valence-shell electrons.

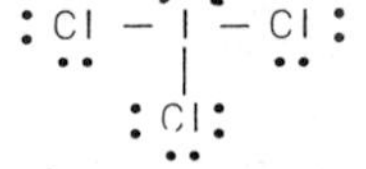

(d) Again 10 electrons must be accommodated in the valence shell of the central atom (*S*). Six of these come from the *S* atom and four from the F atoms.

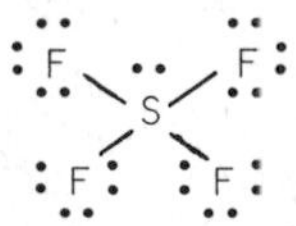

9-27. Write three Lewis structures with *S* as the central atom. In one of the structures use a sulfur-to-nitrogen single bond; in another, a double bond; and in the third, a triple bond. Comment on the plausibility of each structure.

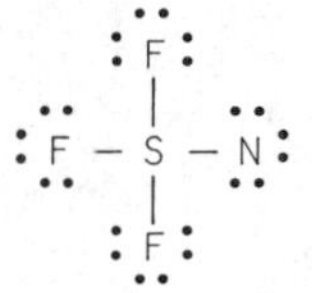

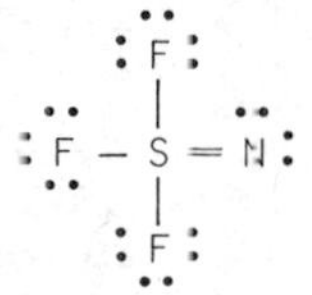

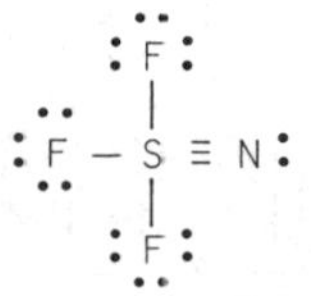

In the single-bond structure, each atom has an outer shell octet but the *S* atom has a formal charge of +2 and *N*, -2. In the double-bond structure the formal charges are reduced to +1 and -1, though the *S* atom must now have an expanded octet--10 valence electrons. In the triple-bond structure, the *S* atom has 12 valence electrons, but there are no formal charges. An expanded octet for *S* is permitted in a Lewis structure, and if formal charges are to be minimized, it seems most probable that the nitrogen-to-sulfur bond is a triple bond.

9-28. The seven Lewis structures referred to here are

I II III V V VI VII

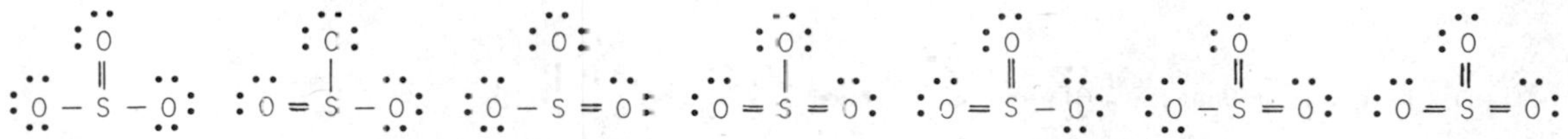

In structures I, II, and III, the S atom has a formal charge of +2; two of the O atoms have a formal charge of -1; and the third O atom, 0. In structures IV, V and VI, the formal charge of S is reduced to +1 and only one O atom carries a formal charge (-1). In structure VII there are no formal charges. Based on formal charge considerations alone, structure VII is the most plausible. Measurement of bond energies and distances could be used to establish whether the sulfur-to-oxygen bonds are double (confirming structure VII) or less-than-double (suggesting some contributions to the resonance hybrid from structures I-VII).

Molecular shapes

9-29. For each species draw a Lewis structure and assign a VSEPR designation. Then find the geometric shape corresponding to this designation in Table 9-2.

(a) Linear: CO is a diatomic molecule and all diatomic molecules are linear.

(b) Tetrahedral: The Lewis structure for $SiCl_4$ is

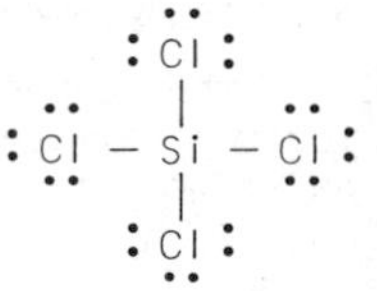

The VSEPR designation is AX_4 (all electron pairs are bond pairs).

(c) Trigonal bipyramidal: The Lewis structure for $SbCl_5$ would show 10 electrons in the valence shell of Sb. These would be five bond pairs (one bond to each Cl atom). The VSEPR designation is AX_5 (no lone pair electrons).

(d) V-shaped: The Lewis structure shows 8 valence electrons for Se, two bond pairs and two lone pairs--AX_2E_2.

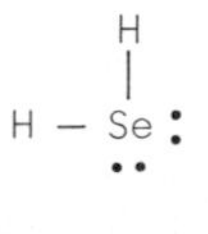

(e) T-shaped: The Lewis structure features an expanded octet for iodine--10 electrons arranged as three bond pairs and two lone pairs.

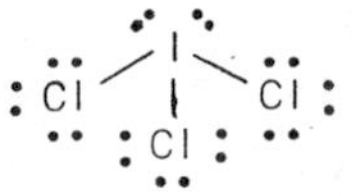

AX_3E_2

(f) Octahedral: The Al atom has 3 valence electrons; each F atom introduces an additional valence electron; and three more electrons are required to convey the charge of -3. Altogether there are 12 valence-shell electrons, arranged as six bond pairs: AX_6.

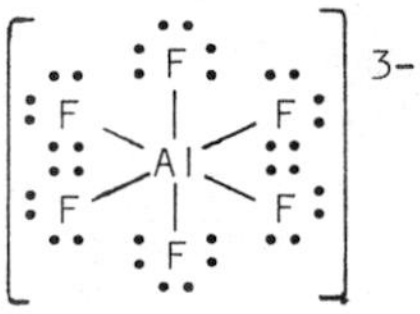

9-30. (a) Linear: :Ö = C = Ö: Treat as if there were only two bond pairs directed from the central C atom--AX_2.

(b) Linear: :N ≡ N — Ö: or :N̈ = N = Ö: In either case treat as two bond pairs--AX_2.

(c) V-shaped: :N ≡ S̈ — F̈: or :N̈ = S̈ — F̈: In either case the required distribution about the S atom is that of three electron pairs, two bond pairs and one lone pair--AX_2E.

(d) Trigonal planar:

The geometry corresponds to three electron pairs--all bond pairs, AX_3.

9-31. The VSEPR notation for this molecule would be AXE_3. Its Lewis structure would be :Ä — X. Because the molecule is diatomic, it would have to be linear. An example would be a hydrogen halide, e.g., :F̈ — H.

9-32. Tetrahedral: The total number of valence electrons is 8 (3 from B, one each from 4 F atoms, and one additional electron which corresponds to the -1 charge). The distribution of four electron pairs is tetrahedral, and each pair is a bond pair. Therefore, the ion has a tetrahedral shape.

9-33. See the solution to Exercise 9-28 for the seven Lewis structures referred to here. Electrons in multiple bonds are treated as if a single electron pair were involved. For each of the seven structures, the distribution corresponds to three electron pairs. Moreover, none of the structures involves lone-pair electrons. All have the VSEPR notation AX_3, and all lead to a prediction of trigonal planar geometry.

9-34. The central I atom of I_3^- has 7 valence electrons. Each of the other two iodine atoms contributes one electron to the valence shell of the central I atom. The extra electron that conveys the ionic charge brings the total number of valence electrons to 10. Five electron pairs are distributed about the cental I atom--two are bond pairs and three are lone pairs. The distribution AX_2E_3 produces a linear species.

Bond distances

9-35. The nitrogen-to-oxygen bonds with a 121 pm bond distance have more multiple bond character than does the 140 pm bond. In the Lewis structure below one nitrogen-to-oxygen bond is shown as a single bond. The other two nitrogen-to-oxygen bonds, because of resonance, are essentially 1-1/2 bonds.

9-36.   Use bond distances between like atoms to establish covalent radii. Then add covalent radii for different atoms to estimate the length of the bond between them.

(a)   covalent radius of H = 1/2(H — H) = 1/2(74) = 37 pm

covalent radius of Cl = 1/2(Cl — Cl) = 1/2(199) = 100 pm

H — Cl bond distance = 137 pm

(b)   C — N bond distance = 1/2(C — C) + 1/2(N — N) = 1/2(154) + 1/2(145) = 149 pm

(c)   C — Cl bond distance = 1/2(C — C) + 1/2(Cl — Cl) = 1/2(154) + 1/2(199) = 177 pm

(d)   C — F bond distance = 1/2(C — C) + 1/2(F — F) = 1/2(154) + 1/2(128) = 141 pm

(e)   N — I bond distance = 1/2(N — N) + 1/2(I — I) = 1/2(145) + 1/2(266) = 205 pm

9-37.   First draw a plausible Lewis structure.

$$H : \overset{\cdot\cdot}{\underset{\cdot\cdot}{N}} - \overset{\cdot\cdot}{\underset{\cdot\cdot}{O}} - H$$
$$H$$

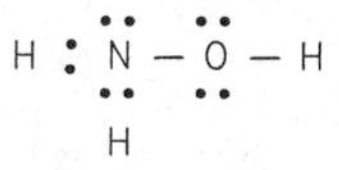

Now, predict the geometrical distribution of electron pairs expected about the N atom and about the O atom. In each case there are four pairs of electrons. For N this corresponds to AX_3E and for O, AX_2E_2. The predicted bond angles are the tetrahedral bond angle, 109.5°. The O — H bond distance is listed in Table 9-3. The N — H distance can be determined by the method of Exercise 9-36-- 1/2(145 + 74) = 110 pm. Data are not available for estimating the N — C bond distance.

Bond energies

9-38.   In C_2H_6 the bonds are

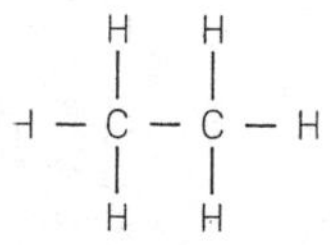

$$H - \overset{H}{\underset{H}{C}} - \overset{H}{\underset{H}{C}} - H$$

1 C — C = 347 kJ/mol
6 C — H = (6 × 414) kJ/mol

Total: 2831 kJ/mol

In C_2H_4 the bonds are

$$H - \overset{H}{C} = \overset{H}{C} - H$$

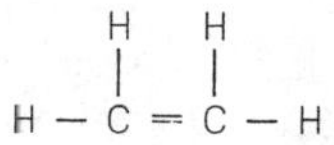

Compared to C_2H_6, there is one C = C in place of C — C. This corresponds to (611 − 347) kJ/mol = 264 kJ/mol of additional energy. However, the molecule has only 4 C — H bonds instead of 6, resulting in a reduction in bond energy of 2 × 414 = 828 kJ/mol. Overall the bond energy in C_2H_4 (2267 kJ/mol) is less than in C_2H_6 (2831 kJ/mol).

9-39.   (a) $H - \overset{H}{\underset{H}{C}} - \overset{H}{\underset{H}{C}} - H \ + \ Cl - Cl \ \longrightarrow \ H - \overset{H}{\underset{H}{C}} - \overset{H}{\underset{H}{C}} - Cl \ + \ H - Cl$

Bonds broken: 1 C — H = +414 kJ/mol
                1 Cl — Cl = +243 kJ/mol
Bonds formed: 1 C — Cl = −326 kJ/mol
                1 H — Cl = −431 kJ/mol

ΔH_{rx} = 414 + 243 − 326 − 431 = −100 kJ/mol

(b)
$$
H-\overset{\displaystyle H}{\underset{\displaystyle |}{C}}=\overset{\displaystyle H}{\underset{\displaystyle |}{C}}-H \;+\; H-H \;\longrightarrow\; H-\overset{\displaystyle H}{\underset{\displaystyle \underset{\displaystyle H}{|}}{C}}-\overset{\displaystyle H}{\underset{\displaystyle \underset{\displaystyle H}{|}}{C}}-H
$$

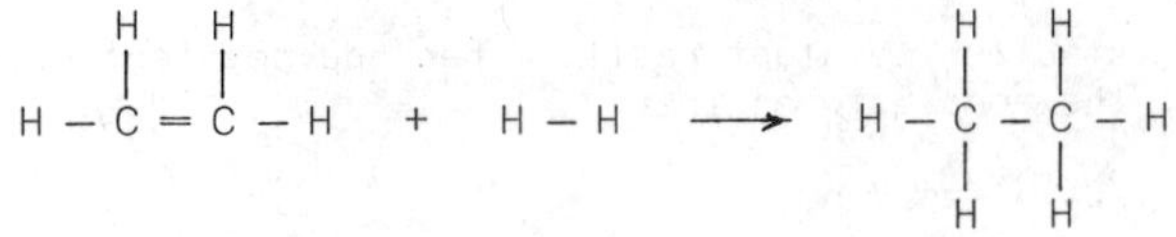

Bonds broken: 1 C = C = +611 kJ/mol
1 H — H = +435 kJ/mol
Bonds formed: 1 C — C = -347 kJ/mol
2 C — H = 2 × (-414)kJ/mol

ΔH_{rx} = 611 + 435 - 347 - 2 × 414 = -129 kJ/mol

9-40.   Compare energies of the bonds broken and formed and see if the total (ΔH_{rx}) is positive or negative.

(a) Endothermic: Break one C — H bond (+414 kJ/mol) and form one H — I (-297 kJ/mol). $\Delta H > 0$.

(b) Exothermic: Break one H — H bond (+435 kJ/mol) and one I — I bond (151 kJ/mol). Form two
H — I bonds (-2 × 297 kJ/mol). ΔH = -8 kJ/mol; therefore $\Delta H < 0$.

(c) Exothermic: Break one C = C bond in C_2H_4 (+611 kJ/mol) and one Cl — Cl bond (+243 kJ/mol).
Form two C — Cl bonds (-2 × 326 kJ/mol) and one C — C bond (-347 kJ/mol). $\Delta H < 0$.

9-41. $N \equiv N(g)\; +\; 3\,H-H(g)\;\longrightarrow\; 2\;\overset{\displaystyle H}{\underset{\displaystyle \underset{\displaystyle H}{|}}{N}}-H(g)$

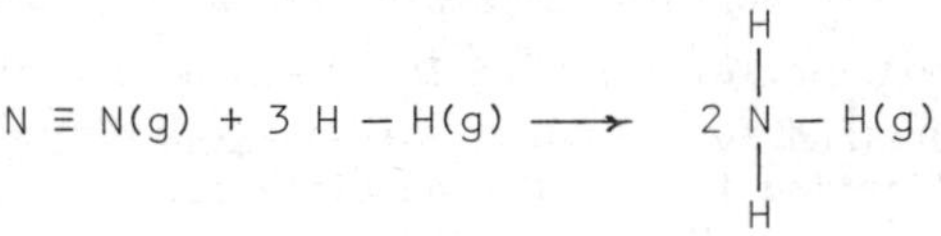

Bonds broken: 1 N ≡ N = +946 kJ
3 H — H = +3 × 435 = +1305 kJ
Bonds formed: 6 N — H = -6 × 389 = -2334 kJ

ΔH_{rx} = 946 + 1305 - 2334 = -83 kJ

per mol NH_3: ΔH_{rx} = 1/2 × -83 = -42 kJ/mol   tabulated value of $\Delta \overline{H}^{\circ}_f[NH_3(g)]$ = -46.19 kJ/mol

9-42.   Base your calculation on the formation reaction, for which $\Delta \overline{H}^{\circ}_f[NO(g)]$ is listed in Appendix D.

1/2 $N_2(g)$ + 1/2 $O_2(g)$ $\longrightarrow$ NO(g) $\Delta \overline{H}^{\circ}_f[NO(g)]$ = +90.37 kJ/mol

1/2 N ≡ N(g) + 1/2 $O_2(g)$ $\longrightarrow$ NO(g)

Bonds broken: 1/2 N ≡ N = 1/2 × 946 = +473 kJ
1/2 O_2 = 1/2 × 497 = +248 kJ
Bond formed: 1 NO = $-x$

ΔH_{rx} = $\Delta \overline{H}^{\circ}_f[NO(g)]$ = +90.37 kJ = 473 kJ + 248 kJ - x

x = bond energy of NO = 473 + 248 - 90 = 631 kJ/mol

Note that we did not have to speculate on the nature of the bonds in O_2 and NO (double, triple?),
but we did have to know that the bond in N_2 is a triple bond to select the proper value from Table
9-3.

Polar molecules

9-43.   Proceed as in the illustration for HCl in Section 9-10. Obtain the H — Br bond distance from
Table 9-3--151 pm.

magnitude of charge × bond distance = 0.79 D = 0.79 × 3.34 × 10^{-30} C m

magnitude of charge × 1.51 × 10^{-10} m = 0.79 × 3.34 × 10^{-30} C m

magnitude of charge = 0.79 × 3.34 × 10^{-30}/1.51 × 10^{-10} = 1.75 × 10^{-20} C

fraction of electronic charge $= 1.75 \times 10^{-20}$ C$/1.60 \times 10^{-19}$ C $= 0.11$

percent ionic character of HBr $\simeq 11\%$

9-44.   In each of these molecules the central atom is As with an electronegativity of 2.18 (see Table 8-6). The EN value of H (2.20) is almost the same as that of As. AsH_3 should be essentially nonpolar.

All of the other elements are more electronegative than As, and in the order: I < Br < Cl < F. The order of increasing dipole moments, then, should be $AsH_3 < AsI_3 < AsBr_3 < AsCl_3 < AsF_3$.

9-45.   The shape of each of these molecules has been described previously in the chapter. This information must be combined with knowledge of electronegativities.

(a) SO_2, V-shaped, polar.

(b)   NO, linear, polar.

(c)   HBr, linear, polar.

(d) NH_3, trigonal pyramidal, polar.

(e) H_2S, V-shaped, polar.

(f) C_2H_4,
$$\begin{array}{c}H \\ \diagup \\ H\end{array}C = C\begin{array}{c}H \\ \diagdown \\ H\end{array}$$
, symmetrical planar, nonpolar.

(g) BF_3, trigonal planar, nonpolar. (Bond dipole moments cancel because of the symmetry of the molecule.)

(h) SF_6, octahedral, nonpolar. (This is a symmetrical molecule and the bond dipole moments cancel.)

(i) CH_2Cl_2, tetrahedral, polar. [Because of differences in the bond dipole moments for C — H and C — Cl, there is a nonsymmetrical pull on electrons (recall Figure 9-15).]

9-46.   The H — O bonds in H — O — O — H have bond dipole moments, but if the molecule were linear there would be no resultant dipole moment. H_2O_2 possesses a dipole moment of 2.13 debye; the molecule cannot be linear. (Also, recall Example 9-11.)

Partial ionic character of covalent bonds

9-47.   Use the method of Example 9-17.

For HF: H — F (est.) $= 1/2$(H — H + F — F) $= 1/2(435 + 155) = 295$ kJ/mol

H — F (actual, from Table 9-3) $= 565$ kJ

ionic resonance energy (IRE) $= 565 - 295 = 270$ kJ/mol

For HBr: H — Br (est.) $= 1/2$(H — H + Br — Br) $= 1/2(435 + 192) = 314$ kJ/mol

H — Br (actual, from Table 9-3) $= 364$ kJ/mol

IRE $= 364 - 314 = 50$ kJ/mol

The value derived in the text for HCl was IRE $= 92$ kJ/mol. We expect the HF bond to have the greatest percent ionic character and HBr the least when we compare HF, HCl and HBr. This is the same order obtained for ionic resonance energies, that is IRE(HF) > IRE(HCl) > IRE(HBr).

9-48.   The greater the electronegativity difference (ΔEN) between the bonded atoms, the more ionic character in the bond. The order of increasing ionic character is:
C — H < Br — H < F — H < Na — Cl < K — F.

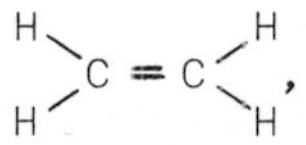

9-49. (a) $(\Delta EN)^2 = \frac{IRE}{96} = \frac{270}{96} = 2.81$ $\Delta EN = \sqrt{2.81} = 1.68$

$E_F - E_H = \Delta EN = 1.68$ (calculated)

$E_F - E_H = 3.98 - 2.20 = 1.78$ (from Table 8-6)

(b) $(\Delta EN)^2 = \frac{IRE}{96} = \frac{50}{96} = 0.52$ $\Delta EN = \sqrt{0.52} = 0.72$

$E_{Br} - E_H = \Delta EN = 0.72$ (calculated)

$E_{Br} - E_H = 2.96 - 2.20 = 0.76$ (from Table 8-6)

9-50. Use electronegativity differences (from Table 8-6) and equation (9.34) to calculate IRE for the N — O bond.

$\Delta EN = E_O - E_N = 3.44 - 3.04 = 0.40$ $IRE = 96(\Delta EN)^2 = 96 \times (0.40)^2 = 15$ kJ/mol

Since the measured N — O bond energy is 201 kJ/mol and the IRE is 15 kJ/mol, the average of N — N and O — O bond energies must be 201 - 15 = 186 kJ/mol.

$$E_{N-O} = \frac{E_{N-N} + E_{O-O}}{2} \quad \frac{163 \text{ kJ/mol} + E_{O-O}}{2} = 186 \text{ kJ/mol}$$

$$E_{O-O} = (2 \times 186 - 163)\text{kJ/mol} = 209 \text{ kJ/mol}$$

Oxidation states

9-51. There is little relationship between oxidation states and formal charges. For example, atoms are assigned oxidation states of 0 only when they are in the free element. In all compounds, the oxidation states are nonzero. In writing Lewis structures one attempts to minimize formal charges, seeking values of zero whenever possible. Rarely is a structure written where a formal charge is higher than 2, but oxidation states may have much higher values, for example, ranging from -1 to +7 for Cl in its compounds. The main reason why formal charges and oxidation states are rarely the same is that in assigning formal charges shared electrons are divided evenly between the shared atoms, whereas in assigning oxidation states electrons are treated as if they had been transferred. For example, in determining oxidation states in the NH_4^+ ion, electrons are treated as if they had been gained by N and lost by H. This produces oxidation states of +1 for H and -3 for N. The formal charges, on the other hand, are 0 for H and +1 for N.

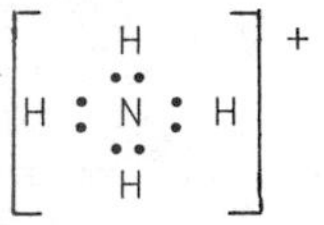

9-52. (a) +3: The total of the oxidation numbers of the atoms in an ion is equal to the ionic charge.

(b) -2: The oxidation state of alkaline earth metal ions (IIA) is +2. That of S^{2-} is -2.

(c) +4: The Mg is in the oxidation state +2, and each O atom, -2. S must have an oxidation state of +4 if all the numbers are to total zero: $+2 + \{3 \times (-2)\} + 4 = 0$.

(d) -2: The Na is in the oxidation state +1 and so is H. This requires O to be in the oxidation state -2.

(e) +5: H is in the oxidation state +1 and each of the three O atoms, -2. This requires an oxidation state of +5 for N.

(f) +7: Each O atom is in the oxidation state -2, leading to a total of -8 for the four O atoms. The ion must carry a charge of -1, and this requires an oxidation state of +7 for I.

(g) +2: Three O atoms yield a total of −6 for their oxidation numbers. The ion carries a charge of −2. This means a total of +4 for the oxidation numbers of two S atoms or an oxidation state of +2 for each S.

(h) +6: Seven O atoms yield a total of −14, and the total of the oxidation numbers for two Cr atoms must be +12; each Cr atom is in the oxidation state +6.

(i) +7: K is in the oxidation state +1 and the total of the oxidation numbers of four O atoms is −8. This requires the assignment of +7 for the oxidation state of Mn.

9-53. The oxidation state of *S* is indicated for each species. Then they are arranged in order of increasing oxidation state of *S*.

+4	+2	+7	+6	−2	+2.5
SO_3^{2-}	$S_2O_3^{2-}$	$S_2O_8^{2-}$	HSO_4^-	HS^-	$S_4O_6^{2-}$

$HS^- < S_2O_3^{2-} < S_4O_6^{2-} < SO_3^{2-} < HSO_4^- < S_2O_8^{2-}$

Nomenclature

9-54. (a) $FeBr_3$ = iron(III) bromide

(b) CrI_3 = chromium(III) iodide

(c) $Ca(ClO_2)_2$ = calcium chlorite

(d) $NaBrO_3$ = sodium bromate

(e) KIO_4 = potassium periodate

(f) $Na_2S_2O_8$ = sodium persulfate

9-55. (a) periodic acid = HIO_4

(b) tin(IV) oxide = SnO_2

(c) sodium selenate = Na_2SeO_4

(d) magnesium perchlorate = $Mg(ClO_4)_2$

(e) gold(III) cyanide = $Au(CN)_3$

(f) potassium iodide = KI

(g) barium telluride = BaTe

Self-test Questions

1. (*b*) Eliminate (d) as being an ionic compound (or a covalent compound with three Al — Cl single bonds). CO_2 is discussed in several places in the text as having double bonds $:\ddot{O}=C=\ddot{O}:$ The NO_3^- ion is given as an example of resonance with one N = O and two N — O bonds. The only possibility is CN^-, for which we can write $[:C \equiv N:]^-$.

2. (*d*) The Lewis structure is 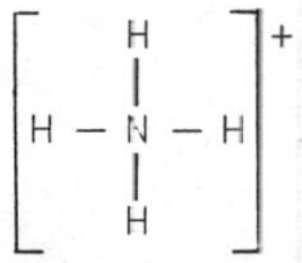 Because there are four electron pairs (all bond pairs) distributed around the central N atom, the structure is tetrahedral (not square planar). The N — H bonds are covalent (only the bond between NH_4^+ and some anion is ionic). One of the N — H bonds can be considered coordinate covalent, but not all four. In the structure we assign 4 electrons to N; it normally has 5 in its valence shell. The N atom carries a formal charge of +1.

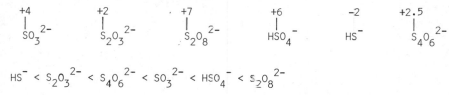

3. (*c*) Use the oxidation state conventions to determine the oxidation state of I and then choose the correct answer. The total of the oxidation numbers of four H atoms is +4, and of six O atoms, −12. The net charge on the ion is −1. The oxidation state of I must be +7.

4. (*a*) Sketch Lewis structures of each molecule to see how the valence shell electron pairs are distributed. Recall that multiple bonds are treated as if they were single bonds. The following are all linear:

$:\ddot{O} = C = \ddot{O}:$, $H - C \equiv N:$, and $H - C \equiv C - H$. SO_2 is not 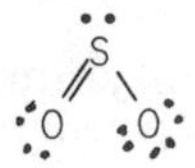

5. (*a*) The nonpolar molecule is the one whose symmetrical geometric shape causes bond dipole moments to cancel. BCl_3 is trigonal planar. It has no resultant dipole moment.

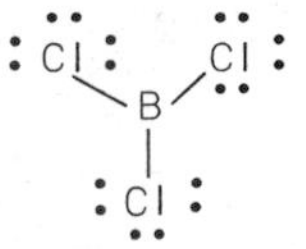 CH_2Cl_2 is tetrahedral and nonsymmetrical 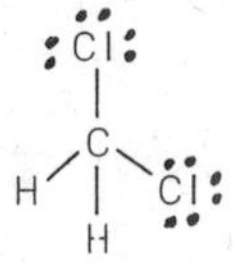

NO is linear and there is an electronegativity difference between N and O. PCl_3 is a trigonal pyramid (like NH_3).

6. (a) Based on 100.0 g of compound,

$$\text{no. mol C} = 24.3 \text{ g C} \times \frac{1 \text{ mol C}}{12.0 \text{ g C}} = 2.02 \text{ mol C}$$

$$\text{no. mol Cl} = 71.6 \text{ g Cl} \times \frac{1 \text{ mol Cl}}{35.5 \text{ g Cl}} = 2.02 \text{ mol Cl}$$

$$\text{no. mol H} = 4.1 \text{ g H} \times \frac{1 \text{ mol H}}{1.01 \text{ g H}} = 4.06 \text{ mol H}$$

$$\text{empirical formula} = C_{2.02}H_{4.06}Cl_{2.02} = CH_2Cl$$

(b) Lewis structure: 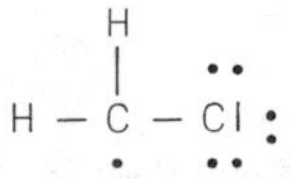

The C atom does not have a complete octet and there is one unpaired electron in the structure.

(c) A more plausible Lewis structure is based on the molecular formula $C_2H_4Cl_2$

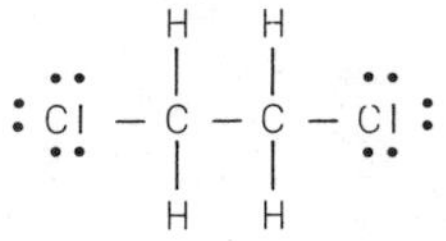

7. (a) The structure shown has only six valence electrons for the C atom. A more plausible structure would be

$[:\ddot{O} = C = \ddot{N}:]^-$

(b) The structure shown has 10 valence electrons for one of the C atoms, but the maximum number it can accomodate is 8. A more plausible structure would be

$[:C \equiv C:]^{2-}$

(c) The structure shown is a plausible one.

(d) This is an odd-electron species, but placing the odd electron on the O atom results in the formal charges: O = +1 and N = -1. A more plausible structure, one without formal charges is

$\cdot\ddot{N} = \ddot{O}:$

8.   First draw plausible Lewis structures. Then try to deduce their geometric shapes.

I

$$H - \underset{\underset{H}{|}}{C} = C = \underset{\underset{H}{|}}{C} - H$$

II

$$H - C \equiv C - \underset{\underset{H}{\overset{H}{|}}}{\overset{|}{C}} - H$$

In structure I the three C atoms lie along the same straight line, but the H atoms cannot lie on the same line. The distribution of three electron pairs about each end carbon atom is trigonal planar. The molecule is not linear. In structure II the three C atoms again lie along the same straight line. The H atom at the left of the structure is situated on the same line, but the H atoms at the right are not. [There is a tetrahedral distribution of the four electron pairs (bond pairs) about the C atom at the right.] Structure II is not linear.

9.   The shortest nitrogen-to-nitrogen bond distance is expected for the structure with the most multiple bond character.

(a) $$H - \underset{\underset{H}{|}}{N} - \underset{\underset{H}{|}}{N} - H$$

(b) $:N \equiv N:$

(c)

(d) $:N \equiv N - \overset{..}{\underset{..}{O}}: \leftrightarrow :\overset{..}{N} = N = \overset{..}{\underset{..}{O}}:$

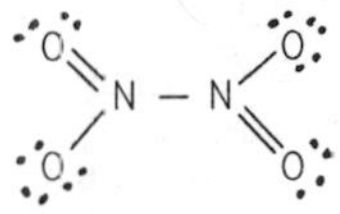

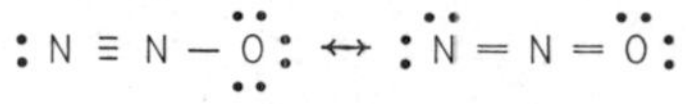

There is but a single triple-bond structure for N_2. For N_2O the true structure is a hybrid of a triple bond structure and structures with less multiple bond character. The shortest nitrogen-to-nitrogen bond distance is expected to be that in N_2.

10. (a)   VSEPR theory predicts the distribution of three electron pairs (with one pair being a lone pair). For the molecule AX_2E the geometry is V-shaped.

(b)   Although other plausible structures can be written as well, all lead to a prediction of trigonal planar geometry.

(c) $$\left[:\overset{..}{\underset{..}{O}} - \underset{\underset{:\overset{..}{\underset{..}{O}}:}{|}}{\overset{:\overset{..}{O}:}{|}} S - \overset{..}{\underset{..}{O}}: \right]^{2-} \quad or \quad \left[:\overset{..}{\underset{..}{O}} - \underset{\underset{:\overset{..}{\underset{..}{O}}:}{|}}{\overset{:O}{||}} S - \overset{..}{\underset{..}{O}}: \right]^{2-} \quad or \quad \left[:\overset{..}{\underset{..}{O}} - \underset{\underset{:\overset{..}{\underset{..}{O}}:}{|}}{\overset{:O}{||}} S = \overset{..}{O}: \right]^{2-}$$

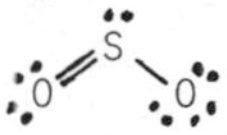

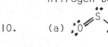

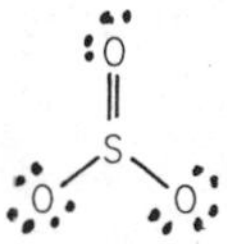

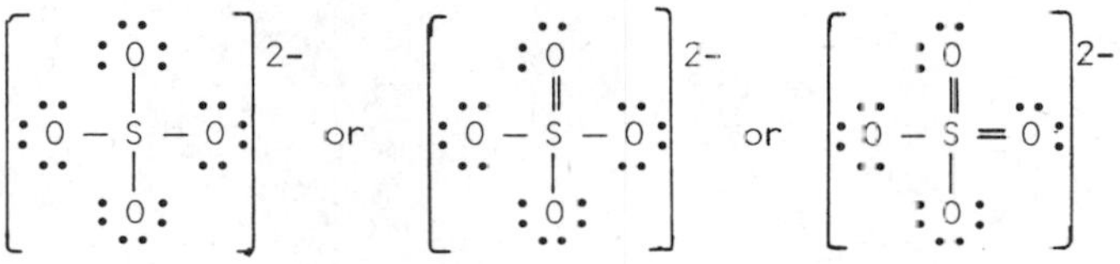

Whichever structure is used, all lead to the prediction of a tetrahedral distribution of four electron pairs (all bond pairs). The SO_4^{2-} ion has a tetrahedral shape.

11. $$2\ NO(g) + 5\ H - H(g) \longrightarrow 2\ \underset{\underset{H}{|}}{\overset{\overset{H}{|}}{N}} - H(g) + 2\ H - \overset{\overset{H}{|}}{O}(g)$$

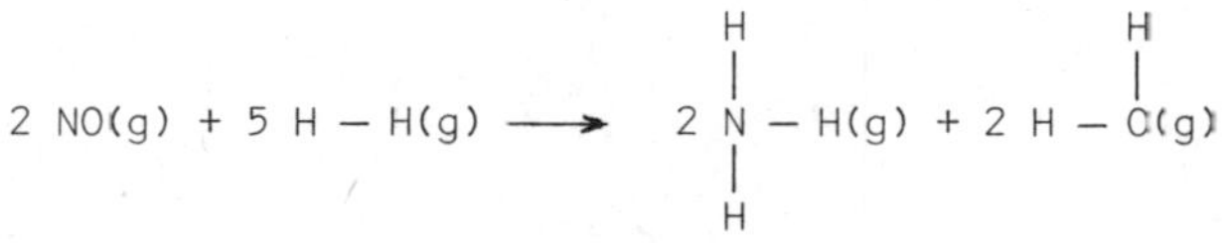

Bonds broken: 2 NO = 2 x 628 = +1256 kJ/mol
               5 H — H = 5 x 435 = +2175 kJ/mol
Bonds formed: 6 N — H = -6 x 389 = -2334 kJ/mol
               4 O — H = -4 x 464 = -1856 kJ/mol

ΔH = 1256 + 2175 - 2334 - 1856 = -759 kJ/mol

12. (a) The three atoms of a triatomic molecule must always lie in the same plane, but sometimes they are situated along a straight line, as in CO_2. Some triatomic molecules, then, are better described as linear than as planar.

(b) An electronegativity difference between bonded atoms always results in a bond dipole moment, but whether there is a resultant dipole moment in the molecule depends on the shape of the molecule. Sometimes, because of the symmetry of a molecule, bond dipole moments cancel out and the molecule as a whole is nonpolar, as is the case with CCl_4, for example.

(c) Although Lewis structures without formal charges are generally preferred, at times the only plausible structures that can be written, or the ones that correspond best to experimental evidence, carry formal charges, for example,

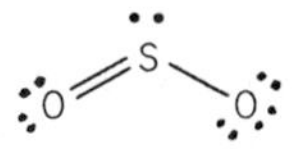

Chapter 10

Chemical Bonding II: Additional Aspects

Valence bond method

10-1. (a) *HCl* H 1s [↓] Cl [Ne] 3s [↓↑] 3p [↓↑|↓↑|↓]

The 1s orbital of the H atom overlaps the half-filled 3p orbital of the Cl atom, and the electrons become paired. The molecule is linear.

(b) *ICl* I [Kr]$4d^{10}$ 5s [↓↑] 5p [↓↑|↓↑|↓] Cl [Ne] 3s [↓↑] 3p [↓↑|↓↑|↓]

The half-filled 3p orbital of Cl and the half-filled 5p orbital of I overlap, and the electrons become paired. The molecule is linear.

(c) H_2Se H 1s [↓] Se [Ar] 3d [↓↑|↓↑|↓↑|↓↑|↓↑] 4s [↓↑] 4p [↓↑|↓|↓]

This structure is like that of H_2S pictured in Figure 10-2, except that the bonding orbitals of Se are 4p rather than 3p.

(d) NI_3 N 1s [↓↑] 2s [↓↑] 2p [↓|↓|↓] I [Kr] 4d [↓↑|↓↑|↓↑|↓↑|↓↑] 5s [↓↑] 5p [↓↑|↓↑|↓]

This structure is similar to that of NH_3 described in Example 10-1 and Figure 10-3, with I atoms substituting for H atoms.

10-2. The best description of the bond angle in H_2Se is, "less than in H_2S, but not less than 90°." In terms of atomic orbital overlap, the orbitals of the Se atom involved in the bonding are two 4p orbitals. These are at right angles to each other, suggesting a bond angle of 90°. For the analogous molecule, H_2O, mutual replusion of the H atoms causes the bond angle to enlarge (to 104.5°). In H_2S the effect is greatly reduced and the bond angle is about 92°. In H_2Se this angle should be still closer to the predicted 90°.

10-3. The electron configuration of nitrogen is 1s [↓↑] 2s [↓↑] 2p [↓|↓|↓] and the Lewis structure is :N ≡ N: .

The lone pair electrons in this structure are the 2s electrons of N. The bonds involve the overlap of the three 2p orbitals of one N atom with those of the other N atom. Electron pairs are shared in the regions of overlap. The only difficulty in describing this structure is in depicting how the overlap occurs. Two of the p orbitals overlap in the end-to-end fashion pictured in Figures 10-2 and 10-3. The other p orbitals must overlap in a "sidewise" fashion (referred to as π bonds and described in Section 10-3).

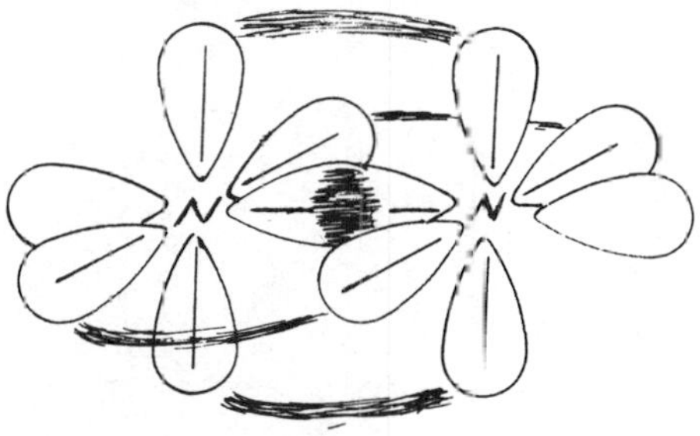

10-4. The principal advantage of the valence bond method over the use of Lewis structures in describing chemical bonding is that a prediction of the geometric structure of the molecule is made possible. Also, when the idea of hybridized atomic orbitals is included, the valence bond method leads to the prediction of multiple bonds in a more direct fashion than the arbitrary shifting of electron dots in an attempt to satisfy the octet rule

10-5. (a) The central C atom employs four $2sp^3$ hybrid orbitals; these have a tetrahedral symmetry. Each of the two H atoms employs a $1s$ orbital, and each of the two Cl atoms, a half-filled $3p$ orbital.

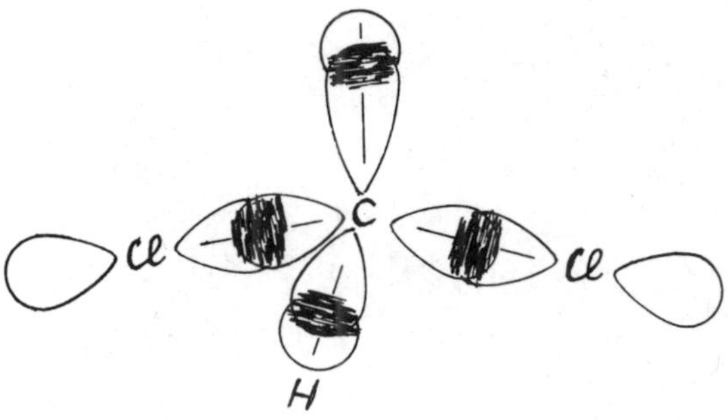

(b) The normal Be atom has the electron configuration 1s [↓↑] 2s [↓↑] 2p [| |]

Based on this ground-state electron configuration, we should expect no bond formation at all. To produce the half-filled orbitals required to form two covalent bonds requires an excited electron configuration.

Be 1s [↓↑] 2sp [↓|↓] 2p [|]

The overlap of the $2sp$ orbitals with the half-filled $3p$ orbitals of the two Cl atoms produces the linear molecule, $BeCl_2$.

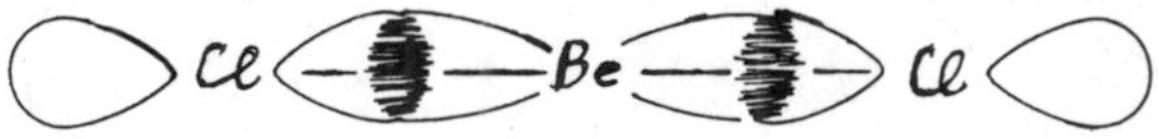

(c) The normal electron configuration of boron suggests an ability to form one covalent bond, not three. 1s [↓↑] 2s [↓↑] 2p [↓| |]

Again, the hybridization of orbitals is required. The geometry is trigonal planar with F — B — F bond angles of 120°.

B 1s [↓↑] $2sp^2$ [↓|↓|↓] 2p [ ]

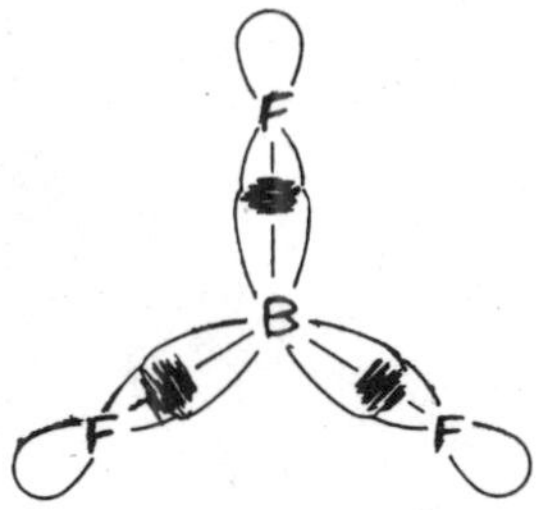

(d) The HCN molecule is linear. The orbital diagram for the required excited C atom is

C 1s [↓↑] 2sp [↓|↓] 2p [↓|↓]

A single bond is formed between the C and H atoms involving the overlap of a $2sp$ orbital of C and a $1s$ orbital of H. The remaining $2sp$ orbital and the two, half-filled $2p$ orbitals of C overlap with the three half-filled $2p$ orbitals of N in a carbon-to-nitrogen triple bond, consisting of one σ and two π bonds.

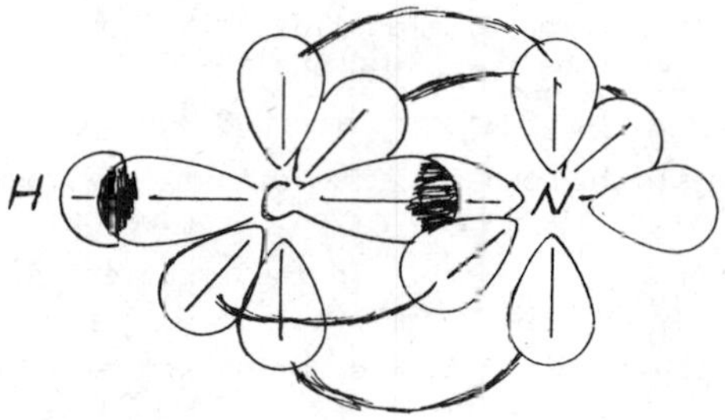

10-6. (a) BrF_5 With the valence-shell electron-pair repulsion method we would predict an octahedral distribution of 12 valence shell electrons, as five bond pairs and one lone pair. The hybridization scheme that results in an octahedral geometry is sp^3d^2 (see Table 10-1).

Br: $[Ar]3d^{10}$ $4s$ [↓↑] $4p$ [↓↑|↓↑|↓] $4d$ [| | | |] "excited" Br: $[Ar]3d^{10}$ $4sp^3d^2$ [↓↑|↓|↓|↓|↓|↓] $4d$ [| |]

(b) CS_2 The Lewis structure reveals two double bonds :S̈ = C = S̈: . The predicted geometry is linear. (Recall that each double bond is treated as if it contained only a single electron pair for the purpose of predicting the geometrical shape of the molecule.) The hybridization scheme leading to a linear geometry is sp.

(c) SiF_4 The Lewis structure is

```
      ..
     :F:
      |
 ..   |   ..
:F — Si — F:
 ..   |   ..
      |
     :F:
      ..
```

The four bond pairs are arranged about the central Si atom in a tetrahedral fashion. The hybridization scheme to account for this is sp^3.

(d) NO_3^- The Lewis structure is

```
[ ..       ..  ]-
[:O — N — O:   ]
[ ..  ||   ..  ]
[    :O:       ]
```

By the valence-shell electron-pair repulsion method we treat this ion as if only three electron pairs were distributed about the N atom. This suggests trigonal planar geometry and an sp^2 hybridization scheme.

(e) AsF_5 This molecule has 10 valence electrons surrounding the As atom, as five bond pairs in a trigonal bipyramidal arrangement. The corresponding hybridization scheme is sp^3d.

As: $[Ar]3d^{10}$ $4sp^3d$ [↓|↓|↓|↓|↓] $4d$ [| | |]

10-7. From the Lewis structure we note four pairs of electrons around the central N atom, all bond pairs. The geometric shape is tetrahedral. The bonding scheme must involve sp^3 hybrid orbitals of the central N atom.

```
[     H     ]+
[     |     ]
[ H — N — H ]
[     |     ]
[     H     ]
```

N $1s$ [↓↑] $2sp^3$ [↓↑|↓|↓|↓]

The overlap of $1s$ orbitals of H atoms with half-filled $2sp^3$ orbitals of the central N atom accounts for three of the four N — H bonds. The fourth N — H bond results from the overlap of an *empty* $1s$ orbital of H (that is, of H^+) with a *filled* $2sp^3$ orbital of N; this fourth bond is coordinate covalent.

10-8. The H — N — H and H — N — O bond angles of 107° are close to the tetrahedral angle of 109.5°. These bond angles would correspond to sp^3 hybridization of the central N atom. The N — O — H bond angle of 102° is also best explained in terms of sp^3 hybridization of the O atom.

10-9. According to VSEPR theory we should predict a trigonal planar distribution of electron pairs about the central C atom, leading to 120° angles for the C — C = O and the O = C — O bonds. The hybridization scheme for the central C atom is sp^2. The C atom of the H_3C- group must use sp^3 hybrid orbitals (because it is able to form four single bonds). The situation with the O atom of the —OH group is not clear, since the C — O — H bond angle is not given. For example, structures could be written in which this O uses $2p$ orbitals or $2sp^2$ or $2sp^3$. In the structure shown below, $2sp^3$ orbitals are used. The hybridization scheme for the O atom of >C = O is also not certain, but for the reason stated in Example 10-2 of the text, an sp^2 hybridization scheme is used below.

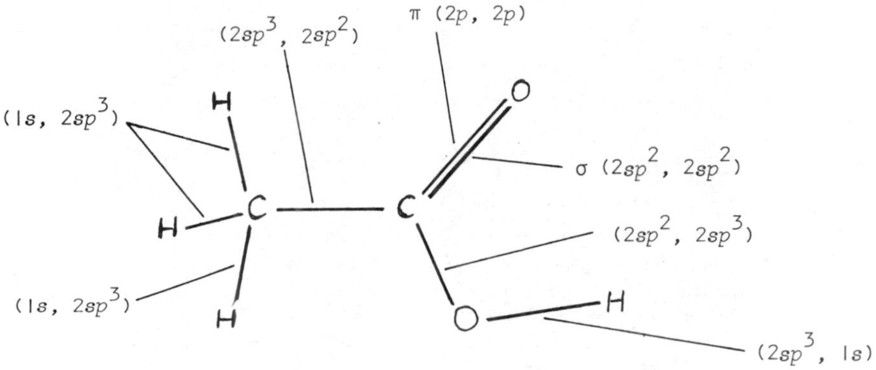

10-10. First, we draw a plausible Lewis structure.

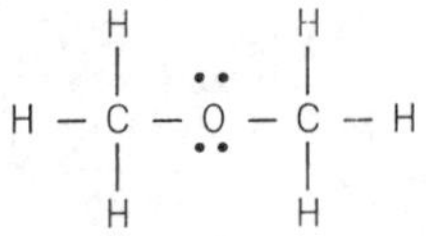

The hybridization scheme for the two C atoms must be sp^3 (to account for the fact that four single bonds are formed by each C atom). For the central O atom VSEPR theory predicts a tetrahedral distribution of the four electron pairs (AX_2E_2) and a tetrahedral angle for the C — O — C bond. The hybridization scheme for this O atom is also sp^3.

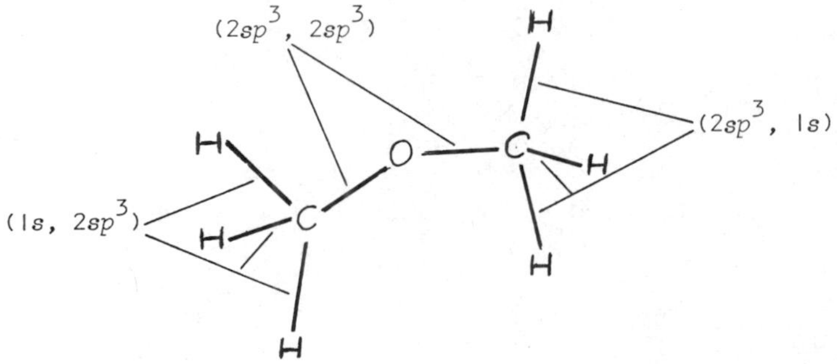

10-11. In the structure ClF_3 there are 10 valence electrons around the central Cl atom (seven from Cl and one each from the F atoms). The VSEPR designation is AX_3E_2. A hybridization scheme consistent with this VSEPR designation is

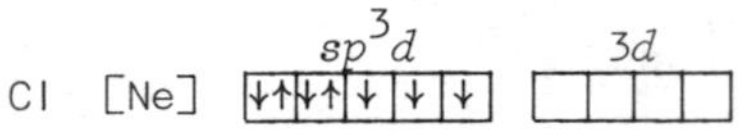

Three of the sp^3d orbitals are involved in the bonding scheme, and two contain lone-pair electrons, as indicated below. (The molecule is T-shaped.)

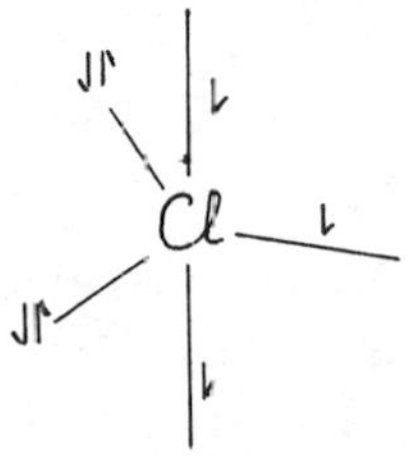

10-12. The basic feature of both molecules is sp hybridization of the carbon atom. The sp hybrid orbitals form σ bonds. The π bonds must involve pure p orbitals of the carbon atom. Hypothetical schemes that lead to the correct conclusions about the nature of the bonds are shown below:

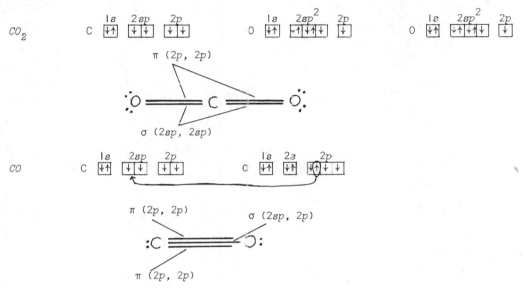

CO_2

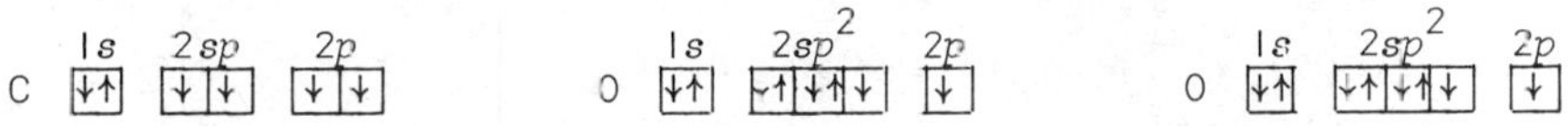

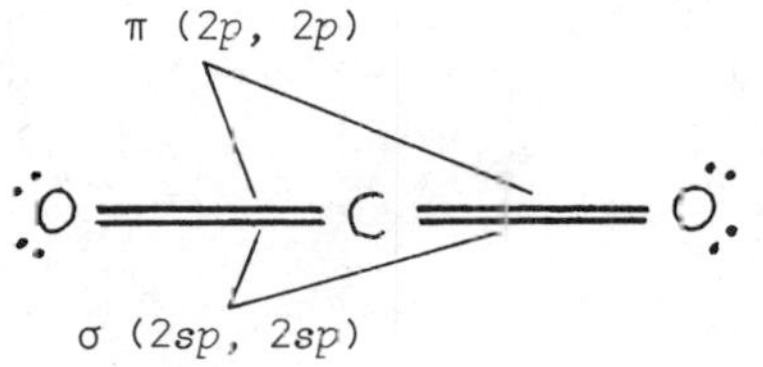

CO

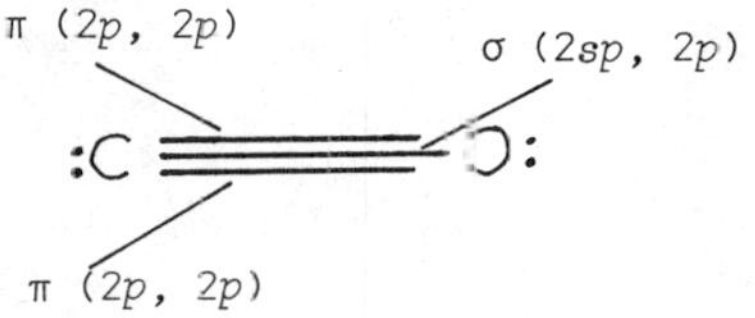

10-13. (a) Linear: The C atom in HCN employs sp orbitals in forming σ bonds with H and N; $2p$ orbitals are involved in the formation of two π bonds to N.

(b) Linear: The basic framework of this molecule involves sp orbitals of the two C atoms. The π bonds between the C and N atoms involve $2p$ orbitals.

(c) Three-dimensional: The F_3C— group has a tetrahedral structure and the —C ≡ N attached to it is linear.

(d) Planar: The H_2C— group is planar and the —C = C = O portion of the molecule is linear. The two taken together produce a planar molecule.

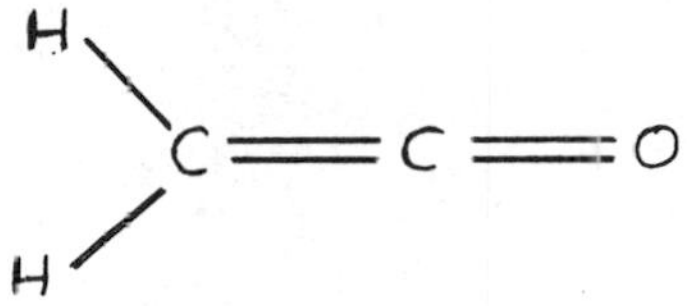

10-14. As a first approximation the strength of a σ bond may be taken as the C — C single bond energy: 347 kJ/mol. The difference between the C = C and C — C bond energies should represent the strength of a π bond: 611 - 347 = 264 kJ/mol. If this assumption is correct, the C ≡ C bond energy should be stronger than the C = C bond by about 264 kJ/mol. Estimate of C ≡ C bond energy: 611 + 264 = 875 kJ/mol. The measured value of the C ≡ C bond energy (Table 9-3) is 837 kJ/mol. The agreement between these two values is only fair, but the line of reasoning is generally correct.

10-15. Of the diatomic species represented in Figure 10-17, those with more bonding than antibonding electrons are stable molecules, that is, Li_2, B_2, C_2, N_2, O_2 and F_2. Among the stable molecules, those with all electrons paired are diamagnetic and those with unpaired electrons are paramagnetic. Diamagnetic: Li_2, C_2, N_2, F_2; paramagnetic: B_2, O_2.

10-16. Start with the electron configuration of N_2 and determine how that configuration is altered in the formation of N_2^- and N_2^{2-}. The test of whether a species is stable is whether the number of bonding electrons exceeds the number of antibonding electrons.

		σ^b_{2s}	σ^*_{2s}	π^b_{2p}	σ^b_{2p}	π^*_{2p}	σ^*_{2p}	
N_2:	KK	↓↑	↓↑	↓↑ ↓↑	↓↑	☐☐	☐	Bond order = 1/2(8 - 2) = 3

For N_2^- an electron enters a π^*_{2p} molecular orbital. This changes the bond order to 1/2(8 - 3) = 2 1/2; the ion is stable. For N_2^{2-} a second electron enters a π^*_{2p} orbital. This reduces the bond order to 2, but the ion is stable.

10-17. Refer to Figure 10-17. The bond order for O_2 is 1/2(8 - 4) = 2. If an electron is lost to produce O_2^+, we should expect this to be an electron from a π^*_{2p} molecular orbital. The bond order for O_2^+ is 1/2(8 - 3) = 2 1/2. Because we expect bond strength to increase with bond order, the bond in O_2^+ should be stronger than in O_2.

10-18. Compare each of the species to the neutral diatomic species depicted in Figure 10-17. Determine the number of unpaired electrons, and then whether the species is diamagnetic or paramagnetic.

(a) F_2, no unpaired electrons, diamagnetic.

(b) N_2^+, one unpaired electron, paramagnetic. (The electron lost when N_2^+ is formed from N_2 is from the σ^b_{2p} molecular orbital.)

(c) O_2^-, one unpaired electron, paramagnetic. (The additional electron that converts O_2 to O_2^- enters the π^*_{2p} molecular orbital.)

10-19. Consider what would be the electron configuration of B_2 if the σ^b_{2p} molecular orbital filled before π^b_{2p}.

		σ^b_{2s}	σ^*_{2s}	σ^b_{2p}	π^b_{2p}	π^*_{2p}	σ^*_{2p}
B_2:	KK	↓↑	↓↑	↓↑	☐☐	☐☐	☐

In this configuration all electrons are paired and the molecule should be diamagnetic. The fact that B_2 is paramagnetic provides experimental evidence for an order of filling in which π^b_{2p} precedes σ^b_{2p}. (Two electrons enter the two π^b_{2p} orbitals singly, producing a molecule with two unpaired electrons.)

10-20. (a)

	σ^b_{1s}	σ^*_{1s}
H_2^-	↓↑	↓

(b)

		σ^b_{2s}	σ^*_{2s}	π^b_{2p}	σ^b_{2p}	π^*_{2p}	σ^*_{2p}
N_2^+	KK	↓↑	↓↑	↓↑ ↓↑	↓	☐☐	☐

(c)

		σ^b_{2s}	σ^*_{2s}	π^b_{2p}	σ^b_{2p}	π^*_{2p}	σ^*_{2p}
F_2^-	KK	↓↑	↓↑	↓↑ ↓↑	↓↑	↓↑ ↓↑	↓

(d) Ne_2^+ is isoelectronic with F_2^- and has the molecular orbital diagram shown in part (c).

10-21. To represent the molecule C_2 by a Lewis structure we would have to write C≣C, involving a quadruple bond between carbon atoms. That is, structures such as :C ≡ C would leave one of the C atoms with an incomplete octet. In Lewis structures electrons either are involved in forming bonds or are excluded totally from the process (lone pair electrons). Molecular orbital theory predicts the existence of antibonding electrons. These electrons actively detract from bond formation. In the molecular orbital diagram for C_2, eight valence electrons are assigned, but two of these are antibonding. The bond order in C_2 is 1/2(6 - 2) = 2.

10-22. The molecular orbitals for the first two electronic shells are diagrammed below in order of increasing energy:

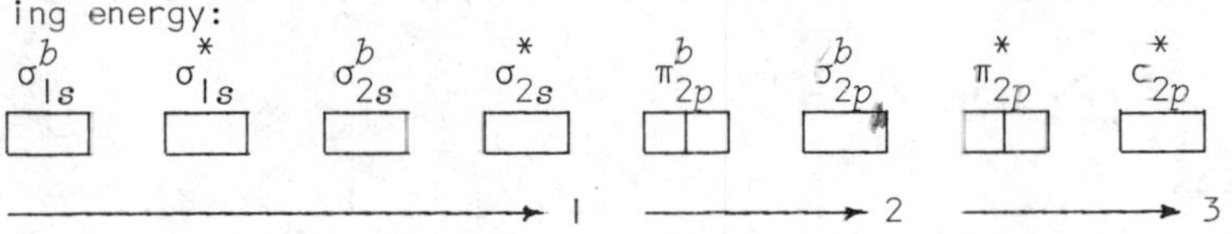

In the filling of orbitals through the σ^*_{2s} orbital (to the point indicated as "1"), the bond order varies between 0 and 1 (specifically: 0 → 1/2 → 1 → 1/2 → 0 → 1/2 → 1 → 1/2 → 0). In the filling of orbitals through σ^b_{2p} (to point "2") the bond order increases progressively since all orbitals are bonding orbitals: 1/2 → 1 → 3/2 → 2 → 5/2 → 3. But the remaining orbitals are antibonding orbitals, and as additional electrons are added (to point "3"), the bond order again decreases: 3 → 5/2 → 2 → 3/2 → 1 → 1/2 → 0. Thus, in no instance is a bond order higher than three encountered.

10-23. In all cases the molecular-orbital diagram is assumed to be the same as in Figure 10-17. The electrons to be assigned to these orbitals are the valence shell electrons of the two atoms in the molecule. In this assignment we overlook the fact that the two atoms do not contribute equal numbers of valence electrons to the molecular orbitals:

			σ^b_{2s}	σ^*_{2s}	π^b_{2p}	σ^b_{2p}	π^*_{2p}	σ^*_{2p}
(a)	*NO*	KK	↓↑	↓↑	↓↑ ↓↑	↓↑	↓	
(b)	*NO*$^+$	KK	↓↑	↓↑	↓↑ ↓↑	↓↑		
(c)	*CO*	KK	↓↑	↓↑	↓↑ ↓↑	↓↑		
(d)	*CN*	KK	↓↑	↓↑	↓↑ ↓↑	↓		
(e)	*CN*$^-$	KK	↓↑	↓↑	↓↑ ↓↑	↓↑		
(f)	*CN*$^+$	KK	↓↑	↓↑	↓↑ ↓↑			
(g)	*BN*	KK	↓↑	↓↑	↓↑ ↓↑			

10-24. Isoelectronic species, each containing 8 valence electrons: CN^+ and BN. Isoelectronic species, each containing 10 valence electrons: CO, CN^- and NO^+.

10-25. Refer to Figure 10-16. If the nodal plane is perpendicular to the line joining the centers of the bonded atoms, there is no way for a high electron charge density to exist between the bonded atoms. A molecular orbital having this type of nodal plane must be antibonding. With the π^b_{2p} orbitals there exists a nodal plane between the two lobes of the orbital. High electron charge density is still possible between the bonded atoms, above and below the nodal plane.

10-26. In writing Lewis structures or structures based on the valence bond method, all electrons are localized to a given bond (or lone pair). If a single structure is inadequate to represent a species, several alternate structures are written, each with a distribution of electrons different from the others. The true structure is a hybrid or "average" of the different plausible structures. Molecular orbital theory allows for the combination of atomic orbitals from several different atoms and the distribution of electrons among the resulting delocalized molecular orbitals. In a sense, the electrons entering these orbitals are "averaged" among several atoms. A plausible structure is written after this averaging has occurred, with the result that only a single structure is needed.

10-27. (a)

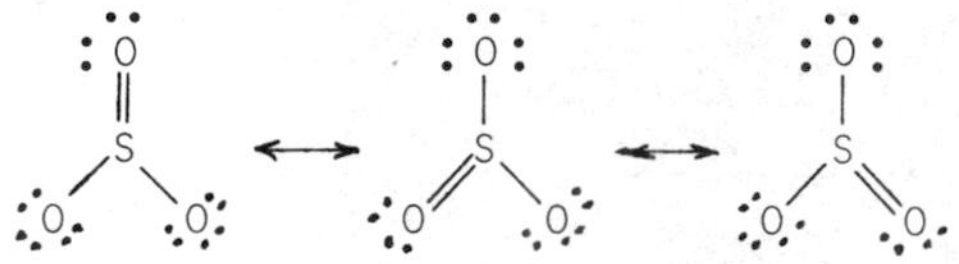

(b) The hybridization scheme for the central S atom that accounts for the σ-bond framework of SO_3 is sp^2. Consider that the O atoms also employ sp^2 hybridization. All of the sp^2 orbitals are either used in σ bond formation or filled with lone pair electrons. This accounts for 18 of the 24 valence electrons of the S and O atoms. (Recall Figure 10-21a depicting the NO_3^- ion.) Each of the four atoms also has a p orbital to be accounted for. Assume that these four p orbitals are combined into four delocalized molecular orbitals--two bonding and two antibonding. Six electrons must be assigned to these molecular orbitals. Four go into bonding orbitals and two into antibonding orbitals. The result is a π bond with a bond order of $1/2(4 - 2) = 1$. This bond is distributed among three sulfur-to-oxygen bonds, making each of these a 1/3 bond. The combination of a σ and 1/3 of a π bond leads to a sulfur-to-oxygen bond order of 1-1/3, the same as predicted from the Lewis structures.

10-28. We expect to find delocalized molecular orbitals in species containing multiple bonds and exhibiting resonance (that is, species for which more than a single Lewis structure must be written).

(a)

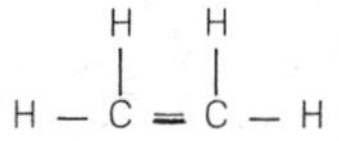

Delocalized molecular orbitals are not necessary to describe bonding in C_2H_4.

(b)

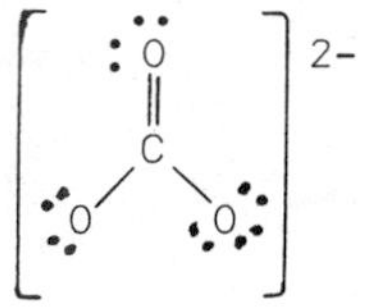

Additional structures must be written in which the double bond is shifted to other O atoms. This is a situation involving resonance. The carbon-to-oxygen π bonding can be described through delocalized molecular orbitals.

(c)

The nitrogen-to-oxygen π bond can be described through a molecular orbital spread over the three atoms.

(d)

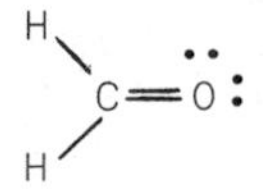

Delocalized molecular orbitals are not needed to describe this structure since multiple bonding is limited to the carbon-to-oxygen bond.

10-29. The line of reasoning here is similar to that of Exercise 10-27. We need to propose a bonding scheme consistent with the structures.

We should employ the hybridization scheme $sp^2 + p$ for each atom. The sp^2 hybrid orbitals, some with bond pairs and some with lone pair electrons, accomodate a total of 14 electrons. There are 18 valence electrons to be accounted for altogether. The three p orbitals (one from each atom) are combined into three delocalized molecular orbitals of the π type. One of these three orbitals is a bonding orbital and one is antibonding. The third orbital is a *nonbonding* orbital--it neither adds to nor detracts from bond formation. The order of increasing energy of these orbitals is bonding < nonbonding < antibonding. Of the four electrons to be assigned to these delocalized molecular orbitals, two enter the bonding orbital and two, the nonbonding. The bond order is 1/2(2) = 1 for a π bond distributed over three atoms. Each sulfur-to-oxygen bond consists of one σ and one half π bond for a bond order of 1-1/2, just as predicted from the Lewis structures.

Metallic bonding

10-30. (a) Although there exists a pattern for the atomic numbers within a group of the periodic table, there is no relationship between atomic number and metallic character of an element. That is there are no relationships of the sort that would say that metals are elements of low atomic number, or that the metallic character of the elements increases continuously with atomic number, and so on.

(b) The situation concerning atomic weight and metallic character is the same as that discussed in part (a) for atomic number.

(c) Here there is a relationship. Metal atoms have small numbers (1, 2, sometimes 3) of valence electrons. Within the representative groups (IA and IIA, for example) the smaller the number of valence electrons the more metallic the element.

(d) Here there is also a relationship. In general, the greater the number of empty valence shell orbitals, the more metallic the element.

(e) Metals occur in every period of the periodic table (except the first period). Thus, there is no relationship between metallic properties and total number of electronic shells in an atom.

10-31. Here are the ground-state electron configurations of the metals in question:

Na [Ne] 3*s* [↓] 3*p* [| |]   *Fe* [Ar] 3*d* [↓↑|↓|↓|↓|↓] 4*s* [↓↑] 4*p* [| |]   *Zn* $[Ar]3d^{10}$ 4*s* [↓↑] 4*p* [| |]

The greatest possibility for the formation of hybrid orbitals and the filling of these orbitals with available electrons exists for Fe, where 3*d*, 4*s* and 4*p* orbitals are all available. In Zn the 4*s* and 4*p* orbitals are available for hybridization and two electrons for sharing with other atoms. In Na, presumably the 3*s* and 3*p* orbitals are available for hybridization, but there is only one electron per atom. We should expect both hardness and melting point to increase in the order: Na < Zn < Fe.

10-32. Each Na atom contributes one atomic orbital for the creation of a set of molecular orbitals or energy levels in the crystal, and each Na atom also contributes one electron to the set of molecular orbitals.

no. energy levels = no. conduction electrons = no. atoms Na

$$= 2.30 \text{ g Na} \times \frac{1 \text{ mol Na}}{23.0 \text{ g Na}} \times \frac{6.02 \times 10^{23} \text{ atoms Na}}{1 \text{ mol Na}} = 6.02 \times 10^{22}$$

Self-test Questions

1. (*d*) Draw Lewis structures for the four molecules listed and determine which one requires a trigonal planar distribution of valence shell electron pairs. This distribution corresponds to sp^2 hybridization.

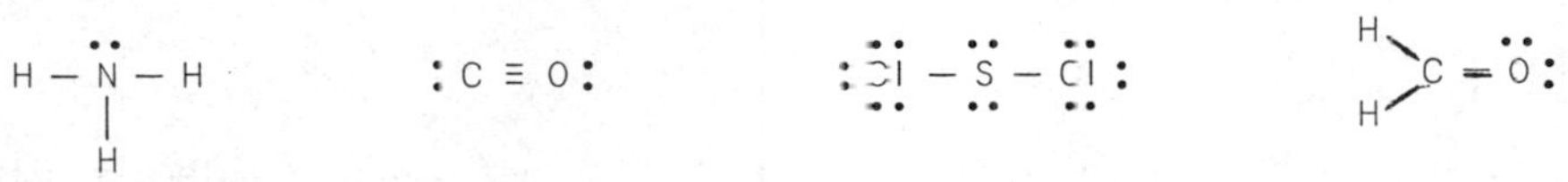

2. (*b*) π bonds are found in multiple covalent bonds and arise from the sidewise overlap of *p* orbitals. In PCl_5 the bonding orbitals of the P atom are sp^3d hybrid orbitals that overlap in an end-to-end fashion with 3*p* orbitals of the Cl atoms. In N_2 each N atom uses three 2*p* orbitals for bond formation. One pair of orbitals overlaps in an end-to-end (σ) fashion and the other two, sidewise (π). The orbital overlap in OF_2 involves 2*p* orbitals of F with 2*p* (or $2sp^3$) orbitals of O,

but the overlap is end-to-end (σ). The species He_2 is not a stable molecule.

3. (b) Hydrogen cannot form multiple bonds. That is, H atoms can be bonded to other atoms only by σ bonds, not π bonds. Thus, (a) is incorrect and (b) is correct. Some carbon-to-carbon bonds are σ bonds (single covalent bonds) and some are combinations of one σ and one π (double bond) or one σ and two π (triple bond). Responses (c) and (d) are both incorrect.

4. (d) For the bond order to be 1, the number of bonding electrons must exceed the number of antibonding electrons by two. In H_2^+ there is only one electron. In H_2^- there are three electrons--two bonding and one antibonding. The bond order is 1/2. He_2 does not exist as a stable molecule; its bond order is zero. Li_2 meets the stated requirement. Of the six electrons in this species, four are in the closed KK shell. The remaining two electrons go into a bonding molecular orbital of the second shell, σ_{2s}^b.

5. Draw Lewis structures of the molecules. Use VSEPR theory to predict the distribution of electron pairs about the C atom. Then propose a hybridization scheme for the central atom that will account for this geometric shape.

(a) $H - C \equiv N$ linear sp hybridization

(b) $:\ddot{C}l - \underset{\underset{\underset{:\ddot{C}l:}{|}}{\overset{\overset{H}{|}}{C}}} - \ddot{C}l:$ tetrahedral sp^3 hybridization

(c) $H - \underset{\underset{H}{|}}{\overset{\overset{H}{|}}{C}} - \ddot{O} - H$ tetrahedral sp^3 hybridization

(d) $H - \underset{\underset{H}{|}}{\ddot{N}} - \overset{\overset{\ddot{O}}{\|}}{C} - \ddot{O} - H$ trigonal planar sp^2 hybridization

6. 6σ and 3π bonds

7. (a) Lewis theory does not tell anything about the shape of the H_2O molecule. For example, both of the following structures are acceptable:

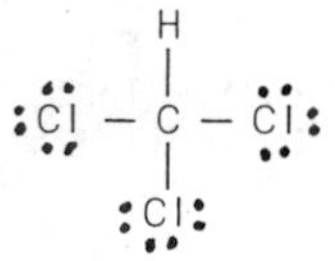

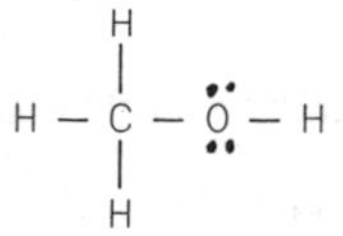

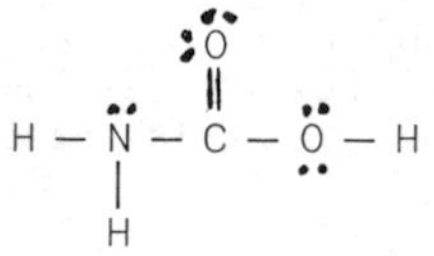

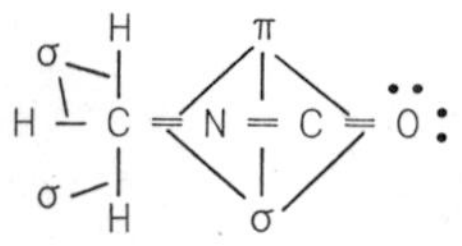

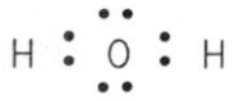

$H : \overset{\cdot\cdot}{\underset{\cdot\cdot}{O}} : H$ and $: \overset{\overset{H}{\cdot\cdot}}{\underset{\cdot\cdot}{O}} : H$

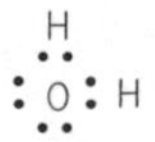

(b) The O atom would use $2p$ orbitals in forming bonds with H atoms. The predicted bond angle is 90°.

$\underset{O - H}{\overset{H}{|}}\!\!\!^{(2p,\ 1s)}$

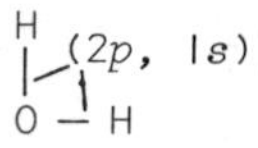

(c) The hybridization scheme for the O atom in H_2O is sp^3. This suggests a bent molecule with a bond angle of 109.5°.

O $\overset{1s}{\boxed{\uparrow\downarrow}}$ $\overset{2sp^3}{\boxed{\uparrow\downarrow|\uparrow\downarrow|\uparrow|\downarrow}}$ $\underset{\underset{H}{\searrow}}{\overset{\overset{H}{\nearrow}}{O}}\!\!^{(2sp^3,\ 1s)}$

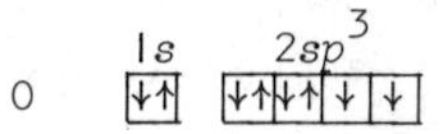

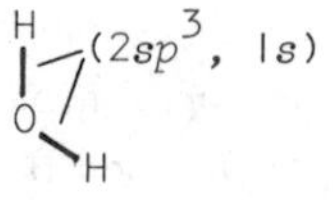

(d) VSEPR predicts a tetrahedral distribution of four electron pairs--two bond pairs and two lone pairs--AX_2E_2. The molecule should be bent and have a bond angle of 109.5°.

8. Whether the bond energy of a diatomic molecule increases or decreases when an electron is lost depends on whether the loss occurs from a bonding or an antibonding orbital. In the case, $O_2 \rightarrow O_2^+ + e^-$, the electron is lost from an antibonding orbital, π^*_{2p}, and the bond energy increases. But in $N_2 \rightarrow N_2^+ + e^-$, the electron is lost from a bonding orbital. The bond energy decreases.

9. The C_6H_6 molecule has a unique structure but it cannot be represented either by Lewis theory (Kekulé structures) or by the valence bond method. At least two structures must be drawn in either case. However, by using sp^2 hybrid orbitals of the six C atoms to construct the σ-bond framework, six p orbitals can be combined into six delocalized molecular orbitals, three bonding and three antibonding. Placement of the six $2p$ electrons into the three bonding orbitals produces three π bonds which are distributed among the six carbon atoms. In this way a single structure can be drawn for C_6H_6.

10. A hybridization scheme for BrF_5 must be able to accomodate 12 valence electrons about the central Br atom--7 from Br and one each from 5 F atoms. The orbital set sp^3d can accomodate only 10 electrons. The required hybridization scheme is sp^3d^2, with five of the six hybrid orbitals receiving a bonding pair and the sixth, a lone pair. That is, the structure of BrF_5 corresponds to the VSEPR designation AX_5E and is depicted in Table 9-2.

Chapter 11

Liquids, Solids, and Intermolecular Forces

Surface tension and related properties

11-1. (a) Surface tension is a force acting at the surface of a liquid that causes the liquid to assume a droplike shape (to minimize the surface area), to rise in a capillary tube, and to exhibit a number of other distinctive properties.

(b) An adhesive force is an intermolecular force of attraction between unlike molecules, such as the attraction between water molecules and the silicate structure of glass (responsible for the spreading of a film of water over glass).

(c) Capillary action refers to the ability of certain liquids to rise in capillary tubes to levels higher than the surrounding liquid. The liquid column is supported in the tube by the surface tension of the liquid.

(d) A wetting agent is a substance that reduces the surface tension of water so that it flows more freely over a surface.

(e) The meniscus is the interface between a liquid and the air above it. It is especially noticeable when the liquid is maintained in a tube of small diameter, and results from the same forces (surface tension) responsible for capillary action.

11-2. Pure water normally wets glass; it flows over the surface in a very thin film. If the glass has spots of oil, grease or other substances that water does not wet, the water does not flow over these spots but adheres to them in the form of droplets.

11-3. If a boot or tent is treated with a silicone oil, water, instead of forming a film on the surface that can be drawn into the material by capillary action, forms droplets that can be shaken off.

11-4. When the wick of the candle is ignited, some of the hydrocarbons (wax) at the tip of the candle melt; the liquid hydrocarbons are drawn into the wick through capillary action; the liquid vaporizes and the gaseous hydrocarbons burn. Heat given off in the combustion causes more wax to melt, to be drawn up the wick, to burn, and so on.

Vaporization

11-5. First determine the number of moles of vapor produced.

$$n = \frac{PV}{RT} = \frac{1 \text{ atm} \times 0.94 \text{ L}}{0.0821 \text{ L atm mol}^{-1} \text{ K}^{-1} \times (273.2 + 80.1)\text{K}} = 0.0324 \text{ mol } C_6H_6(g)$$

$$\Delta H_{vap} = \frac{1.00 \text{ kJ}}{0.0324 \text{ mol } C_6H_6(g)} = 30.9 \text{ kJ/mol } C_6H_6$$

11-6. The heat required to vaporize 1.00 L water at 100°C is

$$q_{water} = 1.00 \text{ L} \times \frac{1000 \text{ cm}^3}{1 \text{ L}} \times \frac{0.958 \text{ g}}{1 \text{ cm}^3} \times \frac{1 \text{ mol } H_2O}{18.0 \text{ g}} \times \frac{40.6 \text{ kJ}}{1 \text{ mol } H_2O} = 2.16 \times 10^3 \text{ kJ}$$

$$q_{water} + q_{combus.} = 0 \qquad q_{combus.} = -q_{water} = -2.16 \times 10^3 \text{ kJ}$$

$$\text{no. mol } CH_4 = -2.16 \times 10^3 \text{ kJ} \times \frac{1 \text{ mol } CH_4}{-890 \text{ kJ}} = 2.43 \text{ mol } CH_4$$

$$V = \frac{nRT}{P} = \frac{2.43 \text{ mol} \times 0.0821 \text{ L atm mol}^{-1} \text{ K}^{-1} \times 298 \text{ K}}{(748/760)\text{atm}} = 60.4 \text{ L } CH_4(g)$$

11-7. (a) When steam condenses on the walls of the inside container heat is evolved--the heat of condensation of the steam (-40.6 kJ/mol). This heat is transferred to the contents of the inner container where cooking occurs.

(b) The maximum temperature that can be reached by the contents of the inside container is 100°C--the temperature of the condensing steam.

11-8. When vaporization of a liquid occurs from a container that can exchange heat with the surroundings, the heat required to vaporize the liquid is drawn from the surroundings; the temperature remains essentially constant. When vaporization occurs from a thermally insulated container, the heat of vaporization is drawn from the liquid itself. This causes the average kinetic energy of the liquid molecules to decrease and the temperature of the liquid to drop. Very little heat can enter the liquid from the surroundings to offset the heat loss to the vapor.

Vapor pressure and boiling point

11-9. (a) The point of intersection of a vertical line at t = 50°C with the vapor pressure curve of benzene appears to come at about 300 mmHg.

(b) The intersection of the line at P = 1 atm with the vapor pressure curve of diethyl ether appears to come at about 35°C.

11-10. (a) From Table 11-1 estimate the temperature at which the vapor pressure of water is 600 mmHg. This is a temperature of about 93.5°C.

(b) Determine the vapor pressure of water at 89°C from Table 11-1. Note that in the interval 90°C to 91°C the vapor pressure increases by 20.2 mmHg, and that from 91°C to 92°C, the vapor pressure increases by 21 mmHg. Assume that in the interval from 89°C to 90°C the difference in vapor pressure is 19 mmHg. This leads to an approximate pressure of 525.8 - 19 = 507 mmHg.

11-11. Use the equilibrium data to calculate the pressure of $Br_2(g)$. This is the vapor pressure of $Br_2(l)$ at 25°C.

$$P = \frac{nRT}{V} = \frac{(0.486/159.8)\text{mol} \times 0.0821\ \text{L atm mol}^{-1}\ \text{K}^{-1} \times 298\ \text{K}}{0.250\ \text{L}} = 0.298\ \text{atm} = 226\ \text{mmHg}$$

11-12. The mass of aniline that vaporizes is 8.050 - 7.938 = 0.112 g. The number of moles of aniline in the 25.0-L vapor volume at 30°C is (0.112/93.1) = 1.20×10^{-3}. Use these data to calculate the partial pressure of aniline in the gaseous mixture. This value is the vapor pressure of liquid aniline at 30.0°C.

$$P = \frac{nRT}{V} = \frac{1.20 \times 10^{-3}\ \text{mol} \times 0.0821\ \text{L atm mol}^{-1}\ \text{K}^{-1} \times 303\ \text{K}}{25.0\ \text{L}} = 1.19 \times 10^{-3}\ \text{atm} = 0.904\ \text{mmHg}$$

11-13. In the gaseous mixture, $P_{tot.}$ = 755 mmHg = $P_{N_2} + P_{CCl_4}$. P_{CCl_4} is simply the vapor pressure of CCl_4 at 45°C--261 mmHg. P_{N_2} = 755 mmHg - 261 mmHg = 494 mmHg. Since the amount of N_2 and its temperature remain constant, we restate the question as a Boyle's law problem: What is the final volume of N_2 at 494 mmHg, if initially there was present 10.0 liters at 755 mmHg?

$$V_f = V_i \times \frac{P_i}{P_f} = 10.0\ \text{L} \times \frac{755\ \text{mmHg}}{494\ \text{mmHg}} = 15.3\ \text{L}$$

The Clausius-Clapeyron equation

11-14. (a) We are asked to find the temperature at which the vapor pressure of aniline = 760 mmHg; log P = 2.88. From Figure 11-9 we see that this condition corresponds to $1/T = 2.19 \times 10^{-3}$; T = 457 K = 184°C.

(b) Corresponding to 75°C we have 348 K and $1/T = 2.87 \times 10^{-3}$. For this value of 1/T, the value of log P for toluene = 2.41. P = 257 mmHg.

11-15. The relevant data for phosphorus are

t, °C	T, K,	1/T, K^{-1}	P, mmHg	log P(mmHg)
76.6	349.8	2.86×10^{-3}	1	0.00
128.0	401.2	2.49×10^{-3}	10	1.00
166.7	439.9	2.27×10^{-3}	40	1.60
197.3	470.5	2.13×10^{-3}	100	2.00
251.0	524.2	1.91×10^{-3}	400	2.60

Plot log P vs. 1/T. Estimate the value of 1/T corresponding to log P = log 760 = 2.88

$1/T \simeq 1.81 \times 10^{-3}$ $\qquad T \simeq 553$ K = 280°C

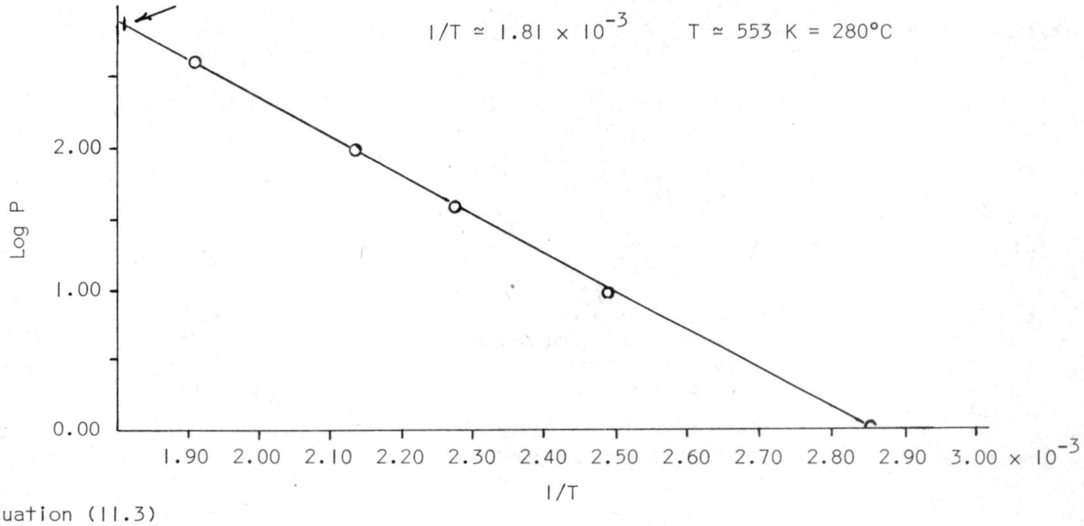

11-16. Use equation (11.3)

(a) $$\log \frac{100.0 \text{ mmHg}}{10.0 \text{ mmHg}} = \frac{\Delta \bar{H}_{vap}}{2.303 \times 8.314 \text{ J mol}^{-1} \text{ K}^{-1}} \left(\frac{312.7 - 275.6}{275.6 \times 312.7}\right) \text{K}^{-1} = 1.00$$

$$\Delta \bar{H}_{vap} = \frac{1.00 \times 2.303 \times 8.314 \text{ J mol}^{-1} \times 275.6 \times 312.7}{(312.7 - 275.6)} = 4.45 \times 10^4 \text{ J/mol}$$

(b) Let T = the boiling point of isopropyl alcohol, expressed in kelvins. Use equation (11.3) again.

$$\log \frac{760 \text{ mmHg}}{100 \text{ mmHg}} = \frac{4.45 \times 10^4}{2.303 \times 8.314} \left(\frac{T - 312.7}{312.7\ T}\right) = 0.8808$$

$$4.45 \times 10^4\ T - 1.39 \times 10^7 = 0.8808 \times 2.303 \times 8.314 \times 312.7\ T$$

$$4.45 \times 10^4\ T - 1.39 \times 10^7 = 5.274 \times 10^3\ T \qquad T = 354 \text{ K} = 81°\text{C}$$

11-17. Let P_1 = 100 mmHg, P_2 = 760 mmHg, and T_2 = 125.8 + 273.2 = 399 K. Solve for T_1 in equation (11.3).

$$\log \frac{760 \text{ mmHg}}{100.0 \text{ mmHg}} = \frac{3.39 \times 10^4 \text{ J/mol}}{2.303 \times 8.314 \text{ J mol}^{-1} \text{ K}^{-1}} \times \left(\frac{399 - T}{399\ T}\right) \text{K}^{-1} = 0.8808$$

$$1.35 \times 10^7 - 3.39 \times 10^4\ T = 0.8808 \times 2.303 \times 8.314 \times 399\ T$$

$$1.35 \times 10^7 - 3.39 \times 10^4 = 6.73 \times 10^3\ T \qquad T = 332 \text{ K} = 59°\text{C}$$

Critical point

11-18. Any substance whose critical temperature is above about 293 K can exist as a liquid at this temperature provided that a sufficient pressure is maintained. Of the substances in Table 11-2 these are CO_2, HCl, NH_3, SO_2, and H_2O.

11-19. SO_2 can be maintained as a liquid at 0°C under moderate pressures (77.7 atm is more than sufficient). Methane cannot be maintained as a liquid at 0°C and 100 atm, because its critical temperature (191.1 K) is well below 0°C.

Fusion

11-20. $$\text{no. kJ} = (10.0\ \text{cm})^3 \times \frac{0.92\ \text{g}}{1\ \text{cm}^3} \times \frac{1\ \text{mol}}{18.0\ \text{g}} \times \frac{6.02\ \text{kJ}}{1\ \text{mol}} = 308\ \text{kJ}$$

11-21. $$q_{\text{lead}} = \left\{0.680\ \text{kg Pb} \times \frac{1000\ \text{g Pb}}{1\ \text{kg Pb}} \times \frac{0.134\ \text{J}}{\text{g Pb}\ ^\circ\text{C}} \times (327.4 - 21.0)^\circ\text{C} \times \frac{1\ \text{kJ}}{1000\ \text{J}}\right\}$$
$$+ \left\{680\ \text{g Pb} \times \frac{1\ \text{mol Pb}}{207\ \text{g Pb}} \times \frac{4.774\ \text{kJ}}{1\ \text{mol Pb}}\right\} = 43.6\ \text{kJ}$$

States of matter and phase diagrams

11-22. In each case determine the pressure that would be exerted if the water were completely vaporized. If this calculated pressure is *less* than the equilibrium vapor pressure, then the sample exists completely as vapor at this pressure. If the calculated pressure is *greater* than the vapor pressure, the sample exists as a liquid-vapor mixture at the equilibrium vapor pressure (see Table 11-1).

(a) $$P = \frac{nRT}{V} = \frac{(0.180/18.0)\text{mol} \times 0.0821\ \text{L atm mol}^{-1}\ \text{K}^{-1} \times 303\ \text{K}}{2.50\ \text{L}} = 0.0995\ \text{atm} = 75.6\ \text{mmHg} > 31.8\ \text{mmHg}$$

The sample exists as a liquid-vapor mixture at 31.8 mmHg pressure.

(b) $$P = \frac{0.0100\ \text{mol} \times 0.0821\ \text{L atm mol}^{-1}\ \text{K}^{-1} \times 323\ \text{K}}{2.50\ \text{L}} = 0.106\ \text{atm} = 80.6\ \text{mmHg}$$

The sample exists entirely as a vapor, at 80.6 mmHg pressure.

(c) $$P = \frac{0.0100\ \text{mol} \times 0.0821\ \text{L atm mol}^{-1}\ \text{K}^{-1} \times 343\ \text{K}}{2.50\ \text{L}} = 0.113\ \text{atm} = 85.6\ \text{mmHg}$$

The sample exists entirely as a vapor, at 85.6 mmHg pressure.

11-23. (a) Calculate the pressure associated with the sample if it were all present as vapor.

$$P = \frac{mRT}{(MW)} = \frac{2.50\ \text{g} \times 0.0821\ \text{L atm mol}^{-1}\ \text{K}^{-1} \times 393\ \text{K}}{18.0\ \text{g/mol} \times 5.00\ \text{L}} = 0.896\ \text{atm}$$

The vapor pressure of water at 120°C is considerably greater than 1 atm; the vapor is unsaturated; and the calculated pressure is the true pressure.

(b) If the vapor is cooled, at constant pressure, to the point at which the vapor pressure of water = 0.896 atm = 681 mmHg, the vapor will condense. This occurs at a temperature of about 97°C (see Table 11-1).

11-24. The $H_2(g)$ and $O_2(g)$ are in exactly stoichiometric amounts, that is, there is twice the number of moles of H_2 as of O_2, just as required by the balanced equation: $2\ H_2 + O_2 \longrightarrow 2\ H_2O$. The net result of the reaction is the production of 0.100 mol H_2O, with no excess H_2 or O_2. Determine the pressure exerted by 0.100 mol H_2O vapor in 20.0 liters at 27°C.

$$P = \frac{nRT}{V} = \frac{0.100 \text{ mol} \times 0.0821 \text{ L atm mol}^{-1} \text{ K}^{-1} \times 300 \text{ K}}{20.0 \text{ L}} = 0.123 \text{ atm} = 94 \text{ mmHg}$$

This calculated pressure is considerably in excess of the equilibrium vapor pressure of water at 27°C. Some of the water vapor condenses and the pressure drops to the vapor pressure of water at 27°C--26.7 mmHg.

11-25. Consider the following quantities of heat: q_{ice} is the heat required to raise the temperature of the ice cubes to 0°C, to melt the cubes, and to raise the temperature of the melted water to a final value of t; q_{water} is the heat associated with the change in temperature of the original water from 32.0°C to t.

First, determine the mass of the two ice "cubes".

$$\text{mass} = 2 \times (4.0 \text{ cm} \times 2.5 \text{ cm} \times 2.7 \text{ cm}) \times \frac{0.917 \text{ g}}{1 \text{ cm}^3} = 49.5 \text{ g}$$

$$q_{ice} = \left\{49.5 \text{ g} \times \frac{2.01 \text{ J}}{\text{g } ^\circ\text{C}} \times [0 - (-25)]^\circ\text{C} \times \frac{1 \text{ kJ}}{1000 \text{ J}}\right\} + \left\{49.5 \text{ g} \times \frac{1 \text{ mol}}{18.0 \text{ g}} \times \frac{6.02 \text{ kJ}}{1 \text{ mol}}\right\}$$
$$+ \left\{49.5 \text{ g} \times \frac{4.18 \text{ J}}{\text{g } ^\circ\text{C}} \times (t - 0)^\circ\text{C} \times \frac{1 \text{ kJ}}{1000 \text{ J}}\right\} = 2.49 + 16.6 + 0.207\, t$$

$$q_{water} = 400.0 \text{ cm}^3 \times \frac{0.998 \text{ g}}{1 \text{ cm}^3} \times \frac{4.18 \text{ J}}{\text{g } ^\circ\text{C}} \times (t - 32.0)^\circ\text{C} \times \frac{1 \text{ kJ}}{1000 \text{ J}} = 1.67\, t - 53.4$$

$$q_{ice} + q_{water} = 0 \qquad 2.49 + 16.6 + 0.207\, t + 1.67\, t - 53.4 = 0$$

t = 18.3°C. The water is present as liquid only.

11-26. Dry ice maintains a constant temperature of -78.5°C, the temperature at which its sublimation pressure is 1 atm. The constant temperature maintained by ordinary ice is its melting point, 0°C. At a temperature of 0°C frozen foods would begin to thaw.

11-27. Both the melting point of ice and the boiling point of water are dependent on atmospheric pressure; this is especially true of the boiling point. Furthermore, at its normal freezing point water must be kept saturated with air (with which it is maintained in contact). The triple point is a unique fixed temperature point. The phases in equilibrium--ice, liquid water, and water vapor--are maintained out of contact with air and under their own unique equilibrium pressure (4.58 mmHg).

11-28. (a) No: Even if sufficiently low temperatures existed, the sublimation pressure of $CO_2(s)$ would be so great that it would sublime completely.

(b) No: The critical temperature of methane (191.1 K = -82°C) is much below ambient temperatures.

(c) Yes: SO_2 normally occurs in the atmosphere in trace amounts.

(d) No: The required temperature to melt iodine under normal atmospheric pressure (114°C) is very much higher than would be found anywhere on the earth's surface.

(e) No: The required temperature to maintain O_2 as a liquid is much too low and the pressure, much too high, for these conditions to be found on earth.

11-29. (a) The path we must trace on the phase diagram (Figure 11-13) is slightly below the broken line, PQ. At a temperature just slightly greater than 0°C the ice will melt. (The melting point of ice under 760 mmHg is 0°C.) The sample remains in the liquid state up to a temperature of about 93.5°C (at which the vapor pressure of water is 600 mmHg). At this temperature complete vaporization of the water occurs. Following this, the temperature is free to rise again, with the volume increasing in accordance with Charles' law.

(b) The sample remains entirely solid, with no vapor present, until the temperature reaches a value slightly below 114°C. Here the solid melts to produce a liquid, but still with no vapor present (recall that the triple point is at 91 mmHg). At a temperature just slightly above 114°C, the liquid vaporizes completely. From this point on the sample remains gaseous.

(c) Since 35°C is above the critical temperature of CO_2, the sample must be completely gaseous at the start. At a temperature approaching -50°C, the gas condenses to pure liquid CO_2. The liquid freezes to $CO_2(s)$ at about -57°C. Further cooling produces no additional phase changes.

11-30. When the pressure reaches about 4.5 mmHg, the vapor condenses to ice. At a pressure somewhat above 1 atm, the ice melts to liquid water. The sample remains as a single liquid phase up to 100 atm pressure.

Van der Waals forces

11-31. $N_2 < F_2 < Ar < O_3 < Cl_2$

mol. wt. 28 < 38 < 40 < 48 < 71

The intermolecular forces in these substances are of the London type. The strength of these forces increases with molecular weight. O_3 is out of place in the original listing.

11-32. The line of reasoning here is the same as illustrated in Figure 11-16. The more compact, symmetrical molecule is the less easily polarized of the two being compared. There are several different octane molecules based on a five-carbon chain, but each has a more compact structure than the straight-chain molecule.

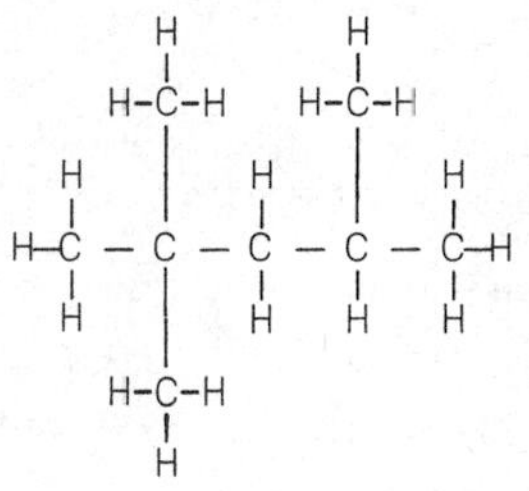

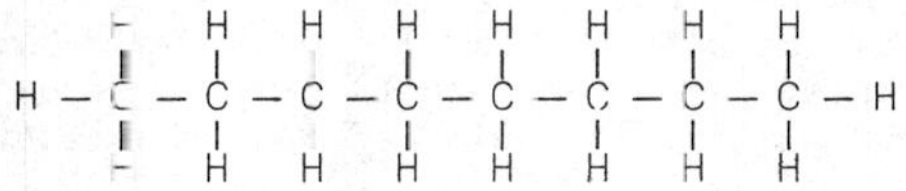

isooctane b. pt. 99.2°C

normal octane b. pt. 125.7°C

11-33. C_3H_8 and N_2 are both nonpolar. The intermolecular foces in these substances are of the London type. We have encountered N_2 and C_3H_8 before and know them to be gases at room temperature. CO, although weakly polar, is a gas at room temperature. It has a low molecular weight (28). This leaves CH_3OH as the liquid. Although its molecular weight is less than that of C_3H_8, we should recognize CH_3OH as a polar molecule and one that also presents a potential for hydrogen bonding. The stronger intermolecular forces in CH_3OH account for its existence as a liquid at room temperature.

11-34. Plot a graph of boiling point versus chain length of the alkane hydrocarbons; extrapolate to the nine-carbon alkane, nonane, C_9H_{20}. The boiling point is slightly greater than 150°C.

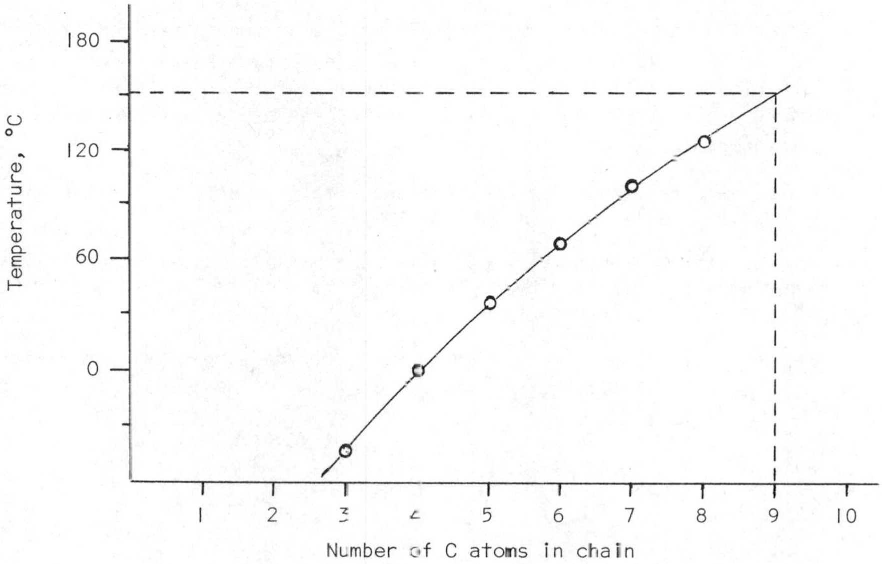

11-35. (a) $C_{10}H_{22}$: The intermolecular forces in C_7H_{16} and $C_{10}H_{22}$ are of the same kind--London forces--but $C_{10}H_{22}$ has the higher molecular weight and the higher boiling point.

(b) $H_3C - O - CH_3$: The molecular weight of this substance (dimethyl ether) is 46. The molecular weight of C_3H_8 (44) is almost the same. But the dimethyl ether is a polar molecule and exhibits stronger intermolecular forces than C_3H_8.

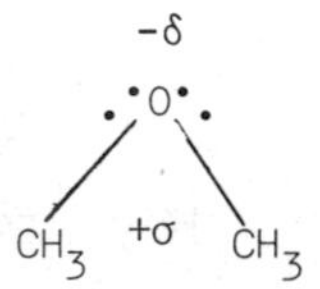

(c) CH_3CH_2OH: The molecules differ only in the O and S atoms. Both molecules are polar, but because the electronegativity difference between C and O is greater than between C and S, the dipole moment of CH_3CH_2OH is greater than that of CH_3CH_2SH. Also, hydrogen bonding occurs in CH_3CH_2OH.

11-36. The substitution of heavier atoms, such as Cl and Br, for H produces an increase in molecular weight and hence in boiling point. This is to be expected. The substitution of —OH for H does not increase the molecular weight as much as does the substitution of either Cl or Br. The reason that C_6H_5OH has the highest boiling point of the group must involve a phenomenon other than the effect of molecular weight on dispersion forces. The new phenomenon encountered in C_6H_5OH is hydrogen bonding between the H atom of the —OH group of one molecule and the O atom of the —OH group of a neighboring molecule.

Hydrogen bonding

11-37. The primary condition required for hydrogen bond formation is that a hydrogen atom covalently bonded to one small electronegative atom (N, O, or F) be in close proximity to another small electronegative atom (N, O, or F) in the same or a neighboring molecule. This is a stronger intermolecular force than the London forces present in all covalent substances.

11-38. *HCl* London forces and dipole-dipole interactions. The Cl atom is too large for hydrogen bonding to be a significant factor. However, the molecule is polar and dipole-dipole interactions should add to the usual London forces in establishing the intermolecular forces in HCl.

Br_2 London forces. Br_2 is a homonuclear, nonpolar molecule.

ICl London forces. Unlike the case of Br_2, the intermolecular forces are not limited to the London type, since the ICl molecule has a small dipole moment. Nevertheless, the dipole-dipole interactions do not contribute significantly to the properties of ICl. For example, its boiling point is roughly intermediate to those of Cl_2 and I_2, which is what would be expected even if London forces were the only intermolecular forces.

HF Hydrogen bonds. The requirements of atomic size and electronegativity that are necessary for hydrogen bonding are met ideally by the fluorine atom.

11-39. Not only must the nonmetal atoms to which hydrogen atoms are bonded be small, but they must also have a high electronegativity in order for hydrogen bonding to occur. The electronegativities of H and C are very nearly equal, so this requirement is not met.

11-40. The situation with NH_3, as pictured on the next page, would be the same as with H_2O--four molecules can be hydrogen-bonded to any given molecule.

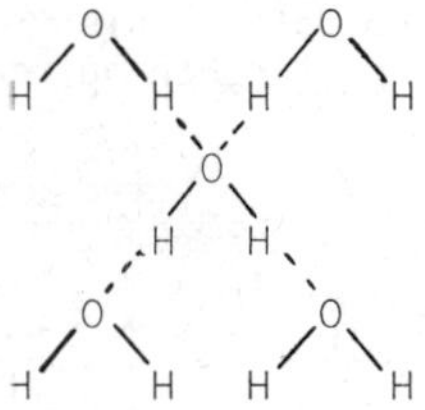

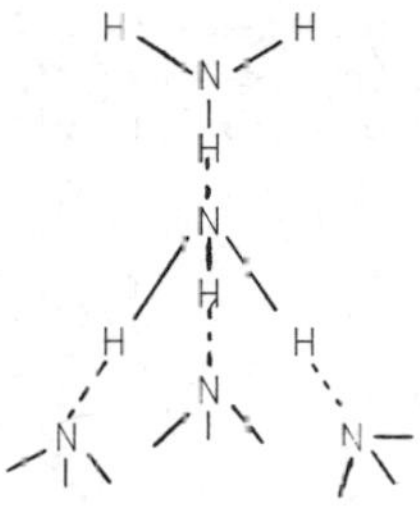

11-41. Were it not for the presence of hydrogen bonds in water, we would expect the data for group VIA hydrides to be in a regular progression (see Figure 11-18). (a) The boiling point of water would be at about 200 K. (b) The freezing point would be perhaps as low as 75 K. (c) The temperature of maximum density of water would be at its freezing point, as with most liquids. (d) The density of solid water (ice) would be greater than that of liquid water, again as with most substances.

11-42. Intramolecular hydrogen bonding requires that two nonmetal atoms within the same molecule be bridged by an H atom. This will occur only if the intermolecular distances are just right.

(a) C_2H_6: No hydrogen bonding.

(b) H_3CCH_2OH: Intermolecular hydrogen bonding. There is only one highly electronegative atom per molecule (the O atom).

(c) H_3CCOOH: Intermolecular hydrogen bonding. The distance between the two O atoms is too short for an H atom to form a bridge between them. (See also, Figure 11-21.)

(d) $C_6H_4(COOH)_2$: Intramolecular hydrogen bonding, as indicated below.

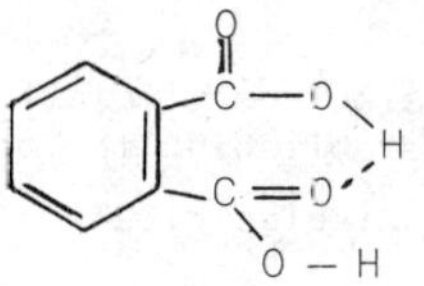

Network covalent solids

11-43. (a) Localized electrons have their charge densities concentrated between two atoms. Delocalized electrons have their charge densities distributed among three or more atoms; the charge density of delocalized electrons is more "spread out".

(b) The delocalized electrons in graphite are the $2p$ electrons of the carbon atoms in hexagonal rings, one electron per carbon atom.

11-44. (a) Simply replace one half of the C atoms by Si atoms in the structures shown in Figure 11-22 in such a way that all the bonds become Si — C bonds.

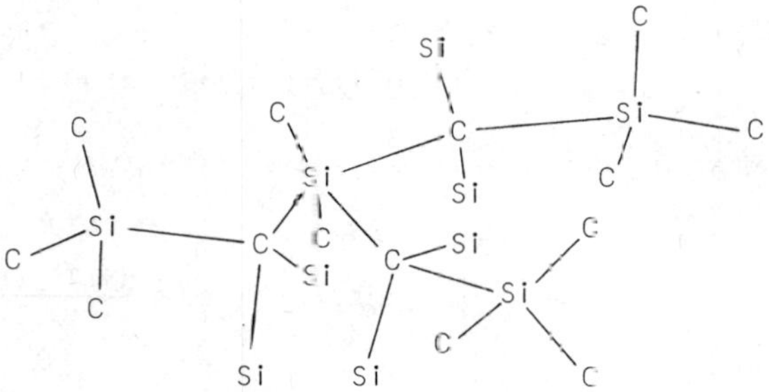

(b) Each B and N atom forms three bonds within a plane by using sp^2 hybrid orbitals. This produces layers of atoms arranged in hexagonal rings. Bonding between layers occurs through delocalized electrons derived from the p orbitals of nitrogen atoms.

	$1s$	$2sp^2$	$2p$
B	[↓↑]	[↓][↓][↓]	[ ]
N	[↓↑]	[↑][↑][↑]	[↓↑]

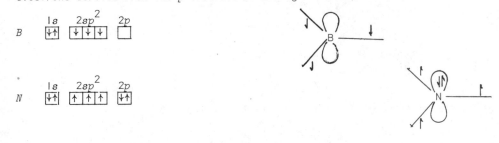

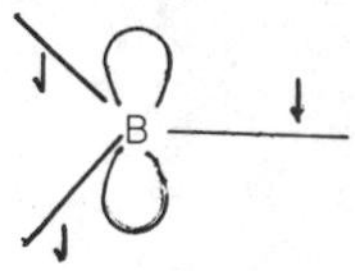

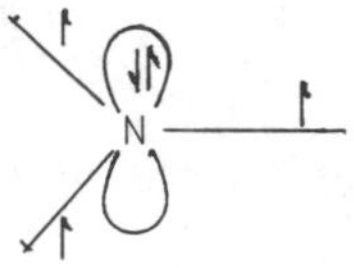

(c) In order for π-bonds to form, as in graphite or BN, there must be an overlap of p orbitals that are oriented parallel to one another. This occurs with $2p$ orbitals; but with $3p$ orbitals, as would be required in the case of silicon, the orbitals are too far apart to overlap effectively.

11-45. Although the carbon atoms within layers in graphite are joined by σ-bonds and have short bond distances, bonding between layers occurs only through π-bonds and these bond distances are greater. In diamond all the bonds are equivalent and are of the σ-type. Because the atoms in diamond are packed more closely, we should expect diamond to have the greater density.

11-46. The property of diamond that makes it useful in glass cutters is its extreme hardness. Graphite could not be used because bonding between layers of carbon atoms is weak. Any attempt to scratch glass with graphite would simply result in flaking of the graphite.

Ionic properties and bonding

11-47. The basic principle in estimating lattice energies is that electrostatic attractions increase as the charges on ions *increase* and as ionic radii *decrease*. In establishing the order indicated below, we note that Mg^{2+}, Ca^{2+}, and O^{2-} each carries two units of net electrical charge, and that Cs^+ and I^- are the largest ions present.

$CsI < MgBr_2 < CaO$

11-48. Melting points parallel the strengths of interionic attractions, which in turn depend on the factors of ionic charge and size. Of the four compounds, each involves Na^+ and a halide ion. The halide ions are alike in charge but differ in ionic radius. We would predict that melting points *increase* in the order in which halide ion radii *decrease*.

$NaI < NaBr < NaCl < NaF$

(observed m. pt. 651 < 755 < 801 < 988°C)

11-49. (a) BaF_2: The ion, Ba^{2+}, is larger than Mg^{2+}. Interionic forces should be weaker in BaF_2 than in MgF_2, suggesting that BaF_2 dissolves to a greater extent in water than does MgF_2.

(b) $MgCl_2$: The ions are of similar types, but since Cl^- is larger than F^- we should expect weaker interionic forces and a higher water solubility for $MgCl_2$ than for MgF_2.

11-50. Coulomb's law is expressed as follows (see Appendix B): $F = Q_1Q_2/\varepsilon r^2$.

NaCl: relative force $= \dfrac{(+1)(-1)}{\varepsilon(276)^2}$

MgO: relative force $= \dfrac{(+2)(-2)}{\varepsilon(205)^2}$

$$\frac{\text{relative force (MgO)}}{\text{relative force (NaCl)}} = \frac{-4/(205)^2}{-1/(276)^2} = 7.25$$

The statement in Figure 11-25 is that intermolecular forces in MgO are about seven times as strong as in NaCl.

Born-Haber cycle

11-51. Proceed either as in Section 11-12 or, as presented below. Write a series of equations that has as its sum the heat of formation of KF(s). In this setup the lattice energy is an unknown in one of the steps ($\Delta\bar{H}_5$ = U).

sublimation of solid K: $K(s) \longrightarrow K(g)$; $\Delta\bar{H}_1 = 90.0$ kJ/mol

ionization of gaseous K: $K(g) \longrightarrow K^+(g) + e^-$; $\Delta\bar{H}_2 = 4.34 \text{ eV} \times \frac{96.5 \text{ kJ/mol}}{1 \text{ eV}}$

dissociation of gaseous F_2: $1/2\ F_2(g) \longrightarrow F(g)$; $\Delta\bar{H}_3 = 1/2 \times 155 = 77.5$ kJ/mol

ionization of gaseous F: $F(g) + e^- \longrightarrow F^-(g)$; $\Delta\bar{H}_4 = -3.57 \text{ eV} \times \frac{96.5 \text{ kJ/mol}}{1 \text{ eV}}$

combination of gaseous ions: $K^+(g) + F^-(g) \longrightarrow KF(s)$; $\Delta\bar{H}_5 = U = ?$

---

net: $K(s) + 1/2\ F_2(g) \longrightarrow KF(s)$; $\Delta\bar{H} = \Delta\bar{H}_1 + \Delta\bar{H}_2 + \Delta\bar{H}_3 + \Delta\bar{H}_4 + U = \Delta\bar{H}^\circ_f[KF(s)]$

$90 + 419 + 78 - 345 + U = -563$

lattice energy, U = -805 kJ/mol KF

The data required for this calculation are derived from page 185, Table 8-4, and Table 9-3.

11-52. The heat of sublimation of Na is obtained from Section 11-12; the ionization energy of Na, from Table 8-4; the heat of sublimation of $I_2(s)$, from Appendix D; the heat of dissociation of $I_2(g)$, from Table 9-3; and the heat of ionization of I(g), from page 185.

$Na(s) \longrightarrow Na(g)$; $\Delta\bar{H}_1 = 108$ kJ/mol

$Na(g) \longrightarrow Na^+(g) + e^-$; $\Delta\bar{H}_2 = 5.14 \text{ eV} \times \frac{96.5 \text{ kJ/mol}}{1 \text{ eV}} = 496$ kJ/mol

$1/2\ I_2(s) \longrightarrow 1/2\ I_2(g)$; $\Delta\bar{H}_3 = 1/2 \times 62.26 = 31.13$ kJ/mol

$1/2\ I_2(g) \longrightarrow I(g)$; $\Delta\bar{H}_4 = 1/2 \times 151 = 75.5$ kJ/mol

$I(g) + e^- \longrightarrow I^-(g)$; $\Delta\bar{H}_5 = -3.06 \text{ eV} \times \frac{96.5 \text{ kJ/mol}}{1 \text{ eV}} = -295$ kJ/mol

$Na^+(g) + I^-(g) \longrightarrow NaI(s)$; $\Delta\bar{H}_6 = U = ?$

---

net: $Na(s) + 1/2\ I_2(s) \longrightarrow NaI(s)$; $\Delta\bar{H} = \Delta\bar{H}_1 + \Delta\bar{H}_2 + \Delta\bar{H}_3 + \Delta\bar{H}_4 + \Delta\bar{H}_5 + U = \Delta\bar{H}^\circ_f[NaI(s)]$

$108 + 496 + 31 + 76 - 295 + U = -288$

lattice energy, U = -704 kJ/mol NaI

Crystal structures

11-53. (a) The closest-packing of spheres refers to an arrangement in which the voids or empty spaces among spheres are reduced to a minimum.

(b) Tetrahedral holes, pictured in Figure 11-26, may be visualized in this way: Bring three spheres into mutual contact. A "triangular" shaped opening exists among them.

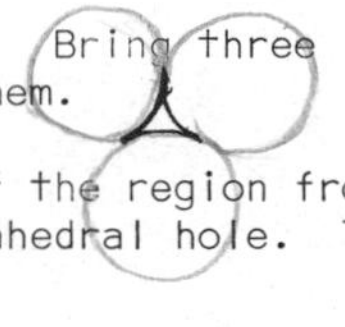

Cover this region with a sphere nestled among the original three; close off the region from below in the same way. The volume bounded by these five spheres is a tetrahedral hole. The hole extends through three layers of spheres.

(c) In an octahedral hole the empty region that results from three spheres in contact is *partially* covered by another set of three spheres that is rotated 60° with respect to the first set, that is,

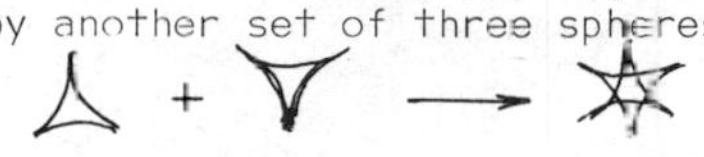

The resulting hole is closed off from above and below by a single sphere. The void among the eight spheres is an octahedral hole. It extends through four layers of spheres (see Figure 11-26).

11-54. When spheres are laid down in layers, two different kinds of voids are found among the spheres in a layer. These are the tetrahedral and octahedral holes referred to in the preceding exercise. Depending on whether one set of voids or the other is covered in the next layer, one of two different closest-packed structures is obtained. 

11-55. Consider the atom in the far upper left corner of the hcp unit cell pictured in Figure 11-26. This atom is surrounded by six others in the same plane, three below the plane, and three above the plane. This yields a total number of nearest neighbors of 12. A similar situation exists for the fcc structure. In the bcc structure there are 8 nearest neighbors.

11-56. (a) The diagonal (d) of the cell face pictured is four times the atomic radius (r), and the cell length (l) is $l = d/\sqrt{2}$. $l = 4 \times 128/\sqrt{2} = 362 \text{ pm} = 3.62 \times 10^{-8}$ cm

(b) volume of unit cell $= l^3 = (3.62 \times 10^{-8} \text{ cm})^3 = 4.74 \times 10^{-23} \text{ cm}^3$

(c) corner atoms = 1/8 × 8 = 1
face-centered atoms = 1/2 × 6 = 3 } atoms per unit cell = 4

(d) The mass contained in a unit cell is the mass of four Cu atoms.

$$\text{no. g Cu} = 4 \text{ Cu atoms} \times \frac{1 \text{ mol Cu}}{6.02 \times 10^{23} \text{ Cu atoms}} \times \frac{63.54 \text{ g Cu}}{\text{mol Cu}} = 4.22 \times 10^{-22} \text{ g Cu}$$

(e) $$\text{density of Cu} = \frac{4.22 \times 10^{-22} \text{ g}}{4.74 \times 10^{-23} \text{ cm}^3} = 8.90 \text{ g/cm}^3$$

11-57. This calculation is most easily based on the hexagonal prism pictured in Figure 11-26; it consists of three unit cells. To determine the number of Mg atoms in this prism, first consider the atoms situated at the centers of the top and bottom faces. These are shared between two hexagonal prisms: 2 × 1/2 = 1. The three atoms in the interior of the prism belong to it entirely: 3 × 1 = 3. Each of the remaining twelve atoms is shared among six hexagonal prisms: 12 × 1/6 = 2. The total number of atoms in the hexagonal prism is 1 + 3 + 2 = 6.

$$\text{mass of hexagonal prism} = 6 \text{ Mg atoms} \times \frac{1 \text{ mol Mg}}{6.02 \times 10^{23} \text{ Mg atoms}} \times \frac{24.32 \text{ g Mg}}{1 \text{ mol Mg}} = 2.42 \times 10^{-22} \text{ g}$$

The most difficult part of this problem is to determine the area of the top and bottom faces of the hexagonal prism. The volume of the prism is the product of this area and the height of the cell. The following construction shows that this area is equivalent to that of six equilateral triangles with sides equal to 3.20 Å.

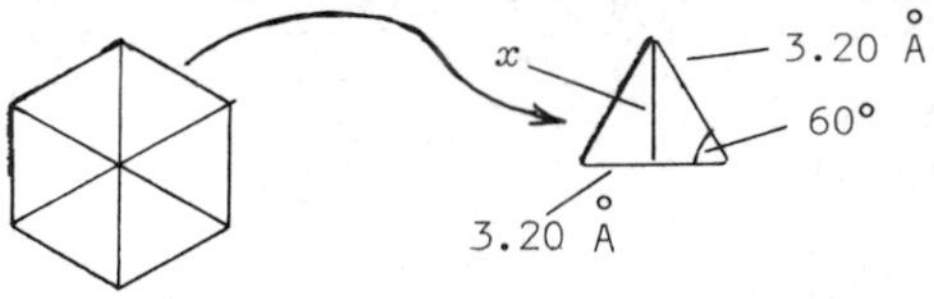

$x = 3.20 \cdot (\sin 60°) = 2.77$ Å   Area = 1/2 (height × base) = 1/2 × 2.77 Å × 3.20 Å = 4.43 Å^2

The area of the hexagon is 6 × 4.43 Å^2 = 26.6 Å^2 = 26.6×10^{-16} cm^2

Volume of hexagonal prism = area × height = $26.6 \times 10^{-16} \text{ cm}^2 \times 5.20 \times 10^{-8}$ cm

$= 138 \times 10^{-24} \text{ cm}^3 = 1.38 \times 10^{-22} \text{ cm}^3$

$$\text{density} = \frac{\text{mass}}{\text{volume}} = \frac{6 \text{ atom Mg} \times \dfrac{1 \text{ mol Mg}}{6.02 \times 10^{23} \text{ atom Mg}} \times \dfrac{24.3 \text{ g Mg}}{1 \text{ mol Mg}}}{1.38 \times 10^{-22} \text{ cm}^3} = 1.75 \text{ g Mg/cm}^3$$

Agreement with the measured density of 1.738 g/cm^3 is good.

11-58. The equation to be solved for the ratio, r_c/r_a, is

$(2r_a)^2 + (2r_a)^2 = (2r_a + 2r_c)^2$; $\cancel{4r_a^2} + 4r_a^2 = \cancel{4r_a^2} + 8r_ar_c + 4r_c^2$; $4r_a^2 = 8r_ar_c + 4r_c^2$;

$r_c^2 + 2r_ar_c - r_a^2 = 0$

Solve the above equation as if r_a were a constant and r_c the "unknown". This can be done through the quadratic formula.

$$r_c = \frac{-2r_a \pm \sqrt{4r_a^2 + 4r_a^2}}{2} = \frac{-2r_a \pm \sqrt{8r_a^2}}{2} \qquad r_c = \frac{-2r_a \pm 2\sqrt{2}r_a}{2} = \sqrt{2}r_a - r_a = (\sqrt{2} - 1)r_a$$

$$\frac{r_c}{r_a} = \sqrt{2} - 1 = 1.414 - 1 = 0.414$$

11-59. The required data from Chapter 8 are ionic radii (see Figure 8-7).

(a) *MgO* $\frac{r(Mg^{2+})}{r(O^{2-})} = \frac{65 \text{ pm}}{140 \text{ pm}} = 0.46$ (CCN = 6) (b) *CsBr* $\frac{r(Cs^+)}{r(Br^-)} = \frac{169 \text{ pm}}{196 \text{ pm}} = 0.862$ (CCN = 8)

11-60. CsCl has a body-centered-cubic unit cell. Consider that a Cs^+ ion is at the very center of the cell and belongs entirely to this cell. Each of the eight corners of the cell is occupied by a Cl^- ion, and each of these Cl^- ions is shared among eight unit cells. The number of Cl^- ions belonging to the cell in question is $8 \times 1/8 = 1$. The unit cell contains the equivalent of one Cs^+ and one Cl^- ion. This is consistent with the formula CsCl.

11-61. *CaF_2*: Each corner Ca^{2+} ion is shared among eight unit cells: $8 \times 1/8 = 1$. Each face-centered Ca^{2+} ion is shared between two unit cells: $6 \times 1/2 = 3$. The total number of Ca^{2+} ions in the unit cell is four. The eight F^- ions are pictured as belonging entirely to the unit cell. The ratio of Ca^{2+} to F^- ions is 4:8 = 1:2, consistent with the formula CaF_2.

TiO_2: Eight Ti^{4+} ions are situated at corners of the unit cell: $8 \times 1/8 = 1$; and one is located at the very center of the cell. Four of the O^{2-} ions are shared between two unit cells: $4 \times 1/2 = 2$. The remaining two are interior to the cell. Thus, the effective number of Ti^{4+} ions is two and O^{2-} ions, four. This ratio is consistent with the formula TiO_2.

11-62. (a) Volume of unit cell = length^3 = $(5.52 \times 10^{-8})^3 \text{ cm}^3 = 1.68 \times 10^{-22} \text{ cm}^3$

(b) Each unit cell contains the equivalent of four formula units of NaCl.

$$\text{no. g NaCl} = 4 \text{ f. u. NaCl} \times \frac{1 \text{ mol NaCl}}{6.02 \times 10^{23} \text{ f.u. NaCl}} \times \frac{58.5 \text{ g NaCl}}{1 \text{ mol NaCl}} = 3.89 \times 10^{-22} \text{ g NaCl}$$

(c) $d = \frac{m}{V} = \frac{3.89 \times 10^{-22} \text{ g}}{1.68 \times 10^{-22} \text{ cm}^3} = 2.32 \text{ g cm}^{-3}$

Self-test Questions

1. (*d*) None of the substances listed is polar. The only type of intermolecular forces to consider are London or dispersion forces. The strengths of these forces increase with increasing molecular weight. Since Br_2 has the highest molecular weight of the substances listed, we should expect it to have the highest boiling point.

2. (*b*) None of the substances listed is a metal, so we should not expect any of them to be an especially good conductor. NaCl(s) is ionic but the ions are fixed in place in a crystalline lattice. Because the ions are not free to move throughout the crystal, NaCl(s) is a nonconductor. Br_2(l) is a typical nonmetal and nonconductor of electricity. SiO_2(s) is a network covalent solid with all electrons localized in covalent bonds. Si(s) is a metalloid (and semiconductor). It is the best conductor of the four substances listed.

3. (*c*) HF, CH_3OH, and N_2H_4 all meet the requirement for hydrogen bonding--a hydrogen atom bonded to a small electronegative atom, such as N, O, or F. In CH_4, although the C atom is small it is not highly electronegative. (C and H have about the same electronegativity.)

4. (*a*) We have not been given enough information in the chapter to say how we should expect ΔH_{vap} and surface tension to vary with temperature. With few exceptions, we know that density should *decrease* with temperature. A point emphasized in this chapter, however, is that vapor pressure always increases with temperature (recall Figure 11-6).

5. (*c*) Graphite and diamond are both pure carbon. [Answer (b) is incorrect.] Diamond is harder than graphite, but graphite is an electrical conductor (because of its delocalized electrons) whereas diamond is not. Diamond has equal bond distances in all directions, but in graphite there is one C — C bond distance for atoms in the hexagonal planes and another C — C bond distance between planes.

6. Since wetting refers to the ability of water to flow over a surface, anything that enhances this ability is a wetting agent and makes water "wetter". There is a basis to the television commercial claim.

7.
(a) The stronger the forces between molecules in a liquid, the lower the tendency for the molecules to pass into the vapor state--the lower the vapor pressure.

(b) The vapor pressure of a liquid *does not* depend on the volume of liquid in the liquid-vapor equilibrium.

(c) The vapor pressure of a liquid *does not* depend on the volume of vapor in the liquid-vapor equilibrium.

(d) As long as liquid-vapor equilibrium is established, the vapor becomes saturated and its pressure is fixed, regardless of the size of the container.

(e) Vapor pressure *does* depend on the temperature of the liquid, always increasing as temperature increases.

8. (*c*) Consider the heat loss when (a) 10 g steam is condensed at 100°C, (b) 10 g of liquid water is cooled from 100°C to 20°C and (c) 110 g water is cooled from 20°C to 0°C. This quantity of heat is greater than that required to melt 100 g ice. The final condition is one of liquid water only.

$$q_a + q_b + q_c = \left\{10\ \text{g} \times \frac{1\ \text{mol}}{18\ \text{g}} \times \frac{-40.7\ \text{kJ}}{1\ \text{mol}}\right\} + \left\{10\ \text{g} \times \frac{4.18\ \text{J}}{\text{g}\ {}^\circ\text{C}} \times (-80^\circ\text{C}) \times \frac{1\ \text{kJ}}{1000\ \text{J}}\right\}$$

$$+ \left\{110\ \text{g} \times \frac{4.18\ \text{J}}{\text{g}\ {}^\circ\text{C}} \times (-20^\circ\text{C}) \times \frac{1\ \text{kJ}}{1000\ \text{J}}\right\} = -35.2\ \text{kJ}$$

$$q_{ice} = 100\ \text{g} \times \frac{1\ \text{mol}}{18\ \text{g}} \times \frac{6.02\ \text{kJ}}{1\ \text{mol}} = +33.4\ \text{kJ}$$

9. If the rate of evacuation is fast enough, the heat of vaporization required to sustain vaporization of the water cannot be drawn from the surroundings and must be taken from the liquid itself. This causes the liquid temperature to drop. If the temperature drops to 0°C as a result, ice may begin to freeze from the water.

10. The student calculation is based on removing a sample of vapor from contact with the liquid with which it is in equilibrium at 20°C. The pressure of this vapor (gas) would then vary with temperature (with amount of gas and volume held constant) in the manner predicted from the gas laws. But to determine the vapor pressure at 50°C requires that the vapor remain *in contact with the liquid* as the temperature is raised from 20°C to 50°C. More liquid vaporizes and the vapor pressure increases to a much greater extent than indicated in the student's calculation. The variation of vapor pressure with temperature must be calculated with equation (11.3).

11. The *fcc* structure simply refers to the location of structural units in a crystalline lattice but not to what these units are or to the type of forces that exist among them. In argon these units are Ar atoms and in carbon dioxide, CO_2 molecules. In both these substances the only intermolecular forces are of the instantaneous dipole-induced dipole type. In sodium chloride the structural units are Na^+ and Cl^- ions and the forces among them are interionic; copper atoms in copper metal are joined by metallic bonds. Thus, both sodium chloride and copper have much higher melting points than argon and carbon dioxide.

12. *Ionic:* The structural units are ions. The intermolecular forces are interionic attractions. In general, ionic compounds have moderate to high melting points and are good electrical conductors in the molten state.

Network covalent: The structural units are atoms. The bonds are covalent. All atoms are bonded together into a giant crystal. If bond strengths are equal in all directions, as in diamond and silica, the solid substance is hard, has a very high melting point, and is a nonconductor.

Molecular: The structural units are discrete molecules. Intermolecular forces are generally weak, involving instantaneous, induced or permanent dipoles, and, in some cases, hydrogen bonds. Melting points are low, and the substances are nonconductors, both as solids and liquids.

Metallic: The structural units are metal ions. These are bound together by a "sea of electrons". The mobility of these electrons accounts for the electrical and thermal conductivity of metals and for their malleability, ductility, and luster.

Chapter 12

Mixtures

Homogeneous and heterogeneous mixtures

12-1. (a) C_2H_5OH is the solute and H_2O is the solvent.

(b) Since equal masses of CH_3OH and H_2O are present it may be difficult to decide which is the solvent and which is the solute. However, since more molecules are present in 50 g H_2O than in 50 g CH_3OH, it is probably appropriate still to refer to H_2O as the solvent.

(c) The CCl_4 is the solute. The C_6H_6-C_7H_8 *mixture* can be thought of as the solvent.

(d) An aqueous solution is indicated. Water is the solvent and Na_2SO_4 is the solute.

12-2. If two substances are similar to one another, then it is likely that intermolecular forces between the different molecules will also be similar and the substances will form a solution. Thus, "like dissolves like". Oils are either hydrocarbons or hydrocarbon derivatives. Oil molecules (nonpolar) and water molecules (polar) do not exert sufficiently strong attractions for one another to keep these different molecules in a homogeneous mixture or solution. Thus, "oil and water don't mix".

12-3. The decrease in volume indicates that ethanol and water molecules exist in close proximity when mixed. This suggests strong intermolecular forces--case 2 of Section 12-1.

12-4. The anions in metal nitrates carry a charge of -1 (NO_3^-) and in metal sulfides, a charge of -2 (S^{2-}). We should expect the lattice energies of metal sulfides to be of greater magnitude than those of metal nitrates. In turn, this means that as a group metal sulfides are less soluble than metal nitrates. Among metal sulfides the most soluble should be those in which the cation is relatively large and has a charge of +1--NH_4^+ and the alkali metal ions, for example.

Percent concentration

12-5. The total solution mass is 144 g KI + 100 g H_2O = 244 g.

$$\%\text{KI, by mass} = \frac{144\text{ g KI}}{244\text{ g total}} \times 100 = 59.0\%\text{ KI}$$

12-6. (a) $$\%\ CH_3OH\ (\text{vol/vol}) = \frac{11.3\text{ ml }CH_3OH}{75.0\text{ ml soln.}} \times 100 = 15.1\%\ CH_3OH$$

(b) $$\%\ CH_3OH\ (\text{mass/vol}) = \frac{11.3\text{ ml }CH_3OH \times \dfrac{0.793\text{ g }CH_3OH}{1.00\text{ ml }CH_3OH}}{75.0\text{ ml soln.}} \times 100 = 11.9\%\ CH_3OH$$

(c) $$\%\ CH_3OH\ (\text{mass/mass}) = \frac{11.3\text{ ml }CH_3OH \times \dfrac{0.793\text{ g }CH_3OH}{1.00\text{ ml }CH_3OH}}{75.0\text{ ml soln.} \times \dfrac{0.980\text{ g soln.}}{1.00\text{ ml soln.}}} \times 100 = 12.2\%\ CH_3OH$$

12-7. $$\text{no. g }HC_2H_3O_2 = 0.500\text{ L} \times \frac{1000\text{ cm}^3}{1.00\text{ L}} \times \frac{1.01\text{ g soln.}}{1.00\text{ cm}^3} \times \frac{6.10\text{ g }HC_2H_3O_2}{100\text{ g soln.}} = 30.8\text{ g }HC_2H_3O_2$$

12-8. Since the density of ethanol is less than that of water, whatever quantities of ethanol and water are mixed the proportion of ethanol to water by mass will always be less than its proportion by volume. As a consequence, the mass percent ethanol is always less than the volume percent in aqueous solutions. If the other component with which ethanol is mixed has a *smaller* density than ethanol, the mass percent ethanol exceeds its volume percent.

12-9. Percent by mass is based on a ratio of masses. Since mass is independent of temperature, so is percent by mass. Percent by volume is based on a ratio of volumes. Volume is temperature dependent, and so too is volume percent.

Molar concentration

12-10.
$$\text{molar concentration} = \frac{11.3\text{ ml } CH_3OH \times \frac{0.793\text{ g } CH_3OH}{1.00\text{ ml } CH_3OH} \times \frac{1\text{ mol } CH_3OH}{32.0\text{ g } CH_3OH}}{0.0750\text{ L}} = 3.73\text{ M } CH_3OH$$

12-11.
$$\text{no. g solute} = 0.2500\text{ L soln.} \times \frac{0.0150\text{ mol } AgNO_3}{1.00\text{ L soln.}} \times \frac{169.9\text{ g } AgNO_3}{1\text{ mol } AgNO_3} \times \frac{100.0\text{ g solute}}{99.68\text{ g } AgNO_3} = 0.639\text{ g solute}$$

12-12.
$$\text{no. g } C_2H_5OH \text{ in final soln.} = 0.5000\text{ L} \times \frac{0.250\text{ mol } C_2H_5OH}{1.00\text{ L}} \times \frac{46.1\text{ g } C_2H_5OH}{1\text{ mol } C_2H_5OH} = 5.76\text{ g } C_2H_5OH$$

From Example 12-1 we see that the original ethanol solution is 8.03%, by mass and has a density of 0.982 g/cm^3.

$$\text{no. ml original soln.} = 5.76\text{ g } C_2H_5OH \times \frac{100.0\text{ g soln.}}{8.03\text{ g } C_2H_5OH} \times \frac{1.00\text{ ml soln.}}{0.982\text{ g soln.}} = 73.0\text{ ml soln.}$$

12-13. Choose a particular solution sample size on which to base these calculations, say 100.0 g. In both cases the numerator represents the number of moles of solute and the denominator, the volume of solution in liters.

at 15°C:
$$\text{molar conc.} = \frac{100.0\text{ g soln.} \times \frac{10.00\text{ g } C_2H_5OH}{100.0\text{ g soln.}} \times \frac{1\text{ mol } C_2H_5OH}{46.07\text{ g } C_2H_5OH}}{100.0\text{ g soln.} \times \frac{1.000\text{ ml soln.}}{0.9831\text{ g soln.}} \times \frac{1.000\text{ L soln.}}{1000\text{ ml soln.}}} = 2.134\text{ M } C_2H_5OH$$

at 25°C:
$$\text{molar conc.} = \frac{100.0\text{ g soln.} \times \frac{10.00\text{ g } C_2H_5OH}{100.0\text{ g soln.}} \times \frac{1\text{ mol } C_2H_5OH}{46.07\text{ g } C_2H_5OH}}{100.0\text{ g soln.} \times \frac{1.000\text{ ml soln.}}{0.9804\text{ g soln.}} \times \frac{1.000\text{ L soln.}}{1000\text{ ml soln.}}} = 2.128\text{ M } C_2H_5OH$$

Molal concentration

12-14.
$$\text{molal conc.} = \frac{1.50\text{ g } C_6H_4Cl_2 \times \frac{1\text{ mol } C_6H_4Cl_2}{147\text{ g } C_6H_4Cl_2}}{35.0\text{ g } C_6H_5 \times \frac{1\text{ kg } C_6H_6}{1000\text{ g } C_6H_6}} = 0.292\text{ m } C_6H_4Cl_2$$

12-15. In the setup below the molality concentration is written as a conversion factor between kg CCl_4 and mol I_2, i.e. 1 kg CCl_4 ≎ 0.175 mol I_2 or 1000 g CCl_4 ≎ 0.175 mol I_2

$$\text{no. g } I_2 = 250.0\text{ ml } CCl_4 \times \frac{1.595\text{ g } CCl_4}{1.000\text{ ml } CCl_4} \times \frac{0.175\text{ mol } I_2}{1000\text{ g } CCl_4} \times \frac{254\text{ g } I_2}{1.00\text{ mol } I_2} = 17.7\text{ g } I_2$$

12-16. Let us base this calculation on 1.00 liter of solution. We must determine the masses of solution and solvent and the number of moles of solute. From these data both the molarity and molality can be determined easily.

$$\text{no. g soln.} = 1.00\text{ L soln.} \times \frac{1000\text{ ml soln.}}{\text{L soln.}} \times \frac{1.101\text{ g soln.}}{1\text{ ml soln.}} = 1101\text{ g soln.}$$

$$\text{no. g HF} = 1101\text{ g soln.} \times \frac{30.0\text{ g HF}}{100\text{ g soln.}} = 330\text{ g HF}$$

$$\text{no. mol HF} = 330 \text{ g HF} \times \frac{1 \text{ mol HF}}{20.0 \text{ g HF}} = 16.5 \text{ mol HF}$$

$$\text{no. kg } H_2O = (1101 - 330)\text{g } H_2O \times \frac{1 \text{ kg } H_2O}{1000 \text{ g } H_2O} = 0.771 \text{ kg } H_2O$$

$$\frac{16.5 \text{ mol HF}}{1.00 \text{ L soln.}} = 16.5 \text{ M HF}; \qquad \frac{16.5 \text{ mol HF}}{0.771 \text{ kg } H_2O} = 21.4 \text{ m HF}$$

12-17. Consider 1.00 L of the solution. This solution weighs 1000 × 1.09 = 1090 g and contains 109.2 g KOH. The mass of water in the solution is 1090 - 109.2 = 981 g H_2O. Use these data to determine the molal concentration of the solution.

$$\text{molal conc.} = \frac{109.2 \text{ g KOH} \times \frac{1 \text{ mol KOH}}{56.1 \text{ g KOH}}}{0.981 \text{ kg } H_2O} = 1.98 \text{ m KOH}$$

To convert this solution to 0.250 m KOH requires that water be added. Set up the following equation based on 100.0 cm^3 (109 g) of the original solution and let x = no. kg H_2O to be added.

$$0.250 \text{ m} = \frac{10.92 \text{ g KOH} \times \frac{1 \text{ mol KOH}}{56.1 \text{ g KOH}}}{(0.0981 + x)\text{kg } H_2O} \qquad 0.250 \times (0.0981 + x) = 0.195$$

$$x = \frac{0.195}{0.250} - 0.0981 \qquad x = 0.682 \text{ kg } H_2O = 682 \text{ g } H_2O$$

Mole fraction, mole percent

12-18. (a) $$X_{C_7H_{16}} = \frac{1.15 \text{ mol } C_7H_{16}}{(1.15 + 1.48 + 2.71)\text{mol}} = 0.215 \qquad X_{C_8H_{18}} = \frac{1.48 \text{ mol } C_8H_{18}}{(1.15 + 1.48 + 2.71)\text{mol}} = 0.277$$

$$X_{C_9H_{20}} = \frac{2.71 \text{ mol } C_9H_{20}}{(1.15 + 1.48 + 2.71)\text{mol}} = 0.507$$

(b) mole percent: 21.5% C_7H_{16}; 27.7% C_8H_{18}; 50.7% C_9H_{20}

12-19. (a) First determine the number of moles of each solution component.

$$\text{no. mol } C_6H_4Cl_2 = 1.50 \text{ g } C_6H_4Cl_2 \times \frac{1 \text{ mol } C_6H_4Cl_2}{147 \text{ g } C_6H_4Cl_2} = 0.0102 \text{ mol } C_6H_4Cl_2$$

$$\text{no. mol } C_6H_6 = 35.0 \text{ g } C_6H_6 \times \frac{1 \text{ mol } C_6H_6}{78.1 \text{ g } C_6H_6} = 0.448 \text{ mol } C_6H_6$$

$$X_{C_6H_4Cl_2} = \frac{0.0102}{0.0102 + 0.448} = 0.0223$$

(b) Unlike molar concentration, mole fraction is independent of temperature. Base the calculation on 100.0 g solution, which consists of 10.00 g C_2H_5OH and 90.00 g H_2O.

$$\text{no. mol } C_2H_5OH = 10.00 \text{ g } C_2H_5OH \times \frac{1 \text{ mol } C_2H_5OH}{46.07 \text{ g } C_2H_5OH} = 0.2171 \text{ mol } C_2H_5OH$$

$$\text{no. mol } H_2O = 90.00 \text{ g } H_2O \times \frac{1 \text{ mol } H_2O}{18.02 \text{ g } H_2O} = 4.994 \text{ mol } H_2O$$

$$X_{C_2H_5OH} = \frac{0.2171}{0.2171 + 4.994} = 0.04166$$

12-20. In Example 12-1 we learned that 100.0 ml of the ethanol solution weighed 98.2 g and consisted of 90.3 g H_2O (5.02 mol) and 7.89 g C_2H_5OH (0.171 mol). Solve the following equation for x, the number of moles of C_2H_5OH to be added.

$$X_{C_2H_5OH} = \frac{(0.171 + x)\text{mol } C_2H_5OH}{[(0.171 + x) + 5.02]\text{mol}} = 0.0500 \qquad 0.171 + x = 0.00855 + 0.0500x + 0.251$$

$$0.950x = 0.089 \qquad x = 0.094 \text{ mol } C_2H_5OH$$

$$\text{no. g } C_2H_5OH = 0.094 \text{ mol } C_2H_5OH \times \frac{46.1 \text{ g } C_2H_5OH}{1 \text{ mol } C_2H_5OH} = 4.3 \text{ g } C_2H_5OH$$

12-21. A 10.0 mol percent solution corresponds to $X_{C_3H_8O_3} = 0.100$. Let V = no. ml glycerol required. Determine the number of moles of glycerol in terms of V.

$$\text{no. mol } C_3H_8O_3 = V \times \frac{1.26 \text{ g}}{1.00 \text{ ml}} \times \frac{1 \text{ mol } C_3H_8O_3}{92.1 \text{ g } C_3H_8O_3} = 0.0137V$$

Next, write an expression for the mole fraction.

$$X_{C_3H_8O_3} = \frac{0.0137V}{0.0137V + \left(1000 \text{ g } H_2O \times \frac{1 \text{ mol } H_2O}{18.02 \text{ g } H_2O}\right)} = \frac{0.0137V}{0.0137V + 55.5} = 0.100$$

$$0.0137V - 0.00137V = 5.55; \qquad V = 450 \text{ ml } C_3H_8O_3$$

Solubility equilibrium

12-22. The data in Figure 12-6 are expressed in g $KClO_4$/100 g soln., that is, percent $KClO_4$, by mass. We must first describe a 1.00 m $KClO_4$ soln. in % $KClO_4$, by mass.

For every 1000 g H_2O, the solution contains 1.00 mol $KClO_4$ = 139 g $KClO_4$.

$$\% \ KClO_4 = \frac{139 \text{ g } KClO_4}{(1000 + 139)\text{g soln.}} \times 100 = 12.2\% \ KClO_4$$

A saturated solution is 12.2% $KClO_4$ at about 80°C.

12-23. (a) The solution in question has 26.0 g $KClO_4$ in (500.0 + 26.0) = 526.0 g solution. Its % $KClO_4$, by mass, is

$$\% \ KClO_4 = \frac{26.0 \text{ g } KClO_4}{526.0 \text{ g soln.}} \times 100 = 4.94\% \ KClO_4 \ (4.94 \text{ g } KClO_4/100 \text{ g soln.})$$

This solution is supersaturated.

(b) The mass of $KClO_4$ per 100 g saturated solution at 20°C is about 2 g $KClO_4$. The mass of $KClO_4$ that should crystallize per 100 g of the given solution is about 3 g $KClO_4$ (that is, 4.94 - 2). For the 526 g supersaturated solution,

$$\text{no. g } KClO_4 \text{ crystallizing} = \frac{3 \text{ g } KClO_4}{100 \text{ g soln.}} \times 526 \text{ g soln.} = 16 \text{ g } KClO_4$$

12-24. (a) Determine the % by mass of each solute in the solution.

$$\% \ NH_4Cl = \frac{(50.0 \times 0.950)\text{g } NH_4Cl}{150.0 \text{ g soln.}} \times 100 = 31.7\% \ NH_4Cl \ (31.7 \ NH_4Cl/100 \text{ g soln.})$$

$$\% \ (NH_4)_2SO_4 = \frac{(50.0 \times 0.050)g\ (NH_4)_2SO_4}{150.0\ g\ soln.} \times 100 = 1.7\% \ (NH_4)_2SO_4 \ [1.7\ g\ (NH_4)_2SO_4/100\ g\ soln.]$$

Reference to Figure 12-6 indicates that the solid sample will dissolve completely.

(b) At 0°C the solubility of NH_4Cl is about 23 g NH_4Cl/100 g soln. Let x = no. g NH_4Cl that crystallize. The original number of grams of NH_4Cl was 0.95 x 50 = 47.5 g. Neglect the presence of the $(NH_4)_2SO_4$.

$$\frac{(47.5 - x)g\ NH_4Cl}{[100 + (47.5 - x)]g\ soln.} = \frac{23\ g\ NH_4Cl}{100\ g\ soln.} \qquad 4750 - 100x = 2300 + 1100 - 23x$$

$$1350 = 77x \qquad x = 18\ g\ NH_4Cl$$

(c) At 0°C the solubility of $(NH_4)_2SO_4$ is about 42 g $(NH_4)_2SO_4$/100 g soln. The original solution at 90°C contained 2.5 g $(NH_4)_2SO_4$ in 150 g soln. No $(NH_4)_2SO_4$ will crystallize when the solution is cooled to 0°C.

Solubility of gases

12-25. Based on data from Example 12-2, we conclude that at 740 mmHg the solubility of H_2S in water is

$$\text{molal conc.} = \frac{0.195\ m}{atm} \times (740/760)atm = 0.190\ m\ H_2S$$

Determine the % H_2S, by mass, in a saturated aqueous solution, i.e., in 0.190 m H_2S.

$$\frac{0.190\ mol\ H_2S \times \frac{34.1\ g\ H_2S}{1\ mol\ H_2S}}{[(0.190 \times 34.1) + 1000]g\ soln.} \times 100 = 0.64\%\ H_2S$$

Since the natural water contains only 0.5% H_2S, by mass, it will dissolve more H_2S.

12-26. First, establish the value of k in the expression C = k x P.

$$\frac{0.02\ g\ CH_4}{kg\ H_2O} = k \times 1\ atm; \qquad k = \frac{0.02\ g\ CH_4}{kg\ H_2O\ \ atm}$$

Under the stated conditions: $C = \frac{0.02\ g\ CH_4}{kg\ H_2O\ \ atm} \times 15\ atm = \frac{0.30\ g\ CH_4}{kg\ H_2O}$

$$\text{no. g natural gas dissolving} = \frac{0.30\ g\ CH_4}{kg\ H_2O} \times 100.0\ kg\ H_2O = 30\ g\ CH_4$$

12-27. According to Henry's law (equation 12.4) the concentration of a dissolved gas is directly proportional to the pressure of the gas in contact with the solution. If this concentration is expressed as molality (mole gas/kg solvent), and if the quantity of solvent is fixed, then the number of moles of dissolved gas is directly proportional to the pressure of the gas. But the mass of a substance is itself directly proportional to the number of moles of a substance. Therefore, the mass of dissolved gas should be directly proportional to the gas pressure, as stated in this exercise.

12-28. Again, the equation in question is $C = k \times P_{gas}$, with the concentration expressed as the number of moles of dissolved gas in a fixed amount of solvent.

$$C = \frac{n}{amt.\ solv.} = k \times P_{gas}$$

But the number of moles of gas in solution, is related to other gas variables through the ideal gas equation.

$$n = \frac{P_{gas} \times V_{gas}}{RT} \qquad C = \frac{P_{gas} \times V_{gas}}{R \times T \times \text{amt. solvent}} = k \times P_{gas}$$

$$V_{gas} = k \times R \times T \times \text{amt. solvent} = \text{constant}$$

At a constant temperature and for a fixed amount of solvent, the volume of dissolved gas is a constant, independent of pressure. Recall, however, that as the gas pressure changes the number of moles in a fixed volume of gas changes proportionately. Thus, although the *volume* of gas that dissolves remains constant as the gas pressure changes, the *number of moles* of gas does change in the expected manner--the higher the gas pressure, the more moles of gas dissolved.

Raoult's law and liquid-vapor equilibrium

12-29. Determine the mole fractions in the liquid solution. Then use Raoult's law to determine partial pressures.

$$\text{no. mol } C_6H_6 = 50.0 \text{ g } C_6H_6 \times \frac{1 \text{ mol } C_6H_6}{78.1 \text{ g } C_6H_6} = 0.640 \text{ mol } C_6H_6$$

$$\text{no. mol } C_7H_8 = 50.0 \text{ g } C_7H_8 \times \frac{1 \text{ mol } C_7H_8}{92.1 \text{ g } C_7H_8} = 0.543 \text{ mol } C_7H_8$$

$$X_{C_6H_6} = \frac{0.640}{0.640 + 0.543} = 0.541 \qquad X_{C_7H_8} = \frac{0.543}{0.640 + 0.543} = 0.459$$

$$P_{C_6H_6} = X_{C_6H_6} \cdot P^\circ_{C_6H_6} = 0.541 \times 95.1 \text{ mmHg} = 51.4 \text{ mmHg}$$

$$P_{C_7H_8} = X_{C_7H_8} \cdot P^\circ_{C_7H_8} = 0.459 \times 28.4 \text{ mmHg} = 13.0 \text{ mmHg}$$

$$P_{total} = 64.4 \text{ mmHg}$$

12-30. Recall expression (5.16) dealing with mixtures of gases, which in this case is written as

$$\frac{n_{C_6H_6}}{n_{tot.}} = X_{C_6H_6} = \frac{P_{C_6H_6}}{P_{tot.}} = \frac{51.4 \text{ mmHg}}{64.4 \text{ mmHg}} = 0.798 \qquad \frac{n_{C_7H_8}}{n_{tot.}} = X_{C_7H_8} = \frac{P_{C_7H_8}}{P_{tot.}} = \frac{13.0 \text{ mmHg}}{64.4 \text{ mmHg}} = 0.202$$

12-31. If the vapor phase contains 62.0 mole % C_6H_6, then in the vapor

$$\frac{n_{C_6H_6}}{n_{tot.}} = \frac{P_{C_6H_6}}{P_{tot.}} = 0.620$$

In the above expression, $P_{C_6H_6} = P^\circ \cdot X_{C_6H_6} = 95.1X_{C_6H_6}$

Also, $P_{C_7H_8} = 28.4X_{C_7H_8} = 28.4(1 - X_{C_6H_6})$. The mol fractions are those of the liquid solution.

$$P_{tot.} = P_{C_6H_6} + P_{C_7H_8} = 95.1X_{C_6H_6} + 28.4(1 - X_{C_6H_6})$$

All of this leads to the following equation, which must be solved for $X_{C_6H_6}$.

$$\frac{95.1X_{C_6H_6}}{28.4(1 - X_{C_6H_6}) + 95.1X_{C_6H_6}} = \frac{95.1X_{C_6H_6}}{28.4 + 66.7X_{C_6H_6}} = 0.620$$

$$95.1X_{C_6H_6} = 17.6 + 41.4X_{C_6H_6}; \qquad X_{C_6H_6} = 0.328$$

12-32. Use the solution concentration data to calculate the mole fraction of water in the aqueous urea solution. Then use Raoult's law.

$$\text{no. mol } CO(NH_2)_2 = 25.0 \text{ g } CO(NH_2)_2 \times \frac{1 \text{ mol } CO(NH_2)_2}{60.1 \text{ g } CO(NH_2)_2} = 0.416 \text{ mol } CO(NH_2)_2$$

$$\text{no. mol } H_2O = 525 \text{ g } H_2O \times \frac{1 \text{ mol } H_2O}{18.0 \text{ g } H_2O} = 29.2 \text{ mol } H_2O$$

$$X_{H_2O} = \frac{29.2 \text{ mol } H_2O}{(29.2 + 0.4)\text{mol total}} = 0.986 \qquad P_{H_2O} = X_{H_2O} \cdot P^{\circ}_{H_2O} = 0.986 \times 23.8 \text{ mmHg} = 23.5 \text{ mmHg}$$

Freezing point depression and boiling point elevation

12-33. The expression required here is (12.7). Solve for (a) the molality of the solution, (b) the number of moles of solute, and (c) the molecular weight of the unknown.

(a) $\Delta T_f = K_f \cdot m; \qquad m = \dfrac{(5.51 - 4.90)°C}{4.90 \dfrac{\text{kg solv. }°C}{\text{mol solute}}} = 0.12 \dfrac{\text{mol solute}}{\text{kg solv.}}$

(b) $\text{no. mol solute} = 75.22 \text{ g solv.} \times \dfrac{1 \text{ kg solv.}}{1000 \text{ g solv.}} \times \dfrac{0.12 \text{ mol solute}}{1 \text{ kg solv.}} = 9.0 \times 10^{-3} \text{ mol solute}$

(c) $\text{molecular weight} = \dfrac{1.10 \text{ g}}{9.0 \times 10^{-3} \text{ mol}} = 1.2 \times 10^{2} \text{ g/mol}$

12-34. Two distinct aspects are involved in this problem. First the method of the preceding exercise is used to determine the molecular weight of the compound. The empirical formula of the compound is established by the method of Example 3-13. A simple comparison of these two results leads to the molecular formula.

Molecular weight determination

$$\Delta T_f = K_f \cdot m; \qquad m = \frac{(5.51 - 1.35)°C}{4.90 \dfrac{\text{kg solv. }°C}{\text{mol solute}}} = 0.849 \frac{\text{mol solute}}{\text{kg solv.}}$$

$$\text{no. mol solute} = 50.0 \text{ ml } C_6H_6 \times \frac{0.879 \text{ g } C_6H_6}{1 \text{ ml } C_6H_6} \times \frac{1 \text{ kg } C_6H_6}{1000 \text{ g } C_6H_6} \times \frac{0.849 \text{ mol solute}}{1 \text{ kg } C_6H_6} = 0.0373 \text{ mol solute}$$

$$\text{molecular weight} = \frac{6.45 \text{ g}}{0.0373 \text{ mol}} = 173 \text{ g/mol}$$

Empirical formula

In 100 grams of the unknown compound,

$$\text{no. mol C} = 42.4 \text{ g C} \times \frac{1 \text{ mol C}}{12.0 \text{ g C}} = 3.53 \text{ mol C} \qquad \text{no. mol H} = 2.4 \text{ g H} \times \frac{1 \text{ mol H}}{1.0 \text{ g H}} = 2.4 \text{ mol H}$$

$$\text{no. mol N} = 16.6 \text{ g N} \times \frac{1 \text{ mol N}}{14.0 \text{ g N}} = 1.19 \text{ mol N} \qquad \text{no. mol O} = 37.8 \text{ g O} \times \frac{1 \text{ mol O}}{16.0 \text{ g O}} = 2.36 \text{ mol O}$$

Empirical formula = $C_{3.5}H_{2.4}N_{1.2}O_{2.4} = C_3H_2NO_2$

Formula weight = $(3 \times 12.0) + (2 \times 1.0) + 14.0 + (2 \times 16.0) = 84$

Molecular weight = 173. [Within the limits of experimental error this value is twice the formula weight.]

Molecular formula = $C_6H_4N_2O_4$

12-35. (a) Data concerning the solution composition are converted to molality, and expresssion (12.7) is solved for K_f.

$$\text{molality of } C_6H_6 \text{ in } C_6H_{12} = \frac{1.00 \text{ g } C_6H_6 \times \dfrac{1 \text{ mol } C_6H_6}{78.1 \text{ g } C_6H_6}}{80.00 \text{ g } C_6H_6 \times \dfrac{1 \text{ kg } C_6H_{12}}{1000 \text{ g } C_6H_{12}}} = 0.160 \text{ m}$$

$$K_f = \frac{\Delta T_f}{m} = \frac{(6.5 - 3.3)°C}{\dfrac{0.160 \text{ mol solute}}{\text{kg solvent}}} = 20 \ \frac{°C \text{ kg solvent}}{\text{mol solute}}$$

(b) Cyclohexane is a better solvent for molecular weight determinations than is benzene. Although the two solvents have about the same freezing point when pure, the addition of a given amount of solute to cyclohexane lowers the freezing point about four times as much as in benzene. [The values of K_f for cyclohexane and benzene are 20 and 4.9, respectively.]

12-36. To ensure protection of the cooling system of an automobile to -10°C requires adding enough ethylene glycol to water to produce ΔT_f = 10°C. The molality corresponding to this freezing point depression is,

$$m = \frac{\Delta T_f}{K_f} = \frac{10°C}{\dfrac{1.86 \text{ kg solv. } °C}{\text{mol solute}}} = 5.4 \ \frac{\text{mol solute}}{\text{kg solvent}}$$

Let us base the remainder of the calculation on 1 liter (1000 ml) of water.

$$\text{no. kg water} = 1000 \text{ ml water} \times \frac{1.00 \text{ g water}}{1 \text{ ml water}} \times \frac{1 \text{ kg water}}{1000 \text{ g water}} = 1.00 \text{ kg water}$$

The number of moles of $C_2H_6O_2$ that must be dissolved in this water to yield a 5.4 m solution is,

$$\text{no. mol } C_2H_6O_2 = 1.00 \text{ kg water} \times \frac{5.4 \text{ mol } C_2H_6O_2}{1 \text{ kg water}} = 5.4 \text{ mol } C_2H_6O_2$$

The volume of $C_2H_6O_2$ follows readily.

$$\text{no. ml } C_2H_6O_2 = 5.4 \text{ mol } C_2H_6O_2 \times \frac{62.1 \text{ g } C_2H_6O_2}{1 \text{ mol } C_2H_6O_2} \times \frac{\text{ml } C_2H_6O_2}{1.12 \text{ g } C_2H_6O_2} = 3.0 \times 10^2 \text{ ml } C_2H_6O_2$$

The required proportions, by volume, are: 3 parts $C_2H_6O_2$ to 10 parts H_2O.

12-37. (a) Freeze damage to citrus occurs if the juice of the fruit is frozen. The juice is a water solution containing sugars, citric acid and other solutes. These solutes lower the freezing point of the juice to a few degrees below the normal freezing point of water. Thus, it is not necessary to begin freeze protection measures at exactly 0°C = 32°F.

(b) Orange juice has a higher sugar content than lemon juice. This higher solute concentration means that the freezing point of orange juice is lower than that of lemon juice.

12-38. Since the solution in question is aqueous, K_f = 1.86. Calculate the expected freezing point of an 0.01 m solution.

$\Delta T_f = K_f \cdot m = 1.86 \times 0.01 = 0.0186°C$

The observed freezing point depression (0.072°C) is almost *four* times as great as expected. The solute must dissociate and produce four ions per formula unit, that is, $\Delta T_f = i \cdot K_f \cdot m$, and i = 4. The expected boiling point elevation is,

$\Delta T_b = i \cdot K_b \cdot m = 4 \times 0.512 \times 0.01 = 0.02°C$

The predicted boiling point of the solution is 100.02°C.

Osmotic pressure

12-39. In both cases osmosis occurs. Water is transported through cell membranes from the more dilute solution within the cells into the more concentrated salt solution. This loss of water is manifested by the wilting of the flowers and the shriveling of the cucumber.

12-40. The simplest verification of the statement is from the osmotic pressure given for the 20% sucrose solution--15 atm. (Note: In Example 5-1 we established that the height of a water column equivalent to one atm is 10.3 m.)

$$\text{no. m water} = 15 \text{ atm} \times \frac{10.3 \text{ m}}{1 \text{ atm}} = 150 \text{ m}$$

12-41. Use the expression $\pi = MRT$

$$M = \frac{\pi}{RT} = \frac{7.7 \text{ atm}}{0.0821 \text{ L atm mol}^{-1} \text{ K}^{-1} \times 298 \text{ K}} = 0.31 \text{ mol/L}$$

A glucose solution isotonic with blood contains 0.31 mol $C_6H_{12}O_6$/L.

12-42. Again, solve for M in the expression $\pi = MRT$

$$M = \frac{\pi}{RT} = \frac{(5.85/760)\text{atm}}{0.0821 \text{ L atm mol}^{-1} \text{ K}^{-1} \times 298 \text{ K}} = 3.15 \times 10^{-4} \text{ mol/L}$$

Now relate the mass of hemoglobin (1.02 g), solution volume (0.0500 L), molarity, and molecular weight (MW), as follows.

$$3.15 \times 10^{-4} \text{ M} = \frac{\left\{1.02 \times \frac{1}{(\text{MW})}\right\} \text{mol}}{0.0500 \text{ L}} \qquad (\text{MW}) = \frac{1.02}{0.0500 \times 3.15 \times 10^{-4}} = 6.48 \times 10^4$$

12-43. Convert the height of liquid column to an equivalent mercury column. This is the osmotic pressure.

$$h_{\text{soln.}} \times d_{\text{soln.}} = h_{\text{Hg}} \times d_{\text{Hg}}$$

$$h_{\text{Hg}} = h_{\text{soln.}} \times \frac{d_{\text{soln.}}}{d_{\text{Hg}}} = 5.1 \text{ mm} \times \frac{0.88 \text{ g/cm}^3}{13.6 \text{ g/cm}^3} = 0.33 \text{ mmHg}$$

Proceed as in Exercise 42.

$$M = \frac{\pi}{RT} = \frac{(0.33/760)\text{atm}}{0.0821 \text{ L atm mol}^{-1} \text{ K}^{-1} \times 298 \text{ K}} = 1.77 \times 10^{-5} \text{ mol/L}$$

$$1.77 \times 10^{-5} \text{ M} = \frac{\frac{0.50}{(\text{MW})} \text{mol}}{0.100 \text{ L}} \qquad (\text{MW}) = \frac{0.50}{0.100 \times 1.77 \times 10^{-5}} = 2.82 \times 10^5$$

Strong, weak, and nonelectrolytes

12-44. There is only one source each of K^+ and Mg^{2+} in the final solution, but two sources exist for Cl^-.

$$\frac{\text{no. mol K}^+}{\text{L}} = \frac{0.10 \text{ mol KCl}}{1 \text{ L}} \times \frac{1 \text{ mol K}^+}{1 \text{ mol KCl}} = 0.10 \text{ M K}^+$$

$$\frac{\text{no. mol Mg}^{2+}}{\text{L}} = \frac{0.20 \text{ mol MgCl}_2}{1 \text{ L}} \times \frac{1 \text{ mol Mg}^{2+}}{1 \text{ mol MgCl}_2} = 0.20 \text{ M Mg}^{2+}$$

$$\frac{\text{no. mol Cl}^-}{\text{L}} = \left\{\frac{0.10 \text{ mol KCl}}{1 \text{ L}} \times \frac{1 \text{ mol Cl}^-}{1 \text{ mol KCl}}\right\} + \left\{\frac{0.20 \text{ mol MgCl}_2}{1 \text{ L}} \times \frac{2 \text{ mol Cl}^-}{1 \text{ mol MgCl}_2}\right\} = 0.10 + 0.40 = 0.50 \text{ M Cl}^-$$

12-45. Determine the total number of moles of Cl^- in the final solution from the two sources indicated below:

(a) $$\text{no. mol } Cl^- = 400 \text{ ml} \times \frac{1 \text{ L}}{1000 \text{ ml}} \times \frac{0.180 \text{ mol } MgCl_2}{1 \text{ L}} \times \frac{2 \text{ mol } Cl^-}{1 \text{ mol } MgCl_2} = 0.144 \text{ mol } Cl^-$$

(b) $$\text{no. mol } Cl^- = 2.00 \text{ g } MgCl_2 \times \frac{1 \text{ mol } MgCl_2}{95.2 \text{ g } MgCl_2} \times \frac{2 \text{ mol } Cl^-}{1 \text{ mol } MgCl_2} = 0.0420 \text{ mol } Cl^-$$

Total number of moles of Cl^- = (a) + (b) = 0.144 + 0.0420 = 0.186 mol Cl^-

$$\frac{\text{no. mol } Cl^-}{\text{L}} = \frac{0.186 \text{ mol } Cl^-}{0.400 \text{ L}} = 0.465 \text{ M } Cl^-$$

12-46. The order of increasing ability to conduct electric current is the same as the order of increasing concentration of ions.

Ion concentrations

(b) 1.0 M $C_2H_5OH \simeq 0$.

(d) 0.01 M $HC_2H_3O_2 < 0.01$ M. This weak acid is only slightly ionized.

(a) 0.01 M NaCl = 0.02 M. This strong electrolyte dissociates to produce two moles of ions per mole of compound.

(c) 1.0 M $MgCl_2$ = 3.0 M. Three moles of ions are produced per mole of compound when this electrolyte dissociates.

Order of increasing ability to conduct electricity: (b) < (d) < (a) < (c)

12-47. Both solutes, NH_3 and $HC_2H_3O_2$, undergo only slight dissociation in aqueous solution; they are weak electrolytes. When mixed in the same solution they react to produce the salt, $NH_4C_2H_3O_2$, which dissociates completely into the ions NH_4^+ and $C_2H_3O_2^-$. The ammonium acetate is a strong electrolyte.

12-48. Begin by predicting the freezing point depression of a nonelectrolyte in an 0.10 m aqueous solution.

$\Delta T_f = K_f \cdot m = 1.86 \times 0.10 = 0.186°C$

The observed freezing point should be about -0.19°C. Now estimate the freezing points of the several solutions by comparison to this value.

(a) urea = -0.19°C: Urea is an undissociated covalent compound--a nonelectrolyte.

(b) NH_4NO_3 = -0.38°C: NH_4NO_3 is an ionic compound that dissociates into the ions NH_4^+ and NO_3^-.

(c) $CaCl_2$ = -0.57°C: $CaCl_2$ dissociates to produce one mole of Ca^{2+} and two moles of Cl^- ions per mole of compound.

(d) $MgSO_4$ = -0.38°C: The ions produced by $MgSO_4$ are Mg^{2+} and SO_4^{2-}.

(e) ethanol = -0.19°C: Ethanol is a nonelectrolyte.

(f) HCl = -0.38°C: Although it is a covalent compound, HCl dissociates in water solution to produce one H^+ and one Cl^- ion per molecule.

(g) $HC_2H_3O_2$ = -0.20°C: According to Example 12-9 in the text, acetic acid is about 4% dissociated in aqueous solution. This corresponds to a van't Hoff factor, *i*, of 1.04. The freezing point should be about 1.04 × (-0.19°C) = -0.20°C.

12-49. True solutions contain solute particles having dimensions of molecular size, say less than 1 nm. In colloidal mixtures the particles have one or more dimensions that exceed 1 nm, sometimes by a great deal. The particles in a colloidal mixture scatter light that is passed through the mixture (Tyndall effect). True solutions do not display the Tyndall effect. For a given mass of solute, true solutions have much more pronounced colligative properties (osmotic pressure, vapor pressure lowering, freezing point depression, and boiling point elevation) than do colloidal mixtures.

12-50. (a) An aerosol is a colloidal dispersion of small particles in a gas. These may be particles of a solid, as in cigarette smoke, or they may be droplets of liquid, as in a fog or mist.

(b) An emulsion is a colloidal dispersion of one liquid in another. One liquid is a continuous phase called a dispersion medium and is analogous to the solvent in a solution. The other liquid is distributed as tiny droplets throughout the dispersion medium. This phase, which is analogous to the solute in a solution, is called the disperse phase.

(c) A foam is a dispersion of microscopic bubbles of a gas or air in a liquid medium. Common examples are soap foams.

(d) A hydrophobic colloid is a dispersion of particles in water in which the suspended particles (disperse phase) have no particular affinity for water. Such colloids owe their stabilities to the fact that the colloidal particles adsorb ions on their surfaces and repel one another because they carry like charges.

(e) Electrophoresis is a process in which the charged particles in a colloidal mixture are made to migrate in an electric field. If the particles have different sizes, shapes and charges, it may be possible to separate different kinds of particles by differences in their mobilities in an electric field.

12-51. (a) The boundary regions between a negatively charged arsenic trisulfide sol and an electrolyte in the electrophoresis apparatus of Figure 12-17 are expected to move as follows: The region in the left arm will move down (descend) and the one in the right arm will move up (ascend).

(b) The effective ion in coagulating a negatively charged sol is the cation (positive ion). The higher the charge on the cation, the more effective it should be. The cations in the three electrolytes listed are K^+, Mg^{2+}, and Al^{3+}. The most effective electrolyte should be $AlCl_3$.

12-52. (a) Determine the volume and mass of one colloidal gold particle. Next, calculate the number of such particles in 1.00 mg gold. Finally, from the number of particles and the area per particle determine the total surface area.

$$\text{volume} = \frac{4}{3}\pi r^3 = \frac{4}{3}\pi\left(100\ \text{nm} \times \frac{10^{-7}\ \text{cm}}{1\ \text{nm}}\right)^3 = 4.19 \times 10^{-15}\ \text{cm}^3$$

$$\text{mass} = \text{volume} \times \text{density} = 4.19 \times 10^{-15}\ \text{cm}^3 \times \frac{19.3\ \text{g}}{1\ \text{cm}^3} = 8.09 \times 10^{-14}\ \text{g}$$

$$\text{no. particles} = 1.00\ \text{mg} \times \frac{1\ \text{g}}{1000\ \text{mg}} \times \frac{1\ \text{particle}}{8.09 \times 10^{-14}\ \text{g}} = 1.24 \times 10^{10}\ \text{particles}$$

$$\text{surface area per particle} = 4\pi r^2 = 4\pi\left(100\ \text{nm} \times \frac{10^{-7}\ \text{cm}}{1\ \text{nm}}\right)^2 = \frac{1.26 \times 10^{-9}\ \text{cm}^2}{1\ \text{particle}}$$

$$\text{total surface area} = 1.24 \times 10^{10}\ \text{particles} \times \frac{1.26 \times 10^{-9}\ \text{cm}^2}{1\ \text{particle}} = 16\ \text{cm}^2$$

(b) A single cube of gold weighing 1.00 mg has the following volume and length.

$$\text{volume} = 1.00\ \text{mg} \times \frac{1\ \text{g}}{1000\ \text{mg}} \times \frac{1\ \text{cm}^3}{19.3\ \text{g}} = 5.18 \times 10^{-5}\ \text{cm}^3$$

$$\text{volume} = (\text{length})^3; \quad \text{length} = (5.18 \times 10^{-5}\ \text{cm}^3)^{1/3} = 3.73 \times 10^{-2}\ \text{cm}$$

$$\text{surface area of cube} = 6 \times (\text{length})^2 = 6 \times (3.73 \times 10^{-2}\ \text{cm})^2 = 8.35 \times 10^{-3}\ \text{cm}^2$$

Self-test Questions

1. (*b*) In 0.01 M CH_3OH there is 0.01 mole CH_3OH (0.32 g) per L solution. A solution that is 0.01% (mass/vol.) would have 0.01 g CH_3OH per 100 cm^3 or 0.1 g CH_3OH per L. Item (a) is incorrect. Because the solution is so dilute (practically pure water), its density should be about 1.00 g/cm^3. One liter of solution would have a mass of about 1.00 kg and practically all of this would be water. A concentration of 0.01 mol/L (0.01 M) would be about the same as 0.01 mol/kg solvent (0.01 m). Item (b) is correct. There is 0.01 mol solute for every 1000/18 = 55.5 mol water. The mole fraction of CH_3OH is much less than 0.01 (it is 0.01/55.5 = 1.8×10^{-4}). The molarity of H_2O in the solution is far greater than 0.99 M (actually it is 55.5 mol/L). Also, note that it is mole fraction concentrations that must always total 1.00, not molarities, molalities, etc.

2. (*c*) Apply the rule that "like dissolves like". The substances $C_6H_6(l)$ and $C_{10}H_8(s)$ are hydrocarbons; they are unlike the polar covalent H_2O. $SiO_2(s)$ is a network covalent solid; the covalent bonds in this substance cannot be broken by interactions with H_2O. $CH_3CH(l)$, on the other hand, is a polar covalent substance with certain similarities to water. (Think of CH_3OH as a molecule in which a $-CH_3$ group substitutes for an $-H$ atom in $H-O-H$.)

3. (*a*) Ethanol and sucrose are nonelectrolytes. Acetic acid is a weak electrolyte and its aqueous solutions are only fair conductors of electricity. NaCl is a strong electrolyte and NaCl(aq) is a good electrical conductor.

4. (*d*) Determine the number of moles of particles present in each solution. In 0.01 m $MgSO_4$ this would be 0.02 m; in 0.01 m NaCl, 0.02 m; in 0.01 m C_2H_5OH, 0.01 m (a nonelectrolyte); 0.008 m MgI_2, 0.024 m. Since $\Delta T_f = K_f \times m$, the solution with the greatest molality of dissolved particles has the greatest freezing point depression and the lowest freezing point.

5. (*c*) Since the mole fractions of A and B in the liquid phase are equal, the mole fractions of A and B in the vapor can be equal (each equal to 0.50) only if the vapor pressures of A and B are equal--this is unlikely. Item (a) is incorrect. Item (b) is also incorrect; the mole fractions of A and B in the vapor could not be equal and have any value other than 0.50. The mole fractions of A and B in the vapor are not likely to be equal (because their vapor pressures are not likely to be equal). Both components are volatile; both will be present in the vapor.

6. (*b*) A polymeric substance has a high molecular weight. Of the colligative properties--osmotic pressure, freezing point depression, and boiling point elevation--only osmotic pressure measurements are useful for substances of high molecular weight (and very dilute solution concentration). Measurement of vapor density [i.e., based on the expression: (MW) = mRT/PV] is feasible only for gases, and substances with high molecular weights are solids or liquids under normal conditions.

7. (a) $$\text{no. g } C_6H_6 = 50.0 \text{ cm}^3\ C_6H_6 \times \frac{0.879 \text{ g } C_6H_6}{1 \text{ cm}^3\ C_6H_6} = 44.0 \text{ g } C_6H_6$$

$$\text{no. g solution} = 44.0 \text{ g } C_6H_6 + 1.00 \text{ g } C_{10}H_8 = 45.0 \text{ g solution}$$

$$\%\ C_{10}H_8 = \frac{1.00 \text{ g } C_{10}H_8}{45.0 \text{ g solution}} \times 100 = 2.22\%\ C_{10}H_8$$

(b) $$\text{molality} = \frac{1.00 \text{ g } C_{10}H_8 \times \dfrac{1 \text{ mol } C_{10}H_8}{128 \text{ g } C_{10}H_8}}{44.0 \text{ g } C_6H_6 \times \dfrac{1 \text{ kg } C_6H_6}{1000 \text{ g } C_6H_6}} = 0.178 \text{ m } C_{10}H_8$$

(c) $$\Delta T_f = K_f \times m = 4.90°C \text{ kg } C_6H_6 \text{ (mol } C_{10}H_8)^{-1} \times \frac{0.178 \text{ mol } C_{10}H_8}{1.00 \text{ kg } C_6H_6} = 0.87°C$$

$$T_f = 5.51 - 0.87 = 4.64°C$$

8. Determine the molality of the solution from the boiling point data.

$$\Delta t_b = K_b \times m \qquad m = \frac{(100.0 - 99.07)°C}{0.512°C \text{ kg solv. (mol solute)}^{-1}} \qquad m = 1.8 \text{ mol solute/kg solv.}$$

Since NaCl dissociates into two ions per formula unit, the molality expressed in terms of NaCl is 0.90 m NaCl.

$$\frac{0.90 \text{ mol NaCl} \times \frac{58.5 \text{ g NaCl}}{1 \text{ mol NaCl}}}{(0.90 \times 58.5)\text{g NaCl} + 1000 \text{ g } H_2O} \times 100 = 5.0\% \text{ NaCl, by mass}$$

9. Neither *pure* liquid is an electrical conductor, but when HCl is dissolved in water it dissociates completely into the ions H^+ and Cl^-; HCl(aq) is a strong electrolyte.

10. It is important to note at the outset that the volume of the final solution is not 350 ml, but (350 + V)ml, where V(in ml) is the volume of 0.25 M $MgCl_2$ to be added. First, determine the no. mol Cl^- in the final solution.

$$\text{no. mol } Cl^- = (350 + V)\text{ml} \times \frac{1 \text{ L}}{1000 \text{ ml}} \times \frac{0.30 \text{ mol } Cl^-}{\text{L}} = 0.105 + 3.0 \times 10^{-4}V \text{ mol } Cl^-$$

Next, calculate the no. mol Cl^- in the original solution.

$$\text{no. mol } Cl^- = 0.350 \text{ L} \times \frac{0.25 \text{ mol NaCl}}{1 \text{ L}} \times \frac{1 \text{ mol } Cl^-}{1 \text{ mol NaCl}} = 0.0875 \text{ mol } Cl^-$$

Now, determine the no. mol Cl^- that must be added to the original solution to produce the final solution.

$$\text{no. mol } Cl^- = 0.105 + 3 \times 10^{-4}V - 0.0875 = 0.017 + 3.0 \times 10^{-4}V$$

Finally, write an expression for the required volume of 0.25 M $MgCl_2$.

$$\text{no. ml} = V = (0.017 + 3.0 \times 10^{-4}V)\text{mol } Cl^- \times \frac{1 \text{ mol } MgCl_2}{2 \text{ mol } Cl^-} \times \frac{1 \text{ L}}{0.250 \text{ mol } MgCl_2} \times \frac{1000 \text{ ml}}{1 \text{ L}} = 34 + 0.60V$$

$$V = 34 + 0.60V \qquad 0.40V = 34 \qquad V = 85 \text{ ml}$$

Chapter 13

Chemical Kinetics

Rates of chemical reactions

13-1. (a) $[A]_0$ refers to the concentration of the reactant A, expressed in moles per liter, that exists at whatever time is taken to be the start of the reaction ($t = 0$).

(b) $[A]_t$ refers to the molar concentration of the reactant A at some time, t, after the start of of a chemical reaction.

(c) $\Delta[A]$ represents the difference in the molar concentration of the reactant A at two different times in a chemical reaction.

(d) Δt represents an interval of time in a chemical reaction.

(e) The ratio of $\Delta[A]$ to Δt represents the rate of change of concentration with time. The negative of this ratio, that is, $-\Delta[A]/\Delta t$, is the rate of the reaction.

(f) $\Delta[B]/\Delta t$ is the rate of increase of concentration of product B with time. This quantity is also equal to the rate of the reaction.

(g) $t_{1/2}$ is the half-life of the reaction--the time required for one half of the quantity of A present initially to react.

13-2. The rate of a chemical reaction is generally proportional to the concentrations of the reacting species. This fact is stated through the rate law expression: Rate = $k[A]^m[B]^n$.... If the rate of a reaction is *independent* of the concentration of one of the reactants, the corresponding exponent in the rate law expression (for example, m, n, ...) must have a value of *zero*. The reaction is said to be *zero-order* in that reactant. If the rate of a reaction is directly proportional to the concentration of one of the reactants, the corresponding exponent in the rate law expression has a value of *one*. The reaction is said to be *first-order* in that reactant. If the rate law expression is proportional to the *square* of a particular reactant concentration, the corresponding exponent has a value of *two*, and the reaction is *second-order* in that reactant. The term order of a reaction is often used to describe the form of the dependence on all concentration terms. In this case the exponents are added together and the reaction is said to have a total or overall order of zero, first, second, and so on.

13-3. rate = $k[CH_3CHO]^2$

13-4. Write a rate equation for each case, rate = $k[A]^m$. Substitute a value for the exponent *m*. Find the units of k that yield units of mol L^{-1} s^{-1} for the rate.

(a) zero order: rate = $k[A]^0$; rate = k; units of k: mol $L^{-1}s^{-1}$

(b) first order: rate = $k[A]^1$; $k = \frac{\text{rate}}{[A]} = \frac{\text{mol } L^{-1}s^{-1}}{\text{mol } L^{-1}}$; units of k: s^{-1}

(c) second order: rate = $k[A]^2$; $k = \frac{\text{rate}}{[A]^2} = \frac{\text{mol } L^{-1}s^{-1}}{\text{mol}^2\ L^{-2}}$; units of k: L $mol^{-1}s^{-1}$

13-5. Use the method of Example 13-1.

(a) $t = 0$ $[N_2O_5] = 0.550$ M $V_{O_2} = 0.00\ cm^3$

$t = \infty$ $[N_2O_5] = 0.000$ M $V_{O_2} = 182\ cm^3$

$t = 85s$ $[N_2O_5] = ?$ $V_{O_2} = 6.2\ cm^3$

fraction of N_2O_5 decomposed at t = 85s: 6.2/182 = 0.034

decrease in $[N_2O_5]$ at t = 85s: 0.034 x 0.550 = 0.019 M

at t = 85s: $[N_2O_5]$ remaining = 0.550 - 0.019 = 0.531 M

(b) initial reaction rate $= \frac{-\Delta[N_2O_5]}{\Delta t} = \frac{0.019 \text{ mol/L}}{85s} = 2.2 \times 10^{-4}$ mol $L^{-1}s^{-1}$

(c) $\Delta[N_2O_5]$ = -initial rate x Δt = -2.2×10^{-4} mol L^{-1} s^{-1} x 120s

$\Delta[N_2O_5] = -2.6 \times 10^{-2}$ mol/L

after 2.0 min: $[N_2O_5]$ = 0.550 - 0.026 = 0.524 M

13-6. $2\ N_2O_5 \longrightarrow 2\ N_2O_4 + O_2(g)$ (13.1)

(a) no. mol N_2O_5 $= 182 \text{ cm}^3 \times \frac{1 \text{ L}}{1000 \text{ cm}^3} \times \frac{1 \text{ mol } O_2}{22.4 \text{ L } O_2(\text{STP})} \times \frac{2 \text{ mol } N_2O_5}{1 \text{ mol } O_2} = 1.62 \times 10^{-2}$ mol N_2O_5

no. ml soln. $= 1.62 \times 10^{-2} \text{ mol } N_2O_5 \times \frac{1.00 \text{ L}}{0.550 \text{ mol } N_2O_5} \times \frac{1000 \text{ ml}}{1 \text{ L}} = 29.5$ ml

(b) rate of formation of O_2 = 1/2 rate of disappearance N_2O_5

initial rate formation of O_2 = $1/2 \times 2.2 \times 10^{-4} = 1.1 \times 10^{-4}$ mol O_2 L^{-1} s^{-1}

(c) Proceed in one of two ways:

1. no. mol N_2O_5 consumed = 2.2×10^{-4} mol L^{-1} s^{-1} x 0.0295 L x 60s = 3.9×10^{-4} mol N_2O_5

no. mol O_2 produced $= 3.9 \times 10^{-4} \text{ mol } N_2O_5 \times \frac{1 \text{ mol } O_2}{2 \text{ mol } N_2O_5} = 1.95 \times 10^{-4}$ mol O_2

2. no. mol O_2 produced = 1.1×10^{-4} mol O_2 L^{-1} s^{-1} x 0.0295 L x 60s = 1.95×10^{-4} mol O_2

no. cm^3 O_2 $= 1.95 \times 10^{-4} \text{ mol } O_2 \times \frac{22.4 \text{ L } O_2(\text{STP})}{1 \text{ mol } O_2} \times \frac{1000 \text{ cm}^3\ O_2}{1 \text{ L } O_2} = 4.4 \text{ cm}^3\ O_2$

13-7. slope of tangent at 1000s $= \frac{\Delta[N_2O_5]}{\Delta t} = \frac{0.67 - 0.85}{400} = -4.5 \times 10^{-4}$ mol L^{-1} s^{-1}

reaction rate = -slope = 4.5×10^{-4} mol L^{-1} s^{-1}

The rate at 1000s should be less than the initial rate but greater than at 1900s because a first-order reaction slows down as a reactant is consumed. [The rate at 1900s is 2.6×10^{-4} mol L^{-1} s^{-1} (see Example 13-2).]

13-8. (a) In the reaction, $A(g) \longrightarrow 2\ B(g) + C(g)$, *three* moles of product replace each mole of reactant. Whatever the original temperature and volume, the amount of A present originally is sufficient to generate a pressure of 1000 mmHg. Since the volume and temperature remain constant, while the amount of gas increases three-fold, the pressure also increases three-fold, to 3000 mmHg.

(b) We are interested in the time at which the pressure of A(g) in the reaction, $A(g) \longrightarrow 2\ B(g) + C(g)$, decreases from 1000 mmHg to 800 mmHg. A number of moles of A(g) decomposes equivalent to 200 mmHg; three times as many moles of product are formed, equivalent to 600 mmHg. The total pressure then is: partial pressure of A (800 mmHg) + partial pressure of products (600 mmHg) = 1400 mmHg.

13-9. (a) The data given in column II correspond to a zero-order reaction. This fact can be easily established in two ways: First, this is the only one of the three sets of data that shows the reaction going to completion. Also, the rate of decrease of [A] is constant; [A] decreases by 0.25 for every 25 s.

(b) The half-life of a first-order reaction is constant. Note the data in column III. The time required for [A] to decrease to 0.50, one half its original value, is 100 sec. But at 200 sec [A] = 0.33, not 0.25 as would be required in a first-order reaction. The first-order reaction must correspond to the data in column I.

(c) By a process of elimination it appears that the second-order reaction corresponds to the data in column III. An alternative approach is also possible. Show that 1/[A] plotted against time is a straight line. For example, at t = 0, 1/[A] = 1.00; t = 25, 1/[A] = 1.25; t = 50, 1/[A] = 1.50; t = 75, 1/[A] = 1.75; t = 100, 1/[A] = 2.00. The increase in 1/[A] over every 25-second interval is constant--0.25. The graph is linear.

13-10. Although graphical methods are best for determining the half-life of a reaction, since we are asked only to give an approximate value, a simple inspection of the data in column I is sufficient. The half-life is somewhat less than 75 s, say approximately 70 s. This appears to be the case because at 75 s [A], which was initially 1.00, has decreased to 0.47. The half-life would be the time at which [A] = 0.50. At t = 140 s, [A] should be 0.25. The data in column I indicate that at t = 150 s, [A] = 0.22. This fact is consistent with a half-life of 70 s. And we should expect a value of [A] = 0.125 at t = 210 s, which is consistent with the observed value of [A] = 0.14 at t = 200 s. Note, finally, that in the 75-second interval from t = 75 s to t = 150 s, [A] decreases from 0.47 to 0.22. This observation, too, suggests that the half-life is slightly less than 75 s. For reaction II, the half-life is 50 s. For reaction III, it is $1/k[A]_0$ and changes with each half-life interval.

13-11. Again, because we are asked only for approximate values, an estimation of reaction rates can be based simply on the tabular data instead of a graph.

(a) The zero-order reaction is described by the data in column II. The reaction is concluded at 100 s. For this reason [A] = 0 at t = 110 s.

(b) The first-order reaction corresponds to the data in column I. The rate of the reaction at 110 s is nearly the same (though slightly less) than at 100 s. In the 25-second interval between t = 75 s and t = 100 s, $\Delta[A] = -0.10$, for an approximate rate of reaction of $-\Delta[A]/\Delta t = 0.10/25 = 0.0040$. In the 50-second interval between t = 100 s and t = 150 s, the corresponding rate of reaction is $-\Delta[A]/\Delta t = 0.15/50 = 0.0030$. Assume that the rate of reaction at t = 110 s is intermediate to these two values, that is, $-\Delta[A]/\Delta t = 0.0035$ mol L^{-1} s^{-1}. In the 10-second interval between 100 and 110 s, [A] decreases by 10 x 0.0035 = 0.035. This suggests [A] at 110 s to be 0.37 - 0.035 = 0.33 M.

(c) Turn to the data in column III and follow the same procedure as in part (b). The approximate rate of reaction at 110 s is $-\Delta[A]/\Delta t \simeq 0.0024$ mol L^{-1} s^{-1}. In the 10-second interval between 100 and 110 s, [A] decreases by 10 x 0.0024 = 0.024. This suggests [A] at 110 s to be 0.50 - 0.02 = 0.48 M.

13-12. Although rates of reaction could be estimated in the same manner as in the preceding exercise, a different method is suggested here. The data, [A] versus time, are plotted below. The rates of reaction are simply the slopes of the tangent lines drawn at t = 75 s.

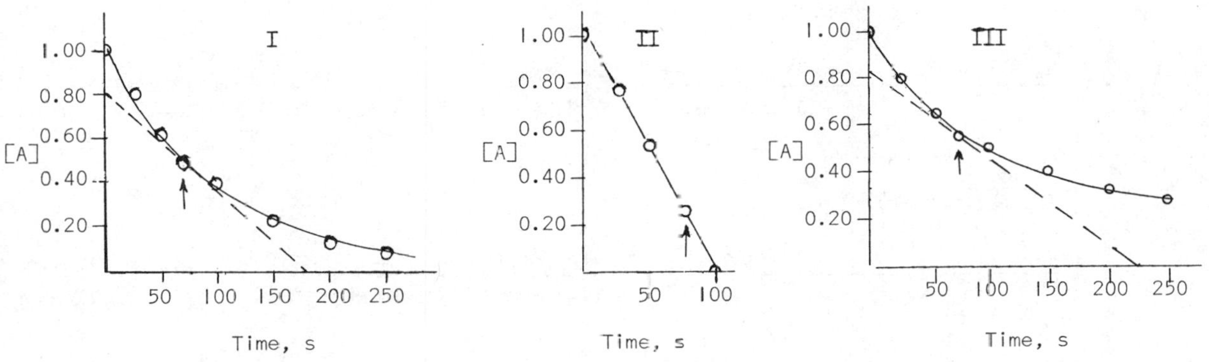

(a) *Zero-order reaction (II)*: The graph is a straight line. The slope (and hence the rate of reaction) is a constant. Rate of reaction = $-\Delta[A]/\Delta t$ = 1.00 mol L^{-1}/100 s = 1.0 x 10^{-2} mol A L^{-1} s^{-1}.

(b) *First-order reaction (I)*: The tangent drawn at $t = 75$ s intersects the y axis at 0.80 mol A/L and the x axis at 175 s. The slope of this tangent line is, Rate of reaction $= -\Delta[A]/\Delta t = 0.80 \text{ mol A L}^{-1}/175 \text{ s} = 4.6 \times 10^{-3} \text{ mol A L}^{-1} \text{ s}^{-1}$.

(c) *Second-order reaction (III)*: The tangent line drawn at 75 s intersects the y axis at 0.84 mol A/L and the x axis at 225 s. Rate of reaction $= -\Delta[A]/\Delta t = 0.84 \text{ mol A L}^{-1}/225 \text{ s} = 3.7 \times 10^{-3} \text{ mol A L}^{-1} \text{ s}^{-1}$.

Method of initial rates

13-13. Use the value of k established in Example 13-5(a) in solving the expression

$$\text{rate} = k[S_2O_8^{2-}][I^-] = 6.1 \times 10^{-3} \text{ L mol}^{-1} \text{ s}^{-1} \times 0.15 \text{ mol/L} \times 0.010 \text{ mol/L} = 9.2 \times 10^{-6} \text{ mol L}^{-1} \text{ s}^{-1}$$

13-14. (a) $\text{rate} = k[HgCl_2]^m [C_2O_4^{2-}]^n$

$$\frac{\text{rate (2)}}{\text{rate (1)}} = \frac{k(0.105)^m (0.30)^n}{k(0.105)^m (0.15)^n} = \frac{\cancel{k(0.105)^m}(2)^n \cancel{(0.15)^n}}{\cancel{k(0.105)^m} \cancel{(0.15)^n}} = 2^n = \frac{7.1 \times 10^{-5}}{1.8 \times 10^{-5}} = 3.94 \simeq 4$$

$n = 2$; reaction is second order in $C_2O_4^{2-}$.

$$\frac{\text{rate (2)}}{\text{rate (3)}} = \frac{k(0.105)^m (0.30)^n}{k(0.052)^m (0.30)^n} = \frac{\cancel{k}(2)^m \cancel{(0.052)^m} \cancel{(0.30)^n}}{\cancel{k(0.052)^m} \cancel{(0.30)^n}} = 2^m = \frac{7.1 \times 10^{-5}}{3.5 \times 10^{-5}} = 2.02 \simeq 2$$

$m = 1$; reaction is first order in $HgCl_2$.

Overall reaction order = 2 + 1 = 3 (third order)

(b) Use representative data, such as for rate (1).

$$k = \frac{\text{rate (1)}}{[HgCl_2][C_2O_4^{2-}]^2} = \frac{1.8 \times 10^{-5} \text{ mol L}^{-1} \text{ min}^{-1}}{0.105 \text{ mol/L} \times (0.15 \text{ mol/L})^2} = 7.6 \times 10^{-3} \text{ L}^2 \text{ mol}^{-2} \text{ min}^{-1}$$

(c) Initial rate $= 7.6 \times 10^{-3} \text{ L}^2 \text{ mol}^{-2} \text{ min}^{-1} \times 0.020 \text{ mol/L} \times (0.22 \text{ mol/L})^2 = 7.4 \times 10^{-6} \text{ mol L}^{-1} \text{min}^{-1}$

13-15. (a) $\text{rate} = k(P_{H_2})^m (P_{NO})^n$. Use appropriate entries from the data listed.

$$\frac{\text{rate (2)}}{\text{rate (3)}} = \frac{k(400 \text{ mmHg})^m (300 \text{ mmHg})^n}{k(400 \text{ mmHg})^m (152 \text{ mmHg})^n} = \frac{\cancel{k(400 \text{ mmHg})^m} (2)^n \cancel{(150 \text{ mmHg})^n}}{\cancel{k(400 \text{ mmHg})^m} \cancel{(152 \text{ mmHg})^n}} = (2)^n = \frac{0.515 \text{ mmHg s}^{-1}}{0.125 \text{ mmHg s}^{-1}}$$

$= 4.12 \simeq 4$; $n = 2$.

The reaction is second order in NO.

$$\frac{\text{rate (1)}}{\text{rate (3)}} = \frac{k(289 \text{ mmHg})^m (400 \text{ mmHg})^n}{k(147 \text{ mmHg})^m (400 \text{ mmHg})^n} = \frac{\cancel{k}(2)^m \cancel{(144 \text{ mmHg})^m} \cancel{(400 \text{ mmHg})^n}}{\cancel{k(147 \text{ mmHg})^m} \cancel{(400 \text{ mmHg})^n}} = (2)^m = \frac{0.800 \text{ mmHg s}^{-1}}{0.395 \text{ mmHg s}^{-1}}$$

$= 2.02 \simeq 2$; $m = 1$.

The reaction is first order in H_2.

Overall reaction order = 2 + 1 = 3.

(b) $\text{rate} = k \times P_{H_2} \times (P_{NO})^2$

13-16. (a) rate = $k[OCl^-]^m [I^-]^n [OH^-]^o$

Order with respect to I^-:
$$\frac{\text{rate }(2)}{\text{rate }(3)} = \frac{k(0.0020)^m (0.0040)^n (1.00)^o}{k(0.0020)^m (0.0020)^n (1.00)^o} = \frac{5.0 \times 10^{-4} \text{ mol L}^{-1} \text{ s}^{-1}}{2.4 \times 10^{-4} \text{ mol L}^{-1} \text{ s}^{-1}}$$

$2^n = 2$; $n = 1$; first order in I^-.

Order with respect to OH^-:
$$\frac{\text{rate }(4)}{\text{rate }(5)} = \frac{k(0.0020)^m (0.0020)^1 (0.50)^o}{k(0.0020)^m (0.0020)^1 (0.25)^o} = \frac{4.6 \times 10^{-4} \text{ mol L}^{-1} \text{ s}^{-1}}{9.4 \times 10^{-4} \text{ mol L}^{-1} \text{ s}^{-1}}$$

$2^o = 1/2$; $o = -1$; order with respect to OH^- is -1.

Order with respect to OCl^-:
$$\frac{\text{rate }(1)}{\text{rate }(3)} = \frac{k(0.0040)^m (0.0020)^1 (1.00)^{-1}}{k(0.0020)^m (0.0020)^1 (1.00)^{-1}} = \frac{4.8 \times 10^{-4} \text{ mol L}^{-1} \text{ s}^{-1}}{2.4 \times 10^{-4} \text{ mol L}^{-1} \text{ s}^{-1}}$$

$2^m = 2$; $m = 1$; first order in OCl^-.

(b) Overall reaction order: $1 - 1 + 1 = 1$.

(c) rate = $k\dfrac{[OCl^-][I^-]}{[OH^-]}$

Use the data for one of the reactions to determine k.

$$k = \frac{\text{rate }[OH^-]}{[OCl^-][I^-]} = \frac{4.8 \times 10^{-4} \text{ mol L}^{-1} \text{ s}^{-1} \times 1.00 \text{ mol/L}}{0.0040 \text{ mol/L} \times 0.0020 \text{ mol/L}} = 60 \text{ s}^{-1}$$

First-order reactions

13-17. (a) Fraction of $C_6H_5N_2Cl$ decomposed = 44.3/58.3 = 0.76

Fraction of $C_6H_5N_2Cl$ remaining = 1.00 − 0.76 = 0.24

$[C_6H_5N_2Cl]_{remaining} = [C_6H_5N_2Cl]_{initially} \times 0.24 = 0.071 \times 0.24 = 0.017$ M $C_6H_5N_2Cl$

(b)

Decomposition of $C_6H_5N_2Cl$

I	II	III	IV	V
Time, min	Δt, min	$[C_6H_5N_2Cl]$ mol liter^{-1}	$\Delta[C_6H_5N_2Cl]$ mol liter^{-1}	$\Delta[C_6H_5N_2Cl]/\Delta t$ mol liter^{-1} min^{-1}
0		0.071		
	3		−0.013	-4.3×10^{-3}
3		0.058		
	3		0.011	3.7
6		0.047		
	3		0.008	2.7
9		0.039		
	3		0.007	2.3
12		0.032		
	3		0.006	2.0
15		0.026		
	3		0.005	1.7
18		0.021		
	3		0.004	1.3
21		0.017		
	3		0.003	1.0

continued on next page

Decomposition of $C_6H_5N_2Cl$ (continued)

I Time, min	*II* Δt, min	*III* $[C_6H_5N_2Cl]$ mol liter^{-1}	*IV* $\Delta[C_6H_5N_2Cl]$ mol liter^{-1}	*V* $\Delta[C_6H_5N_2Cl]/\Delta t$ mol liter^{-1} min^{-1}
24		0.014		
	3		0.002	0.7
27		0.012		
	3		0.002	0.7
30		0.010		

(c)

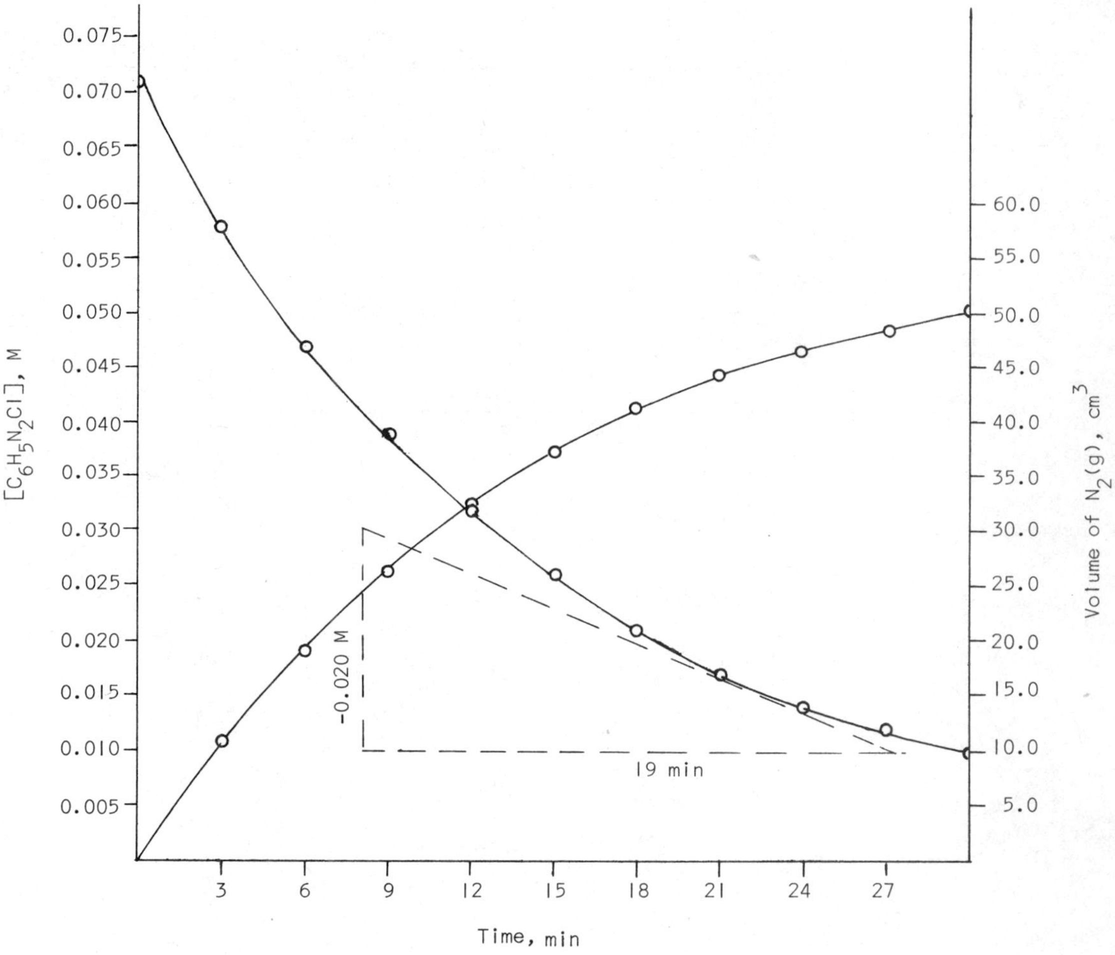

(d) Either draw a tangent line to the curve plotted in part (c) at t = 0, or use the first two data points from the table constructed in part (b).

$$\frac{\Delta[C_6H_5N_2Cl]}{\Delta t} = \frac{(0.058 - 0.071)\text{M}}{3 \text{ min}} = -4.3 \times 10^{-3} \text{ mol L}^{-1} \text{ min}^{-1}$$

$$\text{initial reaction rate} = -\Delta[C_6H_5N_2Cl]/\Delta t = 4.3 \times 10^{-3} \text{ mol L}^{-1} \text{ min}^{-1}$$

(e) The rate of the reaction at t = 21 min is given by the negative of the slope of the tangent line (*t*).

$$\text{Slope} = \frac{\Delta[C_6H_5N_2Cl]}{t} = \frac{(0.010 - 0.030)\text{mol L}^{-1}}{(27.3 - 8.3)\text{ min}} = \frac{-0.020 \text{ mol L}^{-1}}{19 \text{ min}} = -1.1 \times 10^{-3} \text{ mol L}^{-1} \text{ min}^{-1}$$

$\text{Rate} = 1.1 \times 10^{-3} \text{ mol L}^{-1} \text{ min}^{-1}$

(f) The rate law is: rate = $k[C_6H_5N_2Cl]$.

Based on initial data: $k = \dfrac{4.3 \times 10^{-3} \text{ mol L}^{-1} \text{ min}^{-1}}{0.071 \text{ mol L}^{-1}} = 6.1 \times 10^{-2} \text{ min}^{-1}$

Based on data at t = 21 min: $k = \dfrac{1.1 \times 10^{-3} \text{ mol L}^{-1} \text{ min}^{-1}}{0.017 \text{ mol L}^{-1}} = 6.5 \times 10^{-2} \text{ min}^{-1}$

(g) $t_{1/2} = \dfrac{0.693}{6.5 \times 10^{-2} \text{ min}^{-1}} = 11 \text{ min}$

From the graph of part (c), note that t = 0, $[C_6H_5N_2Cl]$ = 0.071. The concentration is half this value, that is, $[C_6H_5N_2Cl]$ = 0.0355, at about 10.5 min.

(h) Half of the substance is decomposed in 11 minutes. Half of what remains is decomposed in another 11 minutes. That is, after 22 minutes, three fourths of the sample is decomposed and one fourth remains.

(i)

t, min	$[C_6H_5N_2Cl]$	$\log[C_6H_5N_2Cl]$
0	0.071	- 1.15
3	0.058	1.24
6	0.047	1.33
9	0.039	1.41
12	0.032	1.49
15	0.026	1.59
18	0.021	1.68
21	0.017	1.77
24	0.014	1.85
27	0.012	1.92
30	0.010	2.00

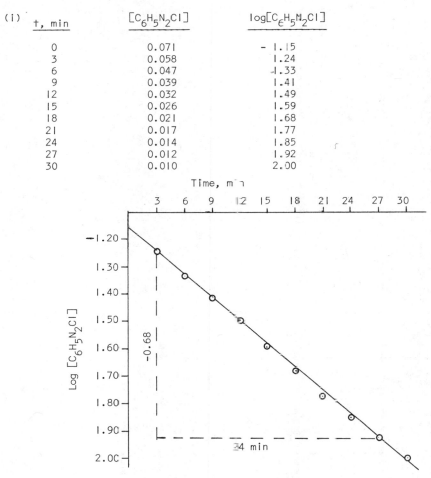

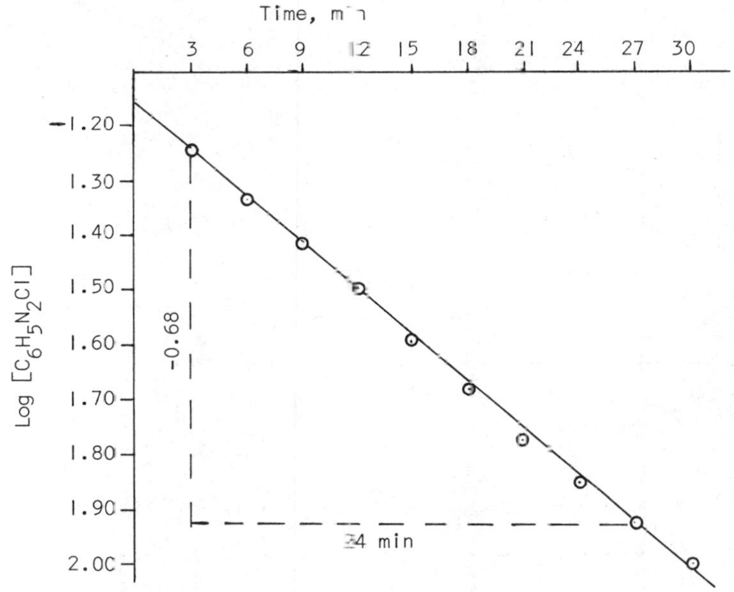

(j) Slope = -0.68/24 min = -0.028 min^{-1}

$k = -2.303 \times \text{slope} = -2.303 \times (-0.028)\text{min}^{-1} = 6.4 \times 10^{-2} \text{ min}^{-1}$

13-18. (a) We need to determine how many half-lives elapse as the concentration of the reactant decreases from [A] = 2.00 M to [A] = 0.250 M.

$$[A] = 2.00 \xrightarrow{t_{1/2}} 1.00 \xrightarrow{t_{1/2}} 0.50 \xrightarrow{t_{1/2}} 0.25$$

at t = 0   t = 200 min

Three half-lives elapse in a 200-minute period. $3 \times t_{1/2} = 200$ min. $t_{1/2} = 67$ min.

(b) $k = 0.693/t_{1/2} = 0.693/67 \text{ min} = 1.0 \times 10^{-2} \text{ min}^{-1}$

13-19. (a) For the decomposition of N_2O_5 in CCl_4 at 45°C, $t_{1/2} = 1100$ s. Starting with 80 g N_2O_5, we should expect the quantities of N_2O_5 remaining at various times to be:

80 g		40 g		20 g		10 g		5 g
t = 0	→	t = 1100 s	→	t = 2200 s	→	t = 3300 s	→	t = 4400 s

The time required for the quantity of N_2O_5 to decrease to 5 g is 4.4×10^3 s.

(b) At the point in question the quantity of N_2O_5 decomposed is 75 g.

$$\text{no. L } O_2 \text{ (STP)} = 75 \text{ g } N_2O_5 \times \frac{1 \text{ mol } N_2O_5}{108 \text{ g } N_2O_5} \times \frac{1 \text{ mol } O_2}{2 \text{ mol } N_2O_5} \times \frac{22.4 \text{ L } O_2}{1 \text{ mol } O_2} = 7.8 \text{ L } O_2$$

13-20. When the substance in question is 80% decomposed, the quantity remaining undecomposed is 20% of the original. The quantities to be substituted into equation (13.9) are $t = 0$, $[A]_0 = 0.50$; $t = ?$, $[A]_t = 0.10$; $k = 1.0 \times 10^{-3} \text{ s}^{-1}$.

$$\log [A]_t - \log [A]_0 = \frac{-kt}{2.303}$$

$$\log (0.10) - \log (0.50) = \frac{-1.0 \times 10^{-3} \text{ s}^{-1} \times t}{2.303}$$

$$-1.00 + 0.30 = (-4.34 \times 10^{-4} \text{ s}^{-1})t$$

$$t = \frac{0.70}{4.34 \times 10^{-4} \text{ s}^{-1}} = 1.6 \times 10^3 \text{ s}$$

13-21. (a) In the manner of Example 13-10 (a) determine which of the three plots yields a straight line. Only the first-order plot does.

t, min	[A]	log [A]
0	0.80	-0.097
8	0.60	0.222
24	0.35	0.456
40	0.20	0.699

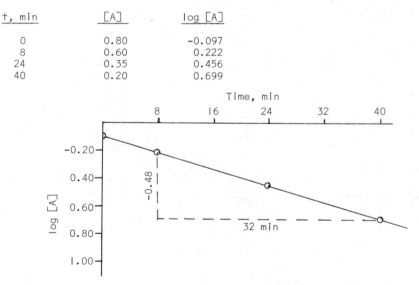

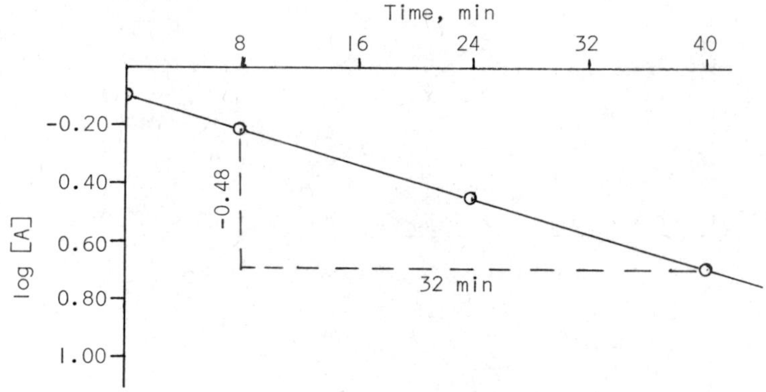

(b) Slope $= \frac{-0.48}{32 \text{ min}} = -1.5 \times 10^{-2} \text{ min}^{-1}$

$k = -2.303 \times \text{slope} = -2.303 \times (-1.5 \times 10^{-2}) \text{min}^{-1} = 3.5 \times 10^{-2} \text{ min}^{-1}$

(c) First calculate [A] at t = 30 min by using equation (13.9)

$$\log\frac{[A]_t}{0.80} = \frac{-3.5 \times 10^{-2} \text{ min}^{-1} \times 30 \text{ min}}{2.303} = -0.456 \qquad [A]_t/0.80 = 0.350; \quad [A]_t = 0.28 \text{ M}$$

Now use the rate equation to calculate the rate of disappearance of A when t = 30 min.

$$\text{rate} = k[A] = 3.5 \times 10^{-2} \text{ min}^{-1} \times 0.28 \text{ M} = 9.8 \times 10^{-3} \text{ mol L}^{-1} \text{ min}^{-1}$$

The rate of formation of B is one half the rate of disappearance of A.

$$\text{rate} = \Delta[B]/\Delta t = 4.9 \times 10^{-3} \text{ mol L}^{-1} \text{ min}^{-1}$$

13-22. At t = 0, [A] = $[A]_0$, and at t = 132 min, [A] = $0.01[A]_0$. (If the reactant is 99% decomposed, 1% remains. This is $0.01[A]_0$.) Use these data in equation (13.9) to solve for k.

$$\log\frac{0.01[A]_0}{[A]_0} = \frac{-k \times 132 \text{ min}}{2.303} = -2.00; \qquad k = 0.0349 \text{ min}^{-1}$$

$$t_{1/2} = 0.693/k = 0.693/0.0349 \text{ min}^{-1} = 19.9 \text{ min}$$

13-23. Since we are seeking the time for a reaction to proceed to a certain extent, we should expect to have to use equation (13.9).

$$\log\frac{[A]_t}{[A]_0} = \frac{-kt}{2.303}$$

The value of $[A]_0$ is 0.105 M. The value of $k = 0.693/t_{1/2} = 0.693/123 \text{ min} = 5.63 \times 10^{-3} \text{ min}^{-1}$. To determine the value of $[A]_t$ we must note the following:

no. mol NH_2NO_2 available = 0.165 L × 0.105 mol NH_2NO_2/L = 0.0173 mol NH_2NO_2

$$\text{no. mol } N_2O(g) \text{ produced} = \frac{PV}{RT} = \frac{[(756 - 12.8)/760]\text{atm} \times 0.050 \text{ L}}{0.0821 \text{ L atm mol}^{-1} \text{ K}^{-1} \times 288 \text{ K}} = 0.0021 \text{ mol } N_2O$$

no. mol NH_2NO_2 remaining = 0.0173 − 0.0021 = 0.0152 mol NH_2NO_2

$[NH_2NO_2]$ at the time in question = 0.0152 mol/0.165 L = 0.0921 M

$$\log\frac{0.0921}{0.105} = \frac{-5.63 \times 10^{-3} \text{ min}^{-1} \times t}{2.303} = -0.0569 \qquad t = 23.3 \text{ min}$$

13-24. (a) Construct the following table:

t, min	P_{DTBP}, mmHg	$\log P_{DTBP}$
0	800	2.90
40	575	2.76
80	400	2.60
120	280	2.45
160	200	2.30
200	140	2.15
240	100	2.00

Then construct the following graph:

$$slope = \frac{-0.90}{240\ min} = -3.8 \times 10^{-3}\ min^{-1}$$

$$k = -2.303 \times slope = -2.303 \times (-3.8 \times 10^{-3})$$

$$= 8.8 \times 10^{-3}\ min^{-1}$$

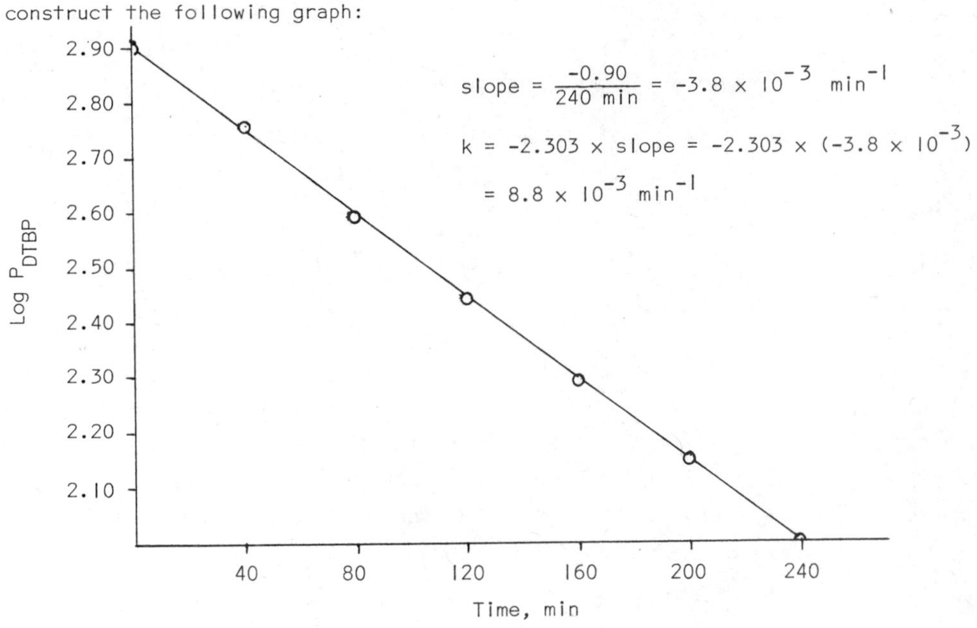

(b) Denote the initial pressure of pure DTBP by P_i. Since 3 mol gas is produced for every mol DTBP consumed, when the partial pressure of DTBP drops by $P_i - P_{DTBP}$, the pressure of the product gases increases by $3(P_i - P_{DTBP})$. This means that at any time the total pressure can be expressed as $P_{tot} = P_{DTBP} + 3(P_i - P_{DTBP})$.

To determine the time at which P_{tot} = 2000 mmHg, first determine the partial pressure of DTBP.
2000 mmHg = $P_{DTBP} + 3(800 - P_{DTBP})$mmHg;   2 P_{DTBP} = 2400 - 2000 = 400 mmHg; P_{DTBP} = 200 mmHg

For P_{DTBP} to drop from 800 mmHg to 200 mmHg, two half-life periods must elapse;
2 $t_{1/2}$ = 2 × 80 min = 160 min.

When the total gas pressure reaches 2100 mmHg: 2100 mmHg = $P_{DTBP} + 3(800 - P_{DTBP})$mmHg

2 P_{DTBP} = 2400 - 2100 = 300 mmHg; P_{DTBP} = 150 mmHg

$$\log\frac{150\ mmHg}{800\ mmHg} = \frac{-(0.693/80)min^{-1} \times t}{2.303} = -0.727 \quad t = 193\ min$$

13-25. (a) Plot log $P_{(CH_3)_2O}$ vs. time to obtain a straight line.

time, s	$P_{(CH_3)_2O}$, mmHg	log $P_{(CH_3)_2O}$
0	312	2.494
390	264	2.422
777	224	2.350
1195	187	2.272
3155	78.5	1.895
∞	2.5	0.40

See graph on next page.

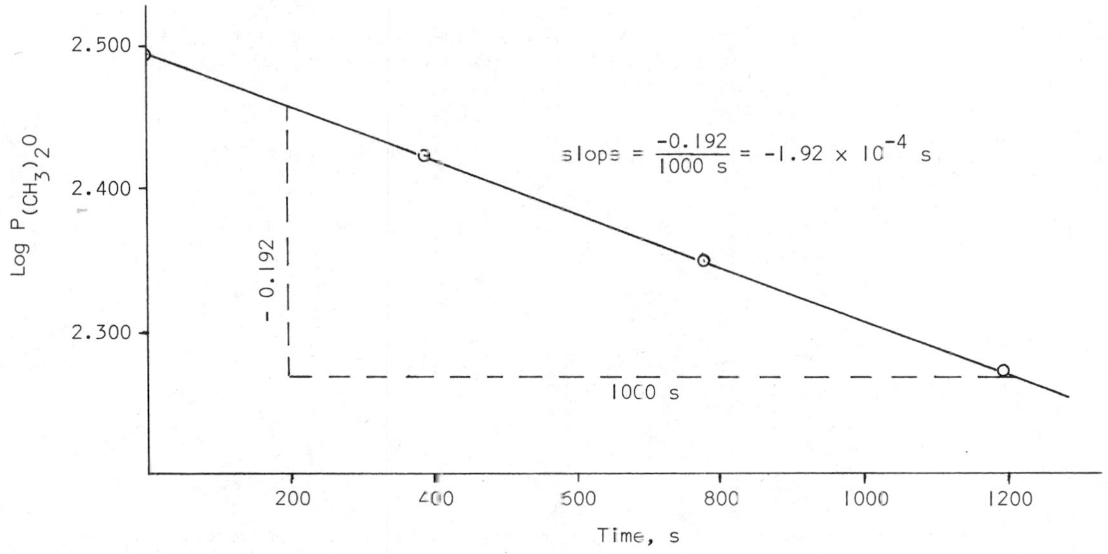

(b) For the straight line obtained in part (a), slope = $-k/2.303$

$k = -2.303 \times \text{slope} = -2.303 \times (-1.92 \times 10^{-4}) = 4.42 \times 10^{-4}\ s^{-1}$

(c) From the table we see that at 390 s, $P_{(CH_3)_2O}$ = 264 mmHg. $\Delta P_{(CH_3)_2O}$ = 312 - 264 = 48 mmHg.

$P_{products} = 3 \times \Delta P_{(CH_3)_2O} = 3 \times 48 = 144$ mmHg. $P_{total} = P_{(CH_3)_2O} + P_{products} = 264 + 144$
= 408 mmHg.

(d) The maximum gas pressure that could develop would be that corresponding to the complete dissociation of $(CH_3)_2O$, since three moles of products are produced for every mole of reactant. Maximum total pressure = 3 x initial $P_{(CH_3)_2O}$ = 3 x 312 = 936 mmHg.

Actually, since the partial pressure of $(CH_3)_2O$ in this particular reaction remains at 2.5 mmHg at $t = \infty$, the maximum pressure is that observed at infinite time.

P_{total} = 2.5 mmHg + 3 x (312 - 2.5)mmHg = 931 mmHg

(e) Here we must use equation (13.13) and solve for the partial pressure of $(CH_3)_2O$ at 1000 s. Use the value of k from part (b).

$$\log \frac{P}{P_o} = \frac{-kt}{2.303} \qquad \log \frac{P}{312} = \frac{-4.4 \times 10^{-4}\ s^{-1} \times 1000\ s}{2.303} = -0.191$$

$\log P = -0.191 + \log 312 = -0.191 + 2.494 = 2.303$ $\qquad P_{(CH_3)_2O}$ = 201 mmHg

P_{total} = 201 mmHg + 3 x (312 - 201)mmHg = 534 mmHg

Collision theory; activation energy

13-26. (a) In order for a collision between molecules to result in a chemical reaction, the molecules must be especially energetic and they must have the correct orientation. As a result, only a tiny fraction of all molecular collisions are effective in producing chemical reaction. The reaction rate is much smaller than the collision frequency.

(b) A critical factor in establishing the rate of a reaction is the fraction of all the molecules that are especially energetic, possessing energies in excess of the activation energy. This fraction, and hence the rate of the reaction itself, increases with temperature at a much faster rate than does the collision frequency.

(c) The effect of a catalyst is to lower the activation energy of a reaction by changing the mechanism of the reaction. If the activation energy is lowered, the fraction of the molecules that are energetic enough to react, and hence the rate of the reaction itself, increases profoundly, even though the temperature remains unchanged.

13-27. (a) Use expression (13.28): $\Delta H = E_a(\text{forward}) - E_a(\text{reverse})$. $\Delta H = 21$ kJ/mol and $E_a(\text{forward}) = 84$ kJ/mol.

$E_a(\text{reverse}) = E_a(\text{forward}) - \Delta H = 84 \text{ kJ/mol} - 21 \text{ kJ/mol} = 63 \text{ kJ/mol}$

(b)

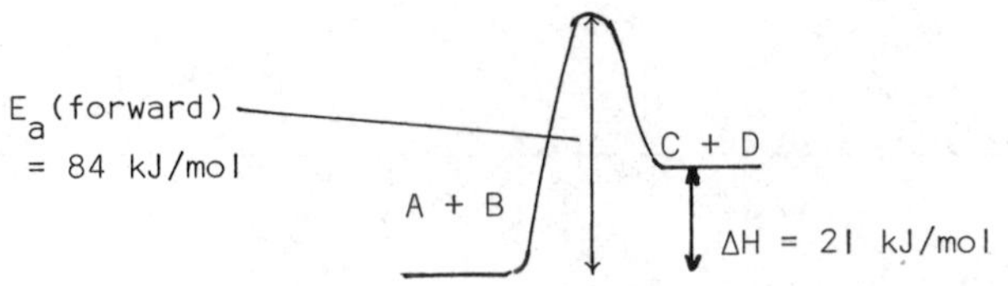

13-28. From the sketches below it can be seen that for the endothermic reaction, no matter what the value of ΔH, the activation energy, E_a, must be greater. With exothermic reactions, however, there is no relationship between the numerical values of E_a and ΔH. For example, for the two cases shown, E_a is seen to be the same but ΔH is very much different.

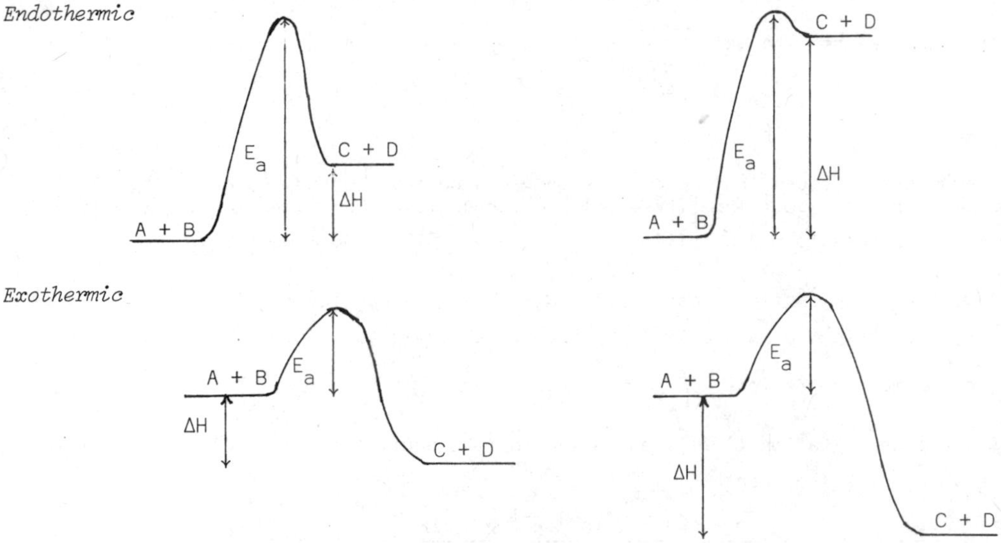

Effect of temperature on reaction rate

13-29. (a) Construct a graph of log k vs. 1/T.

t, °C	T, K	$1/T$, K^{-1}	k, $L\ mol^{-1}\ s^{-1}$	log k
3	276	3.62×10^{-3}	1.4×10^{-3}	-2.85
13	286	3.50×10^{-3}	2.9×10^{-3}	-2.54
24	297	3.37×10^{-3}	6.2×10^{-3}	-2.21
33	306	3.27×10^{-3}	1.2×10^{-2}	-1.92

See graph on next page.

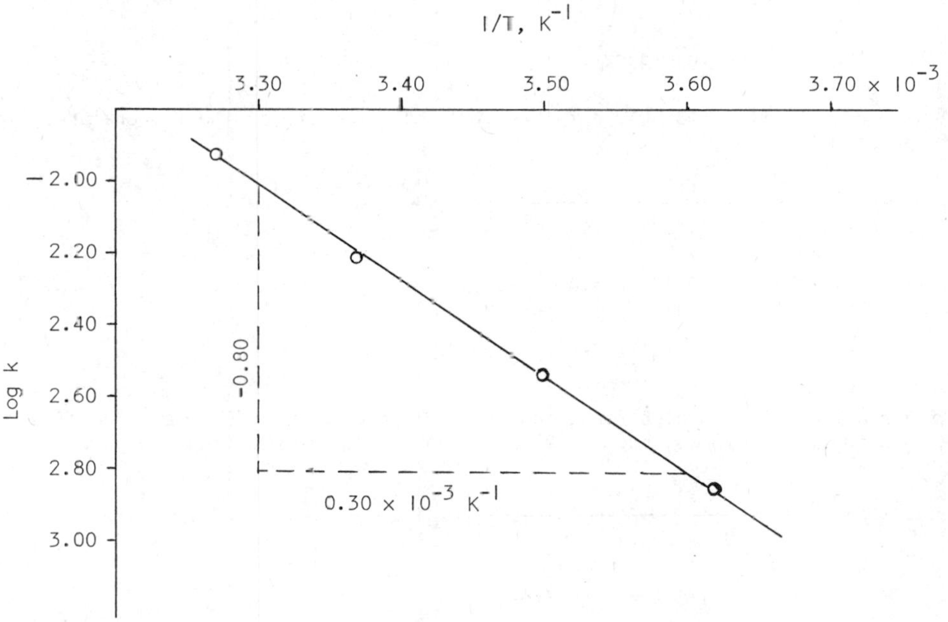

(b) Slope = $-E_a/2.303 \times R = -2.7 \times 10^3$ K

$E_a = 2.303 \times 8.314 \text{ J mol}^{-1} \text{ K}^{-1} \times 2.7 \times 10^3 \text{ K} = 5.2 \times 10^4 \text{ J/mol} = 52 \text{ kJ/mol}$

(c) Use the expression $\log \frac{k_2}{k_1} = \frac{E_a}{2.303 R}\left(\frac{T_2 - T_1}{T_2 T_1}\right)$ with $k_1 = 1.2 \times 10^{-2}$, $T_1 = 306$ K, k_2 = ?, and $T_2 = 313$ K.

From part (b) substitute $E_a = 5.2 \times 10^4$ J/mol

$$\log \frac{k_2}{1.2 \times 10^{-2}} = \frac{5.2 \times 10^4 \text{ J/mol}}{2.303 \times 8.314 \text{ J mol}^{-1} \text{ K}^{-1}}\left(\frac{313 - 306}{313 \times 306}\right) \text{K}^{-1}$$

$\log k_2 - \log 1.2 \times 10^{-2} = 0.20$

$\log k_2 = 0.20 + \log 1.2 \times 10^{-2} = 0.20 - 1.92 = -1.72$

$k_2 = 1.9 \times 10^{-2} \text{ L mol}^{-1} \text{ s}^{-1}$

(d) Proceed as in part (c) to determine k at 50°C. Then use the rate equation to calculate the initial rate.

$$\log \frac{k_2}{1.2 \times 10^{-2}} = \frac{5.2 \times 10^4 \text{ J/mol}}{2.303 \times 8.314 \text{ J mol}^{-1} \text{ K}^{-1}}\left(\frac{323 - 306}{323 \times 306}\right) \text{K}^{-1}$$

$\log k_2 = 0.47 - 1.92 = -1.45$ $\quad\quad k_2 = 3.5 \times 10^{-2} \text{ L mol}^{-1} \text{ s}^{-1}$

initial rate $= k \times [S_2O_8{}^{2-}]_{init} \times [I^-]_{init} = 3.5 \times 10^{-2} \text{ L mol}^{-1} \text{ s}^{-1} \times 0.076 \text{ mol/L} \times 0.030 \text{ mol/L}$

$= 3.0 \times 10^{-5} \text{ mol L}^{-1} \text{ s}^{-1}$

13-30. Use equation (13.30) to solve for E_a

$$\log \frac{3.8 \times 10^{-2}}{1.2 \times 10^{-4}} = \frac{E_a}{2.303 \times 8.314 \text{ J mol}^{-1} \text{ K}^{-1}}\left(\frac{666 - 556}{556 \times 666}\right) \text{K}^{-1} = 2.50$$

$$E_a = 2.50 \times 2.303 \times 8.314 \times \left(\frac{556 \times 666}{666 - 556}\right) = 1.61 \times 10^5 \text{ J/mol} = 161 \text{ kJ/mol}$$

(The value depicted in Figure 13-12 is E_a = 171 kJ/mol.)

13-31. Again, use equation (13.30), but this time solve for one of the temperatures, say T_2 (the higher temperature).

$$\log \frac{1.0 \times 10^{-5}}{1.0 \times 10^{-10}} = \frac{111 \times 10^3 \text{ J/mol}}{2.303 \times 8.314 \text{ J mol}^{-1} \text{ K}^{-1}}\left(\frac{T_2 - 300}{300\ T_2}\right) \text{K}^{-1} = 5.00$$

$$1.11 \times 10^5\ T_2 - 3.33 \times 10^7 = 5.00 \times 2.303 \times 8.314 \times 300\ T_2$$

$$8.23 \times 10^4\ T_2 = 3.33 \times 10^7; \quad T_2 = 405 \text{ K}$$

13-32. If a reaction rate doubles for a temperature increase of 10°C, the value of k must also double. Assume two temperatures, such as 25°C and 35°C, and use equation (13.30).

(a) $$\log \frac{2\not{k}}{\not{k}} = \frac{E_a}{2.303 \times 8.314 \text{ J mol}^{-1} \text{ K}^{-1}} \times \left(\frac{308 - 298}{298 \times 308}\right) \text{K}^{-1} = 0.301$$

$$E_a = 5.3 \times 10^4 \text{ J/mol} = 53 \text{ kJ/mol}$$

(b) The rule of thumb would not apply well to the formation of HI from its elements. E_a for this reaction is shown in Figure 13-12 to be 171 kJ/mol.

13-33. First, determine the initial rate of decomposition for the 1.25 M solution. (Use the value of k listed for 0°C).

$$\text{initial rate} = 7.87 \times 10^{-7} \text{ s}^{-1} \times 1.25 \text{ M} = 9.84 \times 10^{-7} \text{ mol L}^{-1} \text{ s}^{-1}$$

Next, determine a value of k for which the initial rate of decomposition of an 0.15 M solution will be that just calculated.

$$9.84 \times 10^{-7} \text{ mol L}^{-1} \text{ s}^{-1} = k \times 0.15 \text{ mol L}^{-1} \qquad k = 6.56 \times 10^{-6} \text{ s}^{-1}$$

Now, use equation (13.30) to find the appropriate temperature. Use t = 0°C as the second temperature and $E_a = 1.0 \times 10^5$ J/mol.

$$\log \frac{6.56 \times 10^{-6}}{7.87 \times 10^{-7}} = \frac{1.0 \times 10^5 \text{ J/mol}}{2.303 \times 8.314 \text{ J mol}^{-1} \text{ K}^{-1}} \times \left(\frac{T_2 - 273}{273\ T_2}\right) = 0.921$$

$$1.0 \times 10^5\ T_2 - 2.73 \times 10^7 = 4.81 \times 10^3\ T_2 \qquad T_2 = 287 \text{ K}$$

Catalysis

13-34. (a) A catalyst is a substance that speeds up a chemical reaction by entering into the reaction *in such a way that its composition remains unchanged.*

(b) The function of a catalyst is to *change the mechanism* of a chemical reaction to one requiring a lower activation energy.

13-35. An enzyme is a very specific catalyst, catalyzing one reaction and one alone. Also, the conditions of temperature and acid/base concentration under which the enzyme functions are very limited. A platinum catalyst, on the other hand, can catalyze a large number of different reactions and under various conditions of temperature and pressure.

13-36. The order of the reaction can be established by plotting the data in the form, [S] versus *t*, but it is also possible to do this simply by examining the data themselves. The concentration of S decreases by 0.10 mol/L for every 20 minutes. A reaction that proceeds at a *constant* rate is zero-order.

13-37. Both in enzyme action and in heterogeneous catalysis, reaction occurs at an active site. When the concentration (pressure) of reactant is low, active sites are readily available and the reaction rate depends on reactant concentration (pressure); the reaction is first order. At high reactant concentrations (pressures) all active sites tend to be occupied and the reaction rate depends on the rate at which active sites become available. This availability rate is unaffected by reactant concentration (pressure). The reaction proceeds at a constant rate--zero order.

Reaction mechanisms

13-38. An elementary process is a single step in the mechanism of an overall reaction. The molecularity of the elementary process indicates whether an activated molecule undergoes dissociation (unimolecular), whether reaction occurs as a result of a collision between two molecules (bimolecular), and so on. The order of an *elementary process* is related to its molecularity (i.e., unimolecular--first order; bimolecular--second order; etc.). However, the overall reaction generally proceeds by a mechanism involving more than one step and the order of the overall reaction is not related in any direct way to the molecularity of an individual elementary process.

13-39. The rate-determining step in a reaction mechanism is the slowest step and, as in any process that involves several steps, the slowest step acts as a bottleneck. The overall process can proceed no faster than the rate at which events occur in the bottleneck.

13-40. $O_3 \longrightarrow O_2 + \not{O}$

$\not{O} + O_3 \longrightarrow 2\ O_2$

$2\ O_3 \longrightarrow 3\ O_2$

13-41. The mechanism involves a rate determining step in which one molecule each of ICl and H_2 combine to produce one product molecule--HCl--and one molecule of the intermediate--HI. This is the rate determining step and suggests a rate law for the net reaction: rate = $k[H_2][ICl]$. The rate determining step is followed by a fast reaction in which the intermediate HI reacts with a second molecule of ICl to produce a second molecule of HCl and one of I_2. Thus, the kinetics of the reaction is described in terms of the rate determining step, and the stoichiometry, by the combination of the rate determining step and the following fast step.

13-42. Rate of formation of $N_2O_2 = k_1[NO]^2$ Rate of dissociation of $N_2O_2 = k_2[N_2O_2]$

Steady state condition: $k_1[NO]^2 = k_2[N_2O_2]$ $[N_2O_2] = \frac{k_1}{k_2}[NO]^2$

13-43. (a) The rate law, rate = $k[NO]^2[O_2]$, is consistent with the one-step mechanism, $2\ NO + O_2 \longrightarrow 2\ NO_2$.

(b) Despite the fact that the one-step mechanism of part (a) is consistent with the observed rate law, this mechanism is highly unlikely. The one-step mechanism is a termolecular process, requiring the simultaneous collision of three molecules. Such collisions are much less probable than bimolecular collisions. Thus the mechanism of the reaction in question is more likely to involve a combination of uni- and bimolecular steps.

13-44. The steady-state condition in the mechanism has already been described in Exercise 42. The rate of formation of NO_2 is given by:

$$\text{Rate} = k_3[N_2O_2][O_2] = \frac{k_1k_3}{k_2}[NO]^2[O_2] = k[NO]^2[O_2]$$

13-45. In order for a given molecule to dissociate in a unimolecular process, the molecule must first acquire energy in excess of the activation energy. This results from repeated collisions of the given molecule with other molecules. Thus, when dissociation does occur only a single molecule is involved, but molecular collisions must have preceded the dissociation.

Self-test Questions

1. (*a*) Recall the relationship between the order of reaction and the function of [A] that yields a straight line. A plot of [A] vs. t is linear for a zero order reaction; log [A] vs. t for a first order reaction; and 1/[A] vs. t for a second order reaction.

2. (*c*) The decrease in [A] with time is not constant (the reaction slows down with time); the reaction cannot be zero order. The concentration of A decreases to one half of its initial value in 500 s. The second half life is 1000 s. The reaction cannot be first order because the half life is not constant. By a process of elimination we conclude that the reaction is second order. (This conclusion could be verified by plotting 1/[A] vs. time.)

3. (*b*) The half life of a reaction is not one half the time required for a reaction to go to completion [item (a) is incorrect]. At the end of each 100 s interval, half of the reactant present at the beginning of the interval is consumed [item (b) is correct]. If the same quantity were consumed in the second half-life period as in the first half-life period, the reaction would go to completion in two half-life periods. [Item (c) is incorrect for the same reason as item (a).] The reaction starts as soon as the reaction condition is established; there is no waiting time [item (d) is incorrect].

4. (*c*) In the period from 50 s to 100 s, the reaction proceeds at the rate: $-\Delta[A]/\Delta t = -(0.37 - 0.61)M/50\ s = 0.0048\ mol\ L^{-1}\ s^{-1}$. In the period from 100s to 150 s, the rate is $-(0.22 - 0.37)/50\ s = 0.0030\ mol\ L^{-1}\ s^{-1}$. Because a first order reaction slows down continuously, the rate at $t = 100\ s$ must be less than the initial rate of reaction [item (d) is incorrect]. It must also be less than the average rate in the interval from 50 to 100 s (i.e., less than $0.0048\ mol\ L^{-1}\ s^{-1}$). Item (a) is incorrect. But the rate at 100 s must be greater than the average rate in the interval from 100 to 150 s ($0.0030\ mol\ L^{-1}\ s^{-1}$). Item (b) is incorrect.

5. (*d*) The rate equation, rate = k[A]•[B], signifies a second order reaction. Item (a) is incorrect because the unit s^{-1} corresponds to k for a first order reaction. Item (b) is also incorrect because $t_{1/2}$ is a constant only for a first order reaction. Item (c) is incorrect because the value of k for a reaction depends on the particular reaction and the temperature, but not on the initial concentrations of reactants chosen. Item (d) is correct based on the stoichiometry of the reaction--two molecules of A are consumed for each molecule of C produced.

6. (*d*) Here we must recall the method of initial rates. For the second-order decomposition, rate = $k[A]^2$. The initial rate = $k[A]_0^2$. Its value does depend on the concentration chosen for $[A]_0$. [Item (a) is incorrect.] Now compare the initial rates at the following values: $[A]_0 = 0.50$ M, $[A]_0 = 1.00$ M, $[A]_0 = 0.10$ M, and $[A]_0 = 0.25$ M.

   Initial rates: (1) $k(0.50)^2 = 0.25 \cdot k$; (2) $k(1.00)^2 = 1.00 \cdot k$; (3) $k\ (0.10)^2 = 0.01 \cdot k$;
   (4) $k(0.25)^2 = 0.0625 \cdot k$

   Rate (1) is only one quarter of Rate (2). Item (b) is incorrect. Rate (1) is 25 times greater than Rate (3). Item (c) is incorrect. Rate (1) is four times Rate (4). Item (d) is correct.

7. (*b*) Although the average kinetic energy of gas molecules [item (d)] and collision frequency [item (a)] increase with temperature, they do not increase rapidly enough to account for the very sharp increase in reaction rate with temperature. Item (c) must be incorrect, because an increase in the activation energy for a reaction would cause the reaction to slow down. It is the fraction of the molecules that possess energies in excess of the activation energy that increases so rapidly with temperature.

8. (*c*) The activation energy of a reaction is always a positive quantity [item (a) must be incorrect]. Because the reaction is endothermic ($\Delta H > 0$), the activation energy must equal or exceed ΔH. Items (b) and (d) are incorrect and (c) is correct.

9. (*d*) A catalyst can affect neither the average kinetic energies nor the collision frequencies of molecules. Items (a) and (b) are incorrect. A catalyst does *not* increase the activation energy of a reaction; this would slow down a reaction. A catalyst permits a reaction mechanism of *lower* activation energy; if E_a is lowered, the fraction of molecules with energies in excess of E_a increases. Item (d) is the correct response.

10.(*b*) The relationship between k and $t_{1/2}$ in item (a) is for a first-order reaction. If the reaction mechanism involves a *single step*, and if this step is bimolecular, the overall reaction order is second. The rate equation becomes k[A]•[B]. Item (b) is correct. The rate of appearance of C is twice the rate of disappearance of A [item (c) is incorrect]. The equation given in item (d) is for a first-order reaction, not second order.

11. (a) The reaction is first order, and the quantity of A decreases from 1.60 g to 0.40 g in 20 min. This decrease corresponds to two half-life periods: 1.60 g ⟶ 0.80 g ⟶ 0.40 g. The half-life of the reaction, $t_{1/2}$ = 10 min.

(b) Use the value of $t_{1/2}$ to calculate k for the reaction.

$$k = 0.693/t_{1/2} = 0.693/10\ \text{min} = 0.0693\ \text{min}^{-1}$$

Now solve for the mass of A (call it A_t) at t = 33.2 min. (Note that we can deal with mass directly; we do not need to employ molar concentrations.)

$$\log \frac{A_t}{A_0} = \log \frac{A_t}{1.60} = \frac{-(0.0693\ \text{min}^{-1}) \times 33.2\ \text{min}}{2.303} \qquad \log A_t - \log 1.60 = -0.999$$

$$\log A_t = -0.999 + \log 1.60 = -0.999 - 0.204 = -0.795 \qquad A_t = 0.160\ \text{g}$$

12. Use the heat of formation data to establish $\Delta\overline{H}$ for the reaction.

$CH_3CHO(g) \longrightarrow CH_4(g) + CO(g)$; $\Delta\overline{H}$ = ?

$$\Delta\overline{H} = \Delta\overline{H}^\circ_f[CH_4(g)] + \Delta\overline{H}^\circ_f[CO(g)] - \Delta\overline{H}^\circ_f[CH_3CHO(g)]$$

$$= -74.9\ \text{kJ/mol} - 110.5\ \text{kJ/mol} - (-166)\ \text{kJ/mol}$$

$$= -19.4\ \text{kJ/mol}$$

Uncatalyzed reaction:

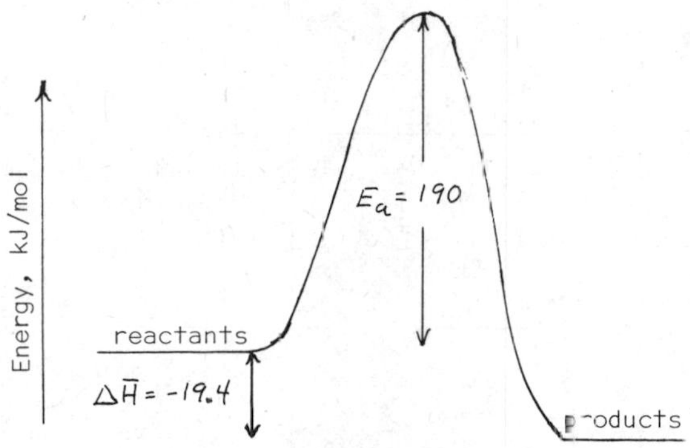

Catalyzed reaction:

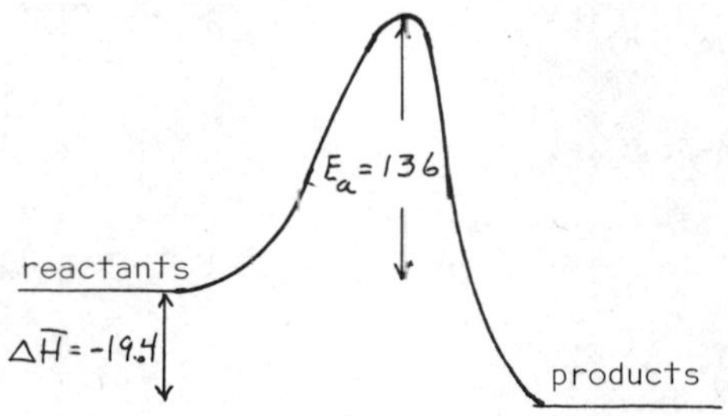

Chapter 14

Principles of Chemical Equilibrium

Writing equilibrium constant expressions

14-1. (a) $K_c = \dfrac{[CO_2][H_2]}{[CO][H_2O]}$; (b) $K_c = \dfrac{[NO_2]^2}{[NO]^2[O_2]}$; (c) $K_c = \dfrac{[CH_4][H_2S]^2}{[CS_2][H_2]^4}$;

(d) $4\ NH_3(g) + 5\ O_2(g) \rightleftharpoons 4\ NO(g) + 6\ H_2O\ (g)$; $K_c = \dfrac{[NO]^4[H_2O]^6}{[NH_3]^4[O_2]^5}$

(e) $2\ NO_2(g) + 7\ H_2(g) \rightleftharpoons 2\ NH_3(g) + 4\ H_2O(g)$; $K_c = \dfrac{[NH_3]^2[H_2O]^4}{[NO_2]^2[H_2]^7}$

14-2. (a) $\frac{1}{2}\ N_2(g) + \frac{1}{2}\ O_2(g) \rightleftharpoons NO(g)$; $K_c = \dfrac{[NO]}{[N_2]^{1/2}[O_2]^{1/2}}$

(b) $\frac{1}{2}\ H_2(g) + \frac{1}{2}\ Cl_2(g) \rightleftharpoons HCl(g)$; $K_c = \dfrac{[HCl]}{[H_2]^{1/2}[Cl_2]^{1/2}}$

(c) $\frac{1}{2}\ N_2(g) + \frac{3}{2}\ H_2(g) \rightleftharpoons NH_3(g)$; $K_c = \dfrac{[NH_3]}{[N_2]^{1/2}[H_2]^{3/2}}$

(d) $\frac{1}{2}\ Cl_2(g) + \frac{3}{2}\ F_2(g) \rightleftharpoons ClF_3(g)$; $K_c = \dfrac{[ClF_3]}{[Cl_2]^{1/2}[F_2]^{3/2}}$

(e) $\frac{1}{2}\ N_2(g) + \frac{1}{2}\ O_2(g) + \frac{1}{2}\ Cl_2(g) \rightleftharpoons NOCl(g)$; $K_c = \dfrac{[NOCl]}{[N_2]^{1/2}[O_2]^{1/2}[Cl_2]^{1/2}}$

14-3. (a) $K_c = [CO_2(g)]$ (b) $K_c = [CO_2(g)][H_2O(g)]$ (c) $K_c = [CO_2(g)]$ (d) $K_c = [(CH_3)_2CO(g)]$

(e) $CS_2(l) + 3\ Cl_2(g) \rightleftharpoons CCl_4(l) + S_2Cl_2(l)$; $K_c = \dfrac{1}{[Cl_2(g)]^3}$

(f) $Na_2CO_3(s) + 4\ C(s) + N_2(g) \rightleftharpoons 2\ NaCN(s) + 3\ CO(g)$; $K_c = \dfrac{[CO(g)]^3}{[N_2(g)]}$

14-4. (a) $CO_2(g) + H_2(g) \rightleftharpoons CO(g) + H_2O(g)$. This equation is written as the *reverse* of the corresponding equation given in the text. Its equilibrium constant value is the *reciprocal* of that given in the text.

$$K_c = \frac{[CO][H_2O]}{[CO_2][H_2]} = \frac{1}{23.2} = 4.31 \times 10^{-2}\ \text{(at 600 K)}$$

(b) $2\ SO_2(g) + O_2(g) \rightleftharpoons 2\ SO_3(g)$. This equation has coefficients that are *twice* those in the corresponding equation in the text. The equilibrium constant value is the *square* of that listed in the text.

$$K_c = \frac{[SO_3]^2}{[SO_2]^2[O_2]} = (56)^2 = 3.1 \times 10^3\ \text{(at 900 K)}$$

(c) $H_2S(g) \rightleftharpoons H_2(g) + 1/2\ S_2(g)$. Here the equation is written with coefficients that are *one half* of those shown in the text. Its equilibrium constant value is the *square root* of the value listed in the text.

$$K_c = \frac{[H_2][S_2]^{1/2}}{[H_2S]} = (2.3 \times 10^{-4})^{1/2} = 1.5 \times 10^{-2} \text{ (at 1405°C)}$$

(d) $NO(g) + 1/2\ O_2(g) \rightleftharpoons NO_2(g)$. In this final case the equation is both *reversed* and written with coefficients that are *one half* of those shown in the text. The equilibrium constant value is the *square root of the reciprocal* of that listed in the text.

$$K_c = \frac{[NO_2]}{[NO][O_2]^{1/2}} = \left(\frac{1}{1.8 \times 10^{-6}}\right)^{1/2} = 7.5 \times 10^{2} \text{ (at 457 K)}$$

14-5. $1/2\ N_2(g) + 1/2\ O_2(g) \rightleftharpoons \cancel{NO(g)}$; $K_c = \left(\frac{1}{2.4 \times 10^{30}}\right)^{1/2} = 6.5 \times 10^{-16}$

$\cancel{NO(g)} + 1/2\ Br_2(g) \rightleftharpoons NOBr(g)$; $K_c = 1.4$

$1/2\ N_2(g) + 1/2\ O_2(g) + 1/2\ Br_2(g) \rightleftharpoons NOBr(g)$; $K_c = 1.4 \times 6.5 \times 10^{-16} = 9.1 \times 10^{-16}$

14-6. $2\ N_2O(g) \rightleftharpoons 2\ \cancel{N_2(g)} + O_2(g)$; $K_c = (1/3.4 \times 10^{-18})^2 = 8.7 \times 10^{34}$

$2\ \cancel{N_2(g)} + 4\ O_2(g) \rightleftharpoons 4\ \cancel{NO_2(g)}$; $K_c = (4.1 \times 10^{-9})^4 = 2.8 \times 10^{-34}$

$4\ \cancel{NO_2(g)} \rightleftharpoons 2\ N_2O_4(g)$; $K_c = (1/4.6 \times 10^{-3})^2 = 4.7 \times 10^{4}$

$2\ N_2O(g) + 3\ O_2(g) \rightleftharpoons 2\ N_2O_4(g)$; $K_c = 8.7 \times 10^{34} \times 4.7 \times 10^{4} \times 2.8 \times 10^{-34} = 1.1 \times 10^{6}$

Experimental determination of equilibrium constants

14-7. $A(g) + B(g) \rightleftharpoons 2\ C(g)$; $K_c = \frac{[C]^2}{[A][B]} = \frac{(0.40)^2}{(0.52)(0.60)} = 0.51$

14-8. number of moles of A, at equilibrium = 0.90 mol A

number of moles of A consumed = 1.20 − 0.90 = 0.30 mol A

number of moles of B consumed = $0.30 \text{ mol A} \times \frac{1 \text{ mol B}}{2 \text{ mol A}} = 0.15 \text{ mol B}$

number of moles of B, at equilibrium = 0.80 − 0.15 = 0.65 mol B

number of moles of C, at equilibrium = $0.30 \text{ mol A} \times \frac{1 \text{ mol C}}{2 \text{ mol A}} = 0.15 \text{ mol C}$

Recall that all of the reactants are present in a vessel of 2.00-liter volume, and substitute appropriate data into the expression for K_c.

$$K_c = \frac{[C]}{[A]^2[B]} = \frac{0.15/2.00}{(0.90/2.00)^2(0.65/2.00)} = \frac{0.15 \times 4.00}{(0.90)^2 \times 0.65} = 1.14$$

14-9. no. mol Cl_2, at equilibrium = $0.25 \text{ g } Cl_2 \times \frac{1 \text{ mol } Cl_2}{70.9 \text{ g } Cl_2} = 3.5 \times 10^{-3} \text{ mol } Cl_2$

no. mol PCl_3, at equilibrium = no. mol Cl_2, at equilibrium = 3.5×10^{-3} mol PCl_3

$$\text{no. mol } PCl_5\text{, originally} = 1.00 \text{ g } PCl_5 \times \frac{1 \text{ mol } PCl_5}{208 \text{ g } PCl_5} = 4.81 \times 10^{-3} \text{ mol } PCl_5$$

$$\text{no. mol } PCl_5\text{, at equilibrium} = 4.81 \times 10^{-3} - 3.5 \times 10^{-3} = 1.3 \times 10^{-3} \text{ mol } PCl_5$$

$$K_c = \frac{[PCl_3][Cl_2]}{[PCl_5]} = \frac{(3.5 \times 10^{-3}/0.250)(3.5 \times 10^{-3}/0.250)}{(1.3 \times 10^{-3}/0.250)} = 3.8 \times 10^{-2}$$

14-10. From the titration data we can establish the no. mol CH_3CO_2H remaining unreacted at equilibrium.

$$\text{no. mol } CH_3CO_2H = 0.02885 \text{ L} \times \frac{0.1000 \text{ mol Ba(OH)}_2}{\text{L}} \times \frac{2 \text{ mol } CH_3CO_2H}{1 \text{ mol Ba(OH)}_2} = 0.00577 \text{ mol } CH_3CO_2H$$

The sample titrated is one-hundredth of the equilibrium mixture. The total amount of CH_3CO_2H at equilibrium = 0.577 mol CH_3CO_2H.

The amount of CH_3CO_2H consumed to reach equilibrium = 1.000 - 0.577 = 0.423 mol. This is also the amount of C_2H_5OH consumed. The amount of C_2H_5OH present at equilibrium = 0.500 - 0.423 = 0.077 mol C_2H_5OH. The amounts of $CH_3CO_2C_2H_5$ and H_2O are both 0.423 mol. Assume that the volume of the reaction mixture is V(liters). Determine the equilibrium concentrations of the reactants and products, substitute into the K_c expression, and obtain a value of K_c.

$$K_c = \frac{[CH_3CO_2C_2H_5][H_2O]}{[C_2H_5OH][CH_3CO_2H]} = \frac{(0.423/V)(0.423/V)}{(0.077/V)(0.577/V)} = \frac{(0.423)^2}{0.077 \times 0.577} = 4.0$$

14-11. Five calculations of the following type are required to determine the concentrations of HI, H_2 and I_2 in each bulb at the time it is opened.

Bulb 1:

$$\text{no. mol } I_2 = 0.02096 \text{ L} \times \frac{0.0150 \text{ mol } Na_2S_2O_3}{\text{L}} \times \frac{1 \text{ mol } I_2}{2 \text{ mol } Na_2S_2O_3} = 1.57 \times 10^{-4} \text{ mol } I_2$$

$$\text{no. mol } H_2 = \text{no. mol } I_2 = 1.57 \times 10^{-4} \text{ mol } H_2$$

$$\text{no. mol HI} = \text{original number moles HI - moles of HI consumed}$$

$$= \left(0.300 \text{ g HI} \times \frac{1 \text{ mol HI}}{127.9 \text{ g HI}}\right) - \left(1.57 \times 10^{-4} \text{ mol } I_2 \times \frac{2 \text{ mol HI}}{1 \text{ mol } I_2}\right)$$

$$= 2.35 \times 10^{-3} \text{ mol HI} - 3.14 \times 10^{-4} \text{ mol HI} = 2.04 \times 10^{-3} \text{ mol HI}$$

Convert these amounts of reactants and products to concentrations and form the reaction quotient, Q.

$$Q = \frac{[H_2][I_2]}{[HI]^2} = \frac{(1.57 \times 10^{-4}/0.400)(1.57 \times 10^{-4}/0.400)}{(2.04 \times 10^{-3}/0.400)^2} = 5.92 \times 10^{-3}$$

Bulb 2:

$$\text{no. mol } I_2 = \text{no. mol } H_2 = 0.02790 \times 0.0150 \times 1/2 = 2.09 \times 10^{-4}$$

$$\text{no. mol HI} = (0.320/127.9) - (2 \times 2.09 \times 10^{-4}) = 2.08 \times 10^{-3}$$

$$Q = \frac{(2.09 \times 10^{-4}/0.400)^2}{(2.08 \times 10^{-3}/0.400)^2} = 1.01 \times 10^{-2}$$

Bulb 3:

$$\text{no. mol } I_2 = \text{no. mol } H_2 = 0.03231 \times 0.0150 \times 1/2 = 2.42 \times 10^{-4}$$

no. mol HI = (0.315/127.9) - (2 × 2.42 × 10^{-4}) = 1.98 × 10^{-3}

$$Q = \frac{(2.42 \times 10^{-4}/0.400)^2}{(1.98 \times 10^{-3}/0.400)^2} = 1.49 \times 10^{-2}$$

Bulb 4:

no. mol I_2 = no. mol H_2 = 0.04150 × 0.0150 × 1/2 = 3.11 × 10^{-4}

no. mol HI = (0.406/127.9) - (2 × 3.11 × 10^{-4}) = 2.55 × 10^{-3}

$$Q = \frac{(3.11 \times 10^{-4}/0.400)^2}{(2.55 \times 10^{-3}/0.400)^2} = 1.49 \times 10^{-2}$$

Bulb 5:

no. mol I_2 = no. mol H_2 = 0.02868 × 0.0150 × 1/2 = 2.15 × 10^{-4}

no. mol HI = (0.280/127.9) - (2 × 2.15 × 10^{-4}) = 1.76 × 10^{-3}

$$Q = \frac{(2.15 \times 10^{-4}/0.400)^2}{(1.76 \times 10^{-3}/0.400)^2} = 1.49 \times 10^{-2}$$

The value of Q assumes a constant value of 1.49 × 10^{-2} in those bulbs opened after about 12 h or more. We conclude that equilibrium was attained in these cases and that K_c = 1.49 × 10^2.

Equilibrium relationships

14-12. For the reaction, $CO(g) + H_2O(g) \rightleftharpoons CO_2(g) + H_2(g)$, K_c = 1.00 at 1100 K

$$K_c = \frac{[CO_2][H_2]}{[CO][H_2O]} = 1.00$$

From the expression for K_c it can be seen that $[CO_2][H_2] = [CO][H_2O] \times 1.00 = [CO][H_2O]$

Of the four statements about the equilibrium condition given in the text, only statement (b) is always correct. It is not necessarily true that any concentration terms must be equal (as suggested by statements a and c), nor that the numerator or denominator must themselves have a value of 1.00 (suggested by statement d).

14-13. (a) The term, V, representing the volume of the reaction mixture, appears the same number of times in the numerator and denominator. It cancels out of the expression for K_c.

$$K_c = \frac{[CO][H_2O]}{[CO_2][H_2]} = \frac{(0.224/\cancel{V})(0.224/\cancel{V})}{(0.276/\cancel{V})(0.276/\cancel{V})}$$

(b) $$K_c = \frac{(0.224)(0.224)}{(0.276)(0.276)} = 6.59 \times 10^{-1}$$

14-14. An implicit assumption in the following calculations is that equilibrium exists. This means that a sufficient amount of each reacting species must somehow have been provided.

(a) Let x = no. mol O_2; y = no. mol SO_2 = no. mol SO_3; volume = 10.0 L.

$$K_c = \frac{[SO_3]^2}{[SO_2]^2[O_2]} = \frac{\cancel{(y/10.0)^2}}{\cancel{(y/10.0)^2}(x/10.0)} = 100; \quad x = \frac{10.0}{100} = 0.100 \text{ mol } O_2$$

(b) Let x = no. mol O_2; y = no. mol SO_2; $2y$ = no. mol SO_3; volume = 10.0 L.

$$K_c = \frac{[SO_3]^2}{[SO_2]^2[O_2]} = \frac{(2y/10.0)^2}{(y/10.0)^2(x/10.0)} = 100 = \frac{\frac{4y^2}{100}}{\frac{y^2}{100} \times \frac{x}{10.0}} \qquad x = \frac{4 \times 10.0}{100} = 0.400 \text{ mol } O_2$$

14-15. Let the required volume of the reaction mixture be V.

$$K_c = \frac{[I]^2}{[I_2]} = \frac{(0.50/V)^2}{1.00/V} = \frac{0.25}{V^2 \times \frac{1.00}{V}} = 1 \times 10^{-2} \qquad V = \frac{0.25}{1.00 \times 1 \times 10^{-2}} = 25 \text{ L}$$

Direction and extent of chemical change

14-16. The concentrations of the components of the mixture are:

$$[SO_3] = \frac{8 \text{ mol } SO_3}{10.0 \text{ L}} = 0.800 \qquad [SO_2] = \frac{1 \text{ mol } SO_2}{10.0 \text{ L}} = 0.100 \qquad [O_2] = \frac{2 \text{ mol } O_2}{10.0 \text{ L}} = 0.200$$

The Reaction Quotient:

$$Q = \frac{[SO_3]^2}{[SO_2]^2[O_2]} = \frac{(0.800)^2}{(0.100)^2(0.200)} = 320 \neq K_c = 100$$

The reaction must proceed further in such a direction that the numerator decreases and the denominator increases. A net reaction occurs in the *reverse* direction.

14-17. (a) $K_c = \frac{[C]^2}{[A]^3[B]}$

(b) If [A] = [B] = [C] = 2.00 mol/1.00 L, the reaction quotient is

$$Q = \frac{[C]^2}{[A]^3[B]} = \frac{(2.00)^2}{(2.00)^3 \times (2.00)} = 0.250 \neq K_c = 9.0$$ The reaction cannot be at equilibrium.

(c) Consider a mixture containing 2.00 mole each of A, B, and C in a volume of V liters.

$$K_c = \frac{[C]^2}{[A]^3[B]} = \frac{(2.00/V)^2}{(2.00/V)^3 \times (2.00/V)} = \frac{V^2}{4.00} = 9.0 \qquad V^2 = 36.0$$

The required volume, V, is 6.0 liters.

14-18. The reaction is

	$CO(g)$ +	$Cl_2(g)$ ⇌	$COCl_2(g)$
initial amounts, mol	1.00	--	1.00
change; mol:	$+x$	$+x$	$-x$
equilibrium amounts, mol:	$(1.00 + x)$	x	$(1.00 - x)$
equilibrium concentrations, M:	$(1.00 + x)/1.50$	$x/1.50$	$(1.00 - x)/1.50$

$$K_c = \frac{[COCl_2]}{[CO][Cl_2]} = \frac{(1.00 - x)/1.50}{\left(\frac{1.00 + x}{1.50}\right)\cdot\left(\frac{x}{1.50}\right)} = \frac{1.50(1.00 - x)}{x(1.00 + x)} = 1.2 \times 10^3$$

Assume $x << 1.00$, and $(1.00 - x) \simeq (1.00 + x) \simeq 1.00$

$$\frac{1.50}{x} = 1.2 \times 10^3 \qquad x = 1.2 \times 10^{-3} \text{ mol } Cl_2$$

14-19. In Example 14-6 it was established that the reaction must proceed to the left. The amounts of CO and H_2O increase (represented by $+x$) and those of CO_2 and H_2 decrease ($-x$).

The reaction is	$CO(g)$	+	$H_2O(g)$	$\rightleftharpoons$	$CO_2(g)$	+	$H_2(g)$
initial amounts, mol:	1.00		1.00		2.00		2.00
change, mol:	$+x$		$+x$		$-x$		$-x$
equilibrium amounts, mol:	$1.00 + x$		$1.00 + x$		$2.00 - x$		$2.00 - x$
equilibrium concentrations, M:	$(1.00 + x)/V$		$(1.00 + x)/V$		$(2.00 - x)/V$		$(2.00 - x)/V$

$$K_c = \frac{[CO_2][H_2]}{[CO][H_2O]} = \frac{(2.00 - x)(2.00 - x)}{(1.00 + x)(1.00 + x)} = 1.00$$

$$\frac{(2.00 - x)^2}{(1.00 + x)^2} = 1.00$$ Take the square root of both sides.

$$\frac{(2.00 - x)}{(1.00 + x)} = 1.00; \quad 2.00 - x = 1.00 + x; \quad 2x = 1.00; \quad x = 0.50 \text{ mol}$$

Equilibrium amounts: 1.50 mol CO, 1.50 mol H_2O, 1.50 mol CO_2, 1.50 mol H_2

14-20. The reaction is

The reaction is	$SbCl_5(g)$	$\rightleftharpoons$	$SbCl_3(g)$	+	$Cl_2(g)$
initial amounts, mol:	--		3.00		1.00
change, mol:	$+x$		$-x$		$-x$
equilibrium amounts, mol:	x		$3.00 - x$		$1.00 - x$
equilibrium concentrations, M	$x/5.00$		$(3.00 - x)/5.00$		$(1.00 - x)/5.00$

$$K_c = \frac{[SbCl_3][Cl_2]}{[SbCl_5]} = \frac{(3.00 - x)/5.00 \times (1.00 - x)/5.00)}{x/5.00} = 2.5 \times 10^{-2}$$

$$\frac{(3.00 - x)(1.00 - x)}{x} = 0.12$$

The simplifying assumption that $x << 1.00$ will not work here. (A very small value of x in the denominator would produce a large quotient, and 0.12 is not "large".)

$$3.00 - 4.00x + x^2 = 0.12x \qquad x^2 - 4.12x + 3.00 = 0$$

$$x = \frac{4.12 \pm \sqrt{(4.12)^2 - 4 \times 3.00}}{2} \qquad x = 0.95$$

Equilibrium mixture: 0.95 mol $SbCl_5$; 2.05 mol $SbCl_3$; 0.05 mol Cl_2

14-21. (a) Form the reaction quotient, Q, based on the given quantities and compare with $K_c = 2.8 \times 10^2$.

$$Q = \frac{[SO_3]^2}{[SO_2]^2[O_2]} = \frac{(0.657/1.90)^2}{(0.390/1.90)^2(0.156/1.90)} = 34.6 < K_c$$

(b) A reaction must proceed in the forward direction (to the right) to establish equilibrium.

14-22. The reaction is

The reaction is	$2\ SO_2(g)$	+	$O_2(g)$	$\rightleftharpoons$	$2\ SO_3(g)$
initial amounts, mol:	0.390		0.156		0.657
change, mol:	$-2x$		$-x$		$+2x$
equilibrium amounts, mol:	$0.390 - 2x$		$0.156 - x$		$0.657 + 2x$
equilibrium concentrations, M:	$(0.390 - 2x)/1.90$		$(0.156 - x)/1.90$		$(0.657 + 2x)/1.90$

$$K_c = \frac{[SO_3]^2}{[SO_2]^2[O_2]} = \frac{(0.657 + 2x)^2(1.90)^2(1.90)}{(1.90)^2(0.390 - 2x)^2(0.156 - x)} = 2.8 \times 10^2$$

$$1.90(0.432 + 2.63x + 4x^2) = (0.156 - x)(0.152 - 1.56x + 4x^2) \times 2.8 \times 10^2$$

$$7.60x^2 + 5.00x + 0.821 = (0.0237 - 0.395x + 2.18x^2 - 4x^3)\ 2.8 \times 10^2$$

$$7.60x^2 + 5.00x + 0.821 = 6.64 - 111x + 610x^2 - 1120x^3$$

$$1120x^3 - 602x^2 + 116x - 5.82 = 0 \qquad x^3 - 0.538x^2 + 0.104x - 0.00520 = 0$$

Solve by a method of successive approximations. For example, first try $x = 0.100$.

$(0.100)^3 - 0.538(0.100)^2 + 0.104(0.100) - 0.00520 = 0.00082 > 0$

Try $x = 0.90$: $(0.090)^3 - 0.538(0.090)^2 + 0.104(0.090) - 0.00520 = 0.00053 > 0$

Try $x = 0.080$: $0.00019 > 0$

Try $x = 0.070$: $-0.0002 < 0$

Try $x = 0.075$: $-4.4 \times 10^{-6} < 0$

Try $x = 0.076$: $+3.5 \times 10^{-5} > 0$

Use $x = 0.075$ to obtain the equilibrium amounts: 0.240 mol SO_2; 0.081 mol O_2; 0.807 mol SO_3.

14-23. The reaction is

	$Ag^+(aq)$	+ $Fe^{2+}(aq)$ $\rightleftharpoons$	$Fe^{3+}(aq)$	+ $Ag(s)$
initial concentrations, M:	1.00	1.00	--	--
changes, M:	$-x$	$-x$	$+x$	--
equilibrium concentrations, M:	$1.00 - x$	$1.00 - x$	x	--

$$K_c = \frac{[Fe^{3+}]}{[Ag^+][Fe^{2+}]} = \frac{x}{(1.00 - x)^2} = 2.98$$

Note that the simplifying assumption that $x << 1.00$ does not work here. (This would lead to the result $x = 2.98$.)

$$x = 2.98(1.00 - 2x + x^2) \qquad 2.98x^2 - 6.96x + 2.98 = 0 \qquad x^2 - 2.34x + 1.00 = 0$$

$$x = \frac{2.34 \pm \sqrt{(2.34)^2 - 4.00}}{2} = 0.56$$

Equilibrium concentrations: $[Ag^+] = [Fe^{2+}] = 0.44$ M; $[Fe^{3+}] = 0.56$ M

14-24. The reaction is

	$2\ Cr^{3+}(aq)$ + $Fe(s)$ $\rightleftharpoons$	$2\ Cr^{2+}(aq)$	+ $Fe^{2+}(aq)$
initial concentrations, M:	0.250	0.0500	0.00100
changes, M:	$-2x$	$+2x$	$+x$
equilibrium concentrations, M:	$0.250 - 2x$	$0.0500 + 2x$	$0.00100 + x$

$$K_c = \frac{[Cr^{2+}]^2[Fe^{2+}]}{[Cr^{3+}]^2} = \frac{(0.0500 + 2x)^2(0.00100 + x)}{(0.250 - 2x)^2} = 10.34$$

To determine whether a simplifying assumption is possible, let us first determine the value of Q based on initial concentrations and compare Q to K_c.

$$Q = \frac{(0.0500)^2(0.00100)}{(0.250)^2} = 4 \times 10^{-5} << K_c$$

In order that $Q = K_c$ the numerator in the above expression must become much larger and the denominator, smaller. This means that x is *not* an extremely small quantity. In fact, we might assume that $x >> 0.00100$, so that $(0.00100 + x) \simeq x$.

$$\frac{x(0.0500 + 2x)^2}{(0.250 - 2x)^2} = 10.34$$

$$x(0.00250 + 0.200x + 4x^2) = 10.34(0.0625 - x + 4x^2)$$

$$4x^3 + (0.200 - 41.36)x^2 + (0.00250 + 10.34)x - 0.646 = 0$$

$$4x^3 - 41.16x^2 + 10.34x - 0.646 = 0 \qquad x^3 - 10.29x^2 + 2.58x - 0.162 = 0$$

To solve this equation use a method of successive approximations. For example, try $x = 0.100$. (Note that x cannot exceed 0.125 or $[Cr^{3+}]$ would become negative.)

$$(0.100)^3 - 10.29(0.100)^2 + 2.58(0.100) - 0.162 = -0.0059 < 0$$

Try $x = 0.11$: $(0.11)^3 - 10.29(0.11)^2 + 2.58(0.11) - 0.162 = -1.38 \times 10^{-3} < 0$

Try $x = 0.12$: $(0.12)^3 - 10.29(0.12)^2 + 2.58(0.12) - 0.162 = 1.15 \times 10^{-3} > 0$

The root we are seeking is $0.11 < x < 0.12$. Let us use $x = 0.11$

Equilibrium concentrations: $[Cr^{3+}] = 0.250 - 2 \times 0.11 = 0.03$ M

$[Cr^{2+}] = 0.0500 + 2 \times 0.11 = 0.27$ M

$[Fe^{2+}] = 0.11$ M

Partial pressure equilibrium constant, K_p

14-25. $CO(g) + H_2O(g) \rightleftharpoons CO_2(g) + H_2(g)$; $K_c = 23.2$; $K_p = 23.2(0.0821 \times 600)^0 = 23.2$

$SO_2(g) + 1/2\ O_2(g) \rightleftharpoons SO_3(g)$; $K_c = 56$; $K_p = 56(0.0821 \times 900)^{-1/2} = 6.5$

$2\ H_2S(g) \rightleftharpoons 2\ H_2(g) + S_2(g)$; $K_c = 2.3 \times 10^{-4}$; $K_p = 2.3 \times 10^{-4}(0.0821 \times 1405) = 2.7 \times 10^{-2}$

$2\ NO_2(g) \rightleftharpoons 2\ NO(g) + O_2(g)$; $K_c = 1.8 \times 10^{-6}$; $K_p = 1.8 \times 10^{-6}(0.0821 \times 457) = 6.8 \times 10^{-5}$

14-26. The relationship between K_p and K_c is $K_p = K_c(RT)^{\Delta n}$. This leads to $K_c = \frac{K_p}{(RT)^{\Delta n}} = K_p(RT)^{-\Delta n}$

(a) $SO_2Cl_2(g) \rightleftharpoons SO_2(g) + Cl_2(g)$; $K_c = 2.9 \times 10^{-2}(0.0821 \times 303)^{-1} = 1.2 \times 10^{-3}$

(b) $2\ NO(g) + O_2(g) \rightleftharpoons 2\ NO_2(g)$; $K_c = 1.48 \times 10^4(0.0821 \times 457)^1 = 5.55 \times 10^5$

(c) $Sb_2S_3(s) + 3\ H_2(g) \rightleftharpoons 2\ Sb(s) + 3\ H_2S(g)$; $K_c = K_p = 0.429$

14-27. Assume 1.00 mol of air originally. This consists of 0.79 mol N_2 and 0.21 mol O_2. (The presence of Ar and other gases is neglected.)

The reaction is	$N_2(g)$	+	$O_2(g)$	$\rightleftharpoons$	$2\ NO(g)$
initial amounts, mol:	0.79		0.21		--
changes, mol:	$-x$		$-x$		$+2x$
equilibrium amounts:	$0.79 - x$		$0.21 - x$		$2x$
equilibrium partial pressures:	$(0.79 - x)RT/V$		$(0.21 - x)RT/V$		$(2x)RT/V$

$$K_p = \frac{(P_{NO})^2}{(P_{N_2})(P_{O_2})} = \frac{\{(2x)RT/V\}^2}{\{(0.79 - x)RT/V\}\{(0.21 - x)RT/V\}} = \frac{4x^2}{(0.79 - x)(0.21 - x)}$$

To obtain a numerical value of K_p, it is first necessary to evaluate x.

The total amount of gas at equilibrium = $(0.79 - x) + (0.21 - x) + 2x = 1.00$

mol % NO = $\frac{2x}{1.00} \times 100 = 1.8$ $\qquad x = 9.0 \times 10^{-3}$

$$K_p = \frac{4(9.0 \times 10^{-3})^2}{\{(0.79) - 9.0 \times 10^{-3}\}\{(0.21) - 9.0 \times 10^{-3}\}} = 2.1 \times 10^{-3}$$

14-28. The total gas pressure is the sum of the equilibrium partial pressures of NH_3 and H_2S. Let us find these quantities in the usual way.

The reation is	$NH_4HS(s)$	$\rightleftharpoons$ $NH_3(g)$	+	$H_2S(g)$
initial amounts, mol:	--	0.0100		--
changes, mol:	--	$+x$		$+x$
equilibrium amounts, mol:	--	$0.0100 + x$		x
equilibrium partial pressures, atm:	--	$(0.0100 + x)RT/V$		xRT/V

$$K_p = (P_{NH_3})(P_{H_2S}) = \frac{x(0.0100 + x) \times (0.0821 \times 298)^2}{(1.60)^2} = 0.108$$

$$599x^2 + 5.99x - 0.276 = 0$$

$$x = \frac{-5.99 \pm \sqrt{(5.99)^2 + (4 \times 599 \times 0.276)}}{2 \times 599} = 0.0170$$

$$P_{NH_3} = \frac{0.0270 \times 0.0821 \times 298}{1.60} = 0.413 \text{ atm} \qquad P_{H_2S} = \frac{0.0170 \times 0.0821 \times 298}{1.60} = 0.260 \text{ atm}$$

$$P_{tot} = 0.413 + 0.260 = 0.673 \text{ atm}$$

14-29. (a) $K_p = (P_{CO_2})(P_{H_2O}) = 0.23$. Since the gases are produced in equal amounts, $P_{CO_2} = P_{H_2O}$.

$(P_{CO_2})^2 = 0.23$ $\qquad P_{H_2O} = P_{CO_2} = \sqrt{0.23} = 0.48$ atm

$P_{tot} = P_{H_2O} + P_{CO_2} = 0.48 + 0.48 = 0.96$ atm

(b) We need to compare Q with K_p.

$Q = (P_{CO_2})(P_{H_2O}) = (2.10)(715/760) = 1.98 > K_p\ (=0.23)$

When equilibrium is established P_{CO_2} and P_{H_2O} will be smaller than their original values.

(c) Since H_2O and CO_2 enter into reaction in a 1:1 molar ratio, if x = no. mol CO_2 reacting, this is also no. mol H_2O reacting. For both gases we can express the decrease in pressure accompanying the reaction of x mol as $\Delta P = \frac{\Delta nRT}{V} = xRT/V$. We can just as well represent this change in pressure as $y = xRT/V$ and use only y in the expression below.

$K_p = (P_{CO_2})(P_{H_2O}) = (2.10 - y)(0.941 - y) = 0.23$

$1.98 - 3.04y + y^2 = 0.23$ $\qquad y^2 - 3.04y + 1.75 = 0$

$$y = \frac{3.04 \pm \sqrt{(3.04)^2 - 4 \times 1.75}}{2} = 0.77 \text{ atm}$$

Equilibrium partial pressures: $P_{CO_2} = 2.10 - 0.77 = 1.33$ atm

$P_{H_2O} = 0.941 - 0.77 = 0.17$ atm

Dissociation reactions

14-30. Transferring the reaction mixture of Example 14-10 to a larger vessel (10.0 L compared to 0.372 L) would favor the forward reaction when equilibrium is restored. The percent dissociation would increase. This conclusion can be based on Le Châtelier's principle or on a comparison of Q and K_c. The equilibrium mixture described in Example 14-10 contains $2x$ mol $NO_2 = 2 \times 3.00 \times 10^{-3}$ $= 6.00 \times 10^{-3}$ mol NO_2 and $0.0240 - x = 0.0240 - 3.00 \times 10^{-3} = 0.0210$ mol N_2O_4

$$Q = \frac{[NO_2]^2}{[N_2O_4]} = \frac{(6.00 \times 10^{-3}/10.0)^2}{(0.0210/10.0)} = 1.71 \times 10^{-4} < K_p (= 4.61 \times 10^{-3})$$

Since $Q < K_p$, a reaction must proceed to the right. The percent dissociation increases.

14-31. The simplest approach here is to return to Example 14-10 and to restate the equilibrium concentrations as

$$[N_2O_4] = \frac{(0.0240 - x)\text{mol}}{10.0 \text{ L}} \quad \text{and} \quad [NO_2] = \frac{2x \text{ mol}}{10.0 \text{ L}}$$

$$K_c = \frac{[NO_2]^2}{[N_2O_4]} = \frac{(2x)^2}{(10.0)^2(0.0240 - x)/10} = \frac{4x^2}{10.0(0.0240 - x)} = 4.61 \times 10^{-3}$$

$$4x^2 + 0.0461x - 0.00111 = 0$$

$$x = \frac{-0.0461 \pm \sqrt{(0.0461)^2 + (4 \times 4 \times 0.00111)}}{8} = 0.0119$$

$$\% \text{ dissoc.} = \frac{0.0119 \text{ mol } N_2O_4 \text{ dissoc.}}{0.0240 \text{ mol } N_2O_4 \text{ initially}} \times 100 = 49.6\%$$

14-32. (a) The fact that I_2 is 5% dissociated into I atoms at 200°C means that from an original 1.00 mol I_2 the equilibrium amounts become 0.95 mol I_2 and 0.10 mol I. Since the reaction volume is 1.00 L, the equilibrium concentrations are $[I_2] = 0.95$ and $[I] = 0.10$.

$$K_c = \frac{[I]^2}{[I_2]} = \frac{(0.10)^2}{0.95} = 1.1 \times 10^{-2}$$

(b) $K_p = K_c(RT)^{\Delta n} = 1.1 \times 10^{-2}(0.0821 \times 1473)^1 = 1.3$

14-33. For the reaction, $2\ HI(g) \rightleftharpoons H_2(g) + I_2(g)$; $K_c = 1/70 = 1.4 \times 10^{-2}$.

In this case, the percent dissociation does not depend on the numbers of moles of reactant and product. Consider, for example, a sample of 1.00 mole HI placed in a volume of V liter. Let x = no. mol H_2 = no. mol I_2 produced; $1.00 - 2x$ = no. mol HI at equilibrium.

$$K_c = \frac{[H_2][I_2]}{[HI]^2} = \frac{(x/V)(x/V)}{[(1.00 - 2x)/V]^2} = \frac{x^2}{1.00 - 4x + 4x^2} = 1.4 \times 10^{-2}$$

$$x^2 = 1.4 \times 10^{-2} - 5.6 \times 10^{-2}x + 5.6 \times 10^{-2}x^2 \qquad 0.94x^2 + 5.6 \times 10^{-2}x - 1.4 \times 10^{-2} = 0$$

$$x = \frac{-5.6 \times 10^{-2} \pm \sqrt{(5.6 \times 10^{-2})^2 + (4 \times 0.94 \times 1.4 \times 10^{-2})}}{2 \times 0.94}$$

$$x = \frac{-5.6 \times 10^{-2} \pm 2.36 \times 10^{-1}}{1.98} = 9.6 \times 10^{-2}$$

No. mol HI dissociated = $2x = 2 \times 9.6 \times 10^{-2} = 19.2 \times 10^{-2} = 1.9 \times 10^{-1}$

% dissociation of HI = $\frac{1.9 \times 10^{-1}}{1.00} \times 100 = 19\%$

14-34. For simplicity, let us base this derivation on an original 1.00 mol PCl_5, of which the fraction dissociated is α.

The reaction is	$PCl_5(g)$	$\rightleftharpoons$	$PCl_3(g)$	+	$Cl_2(g)$
initial amounts, mol:	1.00		--		--
changes, mol:	$-\alpha$		$+\alpha$		$+\alpha$
equilibrium amounts, mol:	$1.00 - \alpha$		α		α

total moles of gas = $(1.00 - \alpha) + \alpha + \alpha = 1.00 + \alpha$

equilibrium partial pressures in terms of total pressure P:	$\frac{(1.00 - \alpha)}{(1.00 + \alpha)} P$	$\frac{\alpha P}{1.00 + \alpha}$	$\frac{\alpha P}{1.00 + \alpha}$

$$K_p = \frac{(P_{PCl_3})(P_{Cl_2})}{(P_{Cl_5})} = \frac{\left(\frac{\alpha P}{1.00 + \alpha}\right)\left(\frac{\alpha P}{1.00 + \alpha}\right)}{\frac{(1.00 - \alpha)}{(1.00 + \alpha)} P} = \frac{\alpha^2 P^2}{(1.00 + \alpha)^2 \frac{(1.00 - \alpha)}{(1.00 + \alpha)} P} = \frac{\alpha^2 P^2}{(1.00 + \alpha)(1.00 - \alpha)P}$$

$$= \frac{\alpha^2 P}{1.00 - \alpha^2}$$

14-35. (a) $K_p = \frac{\alpha^2 P}{1 - \alpha^2} = \frac{\alpha^2 (1.00)}{1 - \alpha^2} = 1.78$ $\qquad \alpha^2 = 1.78 - 1.78\alpha^2$ $\qquad \alpha^2 = 0.640$ $\qquad \alpha = 0.800$

PCl_5 is 80.0% dissociated at 250°C.

(b) If dissociation is to be 10.0%, the value of $\alpha = 0.100$

$$K_p = \frac{(0.100)^2 P}{1 - (0.100)^2} = 1.78 \qquad P = \frac{1.78 - 1.78 \times 10^{-2}}{1.00 \times 10^{-2}} = \frac{1.76}{1.00 \times 10^{-2}} = 176 \text{ atm}$$

Effect of temperature on equilibrium constants

14-36. From Figure 14-4 use the standard molar enthalpy of reaction, $\Delta\bar{H}° = -1.80 \times 10^5$ J/mol. From Table 14-4, select a representative temperature and value of K_p, e.g., $(K_p)_2 = 9.1 \times 10^2$ at $T_2 = 800$ K. At $T_1 = 298$ K, $(K_p)_1 = ?$

$$\log\frac{9.1 \times 10^2}{K_p} = \frac{-1.80 \times 10^5 \text{ J/mol}}{2.303 \times 8.314 \text{ J mol}^{-1} \text{ K}^{-1}} \left(\frac{800 - 298}{298 \times 800}\right) K^{-1} \qquad \log\frac{9.1 \times 10^2}{K_p} = -19.80$$

$$\frac{9.1 \times 10^2}{K_p} = 1.58 \times 10^{-20} \qquad K_p = 5.8 \times 10^{22}$$

14-37. Use the van't Hoff equation with $K_1 = 50.0$ @ $T_1 = 448 - 273 = 721$ K and $K_2 = 66.9$ @ $T_2 = 350 + 273 = 623$ K.

$$\log\frac{66.9}{50.0} = \frac{\overline{\Delta H}°}{2.303 \times 8.314 \text{ J mol}^{-1} \text{ K}^{-1}}\left(\frac{623 - 721}{623 \times 721}\right)\text{K}^{-1} = 0.126$$

$$\overline{\Delta H}° = \frac{0.126 \times 623 \times 721 \times 2.303 \times 8.314}{-98} = -1.11 \times 10^4 \text{ J/mol} = -11.1 \text{ kJ/mol}$$

(The value of $\overline{\Delta H}°$ represented in Figure 13-12 is -13 kJ/mol.)

14-38. From Example 14-7 we obtain a value of $K_c = 4.61 \times 10^{-3}$ at 298 K. The value of K_p at 298 K is $4.61 \times 10^{-3}(0.0821 \times 298) = 1.13 \times 10^{-1}$. Let these values stand for K_1 and T_1. For T_2 use 100°C = 373 K. Before equation (14.25) can be solved for K_2 we must have a value to use for $\overline{\Delta H}°$. This we can get with data from Appendix D.

$$N_2O_4(g) \rightleftharpoons 2\ NO_2(g)$$

$$\overline{\Delta H}° = 2\ \overline{\Delta H}_f°[NO_2(g)] - \overline{\Delta H}_f°[N_2O_4(g)] = 2 \times (33.85) - (9.67) = 58.03 \text{ kJ/mol} = 5.803 \times 10^4 \text{ J/mol}$$

$$\log\frac{K_2}{0.113} = \frac{5.803 \times 10^4 \text{ J/mol}}{2.303 \times 8.314 \text{ J mol}^{-1} \text{ K}^{-1}}\left(\frac{373 - 298}{298 \times 373}\right)\text{K}^{-1} = 2.045 \qquad \frac{K_2}{0.113} = 111 \qquad K_2 = 12.5$$

14-39. (a) Convert temperatures from °C to kelvins. Tabulate $\log K_p$ as a function of $1/T$ as indicated below.

t	T	1/T	K_p	$\log K_p$
30°C	303 K	3.30×10^{-3}	1.66×10^{-5}	-4.780
50	323	3.10×10^{-3}	3.90×10^{-4}	-3.409
70	343	2.92×10^{-3}	6.27×10^{-3}	-2.203
100	373	2.68×10^{-3}	2.31×10^{-1}	-0.636

Plot $\log K_p$ vs $1/T$ and obtain the slope.

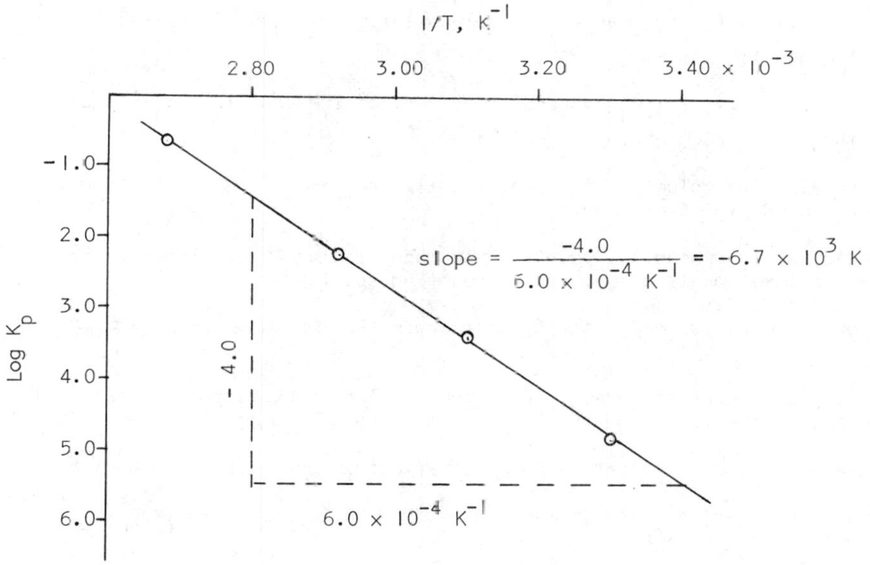

$\Delta\overline{H}° = -2.303 \times R \times \text{slope} = -2.303 \times 8.314 \text{ J mol}^{-1} \text{ K}^{-1} \times (-6.7 \times 10^3)\text{K} = 1.3 \times 10^5 \text{ J/mol}$

$= 130 \text{ kJ/mol}$

(b) If $P_{tot} = 2.00$ atm, then $P_{H_2O} = P_{CO_2} = 1.00$ atm.

$K_p = (P_{CO_2}) \times (P_{H_2O}) = (1.00) \times (1.00) = 1.00$

Calculate the temperature, T_2, at which $K_p = 1.00$, with $T_1 = 373$ K, $K_{p_1} = 0.231$, and $\Delta\overline{H}° = 1.3 \times 10^5$ J/mol.

$$\log\frac{1.00}{0.231} = \frac{1.3 \times 10^5 \text{ J/mol}}{2.303 \times 8.314 \text{ J mol}^{-1} \text{K}^{-1}}\left(\frac{T_2 - 373}{373\ T_2}\right) \text{K}^{-1}$$

$$\log 4.33 = 6.8 \times 10^3\left(\frac{T_2 - 373}{373\ T_2}\right) \qquad 0.636 = 6.8 \times 10^3\left(\frac{T_2 - 373}{373\ T_2}\right)$$

$$237\ T_2 = 6.8 \times 10^3\ T_2 - 2.5 \times 10^6 \qquad 6.6 \times 10^3\ T_2 = 2.5 \times 10^6 \qquad T_2 = 380 \text{ K}$$

Le Châtelier's principle

14-40. In each case decreasing the volume of the reaction mixture has the effect of shifting the equilibrium condition to the side of the equation with the smallest number of moles of reacting species.

(a) The equilibrium condition is displaced to the left.

(b) No effect. [The number of moles of reactants and products are equal.]

(c) The equilibrium condition is displaced to the right.

14-41. When the amount of one of the reacting species in an equilibrium mixture is reduced, by whatever means, the equilibrium condition is shifted in a direction that produces more of that species. Thus, if one of the products of the reaction is removed continuously, the equilibrium condition is displaced toward the products. Eventually, the reaction goes to completion.

14-42. The reversible reaction in question is, $4\ HCl(g) + O_2(g) \rightleftharpoons 2\ H_2O(g) + 2\ Cl_2(g)$.

(a) The addition of $O_2(g)$ causes a displacement of the equilibrium to the right and a *decrease* in the equilibrium amount of HCl(g).

(b) Removal of $Cl_2(g)$ also causes displacement of the equilibrium to the right and a *decrease* in the equilibrium amount of HCl(g).

(c) Increasing the volume of the reaction mixture favors the reverse reaction. The equilibrium amount of HCl(g) *increases*.

(d) A catalyst increases the rate at which equilibrium is attained but has *no effect* on the equilibrium amounts of any of the reacting species.

14-43. The following responses refer to the *exothermic* reaction, $A(g) + B(g) \rightleftharpoons 2\ C(g)$, at equilibrium at 200°C.

(a) True: The number of moles of reacting species is unchanged as the reaction proceeds. Increasing the volume of the reaction mixture has no effect on equilibrium amounts.

(b) False: Addition of a catalyst has no effect on equilibrium amounts of reactants.

(c) False: A lowering of the temperature to 100°C causes a displacement of the equilibrium condition to the right.

(d) True: Addition of a nonreacting gas will not affect appreciably the concentrations of the reacting species.

14-44. (a) Suppose we start with 1.00 mole of SO_2Cl_2 and allow it to come to equilibrium in a reaction vessel of volume, V. Let x = no. mol SO_2Cl_2 dissociated.

$$K_c = \frac{[SO_2][Cl_2]}{[SO_2Cl_2]} = \frac{(x/V)(x/V)}{(1.00 - x)/V} = \frac{x^2}{V(1.00 - x)} \qquad \frac{x^2}{1.00 - x} = K_cV$$

Clearly the value of x will depend on the values of both K_c and V, and since percent dissociation of SO_2Cl_2 = $(x/1.00) \times 100$, the percent dissociation must depend on the volume, V.

This same conclusion is possible using Le Châtelier's principle. Increasing the volume, V, causes the equilibrium condition to be displaced to the right; the percent dissociation increases.

(b) By a similar method to that employed in part (a), we can establish the condition:

$$K_c = \frac{[S_2]}{[CS_2]} = \frac{x/V}{(1.00 - x)/V} = \frac{x}{1.00 - x}$$

Here the value of x depends only on the value of K_c, not on the volume, V.

One mole of gaseous reactant produces one mole of gaseous product. According to Le Châtelier's principle we should expect no effect on equilibrium concentrations as a result of changing the reaction volume.

14-45. An increase in temperature will favor the *endothermic* (heat absorbing) reaction. For those reactions listed where the forward reaction (the dissociation reaction) is endothermic, the percent dissociation increases with increasing temperature--reactions (b) and (d).

14-46. In reactions of the type, $A_2(g) \rightleftharpoons 2\,A(g)$, the bonds, A—A, are broken and no new bonds are formed. Such reactions must be endothermic, and endothermic reactions are favored at high temperatures.

14-47. (a) Because the formation of NO(g) from its elements is an endothermic reaction, high temperatures favor an increase in the equilibrium amounts of NO(g).

(b) Not only is the equilibrium production of NO(g) favored by high temperatures, but the rate of attainment of equilibrium is greatly accelerated. This is because reaction rates increase so rapidly with temperature.

14-48. The application of pressure to ice causes it to melt because the liquid water occupies a smaller volume than a corresponding mass of ice. Stated in terms of Le Châtelier's principle, the application of a stress to an equilibrium mixture causes a displacement of the equilibrium in that direction in which the stress is relieved. The stress in this case is an increase in pressure and the relief comes through a reduction in volume. This behavior is not generally expected since in all but a few cases a liquid occupies a larger volume than the solid from which it is formed.

Self-test Questions

1. (*d*) Based on the availability of 1 mol I_2, if the reaction went to completion, 2 mol HI would form. Since the reaction is reversible, the equilibrium amount of HI is less than 2 mol.

2. (*c*) Write the equilibrium constant expression $K_c = \frac{[SO_3]^2}{[SO_2]^2[O_2]} = 100$

Because the number of moles of SO_2 and SO_3 have been made equal, $[SO_2] = [SO_3]$. The terms $[SO_3]^2$ and $[SO_2]^2$ cancel out in the K_c expression, leaving $1/[O_2] = 100$. This means that $[O_2] = 0.010$ M.

3. (*a*) An increase in reaction volume favors the side of the equation in which the greater number of moles of gas appears. This is the forward reaction. The amounts of $SO_2(g)$ and $Cl_2(g)$ increase.

4. (*c*) For the given condition, K = [C][D]/[A][B] = 10.0. The only one of the listed statements that can be derived from this expression is [A][B] = [C][D]/10.0 = 0.10 [C][D].

5. (*d*) A catalyst does not affect the position of equilibrium [item (a) is incorrect]. An increase of temperature favors the endothermic reaction--the reverse reaction. [Item (b) is incorrect because this would lead to a decrease in the amount of $H_2(g)$.] Transferring the equilibrium mixture to a larger container will have no effect on the amount of $H_2(g)$. The total number of moles of gas is the same on each side of the equation. The correct answer is (d).

6. (*b*) The value of Q for the initial conditions is

$$\frac{[CO_2(g)][H_2(g)]}{[CO(g)][H_2O(g)]} = \frac{(0.10)[H_2]}{(0.10)(0.10)} = 0 \text{ (because } [H_2(g)] = 0)$$

A net reaction must proceed to the right. The amount of $CO_2(g)$ would increase and the amounts of $CO(g)$ and $H_2O(g)$ would decrease. Also, the amount of $H_2(g)$ produced would have to be less than one mole, since the reaction does not go to completion. The correct response is (b). Response (c) must be in error because there is no way for all amounts to exceed 1.00 mol. Response (d) is in error because the amount of $H_2(g)$ cannot exceed 1 mol.

7. (*b*) The given equation must be reversed and divided by 2 to obtain $NO(g) + 1/2\ O_2(g) \rightleftharpoons NO_2(g)$.

$$K_c = 1/\sqrt{1.8 \times 10^{-6}} = 7.5 \times 10^2$$

8. (*a*) For this reaction $K_p = K_c(RT)^{\Delta n} = K_c(RT)^1$. K_p is larger than K_c (or K_c is smaller than K_p) at all temperatures.

9. A balanced equation, through its stoichiometric coefficients, provides the basis for writing an equilibrium constant expression. Also the balanced equation provides factors for relating the changes that occur among the amounts (or concentrations) of the various reactants and products as equilibrium is established. To determine the actual equilibrium concentrations, however, one must have a numerical value of the equilibrium constant. This value cannot be established in any way from the balanced equation alone. Experimental results are required.

10. (a) The rates of the forward and reverse reactions are equal when a reversible reaction reaches equilibrium. However, these rates must be established by the methods of chemical kinetics (Chapter 13) not simply by measuring equilibrium concentrations.

(b) The reaction quotient Q and the equilibrium constant expression K_c are set up in a very similar manner, but the concentrations substituted into the K_c expression must be those that exist at equilibrium. Any set of concentration terms can be substituted into the Q expression. (Depending on how the numerical values of Q and K_c compare one can make predictions about the direction of net chemical reaction.)

(c) The equilibrium constant expression K_c is based on molar concentrations of reactants and products and K_p on partial pressures of gases. The relationship between the two is $K_p = K_c(RT)^{\Delta n}$ (where Δn is the change in number of moles of gaseous species as the reaction proceeds as written, that is, from left to right).

11.

The reaction is	$S_2(g)$	$\rightleftharpoons$	$2\ S(g)$
initial amounts, mol:	0.0010		--
changes, mol:	-0.5×10^{-11}		$+1.0 \times 10^{-11}$
equilibrium amounts, mol:	$0.0010 - 5 \times 10^{-11}$		1.0×10^{-11}
equilibrium concentrations, M:	0.0010/0.500		$1.0 \times 10^{-11}/0.500$

$$K_c = \frac{[S]^2}{[S_2]} = \frac{(1.0 \times 10^{-11}/0.500)^2}{0.0010/0.500} = \frac{1.0 \times 10^{-22}}{0.500 \times 0.0010} = 2.0 \times 10^{-19}$$

12. (a) For the conditions stated:

$$Q = \frac{[NOBr]^2}{[NO]^2[Br_2]} = \frac{(0.0100/1.00)^2}{(0.100/1.00)^2(0.100/1.00)} = 0.10 > K_c \ (= 1.32 \times 10^{-2})$$

A net reaction occurs to the left--in the reverse direction.

(b)

The reaction is	$2\ NO(g)$ +	$Br_2(g)$ $\rightleftharpoons$	$2\ NOBr(g)$
initial amounts, mol:	0.100	0.100	0.0100
changes, mol:	$+2x$	$+x$	$-2x$
equilibrium amounts, mol:	$0.100 + 2x$	$0.100 + x$	$0.0100 - 2x$
equilibrium concentrations, M:	$(0.100 + 2x)/1.00$	$(0.100 + x)/1.00$	$(0.0100 - 2x)/1.00$

$$K_c = \frac{[NOBr]^2}{[NO]^2[Br_2]} = \frac{(0.0100 - 2x)^2}{(0.100 + 2x)^2(0.100 + x)} = 1.32 \times 10^{-2}$$

By inspecting the numerator of the above expression we see that $x < 0.00500$. This means also that $x \ll 0.100$, and that $(0.100 + 2x) \simeq (0.100 + x) \simeq 0.100$.

$$\frac{(0.0100 - 2x)^2}{(0.100)^2(0.100)} = 1.32 \times 10^{-2}$$

$$1.00 \times 10^{-4} - 0.0400x + 4x^2 = 1.32 \times 10^{-5} \qquad 4x^2 - 0.0400x + 8.68 \times 10^{-5} = 0$$

$$x = \frac{+0.0400 \pm \sqrt{(0.0400)^2 - 4 \times 4 \times 8.68 \times 10^{-5}}}{8} = 3.18 \times 10^{-3}$$

no. mol NO = $0.100 + (2 \times 3.18 \times 10^{-3}) = 0.106$

no. mol Br_2 = $0.100 + 3.18 \times 10^{-3} = 0.103$

no. mol NOBr = $0.0100 - (2 \times 3.18 \times 10^{-3}) = 0.0036$

total no. mol = $0.106 + 0.103 + 0.004 = 0.213$

total pressure = $nRT/V = 0.213 \times 0.0821 \times 1000/1.00 = 17.5$ atm

$$P_{NOBr} = \frac{0.0036 \text{ mol NOBr}}{0.213 \text{ mol total}} \times 17.5 \text{ atm} = 0.30 \text{ atm}$$

Chapter 15

Thermodynamics, Spontaneous Change, and Equilibrium

Entropy and disorder

15-1. (a) Decrease: Greater order exists in a solid than in a liquid.

(b) Increase: The gaseous state is more disordered than the solid state. Direct passage of molecules from the solid to the gaseous state (sublimation) should be accompanied by an increase in entropy.

(c) Increase: The burning of a rocket fuel produces large volumes of gases from solid or liquid fuels.

15-2. (a) Increase: A gas is produced from a liquid.

(b) Decrease: Two mol $H_2O(g)$ is consumed for every mol of trihydrate that is converted to pentahydrate.

(c) Indeterminate: There are two moles of gas indicated on each side of the equation.

(d) $2\ H_2S(g) + 3\ O_2(g) \longrightarrow 2\ H_2O(g) + 2\ SO_2(g)$. Five moles of gas are replaced by four. Entropy decreases.

(e) $H_2(g) + I_2(g) \longrightarrow 2\ HI(g)$. The number of moles of reactants is the same as the number of moles of products. Whether entropy increases or decreases cannot be established just by inspecting the balance equation.

15-3. (a) 1 mol H_2(g, 1 atm, 50°C). For a given amount of substance at a given temperature, gaseous matter has a greater entropy than liquid.

(b) 50.0 g Fe(s, 1 atm, 20°C). Entropy is an extensive property. There is more matter in 50.0 g Fe than in 0.80 mol Fe (44.7 g).

(c) 1 mol Br_2(*l*, 1 atm, 58°C). Both the fact that a liquid is being compared to a solid, and that entropy increases with temperature, suggest that $Br_2(l)$ at 58°C will have a higher entropy than $Br_2(s)$ at -10°C.

(d) 0.10 mol O_2(g, 0.10 atm, 25°C). The gas under this condition must occupy a larger volume (100 times larger) than at 10.0 atm. Expanding a gas produces a more disordered structure and thus, a higher entropy.

15-4. (a) If an exothermic process ($\Delta H < 0$) is accompanied by a *decrease* in entropy ($\Delta S < 0$), it might not be spontaneous. For example, the freezing of liquid water is an exothermic process accompanied by a decrease in entropy. The process is spontaneous below 0°C but nonspontaneous above 0°C.

(b) Increase in entropy alone may not be a sufficient factor to make a reaction occur spontaneously if a large positive ΔH is involved. Thus, the process $H_2O(l, 1\ atm) \longrightarrow H_2O(g, 1\ atm)$, for which $\Delta S > 0$, occurs spontaneously only at elevated temperatures--100°C or above.

15-5. According to the first law of thermodynamics (the law of conservation of energy) energy can neither be created nor destroyed. Therefore the energy of the universe (world) must be a constant. [Recall expressions in Chapter 6 of the sort: $q_{reaction} + q_{water} + q_{bomb} = 0$.] According to the second law of thermodynamics, all natural (spontaneous) processes must be accompanied by an increase in total entropy, that is, the entropy of the universe must increase. The combination of all natural processes, then, should cause the entropy of the universe to attain a maximum value.

Free energy and spontaneous change

15-6. For the decomposition of nitrosyl bromide we expect $\Delta\overline{S}° > 0$, since 1.5 mol gas is produced from 1 mol gas. Apply the criterion $\Delta\overline{G}° = \Delta\overline{H}° - T\Delta\overline{S}°$, with $\Delta\overline{H}° > 0$ and $\Delta\overline{S}° > 0$. This corresponds to case (3) in Table 15-1. The higher the temperature, the larger the term $T\Delta S$. At low temperatures, $\Delta G > 0$, and at sufficiently high temperatures, $\Delta G < 0$. We should expect the decomposition to occur to a greater extent at high temperatures.

15-7. (a) Case 3: The dissociation of diatomic molecules must involve $\Delta H > 0$ and $\Delta S > 0$.

(b) Case 2: The value given for ΔH is negative. For this reaction we would also expect a decrease in entropy. Thus, $\Delta H < 0$ and $\Delta S < 0$.

(c) Case 1: An increase in number of moles of gas suggests that $\Delta S° > 0$. $\Delta\overline{H}°$ is -95.4 kJ/mol. The reaction is spontaneous at all temperatures.

(d) Case 4: From the balanced equation we would predict $\Delta S < 0$; the value given for ΔH is positive. The reaction is nonspontaneous at all temperatures.

15-8. There is no heat effect on mixing ideal gases; $\Delta H = 0$. As discussed in connection with Figure 15-3, $\Delta S > 0$ for the mixing process. With this combination of ΔH and ΔS, $\Delta G < 0$. (Recall that $\Delta G = \Delta H - T\Delta S$.)

15-9. The results here would be exactly the same as described for the mixing of ideal gases in Exercise 8, and for the same reasons. In the formation of an ideal solution, $\Delta H = 0$ and $\Delta S > 0$. This means that $\Delta G = \Delta H - T\Delta S < 0$.

Standard free energy change

15-10. Here we substitute the data given for the reaction into the Gibbs-Helmholtz equation (15.6).

$$\Delta\overline{G}° = \Delta\overline{H}° - T\Delta\overline{S}° \qquad T = \frac{\Delta\overline{H}° - \Delta\overline{G}°}{\Delta\overline{S}°}$$

$$T = \frac{-843.7 \text{ kJ/mol} - (-777.8)\text{kJ/mol}}{-0.165 \text{ kJ mol}^{-1} \text{ K}^{-1}} \qquad T = 399 \text{ K}$$

15-11. (a) $N_2(g) + 3\ H_2(g) \longrightarrow 2\ NH_3(g)$

$$\Delta\overline{G}° = 2\Delta\overline{G}^°_f[NH_3(g)] = 2 \times (-16.65)\text{kJ/mol} = -33.30 \text{ kJ/mol}$$

(b) $C_2H_2(g) + 2\ H_2(g) \longrightarrow C_2H_6(g)$

$$\Delta\overline{G}° = \Delta\overline{G}^°_f[C_2H_6(g)] - \Delta\overline{G}^°_f[C_2H_2(g)] = -32.89 - (209.20)\text{kJ/mol} = -242.09 \text{ kJ/mol}$$

(c) $Fe_3O_4(s) + 4\ H_2(g) \longrightarrow 3\ Fe(s) + 4\ H_2O(g)$

$$\Delta\overline{G}° = 4\Delta\overline{G}^°_f[H_2O(g)] - \Delta\overline{G}^°_f[Fe_3O_4(s)] = 4 \times (-228.61) - (-1014.20)\text{kJ/mol} = 99.76 \text{ kJ/mol}$$

(d) $MgO(s) + 2\ HCl(g) \longrightarrow MgCl_2(s) + H_2O(g)$

$$\Delta\overline{G}° = \Delta\overline{G}^°_f[MgCl_2(s)] + \Delta\overline{G}^°_f[H_2O(g)] - \Delta\overline{G}^°_f[MgO(s)] - 2\Delta\overline{G}^°_f[HCl(g)]$$

$$= (-592.33) + (-228.61) - (-569.57) - 2 \times (-95.27) = -60.83 \text{ kJ/mol}$$

15-12. For the reaction $NH_3(g) + HCl(g) \longrightarrow NH_4Cl(s)$

$$\Delta\overline{H}° = \Delta\overline{H}^°_f[NH_4Cl(s)] - \Delta\overline{H}^°_f[NH_3(g)] - \Delta\overline{H}^°_f[HCl(g)] = -315.4 - (-46.2) - (-92.3) = -176.9 \text{ kJ/mol}$$

$$\Delta\overline{G}° = \Delta\overline{G}^°_f[NH_4Cl(s)] - \Delta\overline{G}^°_f[NH_3(g)] - \Delta\overline{G}^°_f[HCl(g)] = -203.9 - (-16.6) - (-95.3) = -92 \text{ kJ/mol}$$

These data may now be substituted in equation (15.6) and the equation solved for $\Delta\overline{S}°$:
$\Delta\overline{G}° = \Delta\overline{H}° - T\Delta\overline{S}°$

$$\Delta\overline{S}° = \frac{\Delta\overline{H}° - \Delta\overline{G}°}{T} = \frac{-176.9 \text{ kJ/mol} - (-92 \text{ kJ/mol})}{298 \text{ K}} = -0.285 \text{ kJ mol}^{-1} \text{ K}^{-1} = -285 \text{ J mol}^{-1} \text{ K}^{-1}$$

15-13. The bond energy of the F_2 molecule should be $\Delta\overline{H}°$ for the reaction $F_2(g) \longrightarrow 2\ F(g)$;
$\Delta\overline{G}° = 123.85$ kJ/mol

$\Delta S° = 2\ \overline{S}°[F(g)] - \overline{S}°[F_2(g)] = 2 \times (158.66) - 187.61 = 129.71 \text{ J mol}^{-1} \text{ K}^{-1}$

$\Delta\overline{G}° = \Delta\overline{H}° - T\Delta\overline{S}°$ $\quad \Delta\overline{H}° = \Delta\overline{G}° + T\Delta\overline{S}° = (123.85 \text{ kJ/mol}) + (298.2 \text{ K} \times 0.12971 \text{ kJ mol}^{-1} \text{ K}^{-1})$

$= 162.53$ kJ/mol

The value listed in Table 9-3 is 155 kJ/mol.

15-14. We need to combine two equations in the manner introduced in Chapter 6 (Hess's law). For the second of the two equations, free energies of formation from Appendix D are used to establish $\Delta\overline{G}°$.

$C_8H_{18}(l) + 25/2\ O_2(g) \longrightarrow 8\ CO_2(g) + 9\ H_2O(l)$; $\Delta\overline{G}° = -5.28 \times 10^3$ kJ/mol

$9\ H_2O(l) \longrightarrow 9\ H_2O(g)$; $\Delta\overline{G}° = 9 \times (-228.61) - 9 \times (-237.19) = +77.22$ kJ/mol

$C_8H_{18}(l) + 25/2\ O_2(g) \longrightarrow 8\ CO_2(g) + 9\ H_2O(g)$; $\Delta\overline{G}° = -5.20 \times 10^3$ kJ/mol

Free energy and equilibrium

15-15. (a) 100°C: The intersection would come at the normal boiling point of water.

(b) At the normal boiling point of a liquid, the liquid is in equilibrium with its vapor; $\Delta G = 0$.

15-16. The condition referred to corresponds to liquid and gaseous water in equilibrium, with the vapor pressure of the water equal to 0.50 atm. This will occur at a temperature above room temperature, but below 100°C (where the vapor pressure is 1 atm). Vapor pressure increases continuously with temperature, and there is only one temperature at which the vapor pressure is 0.50 atm.

15-17. A temperature of 110°C is below the normal melting point of I_2. The process $I_2(s) \longrightarrow I_2(l)$ is nonspontaneous at this temperature, meaning that $\Delta G > 0$. If $\Delta G > 0$ then solid I_2 must have a lower free energy than liquid I_2 at 110°C and 1 atm.

15-18. At -60°C and 1 atm carbon dioxide exists solely as a gas. The conversion of the gas to either a liquid or solid would be nonspontaneous, that is, having $\Delta G > 0$. This means that $CO_2(g)$ has a lower free energy at -60°C and 1 atm than do either $CO_2(l)$ or $CO_2(s)$.

Phase transitions

15-19. All that is required here is to apply data from Appendix D to the process $H_2O(l) \rightleftharpoons H_2O(g)$

$\Delta\overline{H}°_{vap} = \Delta\overline{H}°_f[H_2O(g)] - \Delta\overline{H}°_f[H_2O(l)] = -241.84 - (-285.85) = +44.01$ kJ/mol

$\Delta\overline{S}°_{vap} = \overline{S}°[H_2O(g)] - \overline{S}°[H_2O(l)] = 188.74 - (69.96) = 118.78 \text{ J mol}^{-1} \text{ K}^{-1}$

15-20. Of the three liquids, we should expect appreciable hydrogen bonding to occur in HF and in CH_3OH. This would produce higher-than-normal heats of vaporization and Trouton's rule would fail. In toluene, $C_6H_5CH_3$, the intermolecular forces are of the London type. We should expect this liquid to obey Trouton's rule.

15-21. (a) From Appendix D, determine $\Delta\bar{H}^\circ$ for the process $Br_2(l) \rightleftharpoons Br_2(g)$.

$$\Delta\bar{H}^\circ_{vap} = \Delta\bar{H}^\circ_f[Br_2(g)] - \Delta\bar{H}^\circ_f[Br_2(l)] = 30.71 \text{ kJ/mol} - 0 = 30.71 \text{ kJ/mol}$$

(b) Now use Trouton's rule to estimate T_{bp}.

$$\Delta\bar{S}^\circ_{vap} = \frac{\Delta\bar{H}^\circ_{vap}}{T_{bp}} = \frac{30.71 \times 10^3 \text{ J/mol}}{T_{bp}} = 88 \text{ J mol}^{-1} \text{ K}^{-1}$$

$$T_{bp} = (30.71 \times 10^3/88)\text{K} = 349 \text{ K} = 76°\text{C}$$

15-22. At 298 K for $Hg(l) \rightleftharpoons Hg(g)$ $\Delta\bar{H}^\circ = \Delta\bar{H}^\circ_f[Hg(g)] = 60.84$ kJ/mol

Assuming Trouton's rule: $\Delta\bar{S}^\circ = \frac{\Delta\bar{H}^\circ}{T_{bp}} = \frac{60.84 \text{ kJ/mol}}{T_{bp}} = 0.088 \text{ kJ mol}^{-1} \text{ K}^{-1}$ $T_{bp} = 60.84/0.088 = 691$ K

Relationship of $\Delta\bar{G}$, $\Delta\bar{G}^\circ$, Q, and K

15-23. $\Delta\bar{G}^\circ$ was given in equation (15.12): +8.58 kJ/mol.

The reaction quotient: $$Q = \frac{a_{H_2O(g)}}{a_{H_2O(l)}} = \frac{P_{H_2O(g)}\text{(in atm)}}{1} = \frac{10/760}{1} = 0.0132$$

Now use equation (15.14): $\Delta\bar{G} = \Delta\bar{G}^\circ + 2.303\ RT \log Q$

$$\Delta\bar{G} = 8.58 \times 10^3 \text{ J/mol} + (2.303 \times 8.314 \text{ J mol}^{-1} \text{ K}^{-1} \times 298 \text{ K} \times \log 0.0132)$$

$$= 8.58 \times 10^3 + [2.303 \times 8.314 \times 298 \times (-1.879)] = 8.58 \times 10^3 - 10.72 \times 10^3 = -2.14 \times 10^3 \text{ J/mol}$$

The process in Figure 15-6(c) is pictured to be spontaneous, and this value of $\Delta\bar{G}$ indicates that indeed it should be.

15-24. (a) We are seeking $\Delta\bar{G}^\circ$ for the process $CCl_4(l, 1 \text{ atm}) \longrightarrow CCl_4(g, 1 \text{ atm})$.

$$\Delta\bar{H}^\circ = \Delta\bar{H}^\circ_f[CCl_4(g)] - \Delta\bar{H}^\circ_f[CCl_4(l)] = -106.7 - (-139.3) = +32.6 \text{ kJ/mol}$$

$$\Delta\bar{G}^\circ = \Delta\bar{H}^\circ - T\Delta\bar{S}^\circ = +32.6 \text{ kJ/mol} - (298 \text{ K} \times 0.09498 \text{ kJ mol}^{-1} \text{ K}^{-1}) = +32.6 - 28.3 = +4.3 \text{ kJ/mol}$$

Since the free energy change for the stated process, ΔG°, is a positive quantity, the process does not occur spontaneously.

(b) Use the expression $\Delta\bar{G}^\circ = -2.303 \cdot RT \cdot \log K$ to obtain a value of K. $\Delta\bar{G}^\circ$ was calculated in part (a).

$$\log K = \frac{-4.3 \times 10^3 \text{ J/mol}}{2.303 \times 8.314 \text{ J mol}^{-1} \text{ K}^{-1} \times 298 \text{ K}} = -0.754 \qquad K = 0.176$$

For the process $CCl_4(l) \rightleftharpoons CCl_4(g)$

$$K = \frac{a_{CCl_4(g)}}{a_{CCl_4(l)}} = \frac{P_{CCl_4(g)}}{1} = 0.176$$

The equilibrium vapor pressure of CCl_4 = 0.176 atm = 134 mmHg

15-25. (a) $K_p = K_c(RT)^{\Delta n} = 2.8 \times 10^2(0.0821 \times 1000)^{-1} = 3.4$

(b) $\Delta\bar{G}^\circ = -2.303 \cdot RT \cdot \log K = -2.303 \times 8.314 \times 1000 \times \log 3.4 = -10{,}200 \text{ J/mol} = -10.2 \text{ kJ/mol}$

(c) For the amounts of the gases given, determine their partial pressures and then the reaction quotient, Q.

$$P_{SO_2} = \frac{0.40 \text{ mol} \times 0.0821 \text{ L atm mol}^{-1} \text{ K}^{-1} \times 1000 \text{ K}}{2.50 \text{ L}} = 13 \text{ atm}$$

$$P_{SO_3} = \frac{0.72 \text{ mol} \times 0.0821 \text{ L atm mol}^{-1} \text{ K}^{-1} \times 1000 \text{ K}}{2.50 \text{ L}} = 24 \text{ atm}$$

$$P_{O_2} = \frac{0.18 \text{ mol} \times 0.0821 \text{ L atm mol}^{-1} \text{ K}^{-1} \times 1000 \text{ K}}{2.50 \text{ L}} = 5.9 \text{ atm}$$

$$Q = \frac{(P_{SO_3})^2}{(P_{SO_2})^2(P_{O_2})} = \frac{(24)^2}{(13)^2 \times 5.9} = 0.58$$

Now use the expression $\Delta\overline{G} = \Delta\overline{G}° + 2.303 \cdot RT \cdot \log Q$

$$\Delta G = -10.2 \times 10^3 \text{ J/mol} + (2.303 \times 8.314 \times 1000 \times \log 0.58)\text{J/mol}$$

$$= -10.2 \times 10^3 - 4.5 \times 10^3 = -14.7 \times 10^3 \text{ J/mol}$$

Since $\Delta G < 0$ the reaction proceeds spontaneously in the *forward direction*. An alternative approach is simply to compare Q(0.58) with K_p(3.4). According to criterion (14.22), since $Q < K_p$ a net reaction should occur in the forward direction.

The thermodynamic equilibrium constant

15-26. The quantity K must be dimensionless so that $\Delta\overline{G}°$ has the units J/mol, and K will be dimensionless only if activities are used in its formulation. K_c can be used instead of K if reactants and products are in solution or appear as pure solid(s) and/or liquid(s). Substituting molar concentrations (without units) into K_c yields a numerical value that is the same as K. If reactants and products are gases or appear as pure solid(s) and/or liquid(s), K_p may be used. However an equilibrium constant K_c using molar concentrations of gases could not be substituted for K (unless $K_c = K_p$).

15-27. (a) $$K = \frac{(a_{NO_2(g)})^2}{(a_{NO(g)})^2(a_{O_2})} = \frac{(P_{NO_2})^2}{(P_{NO})^2(P_{O_2})} = K_p$$

(b) $$K = \frac{(a_{MgO(s)})(a_{SO_2(g)})}{(a_{MgSO_3(s)})} = \frac{1 \times (P_{SO_2})}{1} = P_{SO_2} = K_p$$

(c) $$K = \frac{(a_{H^+(aq)})(a_{C_2H_3O_2^-(aq)})}{(a_{HC_2H_3O_2(aq)})} = \frac{[H^+][C_2H_3O_2^-]}{[HC_2H_3O_2]} = K_c$$

(d) $$K = \frac{(a_{Na_2CO_3(s)})(a_{H_2O(g)})(a_{CO_2(g)})}{(a_{NaHCO_3(s)})^2} = \frac{1 \times (P_{H_2O})(P_{CO_2})}{(1)^2} = (P_{H_2O})(P_{CO_2}) = K_p$$

(e) $$K = \frac{(a_{Mn^{2+}(aq)})(a_{H_2O(l)})^2(a_{Cl_2(g)})}{(a_{MnO_2(s)})(a_{H^+(aq)})^4(a_{Cl^-(aq)})^2} = \frac{[Mn^{2+}] \times (1)^2 \times P_{Cl_2}}{(1) \times [H^+]^4[Cl^-]^2} = \frac{[Mn^{2+}] \times P_{Cl_2}}{[H^+]^4[Cl^-]^2} = K$$

15-28. The equilibrium pressures of $H_2(g)$ and $H_2O(g)$ are independent of the quantities of Fe(s) and $Fe_3O_4(s)$ as long as enough of these substances are present to satisfy the stoichiometric requirements of the reaction. That is, the oxygen atoms that must be removed from H_2O to produce H_2 must combine with Fe atoms to form Fe_3O_4. Enough Fe atoms must be present to permit this. Beyond this point the equilibrium condition is independent of how much excess Fe is present. (The same line of reasoning applies to the reverse reaction involving H_2 and Fe_3O_4.) Thus, the conversion of H_2O to H_2 cannot be carried out with total disregard of the amounts of Fe and Fe_3O_4 present.

$\Delta\bar{G}°$ and K

15-29. For this reaction, $K_p = K = 2.45 \times 10^{-7}$ and

$$\Delta\bar{G}° = -2.303\,RT\cdot\log K = -2.303 \times 8.314\ J\ mol^{-1}\ K^{-1} \times 1000\ K \times \log 2.45 \times 10^{-7}$$

$$\Delta\bar{G}° = -2.303 \times 8.314 \times 1000 \times (-6.611) = 1.266 \times 10^{5}\ J/mol = 126.6\ kJ/mol$$

15-30. Here we use data from Appendix D to determine $\Delta\bar{G}°$ and then calculate K_p.

$$2\ NO(g) + O_2(g) \rightleftharpoons 2\ NO_2(g)$$

$$\Delta\bar{G}° = 2\ \Delta\bar{G}_f°[NO_2(g)] - 2\ \Delta\bar{G}_f°[NO(g)] = 2 \times (+51.84) - 2 \times (86.69) = 103.68 - 173.38$$

$$= -69.70\ kJ/mol = -69.70 \times 10^{3}\ J/mol$$

$$\log K_p = \frac{-\Delta\bar{G}°}{2.303\cdot RT} = \frac{+69.70 \times 10^{3}\ J/mol}{2.303 \times 8.314\ J\ mol^{-1}\ K^{-1} \times 298\ K} = 12.2 \qquad K_p = 1.6 \times 10^{12}$$

15-31. (a) At 298 K, $\log K = \dfrac{-130.30 \times 10^{3}\ J/mol}{2.303 \times 8.314\ J\ mol^{-1}\ K^{-1} \times 298\ K} = -22.8 \qquad K = 1.6 \times 10^{-23}$

The equilibrium constant for the decomposition of limestone at room temperature is extremely small. No appreciable decomposition occurs.

(b) Since $\Delta\bar{H}° > 0$ the decomposition reaction is endothermic. According to Le Chatelier's principle the endothermic reaction is favored by raising the temperature.

15-32. From the data given in this exercise we can calculate $\Delta\bar{G}°$.

$$\Delta\bar{G}° = -2.303 \times 8.314\ J\ mol^{-1}\ K^{-1} \times 298\ K \times \log(5.64 \times 10^{35}) = -2.04 \times 10^{5}\ J/mol = -204\ kJ/mol$$

Use data from Appendix D to proceed as follows:

$$CO(g) + Cl_2(g) \rightleftharpoons COCl_2(g)$$

$$\Delta\bar{G}° = \Delta\bar{G}_f°[COCl_2(g)] - \Delta\bar{G}_f°[CO(g)] = -204\ kJ/mol$$

$$\Delta\bar{G}_f°[COCl_2(g)] - (-137.28\ kJ/mol) = -204\ kJ/mol$$

$$\Delta\bar{G}_f°[COCl_2(g)] = -204 - 137 = -341\ kJ/mol$$

15-33. A value of K can be calculated with equation (15.15).

$$\log K = \frac{-\Delta\bar{G}°}{2.303\cdot RT} = \frac{-119.82 \times 10^{3}\ J/mol}{2.303 \times 8.314\ J\ mol^{-1}\ K^{-1} \times 298\ K} = -21.0$$

$$K = K_p = \frac{(P_{CO})^2}{(P_{CO_2})} = 1.0 \times 10^{-21} \qquad (P_{CO})^2 = 1.0 \times 10^{-21}(P_{CO_2}) \qquad P_{CO} = 3.2 \times 10^{-11}\sqrt{P_{CO_2}}$$

Thus, if $CO_2(g)$ is maintained at 298 K at a pressure of 1.00 atm in contact with C(s), the equilibrium partial pressure of CO would be 3.2×10^{-11} atm = 2.4×10^{-8} mmHg. Conversion of $CO_2(g)$ to CO(g) at room temperature is indeed a very limited reaction.

15-34. If K is very large, a reaction goes essentially to completion. If K is very small, a reaction proceeds in the forward direction only to a very limited extent. Let us say that for a range of K values from about 1×10^{-2} to 1×10^{2} we might generally expect significant equilibrium amounts of all reactants and products. Now calculate $\Delta\overline{G}°$ values corresponding to these values of K.

For $K = 1 \times 10^{-2}$

$\Delta\overline{G}° = -2.303 \cdot RT \cdot \log K = -2.303 \times 8.314\ J\ mol^{-1}\ K^{-1} \times 298\ K \log(1 \times 10^{-2})$

$\Delta\overline{G}° = 1 \times 10^{4}\ J/mol = 10\ kJ/mol$

For $K = 1 \times 10^{2}$

$\Delta\overline{G}° = -2.303 \cdot RT \cdot \log K = -2.303 \times 8.314\ J\ mol^{-1}\ K^{-1} \times 298\ K \times \log(1 \times 10^{2})$

$\Delta\overline{G}° = -1 \times 10^{4}\ J/mol = -10\ kJ/mol$

According to this calculation, we expect to find appreciable equilibrium amounts of all reactants and products only if $\Delta\overline{G}°$ is either a small positive or small negative value (say, ranging from about -10 to +10 kJ/mol).

The variation of $\Delta\overline{G}°$ with temperature

15-35. (a) $CO(g) + H_2O(g) \rightleftharpoons CO_2(g) + H_2(g)$

$\Delta\overline{H}° = \Delta\overline{H}_f°[CO_2(g)] - \Delta\overline{H}_f°[CO(g)] - \Delta\overline{H}_f°[H_2O(g)]$

$= -393.51 - (-110.54) - (-241.84) = -41.13\ kJ/mol$

$\Delta\overline{S}° = \overline{S}°[CO_2(g)] + \overline{S}°[H_2(g)] - \overline{S}°[CO(g)] - \overline{S}°[H_2O(g)]$

$= 213.64 + 130.58 - 197.90 - 188.74 = -42.42\ J\ mol^{-1}\ K^{-1}$

$\Delta\overline{G}° = \Delta\overline{G}_f°[CO_2(g)] - \Delta\overline{G}_f°[CO(g)] - \Delta\overline{G}_f°[H_2O(g)]$

$= -394.38 - (-137.28) - (-228.61) = -28.49\ kJ/mol$

Also, $\Delta\overline{G}° = \Delta\overline{H}° - T\Delta\overline{S}° = -41.13 - 298(-0.04242) = -41.13 + 12.64 = -28.49\ kJ/mol$

(b) at 1000 K: $\Delta\overline{G}° = -41.13\ kJ/mol - 1100 \times (-0.04242)kJ/mol$

$= -41.13\ kJ/mol + 46.66\ kJ/mol = +5.53\ kJ/mol$

$$\log K = \frac{-\Delta\overline{G}°}{2.303 \cdot RT} = \frac{-5.53 \times 10^{3}\ J/mol}{2.303 \times 8.314\ J\ mol^{-1}\ K^{-1} \times 1100\ K} = -0.263 \qquad K = K_p = 0.546$$

(c) In Example 14-6 the value of K_c was given as 1.00. For this reaction $K_p = K_c(RT)^{\Delta n} = K_c(RT)^0$. $K_p = K_c = 1.00$. Agreement between this value and the one calculated in part (b) is rather good, given the long extrapolation of data from 298 K to 1100 K.

15-36. Use data from Appendix D to establish $\Delta\bar{H}°$ and $\Delta\bar{S}°$ at 298 K.

$\Delta\bar{H}° = 2\ \Delta\bar{H}_f°[SO_3(g)] - 2\ \Delta\bar{H}_f°[SO_2(g)] = 2 \times (-395.18\ kJ/mol) - 2 \times (-296.90\ kJ/mol) = -196.56\ kJ/mol$

$\Delta\bar{S}° = 2\ \bar{S}°[SO_3(g)] - 2\ \bar{S}°[SO_2(g)] - \bar{S}°[O_2(g)] = 2 \times (256.23) - 2 \times (248.53) - 205.02$

$= -189.62\ J\ mol^{-1}\ K^{-1}$

At the temperature in question, $\Delta\bar{G}° = \Delta\bar{H}° - T\Delta\bar{S}° = -2.303 \cdot RT \cdot \log K$

$\Delta\bar{G}° = (-196.56 \times 10^3) - T(-189.62) = -2.303 \times 8.314 \cdot T \cdot \log 1.0 \times 10^6$

$189.62\ T + 115\ T = 196.56 \times 10^3 \qquad T = 645\ K$

The value calculated in Example 14-12 was 635 K. Agreement between the two methods is good.

15-37. (a) Determine $\Delta\bar{H}°$ for the reaction $C(s) + CO_2(g) \rightleftharpoons 2\ CO(g)$

$\Delta\bar{H}° = 2\ \Delta\bar{H}_f°[CO(g)] - \Delta\bar{H}_f°[CO_2(g)] = 2 \times (-110.54) - (-393.51) = +172.43\ kJ/mol$

Since the forward reaction is endothermic, the conversion of $CO_2(g)$ to $CO(g)$ is favored at high temperatures.

(b) Determine $\Delta\bar{S}°$ for the reaction in part (a).

$\Delta\bar{S}° = 2\ \bar{S}°[CO(g)] - \bar{S}°[CO_2(g)] - \bar{S}°[C(graphite)] = (2 \times 197.90) - 213.64 - 5.69$

$= 176.47\ J\ mol^{-1}\ K^{-1}$

We are looking for the equilibrium condition: $C(graphite) + CO_2(g, 1\ atm) \rightleftharpoons 2\ CO(g, 1\ atm)$

$K = K_p = \frac{(P_{CO})^2}{(P_{CO_2})} = \frac{(1)^2}{(1)} = 1.00 \qquad \Delta\bar{G}° = -2.303 \cdot RT \cdot \log K_p = -2.303\ RT\ \log 1.00 = 0$

Now solve the following expression for T:

$\Delta\bar{G}° = \Delta\bar{H}° - T\Delta\bar{S}° = 0 \qquad T\Delta\bar{S}° = \Delta\bar{H}°$

$T = \frac{\Delta\bar{H}°}{\Delta\bar{S}°} = \frac{172.43\ kJ/mol}{0.17647\ kJ\ mol^{-1}\ K^{-1}} = 977\ K$

15-38. $\Delta\bar{S}°$ is given. $\Delta\bar{H}°_{vap}$ can be calculated as follows:

$\Delta\bar{H}°_{vap} = T \times \Delta\bar{S}°_{vap} = (78.4 + 273.2)K \times 0.121\ kJ\ mol^{-1}\ K^{-1} = 39.41\ kJ/mol$

at 298 K: $\Delta\bar{G}°_{vap} = \Delta\bar{H}°_{vap} - T\Delta\bar{S}°_{vap} = 39.41\ kJ/mol - (298 \times 0.1121)kJ/mol = 6.00\ kJ/mol$

Now, for the process $C_2H_5OH(l) \rightleftharpoons C_2H_5OH(g)$

$\Delta\bar{S}° = \bar{S}°[C_2H_5OH(g)] - \bar{S}°[C_2H_5OH(l)] = \bar{S}°[C_2H_5OH(g)] - 160.67 = 112.1$

$\bar{S}°[C_2H_5OH(g)] = 272.8\ J\ mol^{-1}\ K^{-1}$

$\Delta\bar{H}° = \Delta\bar{H}_f°[C_2H_5OH(g)] - \Delta\bar{H}_f°[C_2H_5OH(l)] = \Delta\bar{H}_f°[C_2H_5OH(g)] - (-277.65) = 39.41$

$\Delta\bar{H}_f°[C_2H_5OH(g)] = 39.41 - 277.65 = -238.24\ kJ/mol$

$\Delta\bar{G}° = \Delta\bar{G}_f°[C_2H_5OH(g)] - \Delta\bar{G}_f°[C_2H_5OH(l)] = \Delta\bar{G}_f°[C_2H_5OH(g)] - (-174.77) = 6.00$

$\Delta\bar{G}_f°[C_2H_5OH(g)] = 6.00 - 174.77 = -168.77\ kJ/mol$

Heat engines

15-39. (a) efficiency $= \frac{T_h - T_l}{T_h} = \frac{T_h - 313}{T_h} = 0.36$ $T_h - 313 = 0.36\ T_h$ $0.64\ T_h = 313$ $T_h = 489$ K

(b) In order to offset other losses, e.g. between the turbine and the generator, the thermodynamic cycle would have to be more than 36% efficient if the overall conversion of heat to electrical work is to be 36% efficient. This higher efficiency for the thermodynamic cycle would require a higher steam temperature.

15-40. Use data from Appendix D to determine $\Delta\overline{H}^\circ_{vap}$ at 298 K

$H_2O(l) \rightleftharpoons H_2O(g)$ $\Delta\overline{H}^\circ_{vap} = -241.84 - (-285.85) = +44.01$ kJ/mol

Use this value in equation (11.3) to find a pressure, P_2, at the temperature $T_2 = 489$ K. Use $P_1 = 1.00$ atm at $T_1 = 373$ K.

$$\log\frac{P_2}{1.00} = \frac{44.01 \times 10^3 \text{ J/mol}}{2.303 \times 8.314 \text{ J mol}^{-1} \text{ K}^{-1}}\left(\frac{489 - 373}{373 \times 489}\right) \text{K}^{-1} \qquad \log P_2 = 1.46 \qquad P_2 = 28.8 \text{ atm}$$

Self-test Questions

1. (*d*) It is not always the case that the entropy of a system increases in a spontaneous process (e.g., the freezing of water). Neither is it required that the entropy of the surroundings increase. Given these facts, a spontaneous process does not require that the entropy of both the system and surroundings increase. What is required is that the total entropy--the entropy of the universe--increase.

$\Delta S_{univ.} = \Delta S_{sys.} + \Delta S_{sun} > 0.$

2. (*b*) The heat of a reaction is related to ΔH; the change in molecular disorder, to ΔS; and the rate of a reaction to the rate constant, k, and the rate law. The change in free energy, ΔG, is related to the direction of spontaneous change. If $\Delta G < 0$ the forward reaction is spontaneous, and if $\Delta G > 0$, the reverse reaction.

3. (*a*) Consider the expression $\Delta G = \Delta H - T\Delta S$. If $\Delta H < 0$ and $\Delta S < 0$, at low temperatures the magnitude of ΔH exceeds that of TΔS; $\Delta G < 0$ and the forward reaction is spontaneous. At high temperatures, $-T\Delta S$ is a positive quantity that exceeds ΔH; $\Delta G > 0$.

4. (*c*) If it is necessary to use an external agent (electricity) to produce a change, the change is nonspontaneous. For a nonspontaneous change, $\Delta G > 0$. The other values listed, ΔH and ΔS, might either be positive or negative.

5. (*b*) This is a dissociation reaction in which Br—Br bonds are broken ($\Delta H > 0$). The dissociation is accompanied by an increase in entropy ($\Delta S > 0$). The reaction is spontaneous at some temperatures ($\Delta G < 0$) but not at all temperatures.

6. (*d*) Since $\Delta\overline{G}^\circ = -2.303 \cdot RT \cdot \log K$, if $\Delta\overline{G}^\circ = 0$ then $\log K = 0$. $\log K = 0$ if $K = 1$. Based on the expression $\Delta\overline{G}^\circ = \Delta\overline{H}^\circ - T\Delta\overline{S}^\circ$, if $\Delta\overline{G}^\circ = 0$ then $\Delta\overline{H}^\circ = T\Delta\overline{S}^\circ$. This does not require that either $\Delta\overline{H}^\circ$ or $\Delta\overline{S}^\circ$ be equal to zero.

7. (a) The criterion for spontaneous change is $\Delta G = \Delta H - T\Delta S < 0$. If $\Delta S > 0$ and $\Delta H < 0$, then clearly $\Delta G < 0$; the change is spontaneous. However, even though $\Delta S > 0$, if $\Delta H > 0$, at low temperatures $\Delta G > 0$; the change is nonspontaneous. Thus, we must know both ΔH and ΔS, not ΔS alone, in order to predict the direction of spontaneous change.

(b) The expression $\Delta\overline{G} = \Delta\overline{G}^\circ + 2.303 \cdot RT \cdot \log Q$ allows us to calculate ΔG for any set of activities of reactants and products expressed through the reaction quotient, Q. If $\Delta G < 0$ the reaction is spontaneous for the given conditions; if $\Delta G > 0$, the reaction is nonspontaneous. But in order to use this expression we must have a value of $\Delta\overline{G}^\circ$--the free energy change when reactants and products are in their standard states.

8. We start with the basic expression $\Delta\overline{G} = \Delta\overline{G}^\circ + 2.303 \cdot RT \cdot \log Q$. If a reaction is at equilibrium, $\Delta\overline{G} = 0$ and $Q = K$. This leads to the expression $0 = \Delta\overline{G}^\circ + 2.303 \cdot RT \cdot \log K$ and $\Delta\overline{G}^\circ = -2.303 \cdot RT \cdot \log K$.

9. (a) $C_5H_{10}(l) \longrightarrow C_5H_{10}(g)$

$\Delta\overline{H}^\circ_{vap} = \Delta\overline{H}^\circ_f[C_5H_{10}(g)] - \Delta\overline{H}^\circ_f[C_5H_{10}(l)] = -77.2 - (-105.9) = 28.7$ kJ/mol

To estimate the normal boiling point, assume Trouton's rule:

$\Delta\overline{S}^\circ_{vap} = 88$ J mol^{-1} K^{-1} and

$$T = \frac{\Delta\overline{H}^\circ}{\Delta\overline{S}^\circ} = \frac{28.7 \text{ kJ/mol}}{0.088 \text{ kJ mol}^{-1} \text{ K}^{-1}} = 326 \text{ K}$$

(b) $\Delta\overline{G}^\circ_{vap} = \Delta\overline{H}^\circ_{vap} - T\Delta\overline{S}^\circ_{vap} = 28.7$ kJ/mol $- (298$ K $\times 0.088$ kJ mol^{-1} K$^{-1})$

$= 28.7$ kJ/mol $- 26.2$ kJ/mol $= 2.5$ kJ/mol

(c) The positive sign of $\Delta\overline{G}^\circ$ signifies that the production of $C_5H_{10}(g)$ at 1.00 atm pressure from $C_5H_{10}(l)$ will not proceed spontaneously at 298 K. That is, the equilibrium vapor pressure of C_5H_{10} at 298 K must be less than 1.00 atm.

10. (a) $NH_4NO_3(s) \longrightarrow N_2O(g) + 2\ H_2O(l)$

$\Delta\overline{H}^\circ = \Delta\overline{H}^\circ_f[N_2O(g)] + 2\ \Delta\overline{H}^\circ_f[H_2O(l)] - \Delta\overline{H}^\circ_f[NH_4NO_3(s)]$

$= 81.55 + 2 \times (-285.85) - (-365.56) = -124.59$ kJ/mol

The reaction is exothermic.

(b) $\Delta\overline{S}^\circ = \overline{S}^\circ[N_2O(g)] + 2\ \overline{S}^\circ[H_2O(l)] - \overline{S}^\circ[NH_4NO_3(s)]$

$= 219.99 + (2 \times 69.96) - 151.08 = 208.8$ J mol^{-1} K^{-1}

$\Delta\overline{G}^\circ = \Delta\overline{H}^\circ - T\Delta\overline{S}^\circ = -124.59 - (298 \times 0.2088) = -186.81$ kJ/mol

(c) $$\log K = \frac{-\Delta\overline{G}^\circ}{2.303 \cdot RT} = \frac{-(-186.81) \times 10^3 \text{ J/mol}}{2.303 \times 8.314 \text{ J mol}^{-1} \text{ K}^{-1} \times 298 \text{ K}} = 32.7 \qquad K = 5.0 \times 10^{32}$$

(d) Because $\Delta\overline{H}^\circ < 0$ and $\Delta\overline{S}^\circ > 0$ the reaction is spontaneous at all temperatures (see case 1, Table 15-1).

Chapter 16

Solubility Equilibria in
Aqueous Solutions

The meaning of K_{sp}

16-1. (a) $K_{sp} = [Ag^+]^2[SO_4^{2-}]$ (b) $K_{sp} = [Hg_2^{2+}][C_2O_4^{2-}]$

(c) $K_{sp} = [Ra^{2+}][IO_3^-]^2$ (d) $K_{sp} = [Ni^{2+}]^3[PO_4^{3-}]^2$

(e) $K_{sp} = [PuO_2^{2+}][CO_3^{2-}]$

16-2. (a) $Fe(OH)_3(s) \rightleftharpoons Fe^{3+}(aq) + 3\ OH^-(aq)$

(b) $BiOOH(s) \rightleftharpoons BiO^+(aq) + OH^-(aq)$

(c) $Hg_2I_2(s) \rightleftharpoons Hg_2^{2+}(aq) + 2\ I^-(aq)$

(d) $Pb_3(AsO_4)_2(s) \rightleftharpoons 3\ Pb^{2+}(aq) + 2\ AsO_4^{3-}(aq)$

(e) $Cu_2[Fe(CN)_6](s) \rightleftharpoons 2\ Cu^{2+}(aq) + [Fe(CN)_6]^{4-}(aq)$

(f) $MgNH_4PO_4(s) \rightleftharpoons Mg^{2+}(aq) + NH_4^+ + (aq) + PO_4^{3-}(aq)$

16-3. (a) If $Q < K_{sp}$ a solution is unsaturated.

(b) If $Q > K_{sp}$ and no precipitate has formed, a solution must be supersaturated.

16-4. The molar solubility of a solute is S mol/L. If the solute is of the type XY the ionic concentrations in solution are $[X^{n+}] = S$ and $[Y^{n-}] = S$, and $K_{sp} = S \times S = S^2$. If the solute is of the type X_2Y, $[X^{n+}] = 2S$; $[Y^{2n-}] = S$; and $K_{sp} = (2S)^2(S) = 4S^3$. No matter what the solute, K_{sp} will be equal to S^2 or some higher power of S. (If the solubility of a solute of the type XY were S = 1.00 mol/L one might argue that $K_{sp} = S \times S = 1.00$. Recall, however, that the solubility product expression loses its meaning in solutions as concentrated as this.)

K_{sp} and solubility

16-5. $Pb(IO_3)_2 \rightleftharpoons Pb^{2+}(aq) + 2\ IO_3^-(aq)$

2.15×10^{-5} M $\quad 2 \times 2.15 \times 10^{-5}$ M

$$K_{sp} = [Pb^{2+}][IO_3^-]^2 = (2.15 \times 10^{-5})(2 \times 2.15 \times 10^{-5})^2 = 3.98 \times 10^{-14}$$

16-6. $$\text{no. mol } BaC_2O_4/L = \frac{22 \text{ mg } BaC_2O_4}{L} \times \frac{1 \text{ g } BaC_2O_4}{1000 \text{ mg } BaC_2O_4} \times \frac{1 \text{ mol } BaC_2O_4}{225 \text{ g } BaC_2O_4} = 9.8 \times 10^{-5} \text{ M}$$

$BaC_2O_4(s) \rightleftharpoons Ba^{2+}(aq) + C_2O_4^{2-}(aq)$

9.8×10^{-5} M $\quad 9.8 \times 10^{-5}$ M

$$K_{sp} = [Ba^{2+}][C_2O_4^{2-}] = (9.8 \times 10^{-5})^2 = 9.6 \times 10^{-9}$$

16-7. $Ag_2SO_4(s) \rightleftharpoons 2\ Ag^+(aq) + SO_4^{2-}(aq)$

from Ag_2SO_4:	9.2×10^{-3} M	$(1/2) \times 9.2 \times 10^{-3}$ M
from Na_2SO_4:		0.200 M
at equil:	9.2×10^{-3} M	0.205 M

$K_{sp} = [Ag^+]^2[SO_4^{2-}] = (9.2 \times 10^{-3})^2(0.205) = 1.7 \times 10^{-5}$

16-8. (a) Let the molar solubility = S. $[Pb^{2+}]$ = S and $[I^-]$ = 2S

$PbI_2(s) \rightleftharpoons Pb^{2+}(aq) + 2\ I^-(aq)$

$K_{sp} = [Pb^{2+}][I^-]^2 = (S)(2S)^2 = 4S^3 = 7.1 \times 10^{-9}$

$S^3 = 1.8 \times 10^{-9}$ $\quad S = 1.2 \times 10^{-3}$ mol PbI_2/L

(b) $PbI_2(s) \rightleftharpoons Pb^{2+}(aq) + 2\ I^-(aq)$

from PbI_2:	S mol/L	2 S mol/L
from 0.010 M KI:	--	0.010 mol/L
at equil:	S mol/L	(0.010 + 2S)mol/L

$K_{sp} = [Pb^{2+}][I^-]^2 = (S)(0.010 + 2S)^2 = 7.1 \times 10^{-9}$

Assume S << 0.010: $\quad (0.010)^2S = 7.1 \times 10^{-9}$ $\quad S = 7.1 \times 10^{-5}$ mol PbI_2/L

(c) $PbI_2(s) \quad Pb^{2+}(aq) + 2\ I^-(aq)$

from PbI_2:	S mol/L	2S mol/L
from 0.030 M $Pb(NO_3)_2$:	0.030 mol/L	--
at equil:	(0.030 + S)mol/L	2S mol/L

$K_{sp} = [Pb^{2+}][I^-]^2 = (0.030 + S)(2S)^2 = 0.030 \times 4S^2 = 7.1 \times 10^{-9}$

Assume S << 0.030: $\quad S^2 = 5.9 \times 10^{-8}$ $\quad S = 2.4 \times 10^{-4}$ mol PbI_2/L

16-9. Refer to Table 16-1 and write a solubility product constant expression for each solute in terms of its solubility S (in mol/L). Solve each expression for S; relate $[Mg^{2+}]$ to S; and find the largest of the three.

(a) $[Mg^{2+}][CO_3^{2-}] = (S)(S) = 3.5 \times 10^{-8}$ $\quad S = 1.9 \times 10^{-4}$

$[Mg^{2+}] = S = 1.9 \times 10^{-4}$ M

(b) $[Mg^{2+}][F^-]^2 = (S)(2S)^2 = 4S^3 = 3.7 \times 10^{-8}$ $\quad S = 2.1 \times 10^{-3}$

$[Mg^{2+}] = S = 2.1 \times 10^{-3}$ M

(c) $Mg_3(PO_4)_2(s) \rightleftharpoons 3\ Mg^{2+}(aq) + 2\ PO_4^{3-}(aq)$

S $\longrightarrow$ 3S $\quad$ 2S

$[Mg^{2+}]^3[PO_4^{3-}]^2 = (3S)^3(2S)^2 = 27S^3 \times 4S^2 = 108S^5 = 1 \times 10^{-25}$

$S = 3.9 \times 10^{-6}$ $\quad [Mg^{2+}] = 3S = 3 \times 3.9 \times 10^{-6} = 1.2 \times 10^{-5}$ M

The highest concentration of Mg^{2+} is found in saturated MgF_2.

16-10. $CaF_2(s) \rightleftharpoons Ca^{2+}(aq) + 2\ F^-(aq)$

at equil: S mol/L   2 S mol/L

$[Ca^{2+}][F^-]^2 = S \times (2S)^2 = 4S^3 = 2.7 \times 10^{-11}$ $S^3 = 6.8 \times 10^{-12}$

$S = 1.9 \times 10^{-4}$ $[F^-] = 2S = 3.8 \times 10^{-4}$ mol F^-/L

Assume that 1.00 L of the saturated solution has a mass of 1000 g. The volume of solution weighing 1×10^6 g would be 1000 L. Determine the number of grams of F^- in 1000 L of saturated solution.

$$\text{no. g } F^- = 1000 \text{ L} \times \frac{3.8 \times 10^{-4} \text{ mol } F^-}{\text{L}} \times \frac{19.0 \text{ g } F^-}{1 \text{ mol } F^-} = 7.2 \text{ g } F^-$$

The saturated solution contains 7.2 ppm F^-.

16-11. Let us base the entire calculation on 1.00 L of the water sample.

$$\text{no. mol } CaSO_4 = 1.00 \text{ L} \times \frac{1000 \text{ cm}^3}{1 \text{ L}} \times \frac{1.00 \text{ g water}}{1.00 \text{ cm}^3} \times \frac{130 \text{ g } CaSO_4}{1 \times 10^6 \text{ g water}} \times \frac{1 \text{ mol } CaSO_4}{136 \text{ g } CaSO_4}$$

$$= 9.56 \times 10^{-4} \text{ mol } CaSO_4$$

Next, let us determine the molar solubility of $CaSO_4$ in water.

$CaSO_4(s) \rightleftharpoons Ca^{2+}(aq) + SO_4^{2-}(aq)$

S mol/L   S mol/L

$K_{sp} = [Ca^{2+}][SO_4^{2-}] = S \times S = 9.1 \times 10^{-6}$ $S = 3.0 \times 10^{-3}$ mol $CaSO_4$/L

The liter of water at the outset is not saturated. It contains 9.56×10^{-4} mol $CaSO_4$ but could tolerate 3.0×10^{-3} mol $CaSO_4$. Let us find the volume of a 3.0×10^{-3} M $CaSO_4$ solution that contains 9.56×10^{-4} mol $CaSO_4$.

$$\text{no. L} = 9.56 \times 10^{-4} \text{ mol } CaSO_4 \times \frac{1.00 \text{ L}}{3.0 \times 10^{-3} \text{ mol } CaSO_4} = 0.32 \text{ L}$$

To reduce the original 1.00 L of solution to a volume of 0.32 L (at which point $CaSO_4$ begins to precipitate) requires that 0.68 L be evaporated. The fraction of the water that must be evaporated, then, is 0.68 (or 68%).

16-12. First, determine the molarity of saturated PbI_2. (Again, refer to this as S.)

$PbI_2(s) \rightleftharpoons Pb^{2+}(aq) + 2\ I^-(aq)$

S mol/L   2 S mol/L

$K_{sp} = [Pb^{2+}][I^-]^2 = (S)(2S)^2 = 4S^3 = 7.1 \times 10^{-9}$ $S = 1.2 \times 10^{-3}$ mol PbI_2/L

The titration reaction is $I^-(aq) + Ag^+(aq) \longrightarrow AgI(s)$.

$$\text{no. mol } AgNO_3 = 50.00 \text{ ml} \times \frac{1.00 \text{ L}}{1000 \text{ ml}} \times \frac{1.2 \times 10^{-3} \text{ mol } PbI_2}{\text{L}} \times \frac{2 \text{ mol } I^-}{1 \text{ mol } PbI_2} \times \frac{1 \text{ mol } Ag^+}{1 \text{ mol } I^-} \times \frac{1 \text{ mol } AgNO_3}{1 \text{ mol } Ag^+}$$

$$= 1.2 \times 10^{-4} \text{ mol } AgNO_3$$

This amount of $AgNO_3$ was found in 16.2 ml of solution. The molar concentration of this solution is:

$$\frac{1.2 \times 10^{-4} \text{ mol } AgNO_3}{0.0162 \text{ L}} = 7.4 \times 10^{-3} \text{ M } AgNO_3$$

16-13. Use the titration data to determine $[C_2O_4^{2-}]$ in the saturated solution. (Note also that $[Ca^{2+}] = [C_2O_4^{2-}]$ in this solution.)

$$\text{no. mol } C_2O_4^{2-} = 2.1 \text{ ml} \times \frac{1.00 \text{ L}}{1000 \text{ ml}} \times \frac{0.00122 \text{ mol } MnO_4^-}{1.00 \text{ L}} \times \frac{5 \text{ mol } C_2O_4^{2-}}{2 \text{ mol } MnO_4^-} = 6.4 \times 10^{-6} \text{ mol } C_2O_4^{2-}$$

$$[C_2O_4^{2-}] = \frac{6.4 \times 10^{-6} \text{ mol } C_2O_4^{2-}}{0.1000 \text{ L}} = 6.4 \times 10^{-5} \text{ M}$$

$$K_{sp} = [Ca^{2+}][C_2O_4^{2-}] = (6.4 \times 10^{-5})^2 = 4.1 \times 10^{-9}$$

16-14. First, we must establish $[Ag^+]$ in saturated $AgBrO_3$(aq).

$$2\, Ag^+(aq) + H_2S(g) \longrightarrow Ag_2S + 2\, H^+$$

$$\text{no. mol } H_2S = n = \frac{PV}{RT} = \frac{(748/760) \times 0.0304}{0.0821 \times 296} = 1.23 \times 10^{-3} \text{ mol } H_2S$$

$$\text{no. mol } Ag^+ = 1.23 \times 10^{-3} \text{ mol } H_2S \times \frac{2 \text{ mol } Ag^+}{1 \text{ mol } H_2S} = 2.46 \times 10^{-3} \text{ mol } Ag^+$$

$$[Ag^+] \text{ in saturated } AgBrO_3(aq) = \frac{2.46 \times 10^{-3} \text{ mol } Ag^+}{0.338 \text{ L}} = 7.28 \times 10^{-3} \text{ M}$$

$$[BrO_3^-] = [Ag^+] = 7.28 \times 10^{-3} \text{ M}$$

$$K_{sp} = [Ag^+][BrO_3^-] = (7.28 \times 10^{-3})^2 = 5.30 \times 10^{-5}$$

16-15. (a) $Mg(OH)_2(s) \rightleftharpoons Mg^{2+}(aq) + 2\, OH^-(aq)$

S $\longrightarrow$ S 2S

$$K_{sp} = [Mg^{2+}][OH^-]^2 = (S)(2S)^2 = 4S^3$$

$$S^3 = \frac{K_{sp}}{4} \qquad S = \left(\frac{K_{sp}}{4}\right)^{1/3} \qquad S = \left(\frac{2 \times 10^{-11}}{4}\right)^{1/3} = 1.7 \times 10^{-4} \text{ mol } Mg(OH)_2/L$$

(b) $Ag_2CO_3(s) \rightleftharpoons 2\, Ag^+(aq) + CO_3^{2-}(aq)$

S $\longrightarrow$ 2S S

$$K_{sp} = [Ag^+]^2[CO_3^{2-}] = (2S)^2(S) = 4S^3 \qquad S^3 = \frac{K_{sp}}{4}$$

$$S = \left(\frac{K_{sp}}{4}\right)^{1/3} = \left(\frac{8.1 \times 10^{-12}}{4}\right)^{1/3} = 1.3 \times 10^{-4} \text{ mol } Ag_2CO_3/L$$

(c) $Al(OH)_3(s) \rightleftharpoons Al^{3+}(aq) + 3\, OH^-(aq)$

S $\longrightarrow$ S 3S

$$K_{sp} = [Al^{3+}][OH^-]^3 = (S)(3S)^3 = 27S^4 \qquad S^4 = \frac{K_{sp}}{27}$$

$$S = \left(\frac{K_{sp}}{27}\right)^{1/4} = \left(\frac{1.3 \times 10^{-33}}{27}\right)^{1/4} = 2.6 \times 10^{-9} \text{ mol } Al(OH)_3/L$$

(d) $Li_3PO_4(s) \rightleftharpoons 3\, Li^+(aq) + PO_4^{3-}(aq)$

S $\longrightarrow$ 3S S

$$K_{sp} = [Li^+]^3[PO_4^{3-}] = (3S)^3(S) = 27S^4 \qquad S^4 = \frac{K_{sp}}{27}$$

$$S = \left(\frac{K_{sp}}{27}\right)^{1/4} = \left(\frac{3.2 \times 10^{-9}}{27}\right)^{1/4} = 3.3 \times 10^{-3} \text{ mol } Li_3PO_4/L$$

(e) $Bi_2S_3(s) \rightleftharpoons 2\,Bi^{3+}(aq) + 3S^{2-}(aq)$

$S \longrightarrow \quad 2S \quad 3S$

$$K_{sp} = [Bi^{3+}]^2[S^{2-}]^3 = (2S)^2(3S)^3 = (4S^2)(27S^3) = 108S^5 \qquad S^5 = \frac{K_{sp}}{108} \qquad S = \left(\frac{K_{sp}}{108}\right)^{1/5}$$

$$S = \left(\frac{1 \times 10^{-97}}{108}\right)^{1/5} = 1.6 \times 10^{-20} \text{ mol } Bi_2S_3/L$$

The common ion effect

16-16. Through the common ion I^-, KI displaces the solubility equilibrium of AgI to the left, that is toward its precipitation. Thus AgI(s) is less soluble in KI(aq) than in water. KNO_3, on the other hand, reduces the activities of the Ag^+ and I^- ions in solution. Additional AgI must dissolve to maintain equilibrium. The solubility of AgI(s) is increased somewhat by the presence of K^+ and NO_3^- ions (the salt effect).

16-17. The method employed in Example 16-4 was

$Ag_2CrO_4(s) \rightleftharpoons$	$2\,Ag^+(aq)$ +	$CrO_4^{2-}(aq)$
from Ag_2CrO_4:	2S mol/L	S mol/L
from 0.10 M $AgNO_3$:	0.10 mol/L	--
equil. concn:	(0.10 + 2S)mol/L	S mol/L

$$K_{sp} = [Ag^+]^2[CrO_4^{2-}] = (0.10 + 2S)^2(S) = 2.4 \times 10^{-12}$$

Assume $S \ll 0.10$: $(0.10)^2 \times S = 2.4 \times 10^{-12}$ $\qquad S = 2.4 \times 10^{-10}$ mol Ag_2CrO_4/L

in 0.10 M $AgNO_3$: $S = 2.4 \times 10^{-10}$ mol Ag_2CrO_4/L

in 0.10 M K_2CrO_4: $S = 2.4 \times 10^{-6}$ mol Ag_2CrO_4/L

in pure water: $S = 8.4 \times 10^{-5}$ mol Ag_2CrO_4/L

The common ion effect due to Ag^+ is seen to be much more pronounced than that of CrO_4^{2-}.

16-18. Let S = no. mol $Pb(IO_3)_2/L$ and M = molarity of KIO_3. The calculation of some data points follows:

$$Pb(IO_3)_2(s) \rightleftharpoons Pb^{2+}(aq) + 2\,IO_3^-(aq); \; K_{sp} = 3.2 \times 10^{-13}$$

$$K_{sp} = [Pb^{2+}][IO_3^-]^2 = S(2S + M)^2 = 3.2 \times 10^{-13}$$

Assume $S \ll M$: $S \cdot M^2 = 3.2 \times 10^{-13}$ $\qquad S = \dfrac{3.2 \times 10^{-13}}{M^2}$

in 0.10 M KIO_3: $S = \dfrac{3.2 \times 10^{-13}}{(0.10)^2} = 3.2 \times 10^{-11}$ mol $Pb(IO_3)_2/L$ $\qquad \log S = -10.5$

in 0.050 M KIO_3: $S = \dfrac{3.2 \times 10^{-13}}{(0.05)^2} = 1.3 \times 10^{-10}$ mol $Pb(IO_3)_2/L$ $\qquad \log S = -9.9$

in 0.020 M KIO_3: $S = \frac{3.2 \times 10^{-13}}{(0.020)^2} = 8.0 \times 10^{-10}$ mol $Pb(IO_3)_2$/L log S = - 9.1

in 0.010 M KIO_3: $S = \frac{3.2 \times 10^{-13}}{(0.010)^2} = 3.2 \times 10^{-9}$ mol $Pb(IO_3)_2$/L log S = - 8.5

in 0.0050 M KIO_3: $S = \frac{3.2 \times 10^{-13}}{(0.0050)^2} = 1.3 \times 10^{-8}$ mol $Pb(IO_3)_2$/L log S = - 7.9

in pure water: $4S^3 = 3.2 \times 10^{-13}$ $S = 4.3 \times 10^{-5}$ mol $Pb(IO_3)_2$/L log S = - 4.4

Because of the extreme range of solubilities, a logarithmic plot is necessary.

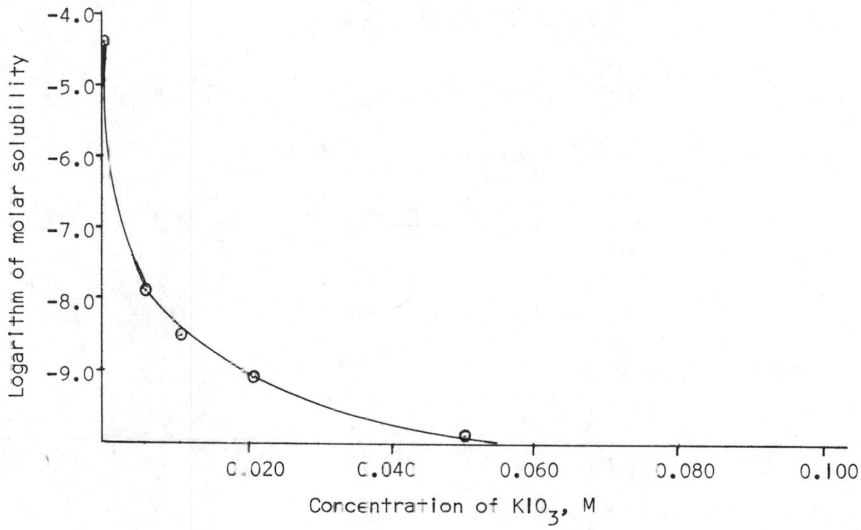

16-19. (a) The solution volume is increased from 500.0 ml to 1000.0 ml. Additional $Mg(OH)_2$ dissolves but the concentration of the saturated solution is unchanged.

$$Mg(OH)_2(s) \rightleftharpoons \underset{S \text{ mol/L}}{Mg^{2+}} + \underset{2\,S \text{ mol/L}}{2\,OH^-(aq)}; \quad K_{sp} = 2 \times 10^{-11}$$

$$K_{sp} = [Mg^{2+}][OH^-]^2 = S \times (2S)^2 = 4S^3 = 2 \times 10^{-11}$$

$$[Mg^{2+}] = S = 1.7 \times 10^{-4}\text{ M}$$

(b) This involves a dilution of the solution described above.

$$[Mg^{2+}] = \frac{0.1000\text{ L} \times \frac{1.7 \times 10^{-4}\text{ mol }Mg^{2+}}{L}}{0.6000\text{ L}} = 2.8 \times 10^{-5}\text{ M}$$

(c) The addition of $MgCl_2$ to the saturated solution of $Mg(OH)_2$ would, through the common-ion-effect, cause the precipitation of some $Mg(OH)_2(s)$. However, the amount of $Mg(OH)_2(s)$ precipitated in this way would be very small. At most, it would correspond to one half the number of moles of OH^- present in the saturated solution.

max. no. mol $Mg(OH)_2$ precipitating = max. no. mol Mg^{2+} removed by pptn
$= 0.02500\text{ L} \times 1.7 \times 10^{-4}$ mol Mg^{2+}/L $= 4.2 \times 10^{-6}$ mol Mg^{2+}.

The final solution, then, contains all the Mg^{2+} ion from the 250.0 ml 0.065 M $MgCl_2$ and some of the Mg^{2+} from the 25.00 ml saturated $Mg(OH)_2(aq)$. And the first source is far more important than the second.

no. mol Mg^{2+} = 0.2500 L × 0.065 mol Mg^{2+}/L = 0.016 mol Mg^{2+}

$$[Mg^{2+}] = \frac{0.016 \text{ mol } Mg^{2+}}{0.2750 \text{ L}} = 0.058 \text{ M}$$

(d) The 0.150 M KOH solution is diluted by the addition of 50.00 ml saturated $Mg(OH)_2(aq)$, and again some slight precipitation of $Mg(OH)_2(s)$ occurs because of the common ion effect. In the mixed solution:

$$[OH^-] = \frac{0.150 \text{ L} \times 0.150 \text{ mol } OH^-/\text{L}}{0.200 \text{ L}} = 0.112 \text{ M}$$

$$[Mg^{+}][OH^-]^2 = [Mg^{2+}](0.112)^2 = 2 \times 10^{-11} \qquad [Mg^{2+}] = 1.6 \times 10^{-9} \text{ M}$$

16-20. Convert the Ca^{2+} content to molarity. Then use the K_{sp} expression to solve for $[F^-]$.

$$[Ca^{2+}] = \frac{130 \text{ g } Ca^{2+}}{1 \times 10^6 \text{ g water}} \times \frac{1 \times 10^3 \text{ g water}}{1 \text{ L water}} \times \frac{1 \text{ mol } Ca^{2+}}{40.1 \text{ g } Ca^{2+}} = 3.24 \times 10^{-3} \text{ M}$$

$$K_{sp} = [Ca^{2+}][F^-]^2 = (3.24 \times 10^{-3})[F^-]^2 = 2.7 \times 10^{-11} \qquad [F^-]^2 = 8.3 \times 10^{-9} \qquad [F^-] = 9.1 \times 10^{-5} \text{ M}$$

Now convert $[F^-]$ to ppm F^-.

$$\frac{9.1 \times 10^{-5} \text{ mol } F^-}{\text{L water}} \times \frac{19.0 \text{ g } F^-}{1 \text{ mol } F^-} \times \frac{1 \text{ L water}}{1000 \text{ g water}} = \frac{1.7 \times 10^{-6} \text{ g } F^-}{\text{g water}} \times \frac{10^6}{10^6} = \frac{1.7 \text{ g } F^-}{10^6 \text{ g water}} = 1.7 \text{ ppm } F^-$$

16-21. Display the data for this exercise in the usual form:

$MgF_2(s)$	$\rightleftharpoons$ $Mg^{2+}(aq)$	+	$2\ F^-(aq)$
from MgF_2:	S mol/L		2S mol/L
from $MgCl_2(aq)$:	5.50×10^{-4} mol/L		--
equil. concn:	$(S + 5.50 \times 10^{-4})$mol/L		2S mol/L

$$K_{sp} = [Mg^{2+}][F^-]^2 = (S + 5.50 \times 10^{-4})(2S)^2$$

If we make the usual assumption, it would be $S << 5.50 \times 10^{-4}$; $5.50 \times 10^{-4}(2S)^2 = 3.7 \times 10^{-8}$; $S = 4.1 \times 10^{-3}$. But 4.1×10^{-3} is not greatly smaller than 5.50×10^{-4}; it is larger. The assumption is not valid.

$$K_{sp} = 4S^2(S + 5.50 \times 10^{-4}) = 4S^3 + 2.2 \times 10^{-3}S^2 = 3.7 \times 10^{-8}$$

$$S^3 + 5.5 \times 10^{-4}S^2 - 9.2 \times 10^{-9} = 0$$

Try $S = 1.0 \times 10^{-3}$: $1.0 \times 10^{-9} + 5.5 \times 10^{-10} - 9.2 \times 10^{-9} = -7.6 \times 10^{-9} < 0$

Try $S = 2.0 \times 10^{-3}$: $8.0 \times 10^{-9} + 2.2 \times 10^{-9} - 9.2 \times 10^{-9} = +1.0 \times 10^{-9} > 0$

Try $S = 1.8 \times 10^{-3}$: $5.8 \times 10^{-9} + 1.8 \times 10^{-9} - 9.2 \times 10^{-9} = -1.6 \times 10^{-9} < 0$

Try $S = 1.9 \times 10^{-3}$: $6.9 \times 10^{-9} + 2.0 \times 10^{-9} - 9.2 \times 10^{-9} = -0.3 \times 10^{-9} < 0$

To two significant figures the molar solubility of MgF_2 in 5.50×10^{-4} M $MgCl_2(aq)$ is 1.9×10^{-3} mol MgF_2/L.

Criterion for precipitation from solution

16-22. If precipitation is just to occur, $Q = [Fe^{3+}][OH^-]^3 = (0.25)[OH^-]^3 = K_{sp} = 4 \times 10^{-38}$

$$[OH^-]^3 = 1.6 \times 10^{-37} \qquad [OH^-] = 5.4 \times 10^{-13}\ M$$

16-23. First determine $[Mg^{2+}]$ in the solution in question.

$$[Mg^{2+}] = \frac{27.0\ mg\ MgCl_2 \cdot 6\ H_2O \times \dfrac{1\ g\ MgCl_2 \cdot 6\ H_2O}{1000\ mg\ MgCl_2 \cdot 6\ H_2O} \times \dfrac{1\ mol\ MgCl_2 \cdot 6\ H_2O}{203\ g\ MgCl_2 \cdot 6\ H_2O} \times \dfrac{1\ mol\ Mg^{2+}}{1\ mol\ MgCl_2}}{0.450\ L}$$

$[Mg^{2+}] = 2.96 \times 10^{-4}\ M$

$Q = [Mg^{2+}][F^-]^2 = (2.96 \times 10^{-4})(0.050)^2 = 7.4 \times 10^{-7} > 3.7 \times 10^{-8} (K_{sp})$

Precipitation of $MgF_2(s)$ should occur.

16-24. Here each ion concentration after mixing must first be determined.

$$[Pb^{2+}] = \frac{0.245\ L \times 0.153\ mol\ Pb(NO_3)_2/L \times 1\ mol\ Pb^{2+}/mol\ Pb(NO_3)_2}{(0.245 + 0.155)L}$$

$[Pb^{2+}] = 9.37 \times 10^{-2}\ M$

$$[Cl^-] = \frac{0.155\ L \times 0.016\ mol\ KCl/L \times 1\ mol\ Cl^-/mol\ KCl}{(0.245 + 0.155)L} = 6.2 \times 10^{-3}\ M$$

$Q = [Pb^{2+}][Cl^-]^2 = (9.37 \times 10^{-2})(6.2 \times 10^{-3})^2 = 3.6 \times 10^{-6} < 1.6 \times 10^{-5} (K_{sp})$

Precipitation of $PbCl_2(s)$ will not occur.

16-25. (a) $$[Cl^-] = \frac{1.0\ mg\ NaCl \times \dfrac{1.00\ g\ NaCl}{1000\ mg\ NaCl} \times \dfrac{1\ mol\ NaCl}{58.5\ g\ NaCl} \times \dfrac{1\ mol\ Na^+}{1\ mol\ NaCl}}{1.00\ L} = 1.7 \times 10^{-5}\ M$$

$Q = [Ag^+][Cl^-] = (0.10)(1.7 \times 10^{-5}) = 1.7 \times 10^{-6} > 1.6 \times 10^{-10} (K_{sp})$

Precipitation of AgCl(s) should occur.

(b) $$[Br^-] = \frac{0.05\ ml \times \dfrac{1\ L}{1000\ ml} \times \dfrac{0.20\ mol\ KBr}{1.00\ L} \times \dfrac{1\ mol\ Br^-}{1\ mol\ KBr}}{0.200\ L} = 5.0 \times 10^{-5}\ M$$

In saturated AgCl(aq), $[Ag^+] = [Cl^-]$ and $[Ag^+][Cl^-] = K_{sp} = 1.6 \times 10^{-10}$; $[Ag^+]^2 = 1.6 \times 10^{-10}$; $[Ag^+] = 1.3 \times 10^{-5}$ M.

To test for precipitation:

$Q = [Ag^+][Br^-] = (1.3 \times 10^{-5})(5.0 \times 10^{-5}) = 6.5 \times 10^{-10} > 5.0 \times 10^{-13} (K_{sp})$

Precipitation of AgBr(s) should occur.

(c) $$[Mg^{2+}] = \frac{2.0\ mg\ Mg^{2+} \times \dfrac{1.00\ g\ Mg^{2+}}{1000\ mg\ Mg^{2+}} \times \dfrac{1\ mol\ Mg^{2+}}{24.3\ g\ Mg^{2+}}}{1.00\ L} = 8.2 \times 10^{-5}\ M$$

$$[OH^-] = \frac{0.05\ ml \times \dfrac{1.00\ L}{1000\ ml} \times \dfrac{0.0150\ mol\ NaOH}{1.00\ L} \times \dfrac{1\ mol\ OH^-}{1\ mol\ NaOH}}{5.0\ L} = 1.5 \times 10^{-7}\ M$$

$Q = [Mg^{2+}][OH^-]^2 = (8.2 \times 10^{-5})(1.5 \times 10^{-7})^2 = 1.8 \times 10^{-18} < 2 \times 10^{-11} (K_{sp})$

Precipitation of $Mg(OH)_2(s)$ will not occur.

16-26. First determine $[Ag^+]$ in saturated $Ag_2CO_3(aq)$. Let the molar solubility be S.

$$Ag_2CO_3(s) \rightleftharpoons 2\ Ag^+(aq) + CO_3^{2-}(aq)$$

$$S \longrightarrow \quad 2S \qquad S$$

$$K_{sp} = [Ag^+]^2[CO_3^{2-}] = (2S)^2(S) = 4S^3 = 8.1 \times 10^{-12} \qquad S = 1.3 \times 10^{-4}\ M$$

$$[Ag^+] = 2S = 2 \times 1.3 \times 10^{-4} = 2.6 \times 10^{-4}\ M$$

$$[Cl^-] = \frac{0.80\ g\ KCl \times \frac{1\ mol\ KCl}{74.6\ g\ KCl} \times \frac{1\ mol\ Cl^-}{1\ mol\ KCl}}{0.75\ L} = 1.4 \times 10^{-2}\ M$$

$$Q = [Ag^+][Cl^-] = (2.6 \times 10^{-4})(1.4 \times 10^{-2}) = 3.6 \times 10^{-6} > 1.6 \times 10^{-10} (K_{sp})$$

Precipitation of AgCl(s) should occur.

Completeness of precipitation

16-27. (a) The mixing of the two solutions causes each ion concentration to be diluted to one half of its original value.

$$[Ag^+] = \frac{0.200\ L \times 0.100\ mol\ Ag^+/L}{0.400\ L} = 0.0500\ M \qquad [CrO_4^{2-}] = \frac{1}{2} \times 0.350 = 0.175\ M$$

$$Q = [Ag^+]^2[CrO_4^{2-}] = (0.0500)^2(0.175) = 4.4 \times 10^{-4} > 2.4 \times 10^{-12} (K_{sp})$$

Precipitation of Ag_2CrO_4 should occur.

(b) Write down the information in the manner shown below:

$Ag_2CrO_4(s)$	$\rightleftharpoons$	$2\ Ag^+(aq)$	+	$CrO_4^{2-}(aq)$
after mixing:		0.0500 M		0.175 M
consumed in pptn:		$0.0500 - x$		$1/2(0.0500 - x)$
equil. concn:		x		$0.175 - 1/2(0.0500 - x)$
				$= 0.175 - 0.0250 + x/2$
				$= 0.150 + x/2$

$$K_{sp} = [Ag^+]^2[CrO_4^{2-}] = (x)^2(0.150 + x/2) = 2.4 \times 10^{-12}$$

Assume $x << 0.150$: $\quad x^2 = \frac{2.4 \times 10^{-12}}{0.150} = 1.6 \times 10^{-11} \qquad x = [Ag^+] = 4.0 \times 10^{-6}\ M$

16-28. (a) Calculate $[OH^-]$ in a saturated $Mg(OH)_2(aq)$ solution having $[Mg^{2+}] = 1 \times 10^{-6}$ M.

$$K_{sp} = [Mg^{2+}][OH^-]^2 = (1 \times 10^{-6})[OH^-]^2 = 2 \times 10^{-11} \qquad [OH^-]^2 = 2 \times 10^{-5} \qquad [OH^-] = 4.5 \times 10^{-3}\ M$$

(b) To effect the removal of 90% of the Mg^{2+} means that $[Mg^{2+}]$ must be reduced to 10% of its original value, that is, $[Mg^{2+}] = 0.10 \times 1.0 \times 10^{-2} = 1.0 \times 10^{-3}$ M. Again, determine $[OH^-]$ in a saturated $Mg(OH)_2(aq)$ in which $[Mg^{2+}] = 1.0 \times 10^{-3}$ M.

$$K_{sp} = [Mg^{2+}][OH^-]^2 = (1.0 \times 10^{-3})[OH^-]^2 = 2 \times 10^{-11} \qquad [OH^-]^2 = 2 \times 10^{-8}$$

$$[OH^-] = 1.4 \times 10^{-4}\ M$$

16-29. The ionic concentrations immediately after mixing the solutions are one half of their original values, since equal volumes of solutions are mixed.

	$BaCO_3(s) \rightleftharpoons$	$Ba^{2+}(aq)$	+	$CO_3^{2-}(aq)$
after mixing:		5.0×10^{-4} M		1.0×10^{-3} M
consumed in pptn:		$(5.0 \times 10^{-4} - x)$M		$(5.0 \times 10^{-4} - x)$M
equil. concn:		x M		$1.0 \times 10^{-3} - (5.0 \times 10^{-4} - x)$
				$= (5.0 \times 10^{-4} + x)$M

$$K_{sp} = [Ba^{2+}][CO_3^{2-}] = x(5.0 \times 10^{-4} + x) = 5.1 \times 10^{-9}$$

Assume that $x \ll 5.0 \times 10^{-4}$: $(5.0 \times 10^{-4})x = 5.1 \times 10^{-9}$ $x = [Ba^{2+}] = 1.0 \times 10^{-5}$ M

$$\% \ Ba^{2+} \text{ precipitated} = \frac{(5.0 \times 10^{-4} - 1.0 \times 10^{-5})\text{M}}{5.0 \times 10^{-4} \text{ M}} \times 100 = 98\%$$

16-30. First, calculate the ion concentrations immediately after mixing the solutions.

$$[Pb^{2+}] = \frac{0.135 \text{ L} \times 0.12 \text{ mol } Pb^{2+}/\text{L}}{(0.135 + 0.225)\text{L}} = 0.045 \text{ M} \qquad [Cl^-] = \frac{0.225 \text{ L} \times 0.15 \text{ mol } K^+/\text{L}}{(0.135 + 0.225)\text{L}} = 0.094 \text{ M}$$

Now, write down relevant information in the manner of Example 16-7b.

	$PbCl_2(s) \rightleftharpoons$	$Pb^{2+}(aq)$	+	$2 Cl^-(aq)$
after mixing:		0.045 M		0.094 M
consumed in pptn:		$(0.045 - x)$M		$2 \times (0.045 - x)$M
equil. concn:		x M		$0.094 - 2 \times (0.045 - x)$
				$= 0.094 - 0.090 + 2x$
				$= (0.004 + 2x)$M

$$K_{sp} = [Pb^{2+}][Cl^-]^2 = x(0.004 + 2x)^2 = 1.6 \times 10^{-5}$$

Here try the assumption that $0.004 \ll 2x$: $4x^3 = 1.6 \times 10^{-5}$ $x^3 = 4.0 \times 10^{-6}$

$x = [Pb^{2+}] = 1.6 \times 10^{-2}$ M

The assumption is not completely valid, but 0.004 is a relatively small quantity compared to $2x = 3.2 \times 10^{-2} = 0.032$.

Net ionic equations

16-31. (a) $Na^+ + I^- + Zn^{2+} + SO_4^{2-} \longrightarrow$ no reaction

(b) $Cu^{2+} + \cancel{SO_4^{2-}} + \cancel{2 Na^+} + CO_3^{2-} \longrightarrow CuCO_3(s) + \cancel{2 Na^+} + \cancel{SO_4^{2-}}$

(c) $2 Ag^+ + \cancel{2 NO_3^-} + \cancel{Cu^{2+}} + 2 Cl^- \longrightarrow 2 AgCl(s) + \cancel{Cu^{2+}} + \cancel{2 NO_3^-}$ or $Ag^+ + Cl^- \longrightarrow AgCl(s)$

(d) $Ba^{2+} + S^{2-} + Cu^{2+} + SO_4^{2-} \longrightarrow BaSO_4(s) + CuS(s)$

(e) $CuS(s) + H_2O \longrightarrow$ no reaction

(f) $\cancel{3\ Na^+} + 3\ OH^- + Fe^{3+} + \cancel{3\ Cl^-} \longrightarrow Fe(OH)_3(s) + \cancel{3\ Na^+} + \cancel{3\ Cl^-}$

(g) $3\ Ca^{2+} + \cancel{6\ Cl^-} + \cancel{6\ Na^+} + 2\ PO_4^{3-} \longrightarrow Ca_3(PO_4)_2(s) + \cancel{6\ Na^+} + \cancel{6\ Cl^-}$

(h) $2\ Na^+ + SO_4^{2-} + 2\ NH_4^+ + S_2O_8^{2-} \longrightarrow$ no reaction

16-32. (a) Use $Ca(NO_3)_2(aq)$ and $K_2SO_4(aq)$

$$Ca^{2+}(aq) + \cancel{2\ NO_3^-(aq)} + \cancel{2\ K^+(aq)} + SO_4^{2-}(aq) \longrightarrow CaSO_4(s) + \cancel{2\ K^+(aq)} + \cancel{2\ NO_3^-(aq)}$$

(b) Use $Mg(NO_3)_2(aq)$ and $NaOH(aq)$

$$Mg^{2+}(aq) + \cancel{2\ NO_3^-(aq)} + \cancel{2\ Na^+(aq)} + 2\ OH^-(aq) \longrightarrow Mg(OH)_2(s) + \cancel{2\ Na^+(aq)} + \cancel{2\ NO_3^-(aq)}$$

(c) Use $K_2SO_4(aq)$ and $BaCl_2(aq)$

$$2\ K^+(aq) + SO_4^{2-}(aq) + Ba^{2+}(aq) + 2\ Cl^-(aq) \longrightarrow BaSO_4(s) + 2\ K^+(aq) + 2\ Cl^-(aq)$$

$BaSO_4(s)$ precipitates and $KCl(aq)$ remains.

(d) Use $Ag_2SO_4(s)$ and $NaCl(aq)$. Since Ag_2SO_4 is more soluble than AgCl, as Ag_2SO_4 goes into solution AgCl(s) precipitates.

$$Ag_2SO_4(s) \longrightarrow 2\ Ag^+(aq) + SO_4^{2-}(aq) \qquad Ag^+(aq) + \underset{\text{(from NaCl)}}{Cl^-(aq)} \longrightarrow AgCl(s)$$

Qualitative analysis

16-33. (a) In general, a test for one cation cannot be made until other **interfering** ions have been removed. That is, the precipitating reagents of the qualitative analysis scheme are not specific for individual ions. If one attempted to identify Ba^{2+} by precipitation with $(NH_4)_2CO_3$ there would be interferences from Sr^{2+}, Ca^{2+}, Cu^{2+}, Zn^{2+}, and so on.

(b) The tests used for ions within a group require that there be no ions present from a preceding group. For example, if the group 2 reagent were used before group 1, any Ag^+ present in solution would precipitate as the sulfide, complicating the sulfide separations of group 2. And the test used for Ag^+ in group 1, based on AgCl, would not work for Ag_2S.

16-34. (a) Assume that 1 drop 0.50 M Na_2S is added to 10.0 ml of a solution having $[Cu^{2+}] = 0.02$ M

$$[S^{2-}] = \frac{0.05\ \text{ml} \times \frac{1.00\ \text{L}}{1000\ \text{ml}} \times \frac{0.50\ \text{mol}\ S^{2-}}{1.00\ \text{L}}}{0.0100\ \text{L}} = 2.5 \times 10^{-3}\ \text{M}$$

$$Q = [Cu^{2+}][S^{2-}] = (0.02)(2.5 \times 10^{-3}) = 5 \times 10^{-5} >> 6.3 \times 10^{-36}\ (K_{sp})$$

Therefore CuS should precipitate. The same conclusion would be reached even if only 1 drop of 0.50 M Na_2S were to be added to a very large volume of a solution with $[Cu^{2+}] = 0.02$ M.

(b) Assume the complete precipitation of CuS(s) from 10.0 ml of solution.

$$\text{no. mg CuS} = 10.0\ \text{ml} \times \frac{1.00\ \text{L}}{1000\ \text{ml}} \times \frac{0.02\ \text{mol}\ Cu^{2+}}{1.00\ \text{L}} \times \frac{1\ \text{mol CuS}}{1\ \text{mol}\ Cu^{2+}} \times \frac{95.6\ \text{g CuS}}{1\ \text{mol CuS}} \times \frac{1000\ \text{mg CuS}}{1.00\ \text{g CuS}}$$

$= 19$ mg CuS (This quantity is visible to the unaided eye.)

16-35. In group 1, Pb^{2+} precipitates as the chloride ($K_{sp} = 1.6 \times 10^{-5}$) and in group 2 as the sulfide ($K_{sp} = 8.0 \times 10^{-28}$). The $[Pb^{2+}]$ remaining in a saturated solution of $PbCl_2$ is fairly high, certainly high enough so that the product $[Pb^{2+}][S^{2-}]$ exceeds K_{sp}(PbS) when the solution is later treated with H_2S. No other common cation is first precipitated as a moderately soluble precipitate, followed by treatment with a reagent that yields a much more insoluble precipitate.

16-36. (a) Precipitate the Ba^{2+} as the sulfate or carbonate. That is, use Na_2SO_4(aq) or Na_2CO_3(aq) as the reagent.

(b) Na_2CO_3 is water soluble and $MgCO_3$ is not. Water can be used as the reagent.

(c) Use a chloride ion solution, such as KCl(aq). The $AgNO_3$(s) is converted to AgCl(s) and the KNO_3(s) dissolves.

(d) $Pb(NO_3)_2$ is water soluble and $PbSO_4$ is not. Use water as the reagent to separate them.

16-37. Let the molar solubility of $PbCl_2$ = S. In a saturated solution, $[Pb^{2+}]$ = S and $[Cl^-]$ = 2S.

$K_{sp} = [Pb^{2+}][Cl^-]^2 = (S)(2S)^2 = 4S^3$

at 25°C: $4S^3 = 1.6 \times 10^{-5}$ $\qquad S = 1.6 \times 10^{-2} = 0.016$ M

at 80°C: $4S^3 = 3.3 \times 10^{-3}$ $\qquad S = 9.4 \times 10^{-2} = 0.094$ M

$PbCl_2$ is moderately soluble at both temperatures. The reason that precipitation of $PbCl_2$ can be carried essentially to completion at 25°C is that an excess of Cl^- (a common ion) is maintained in the precipitating solution.

Fractional precipitation

16-38. (a) Determine $[Ca^{2+}]$ in the seawater sample.

$$[Ca^{2+}] = \frac{440 \text{ g } Ca^{2+}}{1000 \text{ kg seawater}} \times \frac{1.00 \text{ kg seawater}}{1000 \text{ g seawater}} \times \frac{1.03 \text{ g seawater}}{1.00 \text{ cm}^3 \text{ seawater}} \times \frac{1000 \text{ cm}^3 \text{ seawater}}{1.00 \text{ L seawater}}$$

$$\times \frac{1 \text{ mol } Ca^{2+}}{40.1 \text{ g } Ca^{2+}} = 1.1 \times 10^{-2} \text{ M}$$

$$Q = [Ca^{2+}][OH^-]^2 = (1.1 \times 10^{-2})(2.0 \times 10^{-3})^2 = 4.4 \times 10^{-8} < 5.5 \times 10^{-6}\ (K_{sp})$$

$Ca(OH)_2$ will not precipitate under these conditions.

(b) In Example 16-6 it was established that precipitation of $Mg(OH)_2$(s) is complete. In part (a) of this exercise it was established that $Ca(OH)_2$(s) does not precipitate while the precipitation of $Mg(OH)_2$(s) is being carried to completion. Therefore the separation of Ca^{2-} and Mg^{2+} by fractional precipitation from seawater is feasible.

16-39. (a) The precipitate that should form first is the one with the smaller value of K_{sp}--AgBr.

(b) Determine the $[Ag^+]$ required to just begin the precipitation of AgCl.

$K_{sp} = [Ag^+][Cl^-] = [Ag^+](0.250) = 1.6 \times 10^{-10}$ $\qquad [Ag^+] = 6.4 \times 10^{-10}$ M

Now determine $[Br^-]$ remaining in solution at this value of $[Ag^+]$.

$K_{sp} = [Ag^+][Br^-] = 5.0 \times 10^{-13}$ $\qquad [Br^-] = \dfrac{5.0 \times 10^{-13}}{6.4 \times 10^{-10}} = 7.8 \times 10^{-4}$ M

$$\% \ Br^- \text{ remaining} = \frac{7.8 \times 10^{-4} \text{ mol } Br^-/L}{2.2 \times 10^{-3} \text{ mol } Br^-/L} \times 100 = 35\%$$

The precipitation of AgBr is not complete at the point where AgCl begins to precipitate. Fractional precipitation does not work here.

16-40. NaCl cannot be used since both $BaCl_2$ and $CaCl_2$ are water soluble. Even though K_{sp} values are listed in Table 16-1 for $Ba(OH)_2$ and $Ca(OH)_2$, an examination of the ion concentrations involved shows that neither K_{sp} value is exceeded and, therefore, neither precipitates. Of the two remaining possibilities--the sulfates and the carbonates--compare the differences in K_{sp} values between the calcium and barrium compound [i.e., compare the difference between $K_{sp}(BaSO_4)$ and $K_{sp}(CaSO_4)$ to the difference between $K_{sp}(BaCO_3)$ and $K_{sp}(CaCO_3)$]. The greatest difference is found for the sulfates. The best reagent to use is 0.50 M Na_2SO_4(aq).

Self-test Questions

1. (*d*) In saturated PbI_2, if $[Pb^{2+}] = S$, $[I^-] = 2S$, $K_{sp} = 4S^3$ and $S = (K_{sp}/4)^{1/3}$. Item (a) is incorrect because $[Pb^{2+}] \neq [I^-]$. Items (b) and (c) are incorrect because $[Pb^{2+}] = S = (K_{sp}/4)^{1/3}$, not K_{sp} and not $\sqrt{K_{sp}}$. Since $[I^-] = 2[Pb^{2+}]$, then $[Pb^{2+}] = [I^-]/2$.

2. (*a*) The common ion effect results from adding Na_2SO_4 to saturated $BaSO_4$(aq). The solubility of $BaSO_4$ is *reduced*. This means that $[Ba^{2+}]$ is *reduced*. ($[SO_4^{2-}]$ is increased because of the added Na_2SO_4.)

3. (*c*) K_2CrO_4 and $AgNO_3$ produce common ions to the saturated Ag_2CrO_4(aq). They cause a decrease in the solubility of Ag_2CrO_4. KNO_3, which has no ions in common with Ag_2CrO_4, produces the salt effect. Ag_2CrO_4 is most soluble in KNO_3(aq).

4. (*b*) Both ions form an insoluble sulfide and neither forms an insoluble nitrate. Use H_2SO_4(aq). $PbSO_4$(s) precipitates and $CuSO_4$ is soluble.

5. (*c*) Ba^{2+}, Ca^{2+}, and Pb^{2+} all form insoluble carbonates. All ammonium salts, including $(NH_4)_2CO_3$, are soluble.

6. (*a*) Because of the large excess of undissolved solute, the addition of pure water to saturated MgF_2(aq) just results in a larger volume of saturated solution. However, since $[Mg^{2+}]$ in saturated MgF_2(aq) is independent of the volume of solution, $[Mg^{2+}]$ does not change in this process.

7.

	$PbI_2(s) \rightleftharpoons$	$Pb^{2+}(aq)$	$2\ I^-(aq)$
from PbI_2:		S mol/L	2S mol/L
from 0.050 M KI:		--	0.050 mol/L
equil. concn:		S mol/L	(0.050 + 2S)mol/L

$$K_{sp} = [Pb^{2+}][I^-]^2 = S(0.050 + 2S)^2 = 7.1 \times 10^{-9}$$

Assume $S << 0.050$: $(0.050)^2 S = 7.1 \times 10^{-9}$ $\qquad S = [Pb^{2+}] = 2.8 \times 10^{-6}$ M

$$\text{no. mg } Pb^{2+}/ml = \frac{2.8 \times 10^{-6} \text{ mol } Pb^{2+}}{L} \times \frac{1.00 \text{ L}}{1000 \text{ ml}} \times \frac{207 \text{ g } Pb^{2+}}{1 \text{ mol } Pb^{2+}} \times \frac{1000 \text{ mg } Pb^{2+}}{1.00 \text{ g } Pb^{2+}} = 5.8 \times 10^{-4} \text{ mg } Pb^{2+}/ml$$

8. For each of the solutions let S = molar solubility. Express the ion concentrations in terms of S. Substitute ion concentrations into the K_{sp} expression. Solve for S, and obtain a value for $[Ag^+]$.

(a) $K_{sp} = [Ag^+]^2[SO_4^{2-}] = (2S)^2(S) = 4S^3 = 1.4 \times 10^{-5}$

$S^3 = 3.5 \times 10^{-6}$ $S = 1.5 \times 10^{-2}$ $[Ag^+] = 2S = 3.0 \times 10^{-2}$ M

(b) $K_{sp} = [Ag^+]^2[CO_3^{2-}] = (2S)^2(S) = 4S^3 = 8.1 \times 10^{-12}$

$S^3 = 2.0 \times 10^{-12}$ $S = 1.3 \times 10^{-4}$ $[Ag^+] = 2S = 2.6 \times 10^{-4}$ M

(c) $K_{sp} = [Ag^+][Cl^-] = (S)(S) = S^2 = 1.6 \times 10^{-10}$

$[Ag^+] = S = 1.3 \times 10^{-5}$ M

(d) $AgNO_3$ is highly soluble.

(e) $K_{sp} = [Ag^+][I^-] = (S)(S) = S^2 = 8.5 \times 10^{-17}$

$[Ag^+] = S = 9.2 \times 10^{-9}$ M

In order of increasing $[Ag^+]$: AgI < AgCl < Ag_2CO_3 < Ag_2SO_4 < $AgNO_3$

9. (a) The first to precipitate should be the compound with the lower K_{sp} (since the two are of similar type). This should be $PbCrO_4$.

(b) At the point where $PbSO_4$ begins to precipitate $K_{sp} = [Pb^{2+}][SO_4^{2-}] = [Pb^{2+}](0.010) = 1.6 \times 10^{-8}$

$[Pb^{2+}] = 1.6 \times 10^{-6}$ M

(c) $[CrO_4^{2-}]$ remaining in solution at point where $PbSO_4$ begins to precipitate:

$K_{sp} = [Pb^{2+}][CrO_4^{2-}] = (1.6 \times 10^{-6})[CrO_4^{2-}] = 2.8 \times 10^{-13}$ $[CrO_4^{2-}] = 1.8 \times 10^{-7}$ M

$$\% \ CrO_4^{2-} \text{ unprecipitated} = \frac{1.8 \times 10^{-7} \text{ mol/L}}{1.0 \times 10^{-2} \text{ mol/L}} \times 100 = 1.8 \times 10^{-3}\%$$

The precipitation of CrO_4^{2-} is essentially complete before precipitation of $PbSO_4$ begins. Separation by fractional precipitation is effective.

10. (a) This statement would be true only for a pair of compounds of the same type, where the relationship between solubility and K_{sp} is the same. For example, for $BaCO_3$ and $MgCO_3$, the relationship is $S = \sqrt{K_{sp}}$. But in comparing $BaCO_3$ and Ag_2CO_3, the relationships are $S = \sqrt{K_{sp}}$ for $BaCO_3$ and $S = (K_{sp}/4)^{1/3}$ for Ag_2CO_3. The K_{sp} of Ag_2CO_3 is smaller than for $BaCO_3$ (see Table 16-1), but the solubility of Ag_2CO_3 is greater.

(b) If a solution contains $MgCO_3$ as the *only* solute, $[Mg^{2+}] = [CO_3^{2-}]$; and if this solution is *saturated,* $[Mg^{2+}][CO_3^{2-}] = 5.3 \times 10^{-8}$. If the solution is unsaturated, $[Mg^{2+}][CO_3^{2-}] < 5.3 \times 10^{-8}$. If a solution of $MgCO_3$ contains a common ion, $[Mg^{2+}] \neq [CO_3^{2-}]$. (If a solution contains uncommon ions, the solubility of $MgCO_3$ increases. Then $[Mg^{2+}][CO_3^{2-}] > 5.3 \times 10^{-8}$.)

Chapter 17

Acids and Bases

Brønsted-Lowry theory of acids and bases

17-1. (a) HNO_2 is a proton donor; it is acidic.

(b) ClO^- cannot be a proton donor. We can only think of it as accepting a proton to form HOCl; it is basic.

(c) In order to act as an acid (proton donor), NH_2^- would have to form the dinegative ion NH^{2-}. More plausible is that NH_2^- should gain a proton to form NH_3. The ion NH_2^- is basic.

(d) NH_4^+ does not have the capacity to form an additional N–H bond; it cannot act as a base. On the other hand, by losing a proton NH_4^+ is converted to the neutral molecule, NH_3. NH_4^+ is acidic.

(e) Similar to NH_4^+, methyl ammonium ion acts as a proton donor to form methyl amine. $C_6H_5NH_3^+$ is acidic.

17-2. In each case the conjugate acid is the product of adding a proton to the anion listed:

(a) HOH (or H_2O) (b) HCl (c) HOCl (d) HCN

17-3. The conjugate base is the product remaining after the species in question loses a proton.

(a) IO_4^- (b) $C_3H_5O_2^-$ (c) $C_6H_5COO^-$ (d) $C_6H_5NH_2$

17-4. (a) OH^- is not amphiprotic. It can easily gain a proton to form H_2O, but the loss of a proton would produce O^{2-}, which does not exist in aqueous solution.

(b) NH_3 is amphiprotic. Loss of a proton produces NH_2^- and gain of a proton, NH_4^+.

(c) H_2O is amphiprotic. Loss of a proton produces OH^-, and gain of a proton, H_3O^+. Both of these species can exist in aqueous solution.

(d) HS^- is amphiprotic. Loss of a proton produces S^{2-} and gain of a proton, H_2S.

(e) NO_3^- can act as a base in very strongly acidic solutions, but it cannot act as an acid.

(f) HCO_3^- is amphiprotic. Loss of a proton produces CO_3^{2-} and gain of a proton, H_2CO_3.

(g) HSO_4^- is amphiprotic. Loss of a proton produces SO_4^{2-} and gain of a proton (in strongly acidic solutions), H_2SO_4.

(h) HNO_3 is a strong acid. It has no basic properties.

17-5. (a)

$$HBrO + H_2O \rightleftharpoons H_3O^+ + BrO^-$$

acid (1) base (2) acid (2) base (1)

(b)

$$HSO_4^- + H_2O \rightleftharpoons H_3O^+ + SO_4^{2-}$$

acid (1) base (2) acid (2) base (1)

(c)

$$C_6H_5NH_2 + H_2O \rightleftharpoons C_6H_5NH_3^+ + OH^-$$

base (1) acid (2) acid (1) base (2)

(d) S^{2-} + H_2O $\rightleftharpoons$ HS^- + OH^-

base (1)   acid (2)   acid (1)   base (2)

17-6. (a) $C_2H_3O_2^-$ + H^+ (from an acid) $\longrightarrow$ $HC_2H_3O_2$ (the solvent)

$C_2H_3O_2^-$ is a base.

(b) $H_2O + HC_2H_3O_2 \longrightarrow (H_2C_2H_3O_2)^+ + OH^-$ $H_2O + HC_2H_3O_2 \longrightarrow H_3O^+ - C_2H_3O_2^-$

H_2O is an acid. H_2O is a base.

(c) $HC_2H_3O_2 + HC_2H_3O_2 \longrightarrow (H_2C_2H_3O_2)^+ + C_2H_3O_2^-$

$HC_2H_3O_2$ is both an acid and a base.

(d) $HClO_4 + HC_2H_3O_2 \longrightarrow (H_2C_2H_3O_2)^+ + ClO_4^-$

$HClO_4$ is an acid.

Lewis theory of acids and bases

17-7. (a) OH^- has the capacity to donate an electron pair, but not to accept one. It is a Lewis base.

$[:\ddot{O}:H]^-$

(b) $B(OH)_3$ can accept an electron pair through the B atom. It is a Lewis acid.

$$H-\ddot{O}-B-\ddot{O}-H$$
$$\phantom{H-\ddot{O}-B}| $$
$$:O:$$
$$|$$
$$H$$

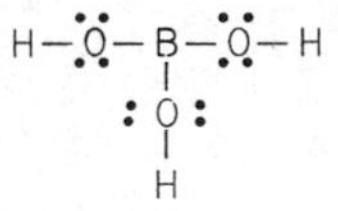

(c) $AlCl_3$ presents a situation similar to $B(OH)_3$ in part (b). The Al atom can accept a pair of electrons. $AlCl_3$ is a Lewis acid. (In the Lewis structure below $AlCl_3$ is pictured as a covalent molecule.)

$$:\ddot{C}l-Al-\ddot{C}l:$$
$$|$$
$$:\ddot{C}l:$$

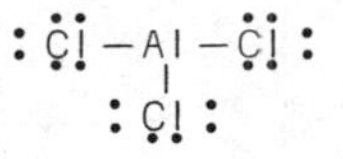

(d) From the Lewis structure below, we see an available pair of electrons on the N atom. CH_3NH_2 is a Lewis base.

$$H$$
$$|\cdot\cdot$$
$$H-C-N-H$$
$$||$$
$$HH$$

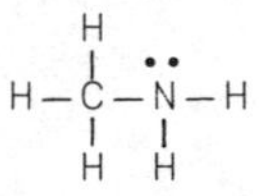

17-8. (a) According to the following Lewis structures, SO_3 appears to be the electron pair acceptor (acid) and H_2O, the electron pair donor (base). Note that an additional sulfur-to-oxygen bond is formed.

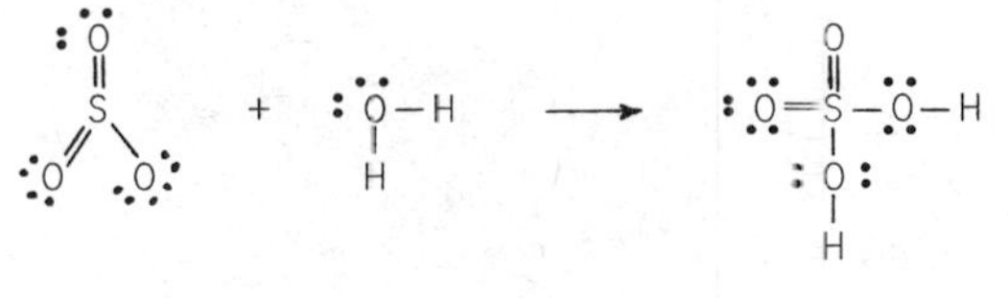

(b) The OH^- has lone pair electrons that it can make available for bond formation with Al^{3+} in $Al(OH)_3$. The result is a complex ion $[Al(OH)_4]^-$. This situation is similar to the formation of $[Zn(NH_3)_4]^{2+}$ described in Example 17-2b. $Al(OH)_3(s)$ is the acid and $OH^-(aq)$ is the base.

17-9. (a) The ion O^{2-} in CaO can be represented as $[:\ddot{O}:]^{2-}$. Because of the presence of available electron pairs, we should expect O^{2-} (and thus CaO) to act as a base. The $SO_2(g)$ must act as an acid. The acid-base reaction is similar to that depicted in Example 17-2(c). One possible representation of the reaction is shown below.

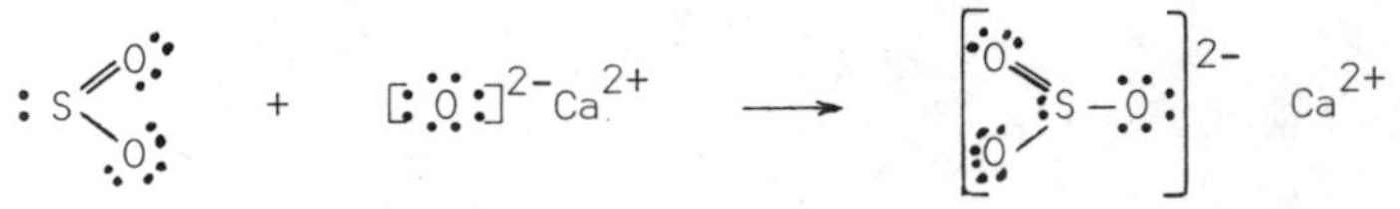

(b) Here, LiOH is a base and CO_2, an acid.

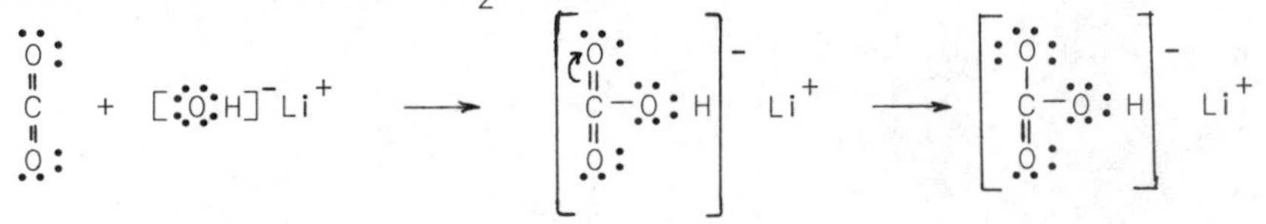

Strong acids, strong bases, and pH

17-10. (a) $[H_3O^+] = 1.0 \times 10^{-3}$ M; $[OH^-] = \dfrac{1.0 \times 10^{-14}}{1.0 \times 10^{-3}} = 1.0 \times 10^{-11}$ M

(b) $[OH^-] = 4.0 \times 10^{-2}$ M; $[H_3O^+] = \dfrac{1.0 \times 10^{-14}}{4.0 \times 10^{-2}} = 2.5 \times 10^{-13}$ M

(c) $[H_3O^+] = 2 \times 0.0020 = 4.0 \times 10^{-3}$ M; $[OH^-] = \dfrac{1.0 \times 10^{-14}}{4.0 \times 10^{-3}} = 2.5 \times 10^{-12}$ M

(d) $[OH^-] = 2 \times 1.3 \times 10^{-3} = 2.6 \times 10^{-3}$ M; $[H_3O^+] = \dfrac{1.0 \times 10^{-14}}{2.6 \times 10^{-3}} = 3.8 \times 10^{-12}$ M

17-11. Proceed in the following steps:

Calculate the number of moles of HCl:

$$PV = nRT; \quad n = \frac{PV}{RT} = \frac{(740/760)\text{atm} \times 0.0248 \text{ L}}{0.0821 \text{ L atm mol}^{-1} \text{ K}^{-1} \times 303 \text{ K}} = 9.71 \times 10^{-4} \text{ mol}$$

Calculate the number of moles of H_3O^+ in solution: $HCl + H_2O \longrightarrow H_3O^+ + Cl^-$

$$\text{no. mol } H_3O^+ = 9.71 \times 10^{-4} \text{ mol HCl} \times \frac{1 \text{ mol } H_3O^+}{1 \text{ mol HCl}} = 9.71 \times 10^{-4} \text{ mol } H_3O^+$$

Calculate $[H_3O^+]$:

$$[H_3O^+] = \frac{9.71 \times 10^{-4} \text{ mol } H_3O^+}{2.50 \text{ L}} = 3.88 \times 10^{-4} \text{ M}$$

17-12. (a) 1×10^{-4} M HCl; $[H_3O^+] = 1 \times 10^{-4}$ M; pH $= -\log [H_3O^+] = -\log (1 \times 10^{-4}) = 4$

(b) 0.00020 M HI; $[H_3O^+] = 2 \times 10^{-4}$ M; pH $= -\log (2 \times 10^{-4})$

pH $= -\log 2 - \log (10^{-4}) = -0.3 + 4.0 = 3.7$

(c) 3.50×10^{-3} M H_2SO_4; $[H_3O^+] = 7.00 \times 10^{-3}$ M; pH = $-\log (7.00 \times 10^{-3})$

pH = $-\log 7.00 - \log (10^{-3}) = -0.85 + 3.00 = 2.15$

(d) 2.50×10^{-4} M NaOH; $[OH^-] = 2.50 \times 10^{-4}$ M; pOH = $-\log [OH^-]$

pOH = $-\log (2.50 \times 10^{-4}) = -\log 2.50 - \log (10^{-4}) = -0.40 + 4.00 = 3.60$

pH = 14.00 − pOH = 14.00 − 3.60 = 10.40

17-13. (a) 1×10^{-3} M KOH; $[OH^-] = 1 \times 10^{-3}$ M. pOH = $-\log [OH^-]$; pOH = $-\log (1 \times 10^{-3}) = 3$

(b) 0.050 M NaOH; $[OH^-] = 5.0 \times 10^{-2}$ M. pOH = $-\log (5.0 \times 10^{-2})$; pOH = $-0.70 + 2.00 = 1.30$

(c) 4.0×10^{-4} M $Ba(OH)_2$; $[OH^-] = 8.0 \times 10^{-4}$ M; pOH = $-\log (8.0 \times 10^{-4})$

pOH = $-\log 8.0 - \log (10^{-4}) = -0.90 + 4.00 = 3.10$

(d) 1.50×10^{-3} M HCl; $[H_3O^+] = 1.50 \times 10^{-3}$ M; pH = $-\log (1.50 \times 10^{-3}) = 2.82$

pOH = 14.00 − pH = 14.00 − 2.82 = 11.18

17-14. First determine $[OH^-]$, then pOH, and finally, pH.

$$[OH^-] = \frac{2.05 \text{ g } Ba(OH)_2 \cdot 8\,H_2O}{0.450 \text{ L}} \times \frac{1 \text{ mol } Ba(OH)_2 \cdot 8\,H_2O}{315 \text{ g } Ba(OH)_2 \cdot 8\,H_2O} \times \frac{2 \text{ mol } OH^-}{1 \text{ mol } Ba(OH)_2 \cdot 8\,H_2O} = 0.0289 \text{ M}$$

pOH = $-\log [OH^-] = -\log (2.89 \times 10^{-2}) = -0.46 + 2.00 = 1.54$

pH = 14.00 − pOH = 14.00 − 1.54 = 12.46

17-15. $$\text{no. mol } H_3O^+ = 0.280 \text{ L} \times \frac{3.0 \times 10^{-3} \text{ mol } H_2SO_4}{1 \text{ L}} \times \frac{2 \text{ mol } H_3O^+}{1 \text{ mol } H_2SO_4} = 1.68 \times 10^{-3} \text{ mol } H_3O^+$$

$$\text{no. mol } H_3O^+ = 0.220 \text{ L} \times \frac{6.40 \times 10^{-2} \text{ mol HCl}}{1 \text{ L}} \times \frac{1 \text{ mol } H_3O^+}{1 \text{ mol HCl}} = 1.41 \times 10^{-2} \text{ mol } H_3O^+$$

Total no. mol $H_3O^+ = 1.68 \times 10^{-3} + 1.41 \times 10^{-2} = 1.58 \times 10^{-2}$

$$[H_3O^+] = \frac{1.58 \times 10^{-2} \text{ mol } H_3O^+}{(0.280 + 0.220)\text{L}} = 3.16 \times 10^{-2} \text{ M}$$

pH = $-\log [H_3O^+] = -\log (3.16 \times 10^{-2}) = -0.50 + 2.00 = 1.50$

17-16. The simplest approach here is to calculate the number of moles of H_3O^+ in the final dilute solution, and then the volume of the concentrated acid required to provide this much H_3O^+. Required first is a calculation of $[H_3O^+]$ from pH.

pH = $-\log [H_3O^+] = 1.65$; $\log [H_3O^+] = -1.65 = 0.35 - 2.00$; $[H_3O^+] = 2.24 \times 10^{-2}$ M

$$\text{no. ml conc. acid} = 4.00 \text{ L} \times \frac{2.24 \times 10^{-2} \text{ mol } H_3O^+}{1 \text{ L}} \times \frac{1 \text{ mol } H_2SO_4}{2 \text{ mol } H_3O^+} \times \frac{98.1 \text{ g } H_2SO_4}{1 \text{ mol } H_2SO_4}$$

$$\times \frac{100 \text{ g conc. acid}}{98.0 \text{ g } H_2SO_4} \times \frac{1 \text{ ml conc. acid}}{1.84 \text{ g conc. acid}} = 2.44 \text{ ml conc. acid}$$

17-17. If pH = 9.50, pOH = 14.00 - 9.50 = 4.50 = $-\log[OH^-]$; $\log[OH^-] = -4.50 = 0.50 - 5 = 3.2 \times 10^{-5}$

If a solution of $Mg(OH)_2$ is to be saturated, $Mg(OH)_2(s) \rightleftharpoons Mg^{2+}(aq) + 2\,OH^-(aq)$

$K_{sp} = [Mg^{2+}][OH^-]^2 = [Mg^{2+}](3.2 \times 10^{-5})^2 = 2 \times 10^{-11}$ $\qquad [Mg^{2+}] = 2 \times 10^{-2}$ M = 0.02 M

17-18. For the reaction $Al(OH)_3(s) \rightleftharpoons Al^{3+}(aq) + 3\,OH^-(aq)$

Let S = molar solubility: S mol/L, 3S mol/L

$K_{sp} = (S)(3S)^3 = 27S^4 = 1.3 \times 10^{-33}$ $\qquad S^4 = 4.8 \times 10^{-35}$ $\qquad S^2 = 6.9 \times 10^{-18}$

$S = 2.6 \times 10^{-9}$ $\qquad [OH^-] = 3S = 7.8 \times 10^{-9}$ M $\qquad$ pOH = 8.11

pH = 14.00 - pH = 14.00 - 8.11 = 5.89

This answer cannot be correct because it suggests that an acidic solution (pH < 7) can somehow be obtained by dissolving a base in water. To modify this calculation one must consider that the OH^- in solution comes principally from the self-ionization of water. The dissolving of some $Al(OH)_3$ adds a small amount of OH^- to that normally present in water, with the result that the pH is slightly greater than 7.

17-19. A solution with pH = 8 is basic. There is no way that a basic solution can be prepared by dissolving an *acid* in water. If one prepared a 1×10^{-8} M HCl solution in water, $[H_3O^+] \neq 1 \times 10^{-8}$ M because in this dilute a solution more H_3O^+ would appear in solution as a result of the self-ionization of water than is derived from the strong acid HCl. Including the self-ionization of water in the calculation of $[H_3O^+]$ would result in $[H_3O^+] > 1 \times 10^{-7}$ M, which it should be for an acidic solution.

Weak acids, weak bases, and pH

17-20. $$\text{no. mol } HC_6H_{11}O_2/L = \frac{11 \text{ g } HC_6H_{11}O_2 \times \dfrac{1 \text{ mol } HC_6H_{11}O_2}{116 \text{ g } HC_6H_{11}O_2}}{1.00 \text{ L}} = 0.095 \text{ M}$$

pH = 2.94 $\qquad \log[H_3O^+] = -2.94 = 0.06 - 3.00$ $\qquad [H_3O^+] = 1.1 \times 10^{-3}$ M

	$HC_6H_{11}O_2(aq)$ +	H_2O ⇌	$H_3O^+(aq)$ +	$C_6H_{11}O_2^-(aq)$
placed in soln:	0.095 M		--	--
changes:	-1.1×10^{-3} M		$+1.1 \times 10^{-3}$ M	$+1.1 \times 10^{-3}$ M
equilibrium:	0.094 M		1.1×10^{-3} M	1.1×10^{-3} M

$$K_a = \frac{[H_3O^+][C_6H_{11}O_2^-]}{[HC_6H_{11}O_2]} = \frac{(1.1 \times 10^{-3})(1.1 \times 10^{-3})}{0.094} = 1.3 \times 10^{-5}$$

17-21. $$\text{no. mol } HCHO_2/L = \frac{25.0 \text{ g } HCHO_2 \times \dfrac{1 \text{ mol } HCHO_2}{46.0 \text{ g } HCHO_2}}{1.400 \text{ L}} = 0.388 \text{ M}$$

	$HCHO_2(aq)$ +	H_2O ⇌	$H_3O^+(aq)$ +	$CHO_2^-(aq)$
dissolve:	0.388 M		--	--
changes:	$-x$ M		$+x$ M	$+x$ M
equilibrium:	$(0.388 - x)$M		x M	x M

$$K_a = \frac{[H_3O^+][CHO_2^-]}{[HCHO_2]} = \frac{x \cdot x}{0.388 - x} = 1.8 \times 10^{-4}$$

Assume $x << 0.388$: $\frac{x^2}{0.388} = 1.8 \times 10^{-4}$ $x^2 = 7.0 \times 10^{-5}$ $x = [CHO_2^-] = 8.4 \times 10^{-3}$ M

17-22. pH = 9.7; pOH = 14.0 - 9.7 = 4.3 = $-\log [OH^-]$; $\log [OH^-] = -4.3 = 0.7 - 5$; $[OH^-] = 5.0 \times 10^{-5}$

$$CH_3C_5H_4N + H_2O \rightleftharpoons CH_3C_5H_4NH^+ + OH^-$$

	$CH_3C_5H_4N$	$CH_3C_5H_4NH^+$	OH^-
placed in soln:	0.250 M	--	--
changes:	-5.0×10^{-5} M	$+5.0 \times 10^{-5}$ M	$+5.0 \times 10^{-5}$ M
equilibrium:	$(0.250 - 5.0 \times 10^{-5})$M	5.0×10^{-5} M	5.0×10^{-5} M

$$K_b = \frac{[CH_3C_5H_4NH^+][OH^-]}{[CH_3C_5H_4N]} = \frac{(5.0 \times 10^{-5})(5.0 \times 10^{-5})}{0.250} = 1.0 \times 10^{-8}$$

17-23. pH = 4.53 = $-\log [H_3O^+]$ $\log [H_3O^+] = -4.53 = 0.47 - 5.00$ $[H_3O^+] = 3.0 \times 10^{-5}$ M

$$HC_6H_4NO_3 + H_2O \rightleftharpoons H_3O^+ + C_6H_4NO_3^-; \quad K_a = 5.9 \times 10^{-8}$$

	$HC_6H_4NO_3$	H_3O^+	$C_6H_4NO_3^-$
dissolve:	x M	--	--
changes:	-3.0×10^{-5} M	$+3.0 \times 10^{-5}$ M	$+3.0 \times 10^{-5}$ M
equilibrium:	$(x - 3.0 \times 10^{-5})$M	3.0×10^{-5} M	3.0×10^{-5} M

Assume $x >> 3.0 \times 10^{-5}$, so that $(x - 3.0 \times 10^{-5}) \simeq x$.

$$K_a = \frac{[H_3O^+][C_6H_4NO_3^-]}{[HC_6H_4NO_3]} = \frac{(3.0 \times 10^{-5})(3.0 \times 10^{-5})}{x} = 5.9 \times 10^{-8}$$

$x = [HC_6H_4NO_3] = 1.5 \times 10^{-2}$ M -- the assumption is valid.

no. g $HC_6H_4NO_3$/L = 1.5×10^{-2} mol $HC_6H_4NO_3$/L $\times$ 139 g $HC_6H_4NO_3$/mol $HC_6H_4NO_3$ = 2.1 g $HC_6H_4NO_3$/L

17-24. The number of moles of acetylsalicylic acid per liter of solution is:

$$\frac{\text{no. mol } HC_9H_7O_4}{L} = 2 \times 0.32 \text{ g } HC_9H_7O_4 \times \frac{\text{mol } HC_9H_7O_4}{80 \text{ g } HC_9H_7O_4} \times \frac{1}{0.250 \text{ L}} = 1.42 \times 10^{-2} \text{ mol } HC_9H_7O_4/L$$

In the **ionization** of acetylsalicylic acid, let $x = [H_3O^+] = [C_9H_7O_4^-]$.

$[HC_9H_7O_4] = 1.42 \times 10^{-2} - x \simeq 1.42 \times 10^{-2}$.

$$K_a = \frac{[H_3O^+][C_9H_7O_4^-]}{[HC_9H_7O_4]} = \frac{x^2}{1.42 \times 10^{-2}} = 2.75 \times 10^{-5}; \quad x^2 = 3.90 \times 10^{-7}$$

$x = [H_3O^+] = 6.24 \times 10^{-4}$ M; pH = $-\log [H_3O^+] = -\log (6.24 \times 10^{-4}) = 3.20$

To test the assumption that $1.42 \times 10^{-2} - x \simeq 1.42 \times 10^{-2}$, substitute $x = 6.24 \times 10^{-4}$.
That is, $1.42 \times 10^{-2} - 6.24 \times 10^{-4} = 1.36 \times 10^{-2} \simeq 1.42 \times 10^{-2}$.

17-25. pH = 1.30 = $-\log [H_3O^+]$ $\log [H_3O^+] = -1.30 = 0.70 - 2.00$ $[H_3O^+] = 5.0 \times 10^{-2}$

$$HC_2HCl_2O_2 + H_2O \rightleftharpoons H_3O^+ + C_2HCl_2O_2^-$$

	$HC_2HCl_2O_2$	H_3O^+	$C_2HCl_2O_2^-$
placed in soln:	0.10 M	--	--
changes:	-0.05 M	+0.05 M	+0.05 M
equilibrium:	0.05 M	0.05 M	0.05 M

$$K_a = \frac{[H_3O^+][C_2HCl_2O_2^-]}{[HC_2HCl_2O_2]} = \frac{0.05 \times 0.05}{0.05} = 5.0 \times 10^{-2}$$

17-26. $pH = 4.50 = -\log [H_3O^+]$ $\log [H_3O^+] = -4.50 = 0.50 - 5.00$ $[H_3O^+] = 3.2 \times 10^{-5}$ M

$$HC_2H_3O_2 + H_2O \rightleftharpoons H_3O^+ + C_2H_3O_2^-$$

	$HC_2H_3O_2$	H_3O^+	$C_2H_3O_2^-$
placed in soln:	x M	--	--
changes:	-3.2×10^{-5} M	$+3.2 \times 10^{-5}$ M	$+3.2 \times 10^{-5}$ M
equilibrium:	$(x - 3.2 \times 10^{-5})$M	3.2×10^{-5} M	3.2×10^{-5} M

$$K_a = \frac{[H_3O^+][C_2H_3O_2^-]}{[HC_2H_3O_2]} = \frac{(3.2 \times 10^{-5})(3.2 \times 10^{-5})}{x - 3.2 \times 10^{-5}} = 1.74 \times 10^{-5}$$

Assume the $x >> 3.2 \times 10^{-5}$, leading to $\frac{(3.2 \times 10^{-5})^2}{x} = 1.74 \times 10^{-5}$

$x = 5.89 \times 10^{-5}$ M. The assumption just made is *not* valid.

$\frac{(3.2 \times 10^{-5})^2}{x - 3.2 \times 10^{-5}} = 1.74 \times 10^{-5}$ $1.0 \times 10^{-9} = 1.74 \times 10^{-5}x - 5.6 \times 10^{-10}$ $x = 9.0 \times 10^{-5}$ M

$$\text{no. mg } HC_2H_3O_2 = 1.00 \text{ L} \times \frac{9.0 \times 10^{-5} \text{ mol } HC_2H_3O_2}{1.00 \text{ L}} \times \frac{60 \text{ g } HC_2H_3O_2}{1 \text{ mol } HC_2H_3O_2} \times \frac{1000 \text{ mg } HC_2H_3O_2}{1.00 \text{ g } HC_2H_3O_2} = 5.4 \text{ mg } HC_2H_3O_2$$

17-27.

$$HC_2H_2ClO_2 + H_2O \rightleftharpoons H_3O^+ + C_2H_2ClO_2^-$$

	$HC_2H_2ClO_2$	H_3O^+	$C_2H_2ClO_2^-$
placed in soln:	5.0×10^{-3} M	--	--
changes:	$-x$ M	$+x$ M	$+x$ M
equilibrium:	$(5.0 \times 10^{-3} - x)$M	x M	x M

Because this acid is rather dilute and the value of K_a is rather large, we should not expect the usual simplifying assumption to hold.

$$K_a = \frac{[H_3O^+][C_2H_2ClO_2^-]}{[HC_2H_2ClO_2]} = \frac{x \cdot x}{(5.0 \times 10^{-3} - x)} = 1.35 \times 10^{-3} \qquad x^2 + 1.35 \times 10^{-3}x - 6.8 \times 10^{-6} = 0$$

$$x = \frac{-1.35 \times 10^{-3} \pm \sqrt{(1.35 \times 10^{-3})^2 + 4 \times 6.8 \times 10^{-6}}}{2} = 2.0 \times 10^{-3} \text{ M}$$

$$pH = -\log [H_3O^+] = -\log (2.0 \times 10^{-3}) = 2.70$$

17-28. $$[C_5H_{11}N] = \frac{0.125 \text{ g } C_5H_{11}N \times \frac{1 \text{ mol } C_5H_{11}N}{85.1 \text{ g } C_5H_{11}N}}{0.250 \text{ L}} = 5.88 \times 10^{-3} \text{ mol } C_5H_{11}N/L$$

$$C_5H_{11}N + H_2O \rightleftharpoons C_5H_{11}NH^+ + OH^-$$

	$C_5H_{11}N$	$C_5H_{11}NH^+$	OH^-
placed in soln:	5.88×10^{-3} M	--	--
changes:	$-x$ M	$+x$ M	$+x$ M
equilibrium:	$(5.88 \times 10^{-3}\ \ x)$M	x M	x M

As in Exercise 27, because we are dealing with a fairly dilute solution of a base with $K_b > 1 \times 10^{-5}$, we should not expect the usual simplifying assumption to work well. That is, 5.88×10^{-3} is not large with respect to x.

$$K_a = \frac{[C_5H_{11}NH^+][OH^-]}{[C_5H_{11}N]} = \frac{x \cdot x}{(5.88 \times 10^{-3} - x)} = 1.6 \times 10^{-3} \qquad x^2 + 1.6 \times 10^{-3}x - 9.4 \times 10^{-6} = 0$$

$$x = \frac{-1.6 \times 10^{-3} \pm \sqrt{(1.6 \times 10^{-3})^2 + 4 \times 9.4 \times 10^{-6}}}{2} = 2.4 \times 10^{-3}$$

$[OH^-] = 2.4 \times 10^{-3}$ M $\qquad pOH = -\log [OH^-] \qquad pOH = -\log (2.4 \times 10^{-3}) \qquad pOH = 2.62$

$pH = 14.00 - 2.62 = 11.38$

Degree of ionization

17-29. $$HCHO_2 + H_2O \rightleftharpoons H_3O^+ + CHO_2^-$$

	$HCHO_2$	H_3O^+	CHO_2^-
placed in soln:	0.50 M	--	--
changes:	$-x$ M	$+x$ M	$+x$ M
equilibrium:	$(0.50 - x)$M	x M	$+x$ M

$$K_a = \frac{[H_3O^+][CHO_2^-]}{[HCHO_2]} = \frac{x \cdot x}{0.50 - x} \simeq \frac{x^2}{0.50} = .8 \times 10^{-4} \qquad x^2 = 9.0 \times 10^{-5}$$

$x = 9.5 \times 10^{-3}$ mol $HCHO_2$ ionized $\qquad$ % ionized $= \dfrac{9.5 \times 10^{-3} \text{ mol}}{0.50 \text{ mol}} \times 100 = 1.9\%$ ionized

17-30. If an $HC_2H_3O_2(aq)$ solution of molarity x is 1.00% ionized, we can write:

$$HC_2H_3O_2 + H_2O \rightleftharpoons H_3O^+ + C_2H_3O_2^-$$

	$HC_2H_3O_2$	H_3O^+	$C_2H_3O_2^-$
placed in soln:	x M	--	--
changes:	$-0.01x$ M	$+0.01x$ M	$+0.01x$ M
equilibrium:	$(x - 0.01x)$M	$0.01x$ M	$0.01x$ M

$$K_a = \frac{[H_3O^+][C_2H_3O_2^-]}{[HC_2H_3O_2]} = \frac{(0.01x)(0.01x)}{0.99x} = 1.74 \times 10^{-5} \qquad 1.0 \times 10^{-4}x = 1.72 \times 10^{-5}$$

$x = 1.72 \times 10^{-1}$ M $HC_2H_3O_2 = 0.172$ M $HC_2H_3O_2$

17-31. If we could make the same simplifying assumption as in Example 17-8 [that x << M (the molarity of acid)], we would expect 0.0010 M $HC_2H_3O_2$ to be 13% ionized and 0.00010 M $HC_2H_3O_2$ to be 42% ionized. But this assumption is not valid when the molarity of the acid is very low (below about 0.01 M), therefore these predictions of the percent ionization of acetic acid are also *invalid*.

17-32. Determine the total moles of solute particles (molecules and ions) in 0.050 M $HC_2H_3O_2$.

	$HC_2H_3O_2$	+	H_2O	$\rightleftharpoons$	H_3O^+	+	$C_2H_3O_2^-$
placed in soln:	0.050 M				--		--
changes:	$-x$ M				$+x$ M		$+x$ M
equilibrium:	$(0.050 - x)$M				x M		x M

$K_a = \frac{[H_3O^+][C_2H_3O_2^-]}{[HC_2H_3O_2]} = \frac{x \cdot x}{0.050 - x} = 1.74 \times 10^{-5}$ Assume $x << 0.050$ $x^2 = 8.7 \times 10^{-7}$

$x = [H_3O^+] = [C_2H_3O_2^-] = 9.3 \times 10^{-4}$ M $[HC_2H_3O_2] = (0.050 - 9.3 \times 10^{-4})M = 0.049$ M

Total concentration of solute particles = $0.049 + (2 \times 9.3 \times 10^{-4}) = 0.051$ M. Assume that an aqueous solution that is 0.051 M is also 0.051 m.

$\Delta T_f = K_f \cdot m = 1.86°C\ (\text{mol solute})^{-1}\ \text{kg solvent} \times \frac{0.051\ \text{mol solute}}{1.00\ \text{kg solvent}} = 0.095°C$

The expected freezing point of 0.050 M $HC_2H_3O_2$ is -0.095°C.

Polyprotic acids

17-33. Calculate $[H_3O^+]$ and pH from K_{a_1}. Assume $[H_3O^+] = [HCO_3^-]$.

$K_{a_1} = \frac{[H_3O^+][HCO_3^-]}{[H_2CO_3]} = \frac{[H_3O^+]^2}{0.034} = 4.2 \times 10^{-7}$ $[H_3O^+]^2 = 1.4 \times 10^{-8}$ $[H_3O^+] = 1.2 \times 10^{-4}$ M

pH = $-\log [H_3O^+] = -\log (1.2 \times 10^{-4}) = 3.92$ $K_{a_2} = \frac{\cancel{[H_3O^+]}[CO_3^{2-}]}{\cancel{[HCO_3^-]}} = 5.6 \times 10^{-11}$

$[CO_3^{2-}] = 5.6 \times 10^{-11}$ M

17-34. Because in each of these solutions the second ionization step is so limited, we can assume that $[H_3O^+] = [HS^-]$ in each solution and that $[S^{2-}] = K_{a_2} = 1.0 \times 10^{-14}$ M.

(a)

	H_2S	+	H_2O	$\rightleftharpoons$	H_3O^+	+	HS^-
placed in soln:	0.075 M				--		--
changes:	$-x$ M				$+x$ M		$+x$ M
equilibrium:	$(0.075 - x)$M				x M		x M

$K_{a_1} = \frac{[H_3O^+][HS^-]}{[H_2S]} = \frac{x \cdot x}{0.075 - x}$ Assume $x << 0.075$ $\frac{x^2}{0.075} = 1.1 \times 10^{-7}$

$x^2 = 8.2 \times 10^{-9}$ $x = 9.1 \times 10^{-5}$ $[H_3O^+] = [HS^-] = 9.1 \times 10^{-5}$ M $[S^{2-}] = 1.0 \times 10^{-14}$M

(b) Assume that $x << 0.005$.

$K_{a_1} = \frac{x \cdot x}{0.005 - x} = \frac{x^2}{0.005} = 1.1 \times 10^{-7}$ $x^2 = 5.5 \times 10^{-10}$ $x = 2.3 \times 10^{-5}$ M

(The assumption is valid.)

$[H_3O^+] = [HS^-] = 2.3 \times 10^{-5}$ M $[S^{2-}] = 1.0 \times 10^{-14}$ M

(c) Assume that $x \ll 1.0 \times 10^{-5}$.

$$K_{a_1} = \frac{x \cdot x}{(1.0 \times 10^{-5} - x)} = \frac{x^2}{1.0 \times 10^{-5}} = 1.1 \times 10^{-7} \qquad x^2 = 1.1 \times 10^{-12} \qquad x = 1.0 \times 10^{-6}$$

$$1.0 \times 10^{-5} - x = 1.0 \times 10^{-5} - 1.0 \times 10^{-6} = 0.9 \times 10^{-5} \simeq 1.0 \times 10^{-5}$$

The assumption works fairly well.

$[H_3O^+] = [HS^-] = 1.0 \times 10^{-6}$ M $\qquad [S^{2-}] = 1.0 \times 10^{-14}$ M

17-35. (a) For the same reasons given in the text in the discussion of a diprotic acid, for a triprotic acid we should expect $K_{a_1} > K_{a_2} > K_{a_3}$.

(b) If $K_{a_1} \gg K_{a_2}$, the extent of ionization in the second step is much less than in the first step.

We can assume that $[H_3O^+] = [H_2A^-]$. Then, $K_{a_2} = \frac{\cancel{[H_3O^+]}[HA^{2-}]}{\cancel{[H_2A^-]}}$. For this expression to hold true it is also necessary that very little HA^{2-} ionize further. This will be the case if $K_{a_2} \gg K_{a_3}$.

(c) We should not expect $[A^{3-}]$ to be equal to K_{a_3}, because in the following expression $[H_3O^+]$ is not equal to $[HA^{2-}]$.

$$K_{a_3} = \frac{[H_3O^+][A^{3-}]}{[HA^{2-}]}$$

17-36. Assume that ionization occurs primarily in the first step. Calculate $[H_3O^+]$, $[H_2PO_4^-]$, and $[H_3PO_4]$ in the usual way.

	H_3PO_4 + H_2O	⇌ H_3O^+	+ $H_2PO_4^{2-}$
placed in soln:	0.100 M	--	--
changes:	$-x$ M	$+x$ M	$+x$ M
equilibrium:	$(0.100 - x)$M	x M	x M

$$K_{a_1} = \frac{[H_3O^+][H_2PO_4^{2-}]}{[H_3PO_4]} = \frac{x \cdot x}{0.100 - x} = 5.9 \times 10^{-3} \qquad x^2 + 5.9 \times 10^{-3}x - 5.9 \times 10^{-4} = 0$$

$$x = \frac{-5.9 \times 10^{-3} \pm \sqrt{(5.9 \times 10^{-3})^2 + 4 \times 5.9 \times 10^{-4}}}{2} = 2.2 \times 10^{-2}$$

Use the K_{a_2} expression to calculate $[HPO_4^{2-}]$: $K_{a_2} = \frac{\cancel{[H_3O^+]}[HPO_4^{2-}]}{\cancel{[H_2PO_4^-]}} = 6.2 \times 10^{-8}$

$[HPO_4^{2-}] = 6.2 \times 10^{-8}$ M

Use the K_{a_3} expression to calculate $[PO_4^{3-}]$: $K_{a_3} = \frac{[H_3O^+][PO_4^{3-}]}{[HPO_4^{2-}]} = \frac{2.2 \times 10^{-2}[PO_4^{3-}]}{6.2 \times 10^{-8}} = 4.8 \times 10^{-13}$

$[PO_4^{3-}] = 1.4 \times 10^{-18}$ M

Equilibrium concentrations: $[H_3PO_4] = 0.100 - x = 0.078$ M; $[H_3O^+] = [H_2PO_4^-] = 0.022$ M;

$[HPO_4^{2-}] = 6.2 \times 10^{-8}$ M; $[PO_4^{3-}] = 1.4 \times 10^{-18}$ M

17-37. (a) $C_{20}H_{24}O_2N_2 + H_2O \rightleftharpoons C_{20}H_{24}O_2N_2H^+ + OH^-$; $K_{b_1} = 1.08 \times 10^{-6}$

$C_{20}H_{24}O_2N_2H^+ + H_2O \rightleftharpoons C_{20}H_{24}O_2N_2H_2^{2+} + OH^-$; $K_{b_2} = 1.5 \times 10^{-10}$

(b) Make the usual assumption that ionization in the first step occurs to a much greater extent than in the second step.

$$K_{b_1} = \frac{[C_{20}H_{24}O_2N_2H^+][OH^-]}{[C_{20}H_{24}O_2N_2]} = 1.08 \times 10^{-6}$$

$[C_{20}H_{24}O_2N_2] = (1.00\text{ g} \times 1\text{ mol}/324\text{ g})/1.900\text{ L} = 0.00162$ mol/L

(In the formulation of the equilibrium constant expression, assume that $0.00162 - x \simeq 0.00162$. Also $[C_{20}H_{24}O_2N_2H^+] = [OH^-]$.)

$$K_{b_1} = \frac{[OH^-]^2}{0.00162} = 1.08 \times 10^{-6} \qquad [OH^-]^2 = 1.75 \times 10^{-9} \qquad [OH^-] = 4.18 \times 10^{-5}\text{ M}$$

$pOH = -\log(4.18 \times 10^{-5}) = 4.38 \qquad pH = 14.00 - 4.38 = 9.62$

Hydrolysis

17-38. (a) $NO_3^- + H_2O \longrightarrow$ no reaction

(b) $BrO^- + H_2O \rightleftharpoons HOBr + OH^-$

(c) $NH_4^+ + H_2O \rightleftharpoons H_3O^+ + NH_3$

(d) $I^- + H_2O \longrightarrow$ no reaction

(e) $C_6H_5NH_3^+ + H_2O \rightleftharpoons H_3O^+ + C_6H_5NH_2$

17-39. (a) KCl (salt of a strong acid and strong base) does not hydrolyze; its aqueous solutions are neutral.

(b) The NH_4^+ ion in NH_4NO_3 hydrolyzes to produce an acidic solution. $NH_4^+ + H_2O \rightleftharpoons H_3O^+ + NH_3$.

(c) $NaNO_3$ (salt of a strong acid and strong base) does not hydrolyze; its aqueous solutions are neutral.

(d) KI (salt of a strong acid and strong base) does not hydrolyze; its aqueous solutions are neutral.

(e) The hypochlorite ion in $Ca(ClO)_2$ hydrolyzes to produce a basic solution.
$ClO^- + H_2O \rightleftharpoons HClO + OH^-$.

17-40. The molar concentration of sodium benzoate is:

$$\text{no. mol } NaC_7H_5O_2/L = \frac{0.10\text{ g } NaC_7H_5O_2 \times \frac{1\text{ mol } NaC_7H_5O_2}{144\text{ g } NaC_7H_5O_2}}{0.100\text{ L}} = 0.0069\text{ M}$$

$$C_7H_5O_2^- + H_2O \rightleftharpoons HC_7H_5O_2 + OH^-$$

	$C_7H_5O_2^-$	$HC_7H_5O_2$	OH^-
placed in soln:	0.0069 M	--	--
changes:	$-x$ M	$-x$ M	$+x$ M
equilibrium:	$(0.0069 - x)$M	x M	x M

$$K_h = \frac{[HC_7H_5O_2][OH^-]}{[C_7H_5O_2^-]} = \frac{x \cdot x}{0.0069 - x} = \frac{K_w}{K_a} = \frac{1.0 \times 10^{-14}}{6.3 \times 10^{-5}} = 1.6 \times 10^{-10}$$

Assume $x << 0.0069$: $\frac{x^2}{0.0069} = 1.6 \times 10^{-10}$ $\quad x^2 = 1.1 \times 10^{-12}$ $\quad x = [OH^-] = 1.0 \times 10^{-6}$

$pOH = -\log [OH^-] = -\log (1.0 \times 10^{-6}) = 6.0$ $\quad pH = 14.0 - 6.0 = 8.0$

17-41. The salt chosen must be that of a strong base and a weak acid if the aqueous solution has pH > 7. Of those listed, this would be KNO_2.

$$NO_2^- + H_2O \rightleftharpoons HNO_2 + OH^-$$

	NO_2^-	HNO_2	OH^-
placed in soln:	x M	--	--
changes:	-5.6×10^{-6} M	$+5.6 \times 10^{-6}$ M	$+5.6 \times 10^{-6}$ M
equilibrium:	$(x - 5.6 \times 10^{-6})$M	5.6×10^{-6} M	5.6×10^{-6} M

The value of $[OH^-]$ listed above comes from pH = 8.75; pOH = 5.25; $\log [OH^-] = 5.25 = 0.75 - 6$; $[OH^-] = 5.6 \times 10^{-6}$ M.

$$K_a = \frac{[HNO_2][OH^-]}{[HNO_2]} = \frac{(5.6 \times 10^{-6})^2}{x - 5.6 \times 10^{-6}} \simeq \frac{(5.6 \times 10^{-6})^2}{x} = \frac{K_w}{K_a} = \frac{1.0 \times 10^{-14}}{5.13 \times 10^{-4}}$$

$\frac{(5.6 \times 10^{-6})^2}{x} = 1.9 \times 10^{-11}$ $\quad x = 1.7$ M KNO_2

17-42.

$$C_6H_5NH_3^+ + H_2O \rightleftharpoons H_3O^+ + C_6H_5NH_2$$

	$C_6H_5NH_3^+$	H_3O^+	$C_6H_5NH_2$
placed in soln:	0.050 M	--	--
changes:	$-x$ M	$+x$ M	$+x$ M
equilibrium:	$(0.050 - x)$M	x M	x M

$$K_h = \frac{[H_3O^+][C_6H_5NH_2]}{[C_6H_5NH_3^+]} = \frac{x \cdot x}{0.050 - x} \simeq \frac{x \cdot x}{0.050} = \frac{K_w}{K_b} = \frac{1.0 \times 10^{-14}}{4.30 \times 10^{-10}} = 2.3 \times 10^{-5}$$

$x^2 = 1.2 \times 10^{-6}$ $\quad x = [H_3O^+] = 1.1 \times 10^{-3}$ M $\quad pH = -\log [H_3O^+] = -\log (1.1 \times 10^{-3}) = 2.96$

17-43. (a) ionization as an acid: $HSO_3^- + H_2O \rightleftharpoons H_3O^+ + SO_3^{2-}$; $K_{a_2} = 6.3 \times 10^{-8}$

hydrolysis: $HSO_3^- + H_2O \rightleftharpoons H_2SO_3 + OH^-$; $K_h = K_w/K_{a_1} = 1.0 \times 10^{-14}/1.3 \times 10^{-2} = 7.7 \times 10^{-13}$

Because $K_{a_2} >> K_h$, the further ionization of HSO_3^- occurs to a greater extent than its hydrolysis. The solution is acidic.

(b) ionization as an acid: $HS^- + H_2O \rightleftharpoons H_3O^+ + S^{2-}$; $K_{a_2} = 1.0 \times 10^{-14}$

hydrolysis: $HS^- + H_2O \rightleftharpoons H_2S + OH^-$; $K_h = K_w/K_{a_1} = 1.0 \times 10^{-14}/1.1 \times 10^{-7} = 9.1 \times 10^{-8}$

Because $K_h >> K_{a_2}$, the hydrolysis of HS^- occurs to a greater extent than its further ionization. The solution is basic.

(c) ionization as an acid: $HC_2O_4^- + H_2O \rightleftharpoons H_3O^+ + C_2O_4^{2-}$; $K_{a_2} = 5.4 \times 10^{-5}$

hydrolysis: $HC_2O_4^- + H_2O \rightleftharpoons H_2C_2O_4 + OH^-$; $K_h = K_w/K_{a_1} = 1.0 \times 10^{-14}/5.4 \times 10^{-2}$
$= 1.9 \times 10^{-13}$

Because $K_{a_2} >> K_h$, ionization of $HC_2O_4^-$ occurs to a greater extent than its hydrolysis and the solution is acidic.

Molecular structure and acid strength

17-44. (a) NH_3 is a stronger base than H_2O (see Table 17-4). This means that $HC_2H_3O_2$ is more able to donate protons in $NH_3(l)$ than in $H_2O(l)$; it is a stronger acid in $NH_3(l)$ than in $H_2O(l)$.

(b) The situation here is that acetic acid is a stronger acid than is water. NH_3 accepts protons from $HC_2H_3O_2$ more readily than from H_2O. Therefore, NH_3 is a stronger base in $HC_2H_3O_2$ than in H_2O.

17-45. (a) This is a combination of a very strong acid (HBr) and a very strong base (OH^-). The reaction proceeds in the forward reaction.

(b) NO_3^- is a weaker base than HSO_4^-; it will not take a proton away from HSO_4^-. The reverse reaction predominates.

(c) Methoxide ion, CH_3O^-, is a very strong base. It will extract a proton from $HC_2H_3O_2$ and will favor the reverse reaction shown.

(d) CO_3^{2-} is a stronger base than $C_2H_3O_2^-$. It will extract a proton from $HC_2H_3O_2$. The forward reaction predominates.

(e) ClO_4^- is an exceptionally weak base. It will not extract a proton from HNO_2. The reverse reaction predominates.

(f) Since carbonate ion, CO_3^{2-}, is a stronger base than bicarbonate ion, HCO_3^-, the forward reaction predominates.

17-46. Because the H—I bond is *weaker* than the H—Cl bond, we should expect HI to ionize *more readily* than HCl; HI is a stronger acid than HCl. And because they are both almost completely **ionized** in aqueous solution, we should expect HCl and HI to be stronger than the other acids listed, all of which are weak. The four weak acids are all substituted acetic acids. The more electronegative the substituent atoms the weaker the O—H bond and the stronger the acid. The order of the acid strength increases as follows: (c) < (f) < (d) < (e) < (b) < (a).

17-47. The conjugate acids are $CH_3CH_2CH_2NH_3^+$ and 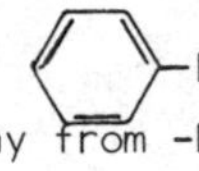 $-NH_3^+$. Because of the inductive effect, the phenyl group, C_6H_5, withdraws electrons away from $-NH_3^+$, making $C_6H_5NH_3^+$ a stronger acid than $CH_3CH_2CH_2NH_3^+$. In turn the conjugate base $C_6H_5NH_2$ (aniline) is a weaker base than is $CH_3CH_2NH_2$ (propylamine). The *stronger* of the two bases is propylamine.

17-48. Refer to the structures in (17.34). Consider that a molecule of HOCl loses a proton and that the "extra" electron, and hence the negative charge is centered on the O atom.

$^-$:Ö—C̈l: (with lone pairs)

With $HClO_2$, the "extra" electron can be spread between two O atoms. This makes ClO_2^- a weaker base than ClO^-, and $HClO_2$ a stronger acid than HOCl.

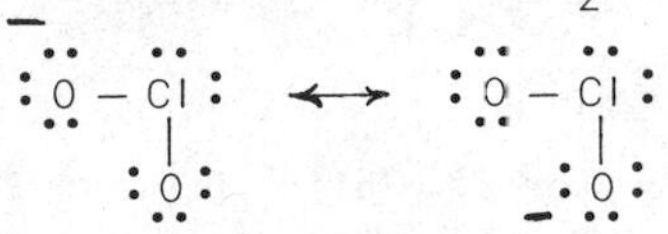

The possibility for spreading the electronic charge increases as the number of O atoms increases. This makes ClO_3^- and ClO_4^- progressively weaker bases, and the acids, $HClO_3$ and $HClO_4$, progressively stronger acids.

17-49. Because both molecules contain one O atom bonded directly to the central P atom, K_{a_1} (H_3PO_3) should be about the same as for H_3PO_4.

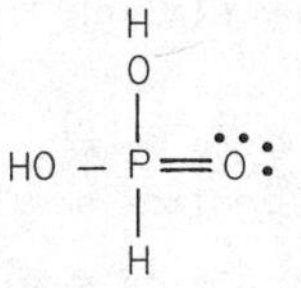

phosphorous acid

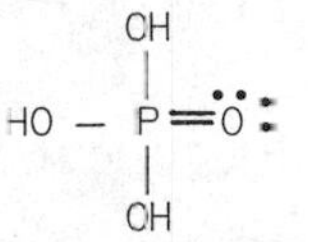

phosphoric acid

The Lewis structure of phosphorous acid is also consistent with the fact that H_3PO_3 is a *diprotic* acid.

17-50. (a) K_{a_1} (H_3AsO_4): 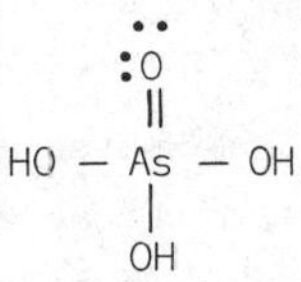 $EO_m(OH)_n$ $m = 1$ $K_{a_1} \approx 1 \times 10^{-2}$

(b) If $pK_{a_1} = 1.1$, the formula of hypophosphorous acid must be of the type, $EO_m(OH)_n$, where $m = 1$.

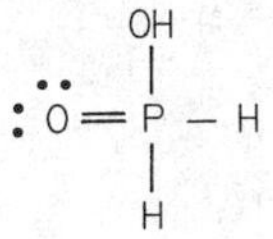

(H_3PO_2, hypophosphorous acid)

Self-test Questions

1. (*c*) The set up leading to a calculation of the number of moles of H_3O^+ is:
$0.30\ L \times 0.0050\ mol\ H_2SO_4/L \times 2\ mol\ H_3O^+/mol\ H_2SO_4 = 0.0030\ mol\ H_3O^+$.

2. (*a*) If the solution pH = 5, the solution is acidic; its pOH = 14 - 5 = 9, and its $[OH^-] = 1 \times 10^{-9}$ M.

3. (*b*) Propionic acid is a weak acid. In a 0.10 M solution of the acid, $[H_3O^+] < 0.10$ M since the acid is largely nonionized. Item (d) is incorrect. So is item (c), since in 0.10 M HBr $[H_3O^+] = 0.10$ M. $[H_3O^+]$ in 0.10 M $HC_3H_5O_2$ and in 0.10 M HNO_2 are not expected to be equal unless K_a has exactly the same value for these two acids (which is quite unlikely). Since $[H_3O^+]$ in 0.10 M HI is 0.10 M, it must also be true that $[H_3O^+]$ in 0.10 M $HC_3H_5O_2$ is smaller than in 0.10 M HI.

4. (*d*) CH_3NH_2 is a *weak* base. A 0.10 M solution must have $[OH^-] < 0.10$ M. Items (a) and (c) are incorrect because both refer to an acidic solution. The solution in question is basic, but with pH < 13. (pH = 13 corresponds to $[OH^-] = 0.10$ M.)

5. (*d*) NaClO is the salt of a weak acid and a strong base. It **hydrolyzes** to produce a basic solution. Its pH > 7, and $[H_3O^+]$ is less than 1.0×10^{-7} M. The $[H_3O^+] \neq 1.0 \times 10^{-12}$ M, however, because this

would correspond to $[OH^-] = 1.0 \times 10^{-2}$ M. Hydrolysis of 0.010 M NaClO would have to go to completion to produce $[OH^-] = 0.010$ M, but the hydrolysis occurs only to a limited extent. $ClO^- + H_2O \rightleftharpoons HOCl + OH^-$

6. (*a*) The amphiprotic ion must contain H if it is to be able to donate a proton. This eliminates CO_3^{2-} and Cl^-. HCO_3^- can lose a proton to form H_2CO_3 or can gain a proton to form H_2CO_3. Although NH_4^+ can lose a proton, it is incapable of gaining an additional proton.

7. (*c*) Several examples were given in the text indicating how a lone pair of electrons on the N atom in NH_3 may be donated to another species. We do not expect a metal ion (Al^{3+}) to be an electron pair donor since it has already lost its available electrons. BF_3 was given as an example of a Lewis acid--a vacant orbital is present on the B atom. The situation with CO_2 is very similar to the one with SO_2 illustrated in the text--a Lewis acid.

8. (*b*) Cl^- is a very weak base and $HClO_4$ is a very strong acid. $HC_2H_3O_2$ can transfer protons to H_2O but it is only partially ionized. $HC_2H_3O_2 + H_2O \rightleftharpoons H_3O^+ + C_2H_3O_2^-$. Because NH_3 is a stronger base than H_2O, ionization of $HC_2H_3O_2$ proceeds essentially to completion in NH_3. $HC_2H_3O_2 + NH_3 \longrightarrow NH_4^+ + C_2H_3O_2^-$.

9. The ten solutions can be arranged according to decreasing $[H_3O^+]$ without need for detailed calculations. The highest $[H_3O^+]$ is expected from the diprotic H_2SO_4; this is followed by the monoprotic HNO_3. $HC_2H_3O_2$, a weak acid, comes next, followed by the still weaker acid, H_2S. An 0.01 M NH_4Cl solution is slightly acidic because of the hydrolysis of NH_4^+. Because no hydrolysis is possible, an 0.01 M NaCl solution is neutral--pH = 7. The $NaNO_2$ solution is slightly basic because of hydrolysis of NO_2^-. NH_3 is a weak base, and NaOH is a strong base. The highest $[OH^-]$ and lowest $[H_3O^+]$ are found in 0.01 M $Ba(OH)_2$. The overall order of decreasing $[H_3O^+]$ is 0.01 M H_2SO_4 > 0.01 M HNO_3 > 0.01 M $HC_2H_3O_2$ > 0.01 M H_2S > 0.01 M NH_4Cl > 0.01 M NaCl > 0.01 M $NaNO_2$ > 0.01 M NH_3 > 0.01 M NaOH > 0.01 M $Ba(OH)_2$.

10. $pH = 2.60 = -\log [H_3O^+]$; $\log [H_3O^+] = -2.60 = 0.40 - 3.00$; $[H_3O^+] = 2.5 \times 10^{-3}$.

	$HC_7H_5O_2$	+ $H_2O \rightleftharpoons$	H_3O^+	+ $C_7H_5O_2^-$
placed in soln:	x M		--	--
changes:	-2.5×10^{-3} M		$+2.5 \times 10^{-3}$ M	$+2.5 \times 10^{-3}$ M
equilibrium:	$(x - 2.5 \times 10^{-3})$M		2.5×10^{-3} M	2.5×10^{-3} M

$$K_a = \frac{[H_3O^+][C_7H_5O_2^-]}{[HC_7H_5O_2]} = \frac{(2.5 \times 10^{-3})^2}{x - 2.5 \times 10^{-3}} \simeq \frac{(2.5 \times 10^{-3})^2}{x} = 6.3 \times 10^{-5} \qquad x = 9.9 \times 10^{-2}\ \text{M } C_7H_5O_2$$

$$\text{no. g } HC_7H_5O_2 = 0.250\ \text{L} \times \frac{9.9 \times 10^{-2}\ \text{mol } C_7H_5O_2}{\text{L}} \times \frac{122\ \text{g } C_7H_5O_2}{1\ \text{mol } C_7H_5O_2} = 3.0\ \text{g } HC_7H_5O_2$$

11. (a) Compare Lewis structures of the two acids.

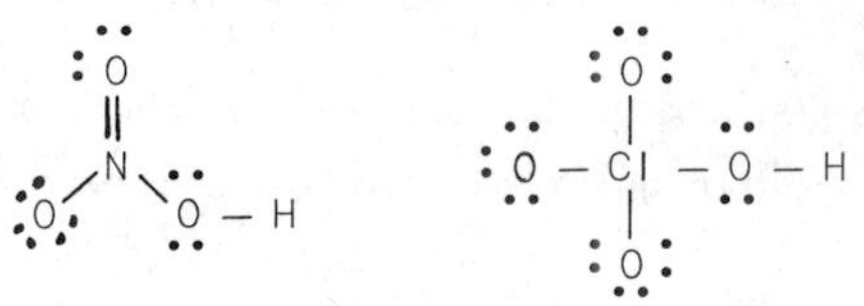

In HNO_3, there are two O atoms and one -OH group bonded to the central nonmetal atom (N). In $HClO_4$ there are three O atoms and one -OH group. Because of the larger number of O atoms bonded directly to the central atom, we should expect $HClO_4$ to be stronger than HNO_3. Also, the oxidation state of Cl is +7, compared to +5 for N. The formal charge on Cl is +3, compared to +1 on N. These are additional factors contributing to the very great acid strength of $HClO_4$.

(b) Electrons are attracted away from the -OH group by the presence of neighboring F atoms in $HC_2F_3O_2$. This leads to an easier loss of protons and to an increased acid strength.

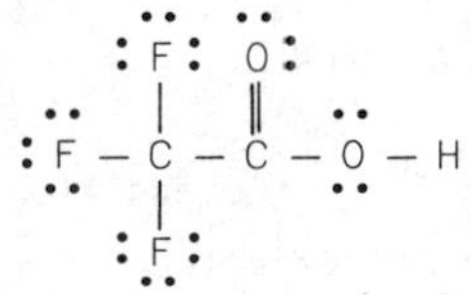

(c) From the structures given for the two molecules, we might reason that the electronegative Cl atom withdraws electrons from the $-NH_2$ group (inductive effect). This makes $C_6H_4ClNH_2$ less able to donate electron pairs (or to receive a proton), and hence a weaker base than $C_6H_5NH_2$. Alternatively, the conjugate acid $C_6H_4ClNH_3^+$ is a stronger acid than $C_6H_5NH_3^+$ because of the withdrawal of electrons from the $-NH_3^-$ group by the presence of Cl in the benzene ring.

12. (a) A strong acid dissociates completely into its ions in water solution. This means that the concentration of ions increases by the same factor as the solution concentration. Thus, if the molarity of a strong acid HX is increased from 0.1 M to 0.2 M (doubled), the $[H_3O^+]$ also increases from 0.1 M to 0.2 M (doubles). For a weak acid solution with [HA] = M, we may write

$$K_{HA} = \frac{[H_3O^+][A^-]}{[HA]} = \frac{[H_3O^+]^2}{M} \;;\quad [H_3O^+]^2 = M \times K_{HA} \;;\quad [H_3O^+] = \sqrt{M \times K_{HA}}$$

For a weak acid solution with [HA] = 2 M,

$$K_{HA} = \frac{[H_3O^+]^2}{2\ M} \;;\quad [H_3O^+]^2 = 2 \times M \times K_{HA} \;;\quad [H_3O^+] = \sqrt{2} \times \sqrt{M \times K_{HA}}$$

(b) One S^{2-} ion and one H_3O^+ ion are produced by the ionization of one HS^- ion. For the HS^- ion to appear in solution, one H_2S molecule must also have ionized, producing one H_3O^+ ion as well. Thus for every S^{2-} that does appear in solution, two H_3O^+ must be formed as well.

$$H_2S + H_2O \rightleftharpoons H_3O^+ + HS^- \qquad\qquad HS^- + H_2O \rightleftharpoons H_3O^+ + S^{2-}$$

However, the vast majority of HS^- ions produced by the ionization of H_2S do not ionize further to S^{2-}. For each of these HS^- ions in solution there must also exist an H_3O^+ ion. Thus, $[H_3O^+] >> 2 \times [S^{2-}]$.

Chapter 18

Additional Aspects of Equilibria in Aqueous Solutions

The common-ion effect in acid-base equilibria

18-1. (a) NO_2^- from $NaNO_2$ favors the *reverse* of the ionization reaction.

$$HNO_2 + H_2O \rightleftharpoons H_3O^+ + NO_2^-$$ This reduces $[H_3O^+]$ and raises the pH.

(b) HNO_3 is a *strong* acid that is completely ionized in aqueous solution. The addition of NO_3^- (from $NaNO_3$) has no effect on its ionization. $[H_3O^+]$ and pH are not affected.

18-2. (a) In this mixture of a strong and a weak acid, we can assume that essentially all of the H_3O^+ is derived from the strong acid. $[H_3O^+] = 0.100$ M

(b) In a combination of a weak acid and its salt, we can assume that essentially all of the anion is derived from the salt. In 0.100 M $NaNO_2$, $[NO_2^-] = 0.100$ M.

(c) All of the Cl^- is derived from the HCl, a strong acid. Moreover Cl^- does not participate in any reaction in solution. $[Cl^-] = 0.200$ M

(d) $C_2H_3O_2^-$ is produced by ionization of the weak acid.

	$HC_2H_3O_2$	+ H_2O $\rightleftharpoons$	H_3O^+	+	$C_2H_3O_2^-$
from weak acid:	$(0.300 - x)$M		x M		x M
from strong acid:	--		0.100 M		--
at equilibrium:	$(0.300 - x)$M		$(0.100 + x)$M		x M

Assume that $x << 0.100$

$$K_a = \frac{[H_3O^+][C_2H_3O_2^-]}{[HC_2H_3O_2]} = \frac{(0.100)x}{(0.300)} = 1.74 \times 10^{-5} \qquad x = [C_2H_3O_2^-] = 5.22 \times 10^{-5}\ M$$

(e)

	NH_3	+ H_2O $\rightleftharpoons$	NH_4^+	+	OH^-
from weak base:	$(0.500 - x)$M		x M		x M
from salt:	--		(2×0.200)M		--
at equilibrium:	$(0.500 - x)$M		$(0.400 + x)$M		x M

Assume $x << 0.400$

$$K_b = \frac{[NH_4^+][OH^-]}{[NH_3]} = \frac{(0.400)x}{(0.500)} = 1.74 \times 10^{-5} \qquad x = [OH^-] = 2.18 \times 10^{-5}\ M$$

18-3. First determine the molar concentration of sodium lactate,

$$\text{no. mol } NaC_3H_5O_3/L = 10.0 \text{ g } NaC_3H_5O_3 \times \frac{1 \text{ mol } NaC_3H_5O_3}{112 \text{ g } NaC_3H_5O_3} \times \frac{1}{0.100 \text{ L}} = 0.893 \text{ M}$$

and then $[H_3O^+]$: $\log [H_3O^+] = -4.11 = 0.89 - 5$ $\qquad [H_3O^+] = 7.8 \times 10^{-5}$ M

$$HC_3H_5O_3 + H_2O \rightleftharpoons H_3O^+ + C_3H_5O_3^-$$

	$HC_3H_5O_3$	H_3O^+	$C_3H_5O_3^-$
from weak acid:	$(0.0500 - x)$M	x M	x M
from salt:	--	--	0.893 M
at equilibrium:	$(0.0500 - x)$M	x M	$(0.893 + x)$M

But $x = 7.8 \times 10^{-5}$ M. Furthermore $x << 0.0500$.

$$K_a = \frac{[H_3O^+][C_3H_5O_3^-]}{[HC_3H_5O_3]} = \frac{(7.8 \times 10^{-5}) \times 0.893}{0.0500} = 1.39 \times 10^{-3}$$

18-4. Let $x = [OH^-]$ and express the following concentrations in terms of x. $[C_6H_5NH_2] = 0.100 - x \simeq 0.100$ (This assumes that $x << 0.100$.)

$$[C_6H_5NH_3^+] = \left\{1.20 \times 10^{-3} \text{ g } C_6H_5NH_3Cl \times \frac{1 \text{ mol } C_6H_5NH_3Cl}{130 \text{ g } C_6H_5NH_3Cl} \times \frac{1 \text{ mol } C_6H_5NH_3^+}{1 \text{ mol } C_6H_5NH_3Cl} \times \frac{1}{2.00 \text{ L}}\right\} + x$$

$$= 4.62 \times 10^{-6} + x$$

$$K_b = \frac{[C_6H_5NH_3^+][OH^-]}{[C_2H_5NH_2]} = \frac{(4.62 \times 10^{-6} + x)x}{0.100} = 4.2 \times 10^{-10} \qquad x^2 + 4.62 \times 10^{-6}x - 4.2 \times 10^{-11} = 0$$

$$x = \frac{-4.62 \times 10^{-6} \pm \sqrt{(4.62 \times 10^{-6})^2 + 4 \times 4.2 \times 10^{-11}}}{2}$$

$$x = \frac{-4.62 \times 10^{-6} \pm 1.38 \times 10^{-5}}{2} = 4.59 \times 10^{-6}$$

$$pOH = -\log [OH^-] = -\log (4.59 \times 10^{-6}) = -0.66 + 6.00 = 5.34$$

18-5. In each case let the volume, in ml, of indicated solution $= x$. Write an expression for $[H_3O^+]$ and set this equal to the value calculated from the pH.

(a) Since this will be a fairly acidic solution (pH = 1.0; $[H_3O^+] = 0.10$ M), assume that the pH is determined solely by the strong acid, HCl. That is, treat the solution as if HCl had been added to pure water.

$$\text{no. mol HCl} = x \text{ ml} \times \frac{1.00 \text{ L}}{1000 \text{ ml}} \times \frac{1.00 \text{ mol HCl}}{1.00 \text{ L}} = 0.00100\, x \text{ mol HCl}$$

$$\text{total volume} = (250 + x)\text{ml} = [(250 + x)/1000] \text{L} \qquad [H_3O^+] = \frac{0.00100\, x}{[(250 + x)/1000]} = \frac{x}{250 + x} = 0.100$$

$$x = 25.0 + 0.100\, x \qquad 0.900\, x = 25.0 \qquad x = 27.8 \text{ ml}$$

(b)

$$HC_3H_7O_2 + H_2O \rightleftharpoons H_3O^+ + C_3H_7O_2^-$$

	$HC_3H_7O_2$	H_3O^+	$C_3H_7O_2^-$
from weak acid:	$(0.100 - x)$M	x M	x M
from salt:	--	--	y M
at equilibrium:	$(0.100 - x)$M	x M	$(x + y)$M

But if pH = 4.00, $[H_3O^+] = x = 1.0 \times 10^{-4}$

Also assume $x << y$ and $x << 0.100$.

$$K_a = \frac{[H_3O^+][C_3H_7O_2^-]}{[HC_3H_7O_2]} = \frac{(1.0 \times 10^{-4}) \times y}{0.100} = 1.35 \times 10^{-5} \qquad y = 0.014$$

The final solution must be 0.014 M in $NaC_3H_7O_2$. Assume that the final solution volume remains at 250 ml.

$$\text{no. mol } NaC_3H_7O_2 = .250\text{ L} \times 0.014\text{ mol/L} = 3.5 \times 10^{-3}\text{ mol } NaC_3H_7O_2.$$

$$\text{no. ml required} = 3.5 \times 10^{-3}\text{ mol } NaC_3H_7O_2 \times \frac{1.00\text{ L}}{1.00\text{ mol } NaC_3H_7O_2} \times \frac{1000\text{ ml}}{1.00\text{ L}} = 3.5\text{ ml}$$

Because the added solution volume (3.5 ml) is much smaller than the initial volume (250 ml), the assumption of a constant solution volume is valid.

(c) One approach is to calculate the pH of 0.100 M $HC_3H_7O_2(aq)$; add 0.15 to this value; determine the corresponding $[H_3O^+]$; establish the molarity of an $HC_3H_7O_2(aq)$ having this $[H_3O^+]$; and, finally, calculate the volume of water to dilute the 0.100 M $HC_3H_7O_2(aq)$ to the new molarity. Another approach, outlined below, does all of this symbolically, without intermediate calculations. Let M_i = initial molarity of the acid solution; pH_i, its initial pH; M_f = final molarity of the acid solution; and pH_f, the final pH. Also, assume that the acid ionizes to such a limited extent that the molar concentration of nonionized acid is equal to the total molarity. [This is the assumption usually expressed in a form such as $(0.100 - x) \simeq 0.100$.]

$$\text{Initially:} \quad K_a = \frac{[H_3O^+][A^-]}{[HA]} = \frac{[H_3O^+]_i^2}{M_i} = K_a$$

$$[H_3O^+]_i = \sqrt{K_a \times M_i} \qquad \log [H_3O^+] = 1/2 \log (K_a \times M_i)$$

$$pH_i = -\log [H_3O^+] = -1/2 \log (K_a \times M_i) \qquad pH_f = pH_i + 0.15$$

$$-1/2 \log (K_a \times M_f) = -1/2 \log (K_a \times M_i) + 0.15$$

$$\cancel{-1/2 \log K_a} - 1/2 \log M_f = \cancel{-1/2 \log K_a} - 1/2 \log M_i + 0.15$$

$$1/2 \log \frac{M_i}{M_f} = 0.15 \qquad \log \frac{M_i}{M_f} = 0.30 \qquad \frac{M_i}{M_f} = 2.0 \quad \text{or} \quad M_f = 1/2\, M_i$$

To raise the pH of the weak acid solution by 0.15 unit requires that the acid solution be diluted to one-half its original molar concentration. In the present case this means adding 250.0 ml H_2O to 250.0 ml 0.100 M $HC_3H_7O_2(aq)$.

Buffer solutions

18-6. (a) 0.100 M NaCl is not a buffer solution. Addition of even small quantities of acid or base will change its pH drastically.

(b) 0.100 M NaCl - 0.100 M NH_4Cl is not a buffer solution. The solution has no capacity to neutralize small added quantities of acid. And although NH_4^+ is capable of reacting with added base, the solution pH would change greatly. [A solution of NH_4^+ is acidic by hydrolysis; a NH_3-NH_4^+ solution is basic.]

(c) A 0.100 M CH_3NH_2 - 0.150 M $CH_3NH_3^+Cl^-$ solution contains a weak base and its salt (in approximately equal concentrations). It is a buffer solution.

(d) Following reaction between HCl and NO_2^-, the solution contains a weak acid, HNO_2, and an excess of strong acid, HCl. This is not a buffer solution.

$$H^+ + Cl^- + Na^+ + NO_2^- \longrightarrow HNO_2 + Na^+ + Cl^-$$

(e) A reaction occurs between a strong acid and the salt of a weak acid. Because there is an excess of the salt, the final solution is that of a weak acid and its salt. This is a buffer solution.

$$H^+ + Cl^- + Na^+ + \underset{\text{(excess)}}{C_2H_3O_2^-} \longrightarrow HC_2H_3O_2 + Na^+ + Cl^-$$

18-7. (a) In the presence of acid: $H_3O^+ + HPO_4^{2-} \longrightarrow H_2PO_4^- + H_2O$

In the presence of base: $OH^- + H_2PO_4^- \longrightarrow HPO_4^{2-} + H_2O$

(b) $pH = pK_{a_2} + \log \dfrac{[HPO_4^{2-}]}{[H_2PO_4^-]}$. This buffer will be most effective when $[HPO_4^{2-}] = [H_2PO_4^-]$.

$pH = -(\log K_{a_2}) + \log 1 = -\log(6.2 \times 10^{-8}) + 0 = -7.21$

(c) $pH = 7.21 + \log \dfrac{0.150}{0.050} = 7.21 + \log 3.0 = 7.69$

18-8. For each of the buffer solutions use the equation: $pH = pK_a + \log \dfrac{[A^-]}{[HA]}$ (or the corresponding equation for a weak base-salt buffer).

(a) $pH = pK_a(HCHO_2) + \log \dfrac{[CHO_2^-]}{[HCHO_2]} = -\log(1.8 \times 10^{-4}) + \log \dfrac{0.082}{0.125} = 3.74 + \log 0.66 = 3.74 - 0.18$

$= 3.56$

(b) $pH = -\log(2.95 \times 10^{-8}) + \log \dfrac{0.216}{0.165} = 7.53 + \log 1.309 = 7.53 + 0.12 = 7.65$

(c) $pOH = -\log(1.74 \times 10^{-5}) + \log \dfrac{2 \times 0.660}{1.52} = 4.76 + \log 0.868 = 4.76 - 0.06 = 4.70$

$pH = 14.00 - pOH = 14.00 - 4.70 = 9.30$

18-9. Our problem is essentially to determine the concentration of NH_4^+ that must be present in 0.100 M NH_3 to yield a solution with a pH of 9.35. $[OH^-]$ in the solution can be calculated from the pH value.)

$NH_3 + H_2O \rightleftharpoons NH_4^+ + OH^-$; $K_b = 1.74 \times 10^{-5}$

$pOH = 14.00 - pH = 14.00 - 9.35 = 4.65$; $\log [OH^-] = -pOH = -4.65$; $pOH = 0.35 - 5.00$;

$[OH^-] = 2.24 \times 10^{-5}$

$$K_b = \frac{[NH_4^+][OH^-]}{[NH_3]} = \frac{[NH_4^+] \times 2.24 \times 10^{-5}}{0.100} = 1.74 \times 10^{-5}; \quad [NH_4^+] = 7.8 \times 10^{-2}$$

$$\text{no. g } (NH_4)_2SO_4 = 250 \text{ ml} \times \frac{1 \text{ L}}{1000 \text{ ml}} \times \frac{7.8 \times 10^{-2} \text{ mol } NH_4^+}{1 \text{ L}} \times \frac{1 \text{ mol } (NH_4)_2SO_4}{2 \text{ mol } NH_4^+} \times \frac{132 \text{ g } (NH_4)_2SO_4}{1 \text{ mol } (NH_4)_2SO_4}$$

$= 1.3 \text{ g } (NH_4)_2SO_4$

18-10. Look up K_a values for the three acids in Tables 17-2 and 17-3, establish the corresponding pK_a values, and substitute into equation (18.9) to obtain:

$pH = 3.74 + \log \dfrac{[CHO_2^-]}{[HCHO_2]}$ for *formic acid-sodium formate*

$$pH = 4.76 + \log \frac{[C_2H_3O_2^-]}{[HC_2H_3O_2]}$$ for *acetic acid-sodium acetate*

$$pH = 2.23 + \log \frac{[H_2PO_4^-]}{[H_3PO_4]}$$ for *phosphoric acid-sodium dihydrogen phosphate*

The capacity of a buffer solution is limited to about one pH unit above and below the pK_a value. This fact suggests that the formic acid-sodium formate buffer is best to use in preparing a buffer solution with pH = 3.50.

Determine the ratio $[CHO_2^-]/[HCHO_2]$ corresponding to pH = 3.50.

$$3.50 = 3.74 + \log \frac{[CHO_2^-]}{[HCHO_2]} \qquad \log \frac{[CHO_2^-]}{[HCHO_2]} = 3.50 - 3.74 = -0.24$$

$$\frac{[CHO_2^-]}{[HCHO_2]} = \text{antilog}(-0.24) = 0.575 \qquad [CHO_2^-] = 0.575\,[HCHO_2]$$

Since the two buffer components are present in the same solution, the ratio of their amounts, in moles, is the same as their ratio of concentrations, 0.575 : 1.00. For convenience let us take *1.00 L 0.100 M* $HCHO_2$ (which contains 0.10 mol $HC_2H_3O_2$). To obtain the desired buffer solution, we must mix this with *575 ml 0.100 M* $NaCHO_2$ (which contains 0.0575 mol $NaCHO_2$).

18-11. This problem differs in two ways from the preceding exercise: (1) Weak acid solutions are not available and (2) an exact volume of buffer solution is required. We can begin, however, at the point where we left off in Exercise 10--$[CHO_2^-]/[HCHO_2] = 0.575$. The required weak acid in the buffer must be produced by reacting the strong acid (1.00 M HCl) with the salt of the weak acid (0.100 M $NaCHO_2$). Let us call the required volumes of these solutions, in liters, x and y, respectively. We need to find two equations to relate these unknowns. The first of the equations is $x + y = 1.00$. The other equation is obtained as follows:

	CHO_2^-	+ H_3O^+	$\longrightarrow$ $HCHO_2$	+ H_2O
initial:	$0.100y$ mol	--	--	
add:	--	$1.00x$ mol		
buffer:	$(0.100y - 1.00x)$mol	pH = 3.50	$1.00x$ mol	

Because the total solution volume is 1.00 L, the molar amounts and the molar concentrations are numerically equal. We can write:

$$pH = pK_a + \log \frac{[CHO_2^-]}{[HCHO_2]} \qquad 3.50 = 3.74 + \log \frac{(0.100y - 1.00x)}{1.00x}$$

$$\frac{0.100y - 1.00x}{1.00x} = \text{antilog}(-0.24) = 0.575 \qquad 0.100y - 1.00x = 0.575x$$

However, since $x + y = 1.00$; $0.100(1.00 - x) - 1.00x = 0.575x \qquad 1.675x = 0.100$

$x = 0.0597$ and $y = 0.9403$. Prepare the buffer solution by mixing 59.7 ml 1.00 M HCl with 940.3 ml 0.100 M $NaCHO_2$.

18-12. The required expression is $pH = pK_a + \log \frac{[HCO_3^-]}{[H_2CO_3]} = 6.4 + \log \frac{20}{1} = 6.4 + 1.3 = 7.7$

A buffer having $[C_2H_3O_2^-]/[HC_2H_3O_2] = 20$ would not function well as a general purpose buffer. It would have considerable capacity to react with added acid ($C_2H_3O_2^- + H_3O^+ \longrightarrow HC_2H_3O_2 + H_2O$), but only 1/20th the capacity to react with added base because of the limited quantity of $HC_2H_3O_2$

present ($HC_2H_3O_2 + OH^- \longrightarrow C_2H_3O_2^- + H_2O$).

18-13. (a) 0.010 M $HC_2H_3O_2$ - 0.010 M $NaC_2H_3O_2$: $pH = -\log(1.74 \times 10^{-5}) + \log \frac{0.010}{0.010} = 4.76 + \log 1 = 4.76$

1.0 M $HC_2H_3O_2$ - 0.50 M $NaC_2H_3O_2$: $pH = -\log(1.74 \times 10^{-5}) + \log \frac{0.50}{1.0} = 4.76 + \log 0.50$

$= 4.76 - 0.30 = 4.46$

(b) 0.010 M $HC_2H_3O_2$ - 0.010 M $NaC_2H_3O_2$ has a capacity of neutralizing 0.010 mol/L of either H_3O^+ OH^- before its buffering action is totally destroyed.

1.0 M $HC_2H_3O_2$ - 0.50 M $NaC_2H_3O_2$ has a capacity of neutralizing 0.50 mol H_3O^+/L or 1.0 mol OH^-/L.

18-14. (a)

	$C_2H_3O_2^-$ +	H_3O^+ $\longrightarrow$	$HC_2H_3O_2$ +	H_2O
original soln:	0.050 mol		0.0150 mol	
add 0.00100 L of 12 M HCl:		0.012 mol		
changes:	-0.012 mol	-0.012 mol	+0.012 mol	
final amounts:	0.038 mol	?	0.027 mol	
final concns:	$\frac{0.038 \text{ mol}}{0.101 \text{ L}} = 0.38$ M	?	$\frac{0.027 \text{ mol}}{0.101 \text{ L}} = 0.27$ M	

$pH = -\log(1.74 \times 10^{-5}) + \log \frac{0.38}{0.27} = 4.76 + \log 1.4 = 4.76 + 0.15 = 4.91$

(b) If 5.00 ml 12 M were added to 100 ml of the buffer this would be equivalent to adding 0.060 mol H_3O^+. All of the $C_2H_3O_2^-$ would be converted to $HC_2H_3O_2$ and there would remain an excess of 0.010 mol H_3O^+.

$[H_3O^+] = \frac{0.010 \text{ mol } H_3O^+}{0.105 \text{ L}} = 0.095$ M $\qquad pH = -\log 0.095 = 1.02$

18-15. $[NH_3] = 1.00 \text{ g } NH_3 \times \frac{1 \text{ mol } NH_3}{17.0 \text{ g } NH_3} \times \frac{1}{0.500 \text{ L}} = 0.118$ M

$[NH_4^+] = 5.00 \text{ g } (NH_4)_2SO_4 \times \frac{1 \text{ mol } (NH_4)_2SO_4}{132 \text{ g } (NH_4)_2SO_4} \times \frac{2 \text{ mol } NH_4^-}{1 \text{ mol } (NH_4)_2SO_4} \times \frac{1}{0.500 \text{ L}} = 0.152$ M

(a) $pOH = -\log(1.74 \times 10^{-5}) + \log \frac{[NH_4^-]}{[NH_3]} = 4.76 + \log \frac{0.152}{0.118} = 4.76 + \log 1.29 = 4.76 + 0.11 = 4.87$

$pH = 14.00 - 4.87 = 9.13$

(b) The addition of 1.00 g NaOH to 0.500 L of the buffer means adding

$1.00 \text{ g NaOH} \times \frac{1 \text{ mol NaOH}}{40.0 \text{ g NaOH}} \times \frac{1 \text{ mol } OH^-}{1 \text{ mol NaOH}} \times \frac{1}{0.500 \text{ L}} = 0.0500 \text{ mol } OH^-/L$

	NH_4^+ +	OH^- $\longrightarrow$	NH_3 +	H_2O
original buffer:	0.152 M		0.113 M	
add:		0.050 M		
changes:	-0.050 M	-0.050 M	+0.050 M	
equil. concns:	0.102 M	?	0.163 M	

$$pOH = 4.76 + \log \frac{0.102}{0.168} = 4.76 + \log 0.607 = 4.76 - 0.22 = 4.54$$

$$pH = 14.00 - pOH = 14.00 - 4.54 = 9.46$$

(c) Here let us work backwards: $pH = 9.00$, $pOH = 5.00$, $pOH = 4.76 + \log \frac{[NH_4^+]}{[NH_3]} = 5.00$

$$\log \frac{[NH_4^+]}{[NH_3]} = 0.24 \qquad \frac{[NH_4^+]}{[NH_3]} = \text{antilog } 0.24 = 1.74$$

The ratio $[NH_4^+]/[NH_3]$ in the original buffer is 0.152/0.118 = 1.29. Thus, some NH_3 must be converted to NH_4^+. Let this quantity, expressed as mol/L, be x.

$$\frac{(0.152 + x)}{(0.118 - x)} = 1.74 \qquad 0.152 + x = 0.205 - 1.74x \qquad 2.74x = 0.053 \qquad x = 0.019$$

Enough 12 M HCl must be added to produce 0.019 M H_3O^+ (which then converts 0.019 mol NH_3/L to 0.019 mol NH_4^+/L).

$$\text{no. drops} = 0.500 \text{ L buffer} \times \frac{0.019 \text{ mol } H_3O^+}{\text{L buffer}} \times \frac{1 \text{ mol HCl}}{1 \text{ mol } H_3O^+} \times \frac{1 \text{ L HCl(aq)}}{12 \text{ mol HCl}} \times \frac{1000 \text{ ml HCl(aq)}}{1 \text{ L HCl(aq)}}$$

$$\times \frac{1 \text{ drop HCl(aq)}}{0.05 \text{ ml HCl(aq)}} = 16 \text{ drops}$$

18-16. (a) Determine the number of moles of the two reactants, $C_2H_3O_2^-$ and H_3O^+.

$$\text{no. mol } C_2H_3O_2^- = 10.0 \text{ g } NaC_2H_3O_2 \times \frac{1 \text{ mol } NaC_2H_3O_2}{82.0 \text{ g } NaC_2H_3O_2} \times \frac{1 \text{ mol } C_2H_3O_2^-}{1 \text{ mol } NaC_2H_3O_2} = 0.122 \text{ mol } C_2H_3O_2^-$$

$$\text{no. mol } H_3O^+ = 0.300 \text{ L} \times \frac{0.200 \text{ mol HCl}}{1 \text{ L}} \times \frac{1 \text{ mol } H_3O^+}{1 \text{ mol HCl}} = 0.0600 \text{ mol } H_3O^+$$

$$\text{no. mol } C_2H_3O_2^- = 0.122 \text{ mol initially} - 0.0600 \text{ mol consumed} = 0.062 \text{ mol } C_2H_3O_2^-$$

These values are now substituted into the equilibrium constant expression.

$$K_a = \frac{[H_3O^+][C_2H_3O_2^-]}{[HC_2H_3O_2]} = \frac{[H_3O^+] \times 0.062/0.300}{0.060/0.300} = 1.74 \times 10^{-5}$$

$$[H_3O^+] = 1.68 \times 10^{-5} \qquad pH = -\log(1.68 \times 10^{-5}) = 4.77$$

(b) The amount of OH^- added to the buffer solution is calculated first.

$$\text{no. mol } OH^- = 1.00 \text{ g } Ba(OH)_2 \times \frac{1 \text{ mol } Ba(OH)_2}{171 \text{ g } Ba(OH)_2} \times \frac{2 \text{ mol } OH^-}{1 \text{ mol } Ba(OH)_2} = 0.0117 \text{ mol } OH^-$$

In the buffer reaction 0.0117 mol $HC_2H_3O_2$ is converted to 0.0117 mol $C_2H_3O_2^-$.

$$HC_2H_3O_2 + OH^- \longrightarrow C_2H_3O_2^- + H_2O$$

In the new equilibrium condition, no. mol $HC_2H_3O_2$ = 0.060 - 0.0117 = 0.048 mol $HC_2H_3O_2$; no. mol $C_2H_3O_2^-$ = 0.062 + 0.0117 = 0.074 mol $C_2H_3O_2^-$.

These new values are now substituted into the equilibrium constant expression.

$$K_a = \frac{[H_3O^+][C_2H_3O_2^-]}{[HC_2H_3O_2]} = \frac{[H_3O^+] \times 0.074/0.300}{0.048/0.300} = 1.74 \times 10^{-5}$$

$$[H_3O^+] = 1.13 \times 10^{-5} \qquad pH = -\log(1.13 \times 10^{-5}) = 4.95$$

(c) The capacity of the buffer toward $Ba(OH)_2$ is simply the amount of $Ba(OH)_2$ required to react with all of the $HC_2H_3O_2$.

$$\text{no. g } Ba(OH)_2 = 0.060 \text{ mol } HC_2H_3O_2 \times \frac{1 \text{ mol } OH^-}{1 \text{ mol } HC_2H_3O_2} \times \frac{1 \text{ mol } Ba(OH)_2}{2 \text{ mol } OH^-} \times \frac{171 \text{ g } Ba(OH)_2}{1 \text{ mol } Ba(OH)_2} = 5.1 \text{ g } Ba(OH)_2$$

(d) Since the amount of $Ba(OH)_2$ added (5.2 g) exceeds the buffer capacity (5.1 g), all the acetic acid is consumed. The resulting solution contains sodium and barium acetates and 0.1 g of excess barium hydroxide, which establishes the pH of the solution.

$$[OH^-] = 0.1 \text{ g } Ba(OH)_2 \times \frac{1 \text{ mol } Ba(OH)_2}{171 \text{ g } Ba(OH)_2} \times \frac{2 \text{ mol } OH^-}{1 \text{ mol } Ba(OH)_2} \times \frac{1}{0.300 \text{ L}} = 3.9 \times 10^{-3} \text{ M}$$

$pOH = -\log (3.9 \times 10^{-3}) = 2.4$ $\quad\quad$ $pH = 14.00 - 2.4 = 11.6$

Acid-base indicators

18-17. (a) In an acid-base titration the pH range where neutralization occurs can be established from an appropriate titration curve. Then an indicator can be selected that changes color in this range. If the pH of an unknown solution can have a value from 0 to 14, several different indicators, each with a pH range of about 2, are required to establish this pH.

(b) An indicator is itself a weak acid and consumes a small quantity of the titrant in being converted to its anion. This volume is treated as though it were part of the volume required for the titration itself. The larger the volume of indicator used, the greater will be the error introduced. (Generally, in laboratory procedures a correction is made for this effect.)

(c) Thymol blue is a diprotic acid, call it H_2B. The first color change corresponds to the equilibrium $H_2B + H_2O \rightleftharpoons H_3O^+ + HB^-$. The second color change, to $HB^- + H_2O \rightleftharpoons H_3O^+ + B^{2-}$. Thus, there are three colors--red (H_2B), yellow (HB^-), and blue (B^{2-}). The first color change corresponds to pK_{a_1} and the second, pK_{a_2}.

18-18. (a) Take the negative logarithms of the K_a values. This yields values of pK_a. For each indicator $pH = pK_a$ at the midpoint of the indicator color change.

acidic solution: bromphenol blue ($pK_a = 3.85$); bromcresol green ($pK_a = 4.68$); 2,4-dinitrophenol ($pK_a = 3.90$); chlorophenol red ($pK_a = 6.00$)

approx. neutral: bromthymol blue ($pK_a = 7.10$)

basic solution: thymolphthalein ($pK_a = 10.00$)

(b) If bromcresol green assumes a green color it is at about the midpoint of its color change. The pH of the solution must be about equal to pK_a for bromcresol green--about pH = 5. Chlorophenol red assumes an orange color at about pH = 6.

18-19. (a) 0.100 M HCl(aq); pH = 1; 2,4-dinitrophenol is colorless.

(b) 1.00 M NaCl(aq); pH = 7; chlorophenol red is red.

(c) In 1.00 M NH_3(aq); $K_b = \frac{[NH_4^+][OH^-]}{[NH_3]} = \frac{[OH^-]^2}{1.00} = 1.74 \times 10^{-5}$ $\quad\quad$ $[OH^-] = 4.17 \times 10^{-3}$ M

$pOH = -\log (4.17 \times 10^{-3}) = 2.38$ $\quad\quad$ $pH = 14.00 - 2.38 = 11.62$

At this pH thymolphthalein is blue.

(d) Hydrolysis of NH_4^+ occurs in NH_4NO_3.

$NH_4^+ + H_2O \rightleftharpoons NH_3 + H_3O^+$ $\quad\quad$ $K_h = K_w/K_a = 1.0 \times 10^{-14}/1.74 \times 10^{-5}$

$$K_h = \frac{[NH_3][H_3O^+]}{[NH_4^+]} = \frac{[H_3O^+]^2}{1.00} = 5.7 \times 10^{-10} \qquad [H_3O^+] = 2.4 \times 10^{-5} \qquad pH = 4.62$$

At this pH bromthymol blue is yellow.

(e) According to Figure 17-3 the pH of seawater is about 8. At this pH bromcresol green is blue.

(f) Considering just the first ionization of H_2CO_3, we can write

$$K_{a_1} = \frac{[H_3O^+][HCO_3^-]}{[H_2CO_3]} = \frac{[H_3O^+]^2}{0.034} = 4.2 \times 10^{-7} \qquad [H_3O^+] = 1.2 \times 10^{-4} \qquad pH = 3.92$$

At this pH bromphenol blue is at about the middle of its change from yellow to blue; the color should be green.

18-20. (a) First calculate the pH of the buffer solution:

$$pH = pK_a + \log \frac{[C_2H_3O_2^-]}{[HC_2H_3O_2]} = -\log (1.74 \times 10^{-5}) + \log \frac{0.10}{0.10} = 4.76$$

Now determine the ratio $[In^-]/[HIn]$ at this pH:

$$pH = pK_a + \log \frac{[In^-]}{[HIn]} = 4.95 + \log\frac{[In^-]}{[HIn]} = 4.76 \qquad \log \frac{[In^-]}{[HIn]} = -0.19 \qquad \frac{[In^-]}{[HIn]} = 0.65$$

If we take $[HIn] = 1.00$, $[In^-] = 0.65$, and total indicator concentration = 1.65. This means the percent of the indicator in the anion form is $(0.65/1.65) \times 100 = 39\%$.

(b) When the indicator is at its pK_a (4.95), the ratio $[In^-]/[HIn] = 1.00$. At the midpoint of its color change (about pH = 5.3) the ratio $[In^-]/[HIn]$ is greater than 1.00. Thus, even though $[HIn] < [In^-]$ at the midpoint, the contribution of HIn to establishing the color of the solution is the same as one would normally expect when $[HIn] = [In^-]$. This must mean that HIn (red) is more strongly colored than In^- (yellow).

Neutralization reactions

18-21. $$\text{no. mol } OH^- = 0.02250 \text{ L} \times \frac{0.0500 \text{ mol } H_2SO_4}{1.00 \text{ L}} \times \frac{2 \text{ mol } H_3O^+}{1 \text{ mol } H_2SO_4} \times \frac{1 \text{ mol } OH^-}{1 \text{ mol } H_3O^+} = 2.25 \times 10^{-3} \text{ mol } OH^-$$

$$[OH^-] = \frac{2.25 \times 10^{-3} \text{ mol } OH^-}{0.02500 \text{ L}} = 0.0900 \text{ M}$$

18-22. $$Ca(OH)_2(s) \rightleftharpoons Ca^{2+}(aq) + 2\,OH^-(aq); \quad K_{sp} = 5.5 \times 10^{-6}$$

dissolve: S mol/L

at equil: S mol/L $\quad 2S$ mol/L

$$K_{sp} = [Ca^{2+}][OH^-]^2 = (S)(2S)^2 = 4S^3 = 5.5 \times 10^{-6} \qquad S = 1.1 \times 10^{-2}$$

$$[OH^-] = 2S = 2 \times 1.1 \times 10^{-2} = 0.022 \text{ M}$$

$$\text{no. ml HCl(aq)} = 0.0500 \text{ L} \times \frac{0.022 \text{ mol } OH^-}{1.00 \text{ L}} \times \frac{1 \text{ mol } H_3O^+}{1 \text{ mol } OH^-} \times \frac{1 \text{ mol HCl}}{1 \text{ mol } H_3O^+} \times \frac{1.00 \text{ L HCl(aq)}}{0.1032 \text{ mol HCl}}$$

$$\times \frac{1000 \text{ ml HCl(aq)}}{1.00 \text{ L HCl(aq)}} = 10.7 \text{ ml HCl(aq)}$$

18-23. Calculate the no. mol H_3O^+ in the acid and no. mol OH^- in the base. Determine which is in excess and then establish the final pH.

Solution A: pH = 2.50 $\quad$ log $[H_3O^+]$ = -2.50 $\quad$ $[H_3O^+] = 3.2 \times 10^{-3}$ M

$$\text{no. mol } H_3O^+ = 0.100 \text{ L} \times 3.2 \times 10^{-3} \text{ mol } H_3O^+/\text{L} = 3.2 \times 10^{-4} \text{ mol } H_3O^+$$

Solution B: pH = 11.00 $\quad$ pOH = 3.00 $\quad$ $[OH^-] = 1.0 \times 10^{-3}$ M

$$\text{no. mol } OH^- = 0.100 \text{ L} \times 1.0 \times 10^{-3} \text{ mol/L} = 1.0 \times 10^{-4} \text{ mol } OH^-$$

The neutralization reaction involves 1.0×10^{-4} mol OH^- reacting with 1.0×10^{-4} mol H_3O^+. The excess reactant is 2.2×10^{-4} mol H_3O^+.

$$[H_3O^+] = \frac{2.2 \times 10^{-4} \text{ mol } H_3O^+}{0.200 \text{ L}} = 1.1 \times 10^{-3} \text{ M} \qquad \text{pH} = 2.96$$

18-24. (a) In the event that the acid and base in Exercise 23 are weak rather than strong, the final pH will be higher than in the strong acid/strong base case. If the molar concentration of weak base to establish a pH = 11.00 is greater than the molar concentration of weak acid to establish a pH = 2.50, then upon mixing excess base will be present. The pH in this case would certainly be greater than 7. Even if weak acid is left in excess following the neutralization reaction, its ionization will be repressed by the salt formed in the neutralization reaction and the final pH will be above 2.50 (although below 7).

(b) K_a and K_b would have to be given to obtain an exact solution to the problem. That is, if K_a of a weak acid and the pH of its solution are known, its molarity can be calculated. The same is true for a weak base. Once the molarities of the weak acid and weak base are known, the result of the neutralization reaction can be worked out.

Titration curves

18-25. The equivalence point in a titration is the point where complete neutralization has occurred. For a given volume of acid (say 25.00 ml) of a fixed concentration (say 0.100 M), the number of moles of acid to be titrated is the same, regardless of whether the acid is strong or weak. The volumes of an NaOH solution required to reach the equivalence point in the two cases will also be the same. The major difference in the two cases is that in the strong acid all the available acid is ionized initially, whereas in a weak acid ionization occurs throughout the titration to the equivalence point.

18-26. (a) The solution being titrated is 25.0 ml of 0.100 M KOH. Initially, $[OH^-] = 0.100$; pOH = 1.00 and *pH = 13.00*. At the equivalence point the solution contains the neutral salt KI; *pH = 7.00*. The volume of 0.200 M HI required to neutralize the base is *12.5 ml*. Because the pH changes so rapidly at the equivalence point, many different indicators may be used in the titration--all of those in Figure 18-2 except alizarin yellow R.

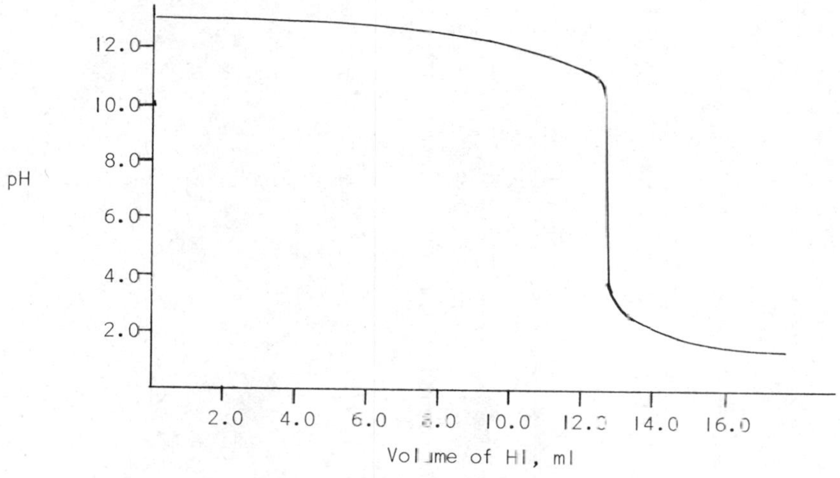

(b) The solution being titrated is 10.0 ml of 1.00 M NH_3.

Initial pH: $K_b = \frac{[NH_4^+][OH^-]}{[NH_3]} = \frac{x^2}{1.00} = 1.74 \times 10^{-5}$ $\qquad x = [OH^-] = 4.17 \times 10^{-3}$

pOH = 2.38 $\qquad$ pH = 11.62

Volume of titrant: no. ml acid = $0.0100 \text{ L} \times \frac{1.00 \text{ mol } NH_3}{1 \text{ L}} \times \frac{1 \text{ mol HCl}}{1 \text{ mol } NH_3} \times \frac{1 \text{ L acid}}{0.250 \text{ mol HCl}}$

$\times \frac{1000 \text{ ml acid}}{1 \text{ L acid}} = 40.0 \text{ ml acid}$

pH at the equivalence point: The volume of 0.250 M HCl required for the titration is 40.0 ml. At this point, 0.0100 mol NH_4Cl is present in 50.00 ml of solution. The molarity of NH_4Cl is 0.0100/0.0500 = 0.200 M NH_4Cl. The pH at the equivalence point is determined by the hydrolysis of NH_4^+.

$$NH_4^+ + H_2O \rightleftharpoons NH_3 + H_3O^+$$

$$K_h = \frac{[H_3O^+][NH_3]}{[NH_4^+]} = \frac{x \cdot x}{0.200} = \frac{K_w}{K_b} = \frac{1.0 \times 10^{-14}}{1.74 \times 10^{-5}} = 5.7 \times 10^{-10}$$

$x^2 = 1.14 \times 10^{-10}$ $\qquad x = [H_3O^+] = 1.07 \times 10^{-5}$ $\qquad$ pH = 4.97

Selection of indicator: The indicator chosen should undergo a color change at pH ≃ 5. Methyl orange and brom cresol green should be satisfactory.

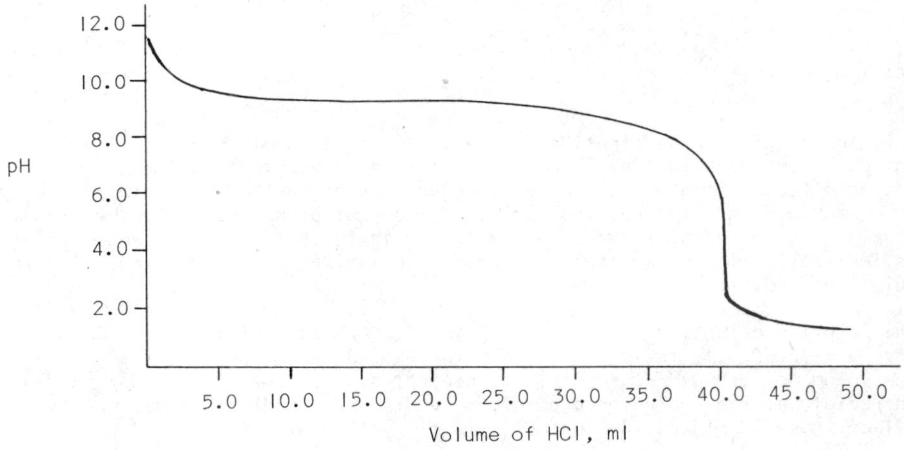

18-27. The initial pH in each case is derived as follows:

$[H_3O^+]^2/0.100 = K_a$ $\qquad [H_3O^+] = (0.100\ K_a)^{1/2}$ $\qquad pH = -\log [H_3O^+]$

The pH at the midpoint of each titration is pH = pK_a.

At the equivalence point the solutions are 0.05 M in the salts, NaX, NaY, and NaZ, respectively. For the hydrolysis of these salts,

$[OH^-]^2 = 0.05 \times K_h = 0.05 \times K_w/K_a$ and $[OH^-] = (0.05\ K_w/K_a)^{1/2}$

pOH = $-\log [OH^-]$ and pH = 14.00 - pOH.

0.100 M HX

initial pH = 2.00

midpoint of titration: $pH = pK_a = -\log(1 \times 10^{-3}) = 3.00$

equivalence point: $[OH^-] = (0.05 \times 1 \times 10^{-14}/1 \times 10^{-3})^{1/2} = 7.1 \times 10^{-7}$ M

$pOH = 6.15 \qquad pH = 14.00 - 6.15 = 7.85$

0.100 M HY

initial pH = 3.00

midpoint of titration: $pH = -\log(1 \times 10^{-5}) = 5.00$

equivalence point: $[OH^-] = (0.05 \times 1 \times 10^{-14}/1 \times 10^{-5})^{1/2} = 7.1 \times 10^{-6}$ M

$pOH = 5.15 \qquad pH = 14.00 - 5.15 = 8.85$

0.100 M HZ

initial pH = 4.00

midpoint of titration: $pH = -\log(1 \times 10^{-7}) = 7.00$

equivalence point: $[OH^-] = (0.05 \times 1 \times 10^{-14}/1 \times 10^{-7})^{1/2} = 7.1 \times 10^{-5}$ M

$pOH = 4.15 \qquad pH = 14.00 - 4.15 = 9.85$

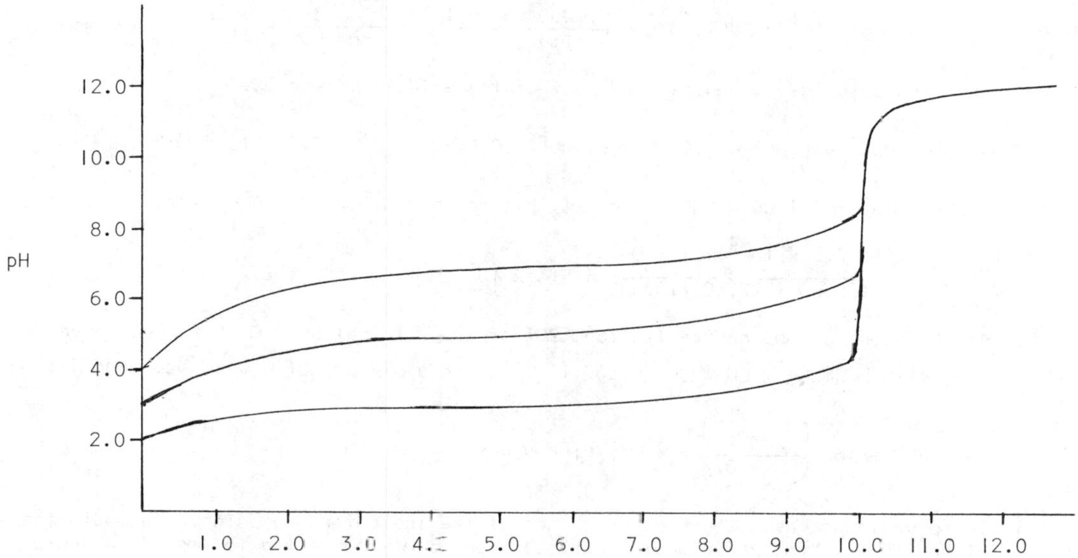

18-28. Refer to Figure 18-5. The first equivalence point corresponds to the conversion of H_3PO_4 to NaH_2PO_4. The volume of 0.0200 M NaOH required is

$$\text{no. ml} = 0.0100 \text{ L} \times \frac{0.0400 \text{ mol } H_3PO_4}{\text{L}} \times \frac{1 \text{ mol NaOH}}{1 \text{ mol } H_3PO_4} \times \frac{1 \text{ L}}{0.0200 \text{ mol NaOH}} \times \frac{1000 \text{ ml}}{1 \text{ L}} = 20 \text{ ml}$$

Present in the solution at the first equivalence point is 4.00×10^{-4} mol NaH_2PO_4 produced by neutralizing the H_3PO_4, *plus* 1.50×10^{-4} mol NaH_2PO_4 present initially. Thus, to reach the second equivalence point, 5.50×10^{-4} mol $H_2PO_4^-$ must be converted to HPO_4^{2-}. The required volume of NaOH, which will be greater than that for the first equivalence point, is

$$\text{no. ml} = 5.50 \times 10^{-4} \text{ mol } H_2PO_4^- \times \frac{\text{mol NaOH}}{1 \text{ mol } H_2PO_4^-} \times \frac{1 \text{ L}}{0.0200 \text{ mol NaOH}} \times \frac{1000 \text{ ml}}{1 \text{ L}} = 27.5 \text{ ml}$$

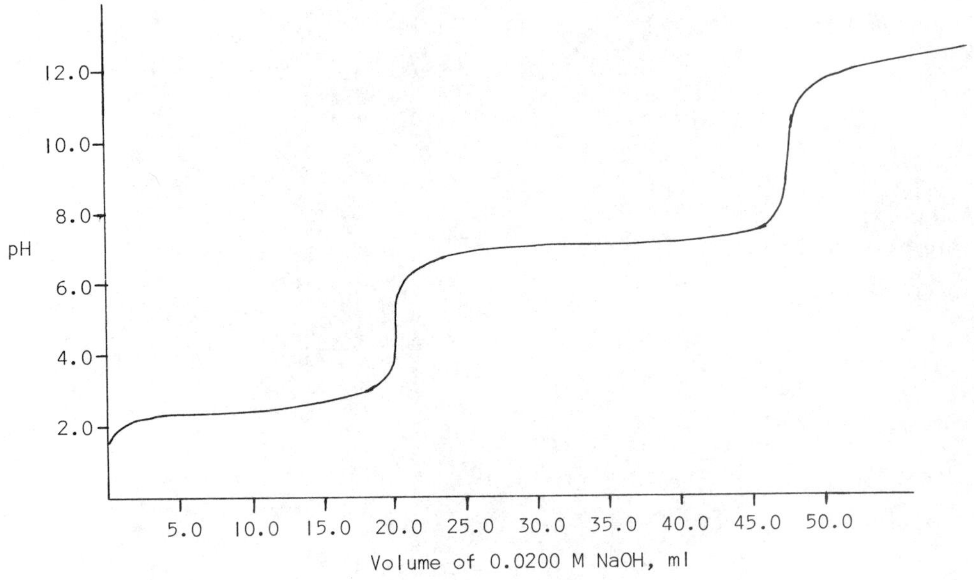

18-29. (a) tot. no. mol $H_3O^+ = 0.02500\ L \times \frac{0.1000\ mol\ HCl}{1.00\ L} \times \frac{1\ mol\ H_3O^+}{1\ mol\ HCl} = 2.500 \times 10^{-3}\ mol\ H_3O^+$

When the acid is 90% neutralized, 10% of the acid is unreacted.

no. mol H_3O^+ unreacted $= 0.10 \times 2.500 \times 10^{-3}\ mol\ H_3O^+ = 2.5 \times 10^{-4}\ mol\ H_3O^+$

The volume of 0.1000 M NaOH added at this point = 0.90 x 25.00 ml = 22.50 ml.

$[H_3O^+] = \frac{2.5 \times 10^{-4}\ mol\ H_3O^+}{[(25.00 + 22.50)/1000]L} = 5.3 \times 10^{-3}\ M$ pH = 2.28

(b) At the point of 90% neutralization, 90% of the original $HC_2H_3O_2$ has been converted to $C_2H_3O_2^-$. The ratio $[C_2H_3O_2^-]/[HC_2H_3O_2]$ is 9:1 = 9. For a mixture of a weak acid and its salt,

$$pH = pK_a + \log \frac{[C_2H_3O_2^-]}{[HC_2H_3O_2]} = 4.76 + \log 9 = 5.71$$

18-30. (a) There would not be a sharp color change at the indicator end point. As indicated in Figure 18-2, thymol blue would have been completely converted to its yellow color before the sharp rise in pH at the equivalence point.

(b) Let the no. ml 0.1000 M NaOH added to reach pH = 2 be x. The number of moles of H_3O^+ unreacted at this point would be 0.02500 x 0.1000 mol H_3O^+ (initially) - $(x/1000) \times 0.1000$ mol H_3O^+ (reacted) $= 2.500 \times 10^{-3} - (1.000 \times 10^{-4})x$.

The volume of solution, in liters, would be $(25.00 + x)/1000$. If pH = 2.00,

$[H_3O^+] = 1.00 \times 10^{-2}$ M. Therefore, $[H_3O^+] = \frac{2.500 \times 10^{-3} - (1.000 \times 10^{-4})x}{(25.00 + x)/1000} = 0.0100$

$2.500 - 0.1000x = 0.2500 + 0.0100x$ $0.1100x = 2.250$ $x = 20.46$ ml 0.1000 M NaOH

For complete neutralization of the HCl, 25.00 ml 0.1000 M NaOH is required. At the point where 20.46 ml has been added, 20.46/25.00 = 0.8184 (81.84%) of the acid has been neutralized. The percent unneutralized = 100.00 - 81.84 = 18.16%.

18-31. (a) Review the solution to part (b) of Exercise 30. In a similar fashion let x = no. ml 0.1000 M NaOH required to reach a pH = 3.00.

$$[H_3O^+] = \frac{2.500 \times 10^{-3} - (1.000 \times 10^{-4})x}{(25.00 + x)/1000} = 0.00100$$

$2.500 - 0.1000x = 0.02500 + 0.00100x \qquad 0.1010x = 2.475 \qquad x = 24.50$ ml 0.1000 M NaOH

(b) Use the equation $pH = pK_a + \log \frac{[C_2H_3O_2^-]}{[HC_2H_3O_2]}$ and solve for the ratio $[C_2H_3O_2^-]/[HC_2H_3O_2]$.

$$pH = 4.76 + \log\frac{[C_2H_3O_2^-]}{[HC_2H_3O_2]} = 5.25 \qquad \log\frac{[C_2H_3O_2^-]}{[HC_2H_3O_2]} = 5.25 - 4.76 = 0.49 \qquad \frac{[C_2H_3O_2^-]}{[HC_2H_3O_2]} = 3.1$$

If at this point $[HC_2H_3O_2] = x$, $[C_2H_3O_2^-] = 3.1x$ and the total acetate concentration = $4.1x$

$$\text{Fraction neutralized} = \frac{[C_2H_3O_2^-]}{\text{total acetate}} = \frac{3.1x}{4.1x} = 0.76$$

For complete neutralization, 25.00 ml 0.1000 M NaOH is required. To reach a pH = 5.25, 0.76 × 25.00 = 19.0 ml 0.1000 M NaOH is required.

(c) When the pH of the solution is 7.50, the titration is that of NaH_2PO_4 being converted to Na_2HPO_4. This occurs in the range from 10.00 to 20.00 ml 0.1000 M NaOH. As in part (b), determine the ratio $[HPO_4^{2-}]/[H_2PO_4^-]$.

$$pH = pK_{a_2} + \log\frac{[HPO_4^{2-}]}{[H_2PO_4^-]} = -\log(6.2 \times 10^{-8}) + \log\frac{[HPO_4^{2-}]}{[H_2PO_4^-]} = 7.50$$

$$\log\frac{[HPO_4^{2-}]}{[H_2PO_4^-]} = 7.50 - 7.21 = 0.29 \qquad [HPO_4^{2-}]/[H_2PO_4^-] = 1.95$$

If at this point $[H_2PO_4^-] = x$, $[HPO_4^{2-}] = 1.95x$ and the total phosphate concentration is $2.95x$.

$$\text{Fraction neutralized} = \frac{[HPO_4^{2-}]}{\text{total phosphate}} = \frac{1.95x}{2.95x} = 0.661$$

For complete conversion of $H_2PO_4^-$ to HPO_4^{2-}, 10.00 ml 0.1000 M NaOH is required. To reach a pH = 7.50, 0.661 × 10.00 = 6.61 ml 0.1000 M NaOH is required, *in addition to* the 10.00 ml required to reach the first equivalence point. Total volume = 16.61 ml.

Solubility and pH

18-32. (a) A mixture of 2×10^{-3} M HI and 2×10^{-3} M NaI is a mixture of a strong acid and its salt. It has $[I^-] = 4 \times 10^{-3}$ M. $[Pb^{2+}] = 1 \times 10^{-3}$ M

$Q = [Pb^{2+}][I^-]^2 = (1 \times 10^{-3})(4 \times 10^{-3})^2 = 16 \times 10^{-9} > 7.1 \times 10^{-9}$ (K_{sp})

Precipitation of $PbI_2(s)$ should occur.

(b) Addition of 1 drop (0.05 ml) 1.00 M NH_3 to 2.50 L of an aqueous solution yields

$$[NH_3] = \frac{0.05 \text{ ml} \times \frac{1.00 \text{ L}}{1000 \text{ ml}} \times \frac{1.00 \text{ mol } NH_3}{1.00 \text{ L}}}{2.50 \text{ L}} = 2 \times 10^{-5} \text{ M}$$

Next, determine $[OH^-]$ in this weak base solution

$$NH_3 + H_2O \rightleftharpoons NH_4^+ + OH^-$$

	NH_3		NH_4^+	OH^-
dissolve:	2×10^{-5} M			
changes:	$-x$ M		$+x$ M	$+x$ M
equil. conc:	$(2 \times 10^{-5} - x)$M		x M	x M

$$K_b = \frac{[NH_4^+][OH^-]}{[NH_3]} = \frac{x \cdot x}{2 \times 10^{-5} - x} = 1.74 \times 10^{-5}$$

Because the solution is so dilute in NH_3, the assumption that $x << 2 \times 10^{-5}$ is probably not valid.

$$x^2 + (1.74 \times 10^{-5})x - 3.48 \times 10^{-10} = 0$$

$$x = \frac{-1.74 \times 10^{-5} \pm \sqrt{(1.74 \times 10^{-5})^2 + 4 \times 3.48 \times 10^{-10}}}{2} = 1.2 \times 10^{-5}$$

$$Q = [Mg^{2+}][OH^-]^2 = (0.0150)(1.2 \times 10^{-5})^2 = 2.2 \times 10^{-12} < 2 \times 10^{-11} \; (K_{sp})$$

$Mg(OH)_2(s)$ will not precipitate under these conditions.

(c) Determine the pH of the $HC_2H_3O_2$ - $NaC_2H_3O_2$ buffer solution.

$$pH = pK_a + \log \frac{[C_2H_3O_2^-]}{[HC_2H_3O_2]} = 4.76 + \log \frac{0.010}{0.010} = 4.76$$

Then determine $[OH^-]$ in the solution. $pOH = 14.00 - pH = 14.00 - 4.76 = 9.24$

$\log [OH^-] = -9.24 = 0.76 - 10.00$ $\qquad [OH^-] = 5.8 \times 10^{-10}$ M

$$Q = [Al^{3+}][OH^-]^3 = (1.0 \times 10^{-2})(5.8 \times 10^{-10})^3 = 2.0 \times 10^{-30} > 1.3 \times 10^{-33} \; (K_{sp})$$

$Al(OH)_3(s)$ should precipitate.

18-33. In the saturated solution $[Mg^{2+}][OH^-]^2 = K_{sp} = 2 \times 10^{-11}$

From the solubility value given:

$$[Mg^{2+}] = \frac{1.00 \text{ g } Mg(OH)_2 \times \frac{1 \text{ mol } Mg(OH)_2}{58.3 \text{ g } Mg(OH)_2} \times \frac{1 \text{ mol } Mg^{2+}}{1 \text{ mol } Mg(OH)_2}}{1.00 \text{ L}} = 0.0172 \text{ M}$$

$(0.0172)[OH^-]^2 = 2 \times 10^{-11}$ $\qquad [OH^-] = 3 \times 10^{-5}$ $\qquad pOH = 4.5$ $\qquad pH = 14.00 - 4.5 = 9.5$

18-34. (a) no. mol $NH_3 = 0.350 \text{ L} \times \frac{0.100 \text{ mol } NH_3}{1 \text{ L}} = 0.0350$ mol NH_3 $\qquad [NH_3] = \frac{0.0350 \text{ mol } NH_3}{0.500 \text{ L}} = 0.0700$ M

$$K_b = \frac{[NH_4^+][OH^-]}{[NH_3]} = \frac{x \cdot x}{7.00 \times 10^{-2}} = 1.74 \times 10^{-5} \qquad x^2 = 1.22 \times 10^{-6} \qquad x = [OH^-] = 1.10 \times 10^{-3} \text{ M}$$

$$\text{no. mol } Mg^{2+} = 0.150 \text{ L} \times \frac{0.100 \text{ mol } MgCl_2}{1 \text{ L}} \times \frac{1 \text{ mol } Mg^{2+}}{1 \text{ mol } MgCl_2} = 1.50 \times 10^{-2} \text{ mol } Mg^{2+}$$

$$[Mg^{2+}] = \frac{1.50 \times 10^{-2} \text{ mol } Mg^{2+}}{0.500 \text{ L}} = 3.0 \times 10^{-2} \text{ M}$$

$$[Mg^{2+}][OH^-]^2 = (3.0 \times 10^{-2}) \times (1.10 \times 10^{-3})^2 = 4 \times 10^{-8} > 2 \times 10^{-11}$$

$Mg(OH)_2$ precipitates under these conditions.

(b) To redissolve the precipitate of $Mg(OH)_2$ requires reducing $[OH^-]$ by adding NH_4^+.

$[Mg^{2+}][OH^-]^2 = (3.0 \times 10^{-2})[OH^-]^2 = 2 \times 10^{-11}$

$[OH^-]^2 = 6.7 \times 10^{-10}$ $\qquad$ $[OH^-] = 2.6 \times 10^{-5}$

$$K_b = \frac{[NH_4^+][OH^-]}{[NH_3]} = \frac{[NH_4^+] \times 2.6 \times 10^{-5}}{7.0 \times 10^{-2}} = 1.74 \times 10^{-5} \qquad [NH_4^+] = 4.7 \times 10^{-2}\ M$$

$$\text{no. g } (NH_4)_2SO_4 = 0.500\ L \times \frac{4.7 \times 10^{-2}\ \text{mol } NH_4^+}{1\ L} \times \frac{1\ \text{mol } (NH_4)_2SO_4}{2\ \text{mol } NH_4^+} \times \frac{132\ \text{g } (NH_4)_2SO_4}{1\ \text{mol } (NH_4)_2SO_4}$$

$= 1.6\ \text{g } (NH_4)_2SO_4$

18-35. Our first calculation must be of $[OH^-]$ in the buffer solution. Then we can form an ion product expression and compare it with K_{sp}.

$$K_a = \frac{[H_3O^+][C_2H_3O_2^-]}{[HC_2H_3O_2]} = \frac{[H_3O^+] \times 0.150}{0.50} = 1.74 \times 10^{-5}$$

$[H_3O^+] = 5.8 \times 10^{-5}$ $\qquad$ $[OH^-] = 1.0 \times 10^{-14}/5.8 \times 10^{-5} = 1.7 \times 10^{-10}$

$[Fe^{3+}][OH^-]^3 = (0.25) \times (1.7 \times 10^{-10})^3 = 1.2 \times 10^{-30} > 6 \times 10^{-38}$

Precipitation of $Fe(OH)_3$ *does* occur.

18-36. (a)

$$CaHPO_4(s) \rightleftharpoons Ca^{2+}(aq) + HPO_4^{2-}(aq)$$

Dissolve $\quad$ *S* mol/L $\longrightarrow$ *S* mol/L $\quad$ *S* mol/L

$K_{sp} = [Ca^{2+}][HPO_4^{2-}] = (S)(S) = 1 \times 10^{-7}$ $\qquad$ $S = 3 \times 10^{-4}$ mol $CaHPO_4$/L

Expressed as g $CaHPO_4 \cdot 2\ H_2O$/L, the calculated solubility is:

$$\text{no. g } CaHPO_4 \cdot 2\ H_2O/L = \frac{3 \times 10^{-4}\ \text{mol } CaHPO_4}{1.00\ L} \times \frac{1\ \text{mol } CaHPO_4 \cdot 2\ H_2O}{1\ \text{mol } CaHPO_4} \times \frac{172\ \text{g } CaHPO_4 \cdot 2\ H_2O}{1\ \text{mol } CaHPO_4 \cdot 2\ H_2O}$$

$= 0.05\ \text{g } CaHPO_4 \cdot 2\ H_2O/L$

These data do not appear to be consistent with one another. The solubility based on K_{sp} is 0.05 g/L and the actual observed solubility is 0.32 g/L.

(b) Several factors may be involved in accounting for this discrepancy. The K_{sp} calculation assumes that HPO_4^{2-} is the only phosphate species, when, in fact, some HPO_4^{2-} hydrolyzes to $H_2PO_4^-$ (and a very small quantity ionizes further to PO_4^{3-}). Also, some ion pair formation might occur ($Ca^{2+})(HPO_4^{2-}$). All of these factors would lead to a greater observed solubility than that calculated from K_{sp}.

18-37. Combine the two equilibrium expressions and obtain a value of K

$$Mg(OH)_2(s) \rightleftharpoons Mg^{2+}(aq) + 2\ OH^-(aq); \quad K_{sp} = 1.8 \times 10^{-11}$$

$$2\ NH_4^+(aq) + 2\ OH^-(aq) \rightleftharpoons 2\ NH_3(aq) + 2\ H_2O; \quad 1/K^2 = 1/(1.74 \times 10^{-5})^2$$

$$Mg(OH)_2(s) + 2\ NH_4^+(aq) \rightleftharpoons Mg^{2+}(aq) + 2\ NH_3(aq) + 2\ H_2O$$

$$K = \frac{1.8 \times 10^{-11}}{(1.74 \times 10^{-5})^2} = 5.9 \times 10^{-2}$$

Let the molar solubility of $Mg(OH)_2 = S$

$$Mg(OH)_2(s) + 2\ NH_4^+(aq) \rightleftharpoons Mg^{2+}(aq) + 2\ NH_3(aq) + 2\ H_2O$$

	NH_4^+	Mg^{2+}	NH_3
initial:	1.00 M		
changes:	$-2S$ M	$+S$ M	$+2S$ M
equil:	$(1.00 - 2S)$M	S M	$2S$ M

$$K = \frac{[Mg^{2+}][NH_3]^2}{[NH_4^+]^2} = \frac{S \times (2S)^2}{(1.00 - 2S)^2} = 5.9 \times 10^{-2}$$

$4S^3 = 5.9 \times 10^{-2}\ (1.00 - 4S + 4S^2)$ $\qquad S^3 - 0.059S^2 + 0.059S - 1.5 \times 10^{-2} = 0$

Solve by successive approximations:

Try $S = 0.20$: $8.0 \times 10^{-3} - 2.4 \times 10^{-3} + 1.2 \times 10^{-2} - 1.5 \times 10^{-2} = 2.6 \times 10^{-3} > 0$

Try $S = 0.19$: $6.9 \times 10^{-3} - 2.1 \times 10^{-3} + 1.1 \times 10^{-2} - 1.5 \times 10^{-2} = 8 \times 10^{-4} > 0$

Try $S = 0.18$: $5.8 \times 10^{-3} - 1.9 \times 10^{-3} + 1.1 \times 10^{-2} - 1.5 \times 10^{-2} = -1 \times 10^{-4} < 0$

The molar solubility is 0.18 mol $Mg(OH)_2$/L.

Precipitation and solubilities of metal sulfides

18-38. The appropriate relationship to use in this problem is equation (18.31). That is, in a solution saturated in H_2S (0.10 M H_2S),

$[H_3O^+]^2[S^{2-}] = 1.1 \times 10^{-22}$ $\qquad$ If pH = 3.5, $\log [H_3O^+] = -3.5 = 0.50 - 4.00$

$[H_3O^+] = 3.2 \times 10^{-4}$ $\qquad (3.2 \times 10^{-4})^2[S^{2-}] = 1.1 \times 10^{-22}$ $\qquad [S^{2-}] = 1.1 \times 10^{-15}$

$[Fe^{2+}][S^{2-}] = (2.0 \times 10^{-3})(1.1 \times 10^{-15}) = 2.2 \times 10^{-18} < 3.0 \times 10^{-17}$

FeS *will not* precipitate from this solution.

18-39. If ZnS is to be kept from precipitating, $[Zn^{2+}][S^{2-}] < K_{sp}$.

$(1 \times 10^{-3}) \times [S^{2-}] < 1 \times 10^{-21}$ $\qquad [S^{2-}] < 1 \times 10^{-18}$

Substitute into equation (18.31) and solve for $[H_3O^+]$. (Note that $[H_2S] = 0.10$ M.)

$[H_3O^+]\ [S^{2-}] = 1.1 \times 10^{-22}$ $\qquad [H_3O^+]^2 \times 1 \times 10^{-18} = 1.1 \times 10^{-22}$ $\qquad [H_3O^+]^2 = 1.1 \times 10^{-4}$

$[H_3O^+] = 1.05 \times 10^{-2}$ $\qquad pH = -\log (1.05 \times 10^{-2}) = 2.0$

If pH < 2.0, $[S^{2-}] < 1 \times 10^{-18}$ and ZnS *will not* precipitate.

18-40. The first step in this solution is to calculate $[Pb^{2+}]$ in saturated $PbCl_2(aq)$. Let $[Pb^{2+}]$ in this solution = x; $[Cl^-] = 2x$.

$[Pb^{2+}][Cl^-]^2 = (x)(2x)^2 = 4x^3 = 1.6 \times 10^{-5}$ $\qquad x^3 = 4.0 \times 10^{-6}$ $\qquad x = [Pb^{2+}] = 1.6 \times 10^{-2}$

Next, calculate $[S^{2-}]$. Since the solution is saturated in H_2S, use equation (18.31) with $[H_2S] = 0.10$ M.

$$[H_3O^+][S^{2-}] = 1.1 \times 10^{-22}$$

The value of $[H_3O^+]$ is determined from the pH.

$$pH = 0.5 \qquad \log [H_3O^+] = -0.50 = 0.50 - 1.00 \qquad [H_3O^+] = 3.2 \times 10^{-1}$$

Now we are in a position to calculate $[S^{2-}]$ in the solution.

$$(3.2 \times 10^{-1})^2 \times [S^{2-}] = 1.1 \times 10^{-22} \qquad [S^{2-}] = 1.1 \times 10^{-21}$$

Finally, compare the ion product expression and K_{sp} for PbS.

$$[Pb^{2+}][S^{2-}] = (1.6 \times 10^{-2}) \times (1.1 \times 10^{-21}) = 1.8 \times 10^{-23} > 8.0 \times 10^{-28}$$

PbS *does* precipitate under the conditions described here.

18-41. Following the hint given in the exercise, first solve for pH and $[H_3O^+]$ in the buffer solution.

$$pH = pK_a + \log \frac{[C_2H_3O_2^-]}{[HC_2H_3O_2]} = 4.76 + \log \frac{0.250}{0.500} = 4.76 - 0.30 = 4.46$$

$$\log [H_3O^+] = -4.46 = 0.54 - 5.00 \qquad [H_3O^+] = 3.5 \times 10^{-5} \text{ M}$$

$[H_3O^+]$ is assumed to remain constant in the following reaction:

$$FeS(s) + 2\ H_3O^+(aq) \rightleftharpoons Fe^{2+}(aq) + H_2S(aq) + 2\ H_2O$$

To obtain K for this reaction proceed in the same fashion as was used to establish equation (18.34) in the text. The result obtained is:

$$K = \frac{K_{sp}}{K_{a_1} \times K_{a_2}} = \frac{6.3 \times 10^{-18}}{1.1 \times 10^{-21}} = 5.7 \times 10^3$$

Let the molar solubility of FeS(s) = $[Fe^{2+}] = [H_2S(aq)] = S$

$$K = \frac{[Fe^{2+}][H_2S]}{[H_3O^+]^2} = \frac{S \times S}{(3.5 \times 10^{-5})^2} = 5.7 \times 10^3 \qquad S^2 = 7.0 \times 10^{-6} \qquad S = 2.6 \times 10^{-3} \text{ M}$$

$$\text{no. g FeS/L} = \frac{2.6 \times 10^{-3} \text{ mol FeS}}{1.00 \text{ L}} \times \frac{87.9 \text{ g FeS}}{1 \text{ mol FeS}} = 0.23 \text{ g FeS/L}$$

18-42. The three equilibrium expressions referred to in the exercise are

$$CoS(s) \rightleftharpoons Co^{2+}(aq) + S^{2-}(aq); \quad K_{sp} = 4 \times 10^{-21}$$

$$S^{2-}(aq) + 2\ H_3O^+(aq) \rightleftharpoons H_2S(aq) + 2\ H_2O; \quad K = 1/(K_{a_1} \times K_{a_2}) = 1/(1.1 \times 10^{-21})$$

$$2\ HC_2H_3O_2(aq) + 2\ H_2O \rightleftharpoons 2\ H_3O^+(aq) + 2\ C_2H_3O_2^-(aq); \quad K = K_a^2 = (1.74 \times 10^{-5})^2$$

$$CoS(s) + 2\ HC_2H_3O_2(aq) \rightleftharpoons Co^{2+}(aq) + 2\ C_2H_3O_2^-(aq) + H_2S(aq)$$

$$K = \frac{K_{sp}\ (K_a)^2}{K_{a_1} \times K_{a_2}} = \frac{4 \times 10^{-21} \times (1.74 \times 10^{-5})^2}{1.1 \times 10^{-21}} = 1.1 \times 10^{-9}$$

Let the molar solubility of CoS = $[Co^{2+}] = S$. Assume $[HC_2H_3O_2]$ remains constant at 0.100 M.

$$K = \frac{[Co^{2+}][C_2H_3O_2^-]^2[H_2S]}{[HC_2H_3O_2]^2} = \frac{S \times (2S)^2 \times S}{(0.100)^2} = \frac{4S^4}{(0.100)^2} = 1.1 \times 10^{-9}$$

$S^4 = 2.8 \times 10^{-12}$ $\qquad S^2 = 1.7 \times 10^{-6}$ $\qquad S = 1.3 \times 10^{-3}$

The molar solubility of CoS in 0.100 M $HC_2H_3O_2$ is 1.3×10^{-3} mol CoS/L.

Net ionic equations

18-43. (a) $\cancel{NH_4^+} + C_2H_3O_2^- + H_3O^+ + \cancel{I^-} \rightleftharpoons HC_2H_3O_2 + \cancel{NH_4^+} + \cancel{I^-} + H_2O$

(b) $Na^+ + I^- + Zn^{2+} + SO_4^{2-} \longrightarrow$ no reaction

(c) $\cancel{Na^+} + HPO_4^{2-} + H_2O \rightleftharpoons \cancel{Na^+} + H_2PO_4^- + OH^-$

This hydrolysis reaction is more significant than the further ionization of HPO_4^{2-}.

(d) $NH_4^+ + \cancel{NO_3^-} + \cancel{Ba^{2+}} + OH^- \rightleftharpoons NH_3 + H_2O + \cancel{Ba^{2+}} + \cancel{NO_3^-}$

(e) $Al(OH)_3(s) + 3\ HC_2H_3O_2(aq) \longrightarrow Al^{3+}(aq) + 3\ C_2H_3O_2^-(aq) + 3\ H_2O$

(f) $\cancel{Na^+} + C_3H_5O_2^- + H_3O^+ + \cancel{Br^-} \rightleftharpoons HC_3H_5O_2 + H_2O + \cancel{Na^+} + \cancel{Br^-}$

(g) $HNO_2(aq) + H_3O^+ + Cl^- \longrightarrow$ no reaction

(h) $NH_3(aq) + H_2CO_3(aq) \longrightarrow NH_4^+(aq) + HCO_3^-(aq)$

18-44. (a) $Cu^{2+}(aq) + H_2S(\text{satd. aq}) \longrightarrow CuS(s) + 2\ H^+(aq)$

The $[S^{2-}]$ in saturated $H_2S(aq)$ is large enough that K_{sp} for CuS is greatly exceeded.

(b) $Mg^{2+}(aq) + H_2S(\text{satd. aq}) \xrightarrow{0.3\ M\ HCl}$ no reaction

MgS is soluble. It does not precipitate as a sulfide anywhere in the qualitative analysis scheme. It remains with the alkali metal ions in the soluble group.

(c) $PbS(s) + HCl(0.3\ M) \longrightarrow$ no reaction.
PbS is essentially insoluble in 0.3 M HCl. In the qualitative analysis scheme Pb^{2+} is precipitated as PbS in an acidic solution (approx. 0.3 M HCl).

(d) $2\ Ag^+(aq) + H_2S(\text{satd. aq}) \xrightarrow{0.3\ M\ HCl} Ag_2S(s) + 2\ H^+$

Ag^+ is precipitated as the chloride prior to the treatment of cations with $H_2S(aq)$ in the qualitative analysis scheme. Nevertheless, reference to Table 16-1 indicates that Ag_2S is highly insoluble ($K_{sp} = 6.3 \times 10^{-50}$) and should surely precipitate from 0.30 M HCl - 0.10 M H_2S, where $[S^{2-}] \simeq 1.0 \times 10^{-22}$ M.

18-45. (a) Two possible precipitates come to mind: $CaHPO_4$ or $Ca_3(PO_4)_2$. Determine the % Ca in each.

$$\% \text{ Ca} = \frac{40.1 \text{ g Ca}}{136 \text{ g CaHPO}_4} \times 100 = 29.5\% \text{ Ca} \qquad \% \text{ Ca} = \frac{(3 \times 40.1)\text{g Ca}}{310 \text{ g Ca}_3(\text{PO}_4)_2} \times 100 = 38.8\% \text{ Ca}$$

The product of the reaction in question is $Ca_3(PO_4)_2(s)$

$$2\ HPO_4^{2-} + 2\ H_2O \rightleftharpoons 2\ H_3O^+ + 2\ PO_4^{3-}$$

$$+$$

$$3\ Ca^{2+}$$

$$\downarrow$$

$$Ca_3(PO_4)_2(s)$$

(b) *white precipitate formation:*

$$H_2O + CO_2(g) \rightleftharpoons \cancel{H_2CO_3(aq)}$$

$$Ca^{2+}(aq) + 2\ OH^-(aq) + \cancel{H_2CO_3(aq)} \longrightarrow CaCO_3(s) + 2\ H_2O$$

$$\text{net: } Ca^{2+}(aq) + 2\ OH^-(aq) + H_2O + CO_2(g) \longrightarrow CaCO_3(s) + 2\ H_2O$$

redissolving of precipitate:

$$H_2O + CO_2(g) \rightleftharpoons \cancel{H_2CO_3(aq)}$$

$$\cancel{H_2CO_3(aq)} + \cancel{H_2O} \rightleftharpoons \cancel{H_3O^+(aq)} + HCO_3^-(aq)$$

$$CaCO_3(s) + \cancel{H_3O^+(aq)} \longrightarrow Ca^{2+}(aq) + HCO_3^-(aq) + \cancel{H_2O}$$

$$\text{net: } CaCO_3(s) + H_2O + CO_2(g) \longrightarrow Ca^{2+}(aq) + 2\ HCO_3^-(aq)$$

Applications of various equilibrium principles

18-46. (a) $pH = pK_a + \log \frac{[C_2H_3O_2^-]}{[HC_2H_3O_2]} = 4.76 + \log \frac{0.050}{[HC_2H_3O_2]} = 4.22$ $\qquad \log \frac{0.050}{[HC_2H_3O_2]} = 4.22 - 4.76 = -0.54$

$\frac{0.050}{[HC_2H_3O_2]} = 0.29$ $\qquad [HC_2H_3O_2] = 0.050/0.29 = 0.17$ M

(b) $pOH = 14.00 - pH = 14.00 - 12.65 = 1.35$ $\qquad pOH = -\log [OH^-]$

$\log [OH^-] = -1.35 = 0.65 - 2.00$ $\qquad [OH^-] = 4.47 \times 10^{-2}$ M

$$\frac{\text{no. mol Ba(OH)}_2}{\text{L}} = \frac{4.47 \times 10^{-2} \text{ mol OH}^-}{\text{L}} \times \frac{1 \text{ mol Ba(OH)}_2}{2 \text{ mol OH}^-} = \frac{2.24 \times 10^{-2} \text{ mol Ba(OH)}_2}{\text{L}}$$

(c) $K_b = \frac{[C_6H_5NH_3^+][OH^-]}{[C_6H_5NH_2]} = 4.30 \times 10^{-10}$ $\qquad$ If pH = 8.95, pOH = 5.05 and $[OH^-] = 8.9 \times 10^{-6}$

$\frac{(8.9 \times 10^{-6})(8.9 \times 10^{-6})}{[C_6H_5NH_2]} = 4.30 \times 10^{-10}$ $\qquad [C_6H_5NH_2] = 0.18$ M

(d) pH = 5.5 $[H_3O^+] = 3.2 \times 10^{-6}$ M

$$NH_4^+ + H_2O \rightleftharpoons H_3O^+ + NH_3 \quad ; \quad K_h = K_w/K_b$$

	NH_4^+	H_3O^+	NH_3
dissolve:	x M		
changes:	-3.2×10^{-6} M	$+3.2 \times 10^{-6}$ M	$+3.2 \times 10^{-6}$ M
equil:	$(x - 3.2 \times 10^{-6})$M	3.2×10^{-6} M	3.2×10^{-6} M

$$K_h = \frac{[H_3O^+][NH_3]}{[NH_4^+]} = \frac{(3.2 \times 10^{-6})^2}{(x - 3.2 \times 10^{-6})} \simeq \frac{(3.2 \times 10^{-6})^2}{x} = \frac{1.0 \times 10^{-14}}{1.74 \times 10^{-5}} = 5.7 \times 10^{-10}$$

$x = [NH_4^+] = 1.8 \times 10^{-2} = 0.018$ M NH_4Cl

18-47. (a) If $[NH_3] = 0.10$ M, $[NH_4^+] = 0.10$ M, $[H_3O^+] = 1 \times 10^{-5}$, and $[OH^-] = 1 \times 10^{-9}$

$$\frac{[NH_4^+][OH^-]}{[NH_3]} = \frac{(1 \times 10^{-1}) \times (1 \times 10^{-9})}{(1 \times 10^{-1})} = 1 \times 10^{-9} \neq K_b = 1.74 \times 10^{-5}$$

Thus, these ion concentrations cannot coexist in aqueous solution.

(b) There is no way that this equilibrium constant expression can be satisfied unless some $HC_2H_3O_2$ is formed.

$$\frac{[H_3O^+][C_2H_3O_2^-]}{[HC_2H_3O_2]} = K_a = 1.74 \times 10^{-5}$$

The solution cannot remain with $[H_3O^+] = 0.20$ M (from the HI) and $[C_2H_3O_2^-] = 0.10$ M (from the $NaC_2H_3O_2$).

(c) No reaction occurs in an aqueous solution containing K^+, Na^+, Cl^-, and NO_3^-. The solution can be simultaneously 0.10 M KCl and 0.50 M $NaNO_3$.

(d) We must answer the question: "Will a precipitate form in a solution with $[Pb^{2+}] = 1 \times 10^{-3}$ M and $[CrO_4^{2-}] = 1 \times 10^{-4}$ M?"

$$[Pb^{2+}][CrO_4^{2-}] = (1 \times 10^{-3})(1 \times 10^{-4}) = 1 \times 10^{-7} \gg K_{sp} = 2.8 \times 10^{-13}$$

A precipitate does form, so the indicated ion concentrations cannot coexist in aqueous solution.

(e) Here the question is: "Will $Mg(OH)_2$ precipitate from a solution with $[Mg^{2+}] = 1.00$ M, pH = 8.0, pOH = 6.0, and $[OH^-] = 1 \times 10^{-6}$?"

$$[Mg^{2+}][OH^-]^2 = 1.00 \times (1 \times 10^{-6})^2 = 1 \times 10^{-12} < K_{sp} = 2 \times 10^{-11}$$

A precipitate does not form; a stable solution can exist with the indicated ion concentrations.

18-48. (a) $HC_2H_3O_2(aq) + H_2O \rightleftharpoons H_3O^+(aq) + C_2H_3O_2^-(aq)$

high conc. high low

This represents the common ion effect on adding a strong acid to a weak acid.

(b) $HC_2H_3O_2(aq) + H_2O \rightleftharpoons H_3O^+(aq) + C_2H_3O_2^-(aq)$

very low conc. very low high

This is the result we would expect for the hydrolysis of $C_2H_3O_2^-$ ($[H_3O^+]$ is so low that the solution is actually basic.)

(c) $HC_2H_3O_2(aq) + H_2O \rightleftharpoons H_3O^+(aq) + C_2H_3O_2^-(aq)$

high conc. low low

This combination of concentrations would result from the ionization of pure $HC_2H_3O_2$ in water.

(d) $HC_2H_3O_2(aq) + H_2O \rightleftharpoons H_3O^+(aq) + C_2H_3O_2^-(aq)$

high conc. low high

This is the situation that prevails in a buffer solution. A salt of the weak acid represses ionization of the weak acid.

Equivalent weight and normality concentration

18-49. (a) $HClO_4$: equiv. wt. = mol. wt. = 100.5

(b) $Mg(OH)_2$: equiv. wt. = 1/2(mol. wt.) = 1/2(58.3) = 29.2

(c) $HC_3H_5O_2$: equiv. wt. = mol. wt. = 74.1

18-50. From the information given about the reaction of CO_3^{2-} and H^+ we see that for Na_2CO_3 or $Na_2CO_3 \cdot 10\ H_2O$, equiv. wt. = 1/2 f. wt.; equiv. wt. $Na_2CO_3 \cdot 10\ H_2O$ = 1/2(286.2) = 143.1

$$\text{no. equiv.} = 2.00\ \text{L} \times \frac{0.175\ \text{equiv. } Na_2CO_3}{1.00\ \text{L}} \times \frac{1\ \text{equiv. } Na_2CO_3 \cdot 10\ H_2O}{1\ \text{equiv. } Na_2CO_3} \times \frac{143.1\ \text{g } Na_2CO_3 \cdot 10\ H_2O}{1\ \text{equiv. } Na_2CO_3 \cdot 10\ H_2O}$$

$$= 50.1\ \text{g } Na_2CO_3 \cdot 10\ H_2O$$

18-51. (a) 0.24 M KOH = 0.24 N KOH

(b) 0.001 M HI = 0.001 N HI

(c) 2.0×10^{-3} M $Ca(OH)_2$ = 4.0×10^{-3} N $Ca(OH)_2$

(d) 0.15 M H_3PO_4 = 0.15 N H_3PO_4 (based on first ionization step only)

= 0.30 N H_3PO_4 (if ionization occurs through two steps)

= 0.45 N H_3PO_4 (if ionization proceeds through third step)

(e) 0.01 M C_6H_5COOH = 0.01 N C_6H_5COOH (only the H atom bonded to an O atom is ionizable)

18-52. Assume that the solution density is approximately 1.00 g/ml, so that the solubility can be expressed as 3.89 g $Ba(OH)_2$ per 100 ml or 38.9 g $Ba(OH)_2$/L.

$$\text{molar concentration} = \frac{38.9\ \text{g } Ba(OH)_2}{1.00\ \text{L}} \times \frac{1\ \text{mol } Ba(OH)_2}{171\ \text{g } Ba(OH)_2} = 0.23\ \text{M}$$

For $Ba(OH)_2$, normality = 2 × molarity = 0.46 N

18-53. $V_{NaOH} \times N_{NaOH} = V_{H_2SO_4} \times N_{H_2SO_4}$ $V_{NaOH} \times 0.115 = 10.00\ \text{ml} \times 0.188$

$$V_{NaOH} = \frac{0.188}{0.115} \times 10.00\ \text{ml} = 16.3\ \text{ml}$$

18-54. The volume of NaOH given is that required for titration to the second equivalence point. To the first equivalence point, the volume required is 31.15/2 = 15.58 ml.

For use in reaction (18.39), $N_{H_3PO_4} = \dfrac{15.58 \text{ ml} \times 0.242 \text{ mequiv/ml}}{25.00 \text{ ml}} = 0.151 \text{ mequiv/ml} = 0.151 \text{ N}$

For use in reaction (18.40), $N_{H_3PO_4} = 2 \times 0.151 = 0.302 \text{ N}$

For use in reaction (18.41), $N_{H_3PO_4} = 3 \times 0.151 = 0.453 \text{ N}$

18-55. $\text{no. g } H_2SO_4 \text{ in sample titrated} = 0.03240 \text{ L} \times \dfrac{0.0100 \text{ equiv Ba(OH)}_2}{1.00 \text{ L}} \times \dfrac{1 \text{ equiv } H_2SO_4}{1 \text{ equiv Ba(OH)}_2}$

$\times \dfrac{49.0 \text{ g } H_2SO_4}{1 \text{ equiv } H_2SO_4} = 0.0159 \text{ g } H_2SO_4$

The sample titrated (10.00 ml) is only a portion of the total solution prepared (250.0 ml).

$\text{total g } H_2SO_4 = \dfrac{0.0159 \text{ g } H_2SO_4}{10.00 \text{ ml}} \times 250.0 \text{ ml} = 0.398 \text{ g } H_2SO_4$

This mass of H_2SO_4 was derived from 1.239 g battery acid.

$\% \; H_2SO_4, \text{ by mass} = \dfrac{0.398 \text{ g } H_2SO_4}{1.239 \text{ g battery acid}} \times 100 = 32.1\% \; H_2SO_4$

Self-test Questions

1. (*c*) The amount of HCl present is 0.50 mol. Adding a weak acid ($HC_2H_3O_2$) to a strong acid (HCl) will not affect the pH of the strong acid. Adding only 0.40 mol NaOH will also not affect the pH significantly, since this will leave 0.10 mol of the acid as free acid. Addition of NaCl will have no effect on the pH of HCl. The addition of 0.60 mol $NaC_2H_3O_2$ converts the strong acid to 0.50 mol $HC_2H_3O_2$ and leaves an excess of 0.10 mol of $NaC_2H_3O_2$. The pH of this $HC_2H_3O_2$ - $NaC_2H_3O_2$ buffer solution will be several units higher (about 3-4) than that of 0.50 M HCl.

2. (*b*) KNO_3 would have essentially no effect on the NH_3 - NH_4^+ equilibrium. Neither would $BaSO_4(s)$ since it is insoluble. The addition of H_3O^+ would convert NH_3 to NH_4^+. To convert NH_4^+ to NH_3 add OH^- ($NH_4^+ + OH^- \longrightarrow NH_3 + H_2O$). This can be accomplished by raising the pH.

3. (*b*) Indicators are weak acids that function in a pH range of about two units with the center of the range being at pH = pK_a(indicator). If K_a for the indicator is 1×10^{-9}, $pK_a = 9$.

4. (*d*) In the neutralization of a weak acid by a strong base, a buffer solution is produced, with $pH = pK_a + \log \frac{[A^-]}{[HA]}$. If the acid is one-half neutralized, $[A^-] = [HA]$, $\log [A^-]/[HA] = 0$, and $pH = pK_a$.

5. (*a*) The solubility of $CaCO_3(s)$ can be increased by increasing H_3O^+ in a solution. This occurs through reactions such as $CO_3^{2-} + H_3O^+ \longrightarrow HCO_3^- + H_2O$ and $HCO_3^- + H_3O^+ \longrightarrow H_2CO_3 + H_2O$ and $H_2CO_3 \longrightarrow H_2O + CO(g)$. The only one of the species listed that has acidic properties is $NaHSO_4$.

6. (*c*) $[H_2S]$ in a solution cannot be raised beyond its saturation limit--0.10 M. Heating a solution will simply expel $H_2S(g)$ and not promote more complete precipitation. The need is to increase $[S^{2-}]$. $H_2S + H_2O \rightleftharpoons H_3O^+ + HS^-$ and $HS^- + H_2O \longrightarrow H_3O^+ + S^{2-}$. By adding OH^- both of these equilibria are shifted to the right. $[S^{2-}]$ increases and the metal ion concentration decreases, ensuring more complete precipitation. The pH must be raised.

7. If the solid has acidic properties, it will be more soluble in basic solution. Solids with basic properties (e.g., carbonates, hydroxides, and sulfides) are more soluble in acidic solution.

more soluble in acidic solution: $MgCO_3$, CdS, $Ca(OH)_2$

more soluble in basic solution: $H_2C_2O_4$

solubility independent of pH: KCl, $NaNO_3$

8. (a) Use the equation $pH = pK_a + \log \frac{[CHO_2^-]}{[HCHO_2]}$ and solve for $[CHO_2^-]$.

$$3.90 = -\log(1.8 \times 10^{-4}) + \log \frac{[CHO_2^-]}{0.650} \qquad 3.90 = 3.74 + \log \frac{[CHO_2^-]}{0.650}$$

$$\log \frac{[CHO_2^-]}{0.650} = 3.90 - 3.74 = 0.16 \qquad \frac{[CHO_2^-]}{0.650} = 1.45 \qquad [CHO_2^-] = 0.942\ M$$

$$\text{no. g } NaCHO_2 = 0.500\ L \times \frac{0.942\ \text{mol } NaCHO_2}{1.00\ L} \times \frac{68.0\ g\ NaCHO_2}{1\ \text{mol } NaCHO_2} = 32.0\ g\ NaCHO_2$$

(b) The concentration of OH^- being added to the buffer solution is:

$$[OH^-] = \frac{0.20\ g\ NaOH \times \frac{1\ \text{mol NaOH}}{40.0\ g\ NaOH} \times \frac{1\ \text{mol } OH^-}{1\ \text{mol NaOH}}}{0.500\ L} = 0.010\ M$$

	$HCHO_2$	+	OH^-	$\longrightarrow$	CHO_2^-	+	H_2O
original:	0.650 M				0.942 M		
add:			0.010 M				
changes:	-0.010 M		-0.010 M		+0.010 M		
equil:	0.640 M		≈ 0		0.952 M		

$$pH = 3.74 + \log \frac{0.952}{0.640} = 3.74 + \log 1.49 = 3.74 + 0.17 = 3.91$$

9. (a) $K_a = \frac{[H_3O^+][C_7H_5O_2^-]}{[HC_7H_5O_2]} = \frac{[H_3O^+]^2}{0.0100} = 6.3 \times 10^{-5} \qquad [H_3O^+]^2 = 6.3 \times 10^{-7}$

$[H_3O^+] = 7.9 \times 10^{-4}$ M $\qquad$ pH = 3.10

(b) no. mol $HC_7H_5O_2$ = 0.0250 L × 0.0100 mol/L = 2.50×10^{-4} mol

no. mol OH^- added = 0.00625 L × 0.0200 mol OH^-/L = 1.25×10^{-4} mol OH^-

no. mol $HC_7H_5O_2$ reacted = 1.25×10^{-4} mol

no. mol $HC_7H_5O_2$ unreacted = 2.50×10^{-4} mol - 1.25×10^{-4} mol = 1.25×10^{-4} mol

$[HC_7H_5O_2] = 1.25 \times 10^{-4}$ mol/(0.0250 + 0.00625)L = 4.0×10^{-3} M

$[C_7H_5O_2^-] = [HC_7H_5O_2]$ (since the acid is half neutralized).

$$pH = -\log (6.3 \times 10^{-5}) + \log \frac{[C_7H_5O_2^-]}{[HC_7H_5O_2]} = 4.20 + \log 1.0 = 4.20$$

(c) At the equivalence point there is present 2.50×10^{-4} mol $NaC_7H_5O_2$ in (25.0 + 12.5) = 37.5 ml.

$$[C_7H_5O_2^-] = \frac{2.50 \times 10^{-4}\ \text{mol}}{0.0375\ \text{L}} = 6.67 \times 10^{-3}\ \text{M}$$

In the hydrolysis reaction $C_7H_5O_2^- + H_2O \rightleftharpoons HC_7H_5O_2 + OH^-$,

$$K_h = \frac{[HC_7H_5O_2][OH^-]}{[C_7H_5O_2^-]} = \frac{[OH^-]^2}{6.67 \times 10^{-3}} = \frac{1.0 \times 10^{-14}}{6.3 \times 10^{-5}} = 1.6 \times 10^{-10} \qquad [OH^-]^2 = 1.1 \times 10^{-12}$$

$[OH^-] = 1.0 \times 10^{-6}$ M pOH = 6.00 pH = 8.00

(d) The addition of 15.00 ml 0.0100 M $Ba(OH)_2$ introduces no. mol OH^- = 0.01500 L × 0.0200 mol OH^-/L = 3.00×10^{-4} mol OH^-; excess mol OH^- = $(3.00 \times 10^{-4}) - (2.50 \times 10^{-4}) = 0.50 \times 10^{-4}$ mol OH^-; soln. volume = 40.00 ml = 0.0400 L.

$$[OH^-] = \frac{0.50 \times 10^{-4}\ \text{mol } OH^-}{0.0400\ \text{L}} = 1.2 \times 10^{-3} \qquad pOH = 2.92 \qquad pH = 11.08$$

10. $pH = -\log (1.74 \times 10^{-5}) + \log \frac{[C_2H_3O_2^-]}{[HC_2H_3O_2]} = 4.76 + \log \frac{0.15}{0.25} = 4.76 - 0.22 = 4.54$

$[H_3O^+] = 2.9 \times 10^{-5}$ M

$$K_{a_1} \times K_{a_2} = \frac{[H_3O^+]^2[S^{2-}]}{[H_2S]} = \frac{(2.9 \times 10^{-5})^2[S^{2-}]}{0.10} = 1.1 \times 10^{-21} \qquad [S^{2-}] = 1.3 \times 10^{-13}\ \text{M}$$

(a) $Q = [Mn^{2+}][S^{2-}] = (0.015)(1.3 \times 10^{-13}) = 2.0 \times 10^{-15} < 2.5 \times 10^{-13} (K_{sp})$

MnS will not precipitate.

(b) To just precipitate MnS: $[S^{2-}] = 2.5 \times 10^{-13}/0.015 = 1.7 \times 10^{-11}$ M

$$\frac{[H_3O^+]^2(1.7 \times 10^{-11})}{0.10} = 1.1 \times 10^{-21} \qquad [H_3O^+]^2 = 6.5 \times 10^{-12} \qquad [H_3O^+] = 2.5 \times 10^{-6}$$

pH = 5.60

To raise the pH of the buffer, increase $[C_2H_3O_2^-]$.

$$pH = 4.76 + \log \frac{[C_2H_3O_2^-]}{[HC_2H_3O_2]} = 4.76 + \log \frac{[C_2H_3O_2^-]}{0.25} = 5.60 \qquad \log \frac{[C_2H_3O_2^-]}{0.25} = 0.84$$

$$\frac{[C_2H_3O_2^-]}{0.25} = 6.9 \qquad [C_2H_3O_2^-] = 1.7\ \text{M}$$

Chapter 19

Oxidation-Reduction and Electrochemistry

Definitions and terminology

19-1. (a) In an oxidation process some element undergoes an increase in oxidation state as a result of a substance losing electrons. In a reduction process a substance gains electrons and an element undergoes a decrease in its oxidation state.

(b) An oxidizing agent gains the electrons lost in an oxidation process; it is reduced. A reducing agent loses electrons and is itself oxidized, thereby making possible a reduction process.

(c) A half-reaction refers either to an oxidation or reduction process. When oxidation and reduction half reactions are combined, a net reaction results.

(d) A voltaic (galvanic) cell produces electricity as a result of a spontaneous oxidation-reduction reaction occurring in an electrochemical cell. In an electrolytic cell a non-spontaneous reaction is produced by the use of electricity.

(e) An anode is an electrode in an electrochemical cell at which oxidation occurs. Reduction occurs at a cathode.

(f) E_{cell} is the electromotive force associated with an oxidation-reduction reaction occurring in an electrochemical cell. If the reactants and products are in their standard states, the value is E°_{cell}.

Balancing oxidation-reduction equations

19-2. (a) *reduction:* $S_2O_8^{2-} + 2e^- \longrightarrow 2\ SO_4^{2-}$

(b) *reduction:* $2\ NO_3^- + 10\ H^+ + 8\ e^- \longrightarrow N_2O + 5\ H_2O$

(c) *oxidation:* $CH_4 + 2\ H_2O \longrightarrow CO_2 + 8\ H^+ + 8\ e^-$

(d) *oxidation:* $Br^- + 6\ OH^- \longrightarrow BrO_3^- + 3\ H_2O + 6\ e^-$

(e) *reduction:* $NO_3^- + 6\ H_2O + 8\ e^- \longrightarrow NH_3 + 9\ OH^-$

19-3. (a) *oxid:* $3\{Cu(s) \longrightarrow Cu^{2+} + 2\ e^-\}$

red: $2\{NO_3^- + 4\ H^+ + 3\ e^- \longrightarrow NO(g) + 2\ H_2O\}$

net: $3\ Cu(s) + 8\ H^+ + 2\ NO_3^- \longrightarrow 3\ Cu^{2+} + 2\ NO(g) + 4\ H_2O$

(b) *oxid:* $4\{Zn(s) \longrightarrow Zn^{2+} + 2\ e^-\}$

red: $NO_3^- + 10\ H^+ + 8\ e^- \longrightarrow NH_4^+ + 3\ H_2O$

net: $4\ Zn(s) + 10\ H^+ + NO_3^- \longrightarrow 4\ Zn^{2+} + NH_4^+ + 3\ H_2O$

(c) *oxid:* $5\{H_2O_2 \longrightarrow O_2(g) + 2\,H^+ + 2\,e^-\}$

red: $2\{MnO_4^- + 8\,H^+ + 5\,e^- \longrightarrow Mn^{2+} + 4\,H_2O\}$

net: $5\,H_2O_2 + 2\,MnO_4^- + 6\,H^+ \longrightarrow 2\,Mn^{2+} + 8\,H_2O + 5\,O_2(g)$

(d) *oxid:* $3\{C_8H_{16}O \longrightarrow C_8H_{14}O + 2\,H^+ + 2\,e^-\}$

red: $Cr_2O_7^{2-} + 14\,H^+ + 6\,e^- \longrightarrow 2\,Cr^{3+} + 7\,H_2O$

net: $3\,C_8H_{16}O + Cr_2O_7^{2-} + 8\,H^+ \longrightarrow 3\,C_8H_{14}O + 2\,Cr^{3+} + 7\,H_2O$

(e) *oxid:* $3\{As_2S_3(s) + 8\,H_2O \longrightarrow 2\,H_3AsO_4 + 3\,S(s) + 10\,H^+ + 10\,e^-\}$

red: $10\{NO_3^- + 4\,H^+ + 3\,e^- \longrightarrow NO(g) + 2\,H_2O\}$

net: $3\,As_2S_3(s) + 10\,H^+ + 10\,NO_3^- + 4\,H_2O \longrightarrow 6\,H_3AsO_4 + 10\,NO + 9\,S$

(f) *oxid:* $Cl_2(g) + 2\,H_2O \longrightarrow 2\,ClO^- + 4\,H^+ + 2\,e^-$

red: $Cl_2(g) + 2\,e^- \longrightarrow 2\,Cl^-$

net: $2\,Cl_2(g) + 2\,H_2O \longrightarrow 2\,ClO^- + 2\,Cl^- + 4\,H^+$

or $Cl_2(g) + H_2O \longrightarrow ClO^- + Cl^- + 2\,H^+$

or $Cl_2(g) + H_2O \longrightarrow HOCl + Cl^- + H^+$

(HOCl is a weak acid that exists mostly in the nonionized form in acidic solution.)

19-4. (a) *oxid:* $Br_2 + 12\,OH^- \longrightarrow 2\,BrO_3^- + 6\,H_2O + 10\,e^-$

red: $5\{Br_2(l) + 2\,e^- \longrightarrow 2\,Br^-\}$

net: $6\,Br_2(l) + 12\,OH^- \longrightarrow 10\,Br^- + 2\,BrO_3^- + 6\,H_2O$

or $3\,Br_2(l) + 6\,OH^- \longrightarrow 5\,Br^- + BrO_3^- + 3\,H_2O$

(b) *oxid:* $N_2H_4(g) + 4\,OH^- \longrightarrow N_2(g) + 4\,H_2O + 4\,e^-$

red: $4\{[Fe(CN)_6]^{3-} + e^- \longrightarrow [Fe(CN)_6]^{4-}\}$

net: $4\,[Fe(CN)_6]^{3-} + N_2H_4 + 4\,OH^- \longrightarrow 4\,[Fe(CN)_6]^{4-} + N_2 + 4\,H_2O$

(c) *oxid:* $As_2S_3(s) + 40\,OH^- \longrightarrow 2\,AsO_4^{3-} + 3\,SO_4^{2-} + 20\,H_2O + 28\,e^-$

red: $14\{H_2O_2 + 2\,e^- \longrightarrow 2\,OH^-\}$

net: $As_2S_3 + 12\,OH^- + 14\,H_2O_2 \longrightarrow 2\,AsO_4^{3-} + 20\,H_2O + 3\,SO_4^{2-}$

d) *oxid:* $2\{CrI_3(s) + 32\,OH^- \longrightarrow CrO_4^{2-} + 3\,IO_4^- + 16\,H_2O + 27\,e^-\}$

red: $27\{H_2O_2 + 2\,e^- \longrightarrow 2\,OH^-\}$

net: $2\,CrI_3 + 27\,H_2O_2 + 10\,OH^- \longrightarrow 2\,CrO_4^{2-} + 6\,IO_4^- + 32\,H_2O$

(e) *oxid:* $3\{P_4(s) + 8\ OH^- \longrightarrow 4\ H_2PO_2^- + 4\ e^-\}$

red: $P_4(s) + 12\ H_2O + 12\ e^- \longrightarrow 4\ PH_3(g) + 12\ OH^-$

net: $4\ P_4 + 12\ OH^- + 12\ H_2O \longrightarrow 12\ H_2PO_2^- + 4\ PH_3$

or $P_4 + 3\ OH^- + 3\ H_2O \longrightarrow 3\ H_2PO_2^- + PH_3$

19-5. (a) $Cl_2(g) + H_2O(g) \longrightarrow HCl(g) + O_2(g)$

gain $1e^-$/Cl

loss 2 e^-/O

$2\ Cl_2(g) + 2\ H_2O(g) \longrightarrow 4\ HCl(g) + O_2(g)$

(b) $PbO(s) + NH_3(g) \longrightarrow Pb(s) + N_2(g) + H_2O(g)$

gain 2 e^-/Pb

loss 3 e^-/N

$3\ PbO(s) + 2\ NH_3(g) \longrightarrow 3\ Pb(s) + N_2(g) + 3\ H_2O$

(c) $Cu(s) + H^+ + NO_3^- \longrightarrow Cu^{2+} + H_2O + NO(g)$

loss 2 e^-/Cu

gain 3 e^-/N

$3\ Cu(s) + 8\ H^+ + 2\ NO_3^- \longrightarrow 3\ Cu^{2+} + 4\ H_2O + 2\ NO(g)$

(d) $Zn(s) + H^+ + NO_3^- \longrightarrow Zn^{2+} + H_2O + N_2O(g)$

loss 2 e^-/Zn

gain 4 e^-/N

$4\ Zn(s) + 10\ H^+ + 2\ NO_3^- \longrightarrow 4\ Zn^{2+} + 5\ H_2O + N_2O(g)$

(e) $MnO_4^- + NO_2^- + H^+ \longrightarrow Mn^{2+} + NO_3^- + H_2O$

gain 5 e^-/Mn

loss 2 e^-/N

$2\ MnO_4^- + 5\ NO_2^- + 6\ H^+ \longrightarrow 2\ Mn^{2+} + 5\ NO_3^- + 3\ H_2O$

19-6. Various possibilities exist for balancing these equations. We will use the ion-electron (half-reaction) method for those in which ionic species are shown. For the other equations we will use the oxidation state change method.

(a) $(NH_4)_2Cr_2O_7(s) \longrightarrow Cr_2O_3(s) + N_2(g) + H_2O(g)$

loss 3 e^-/N

gain 3 e^-/Cr

N and Cr atoms are balanced above—two atoms of each on both sides. To balance the remainder requires finding a coefficient for $H_2O(g)$.

$(NH_4)_2Cr_2O_7(s) \longrightarrow Cr_2O_3(s) + N_2(g) + 4\ H_2O(g)$

(b) *oxid:* $S_2O_3^{2-} + 5\ H_2O \longrightarrow 2\ SO_4^{2-} + 10\ H^+ + 8\ e^-$

red: $4\{Cl_2(g) + 2\ e^- \longrightarrow 2\ Cl^-\}$

net: $S_2O_3^{2-} + 4\ Cl_2(g) + 5\ H_2O \longrightarrow 2\ SO_4^{2-} + 10\ H^+ + 8\ Cl^-$

(c) *oxid:* $3\{CN^- + 2\ OH^- \longrightarrow CNO^- + H_2O + 2\ e^-\}$

red: $2\{MnO_4^- + 2\ H_2O + 3\ e^- \longrightarrow MnO_2(s) + 4\ OH^-\}$

net: $3\ CN^- + 2\ MnO_4^- + H_2O \longrightarrow 3\ CNO^- + 2\ MnO_2(s) + 2\ OH^-$

(d) $Fe_2S_3(s) + H_2O + O_2(g) \longrightarrow Fe(OH)_3(s) + S(s)$

gain $2\ e^-$/O

loss $2\ e^-$/S

$2\ Fe_2S_3(s) + 6\ H_2O + 3\ O_2(g) \longrightarrow 4\ Fe(OH)_3(s) + 6\ S(s)$

(e) *oxid:* $3\{C_2H_5OH + 5\ OH^- \longrightarrow C_2H_3O_2^- + 4\ H_2O + 4\ e^-\}$

red: $4\{MnO_4^- + 2\ H_2O + 3\ e^- \longrightarrow MnO_2(s) + 4\ OH^-\}$

net: $3\ C_2H_5OH + 4\ MnO_4^- \longrightarrow 3\ C_2H_3O_2^- + 4\ MnO_2(s) + OH^- + 4\ H_2O$

(f) $CS_2(g) + H_2S(g) + Cu(s) \longrightarrow Cu_2S(s) + CH_4(g)$

loss $1\ e^-$/Cu

gain $8\ e^-$/C

$CS_2(g) + 2\ H_2S(g) + 8\ Cu(s) \longrightarrow 4\ Cu_2S(s) + CH_4(g)$

(g) *oxid:* $3\{P(s) + 4\ H_2O \longrightarrow H_2PO_4^- + 6\ H^+ + 5\ e^-\}$

red: $5\{NO_3^- + 4\ H^+ + 3\ e^- \longrightarrow NO(g) + 2\ H_2O\}$

net: $3\ P(s) + 5\ NO_3^- + 2\ H_2O + 2\ H^+ \longrightarrow 3\ H_2PO_4^- + 5\ NO(g)$

Oxidizing and reducing agents

19-7.

	oxidizing agent	*reducing agent*
(19.5)	$Ag^+(aq)$	$Cu(s)$
(19.6)	$MnO_4^-(aq)$	$SO_3^{2-}(aq)$
(19.11)	$Cu^{2+}(aq)$	$Zn(s)$
(19.18)	$Cu^{2+}(aq)$	$H_2(g)$
(19.25)	$Cu^{2+}(aq)$	$Al(s)$
(19.37)	$Ag^+(aq)$	$Fe^{2+}(aq)$
(19.43)	$PbO_2(s)$	$Pb(s)$
(19.52)	$MnO_4^-(aq)$	$Fe^{2+}(aq)$
(19.53)	$MnO_4^-(aq)$	$C_2O_4^{2-}(aq)$

19-8. The power of an oxidizing agent is measured by the magnitude of the standard electrode potential for its reduction. For example, consider $F_2(g) + 2\ e^- \longrightarrow 2\ F^-(aq)$ with $E° = +2.87$ V and $I_2(s) + 2\ e^- \longrightarrow 2\ I^-(aq)$ with $E° = +0.54$ V. Fluorine is a better oxidizing agent than iodine. For the species listed, the order is: $Na^+(aq) < Zn^{2+}(aq) < I_2(s) < IO_3^-(aq) < PbO_2(s) < F_2(g)$.

19-9. Oxidizing agents only: $Cr_2O_7^{2-}$, Al^{3+} Reducing agents only: Zn, S^{2-}

Either an oxidizing agent or a reducing agent: H_2SO_3, I_2, S

Standard electrode potentials

19-10. Combine the known electrode potential for the reduction of dichromate ion with the unknown potential for the oxidation of palladium to obtain the measured cell potential for the oxidation-reduction reaction.

$$3\ Pd \longrightarrow 3\ Pd^{2+} + 6\ e^- \qquad E^\circ_{ox} = -E^\circ_{red}$$

$$Cr_2O_7^{2-} + 14\ H^+ + 6\ e^- \longrightarrow 2\ Cr^{3+} + 7\ H_2O \qquad E^\circ_{red} = +1.33\ V$$

$$3\ Pd + Cr_2O_7^{2-} + 14\ H^+ \longrightarrow 3\ Pd^{2+} + 2\ Cr^{3-} + 7\ H_2O \qquad E^\circ_{cell} = +0.34\ V$$

$$-E^\circ_{red} + 1.33\ V = +0.34\ V \qquad E^\circ_{red} = 1.33\ V - 0.34\ V = +0.99\ V$$

19-11. (a) Because the metal does not dissolve in HCl(aq), its standard reduction potential must be positive. The metal displaces silver ion, so the reduction potential must be less than +0.799 V. It does not displace copper ion, so its reduction potential must be greater than +0.337 V. For the reduction process, $M^{2+}(aq) + 2\ e^- \longrightarrow M(s)$, $+0.337 < E^\circ < +0.799$ V.

(b) Because the metal dissolves in HCl(aq), its standard reduction potential must be negative. The fact that it displaces neither zinc ion ($E^\circ = -0.763$ V) nor ferrous ion ($E^\circ = -0.440$ V) means that $-0.440 < E^\circ < 0.000$ V.

19-12. Arrange the available metal ion solutions in decreasing order of standard electrode potentials. Determine which metals indium displaces from solutions of their ions and which it does not. This will enable you to bracket the standard electrode potential between the known values of two other metals. For example, indium is found to displace Sn^{2+} but not Fe^{2+}. This suggests that for the reduction process, $In^{3+}(aq) + 3\ e^- \longrightarrow In(s)$, $-0.440 < E^\circ < -0.136$ V. (The tabulated value is -0.345 V.)

19-13. Consider the second reaction first. Express it as the sum of two half-reactions.

oxid: $V^{3+} + H_2O \longrightarrow VO^{2+} + 2\ H^+ + e^- \qquad E^\circ_{ox} = -E^\circ_{red} = ?$

red: $Ag^+ + e^- \longrightarrow Ag(s) \qquad E^\circ_{red} = +0.799\ V$

net: $V^{3+} + Ag^+ + H_2O \longrightarrow VO^{2+} + 2\ H^+ + Ag(s) \qquad E^\circ_{cell} = +0.439\ V$

$$E^\circ_{cell} = 0.799\ V - E^\circ_{red} = +0.439\ V \qquad E^\circ_{red} = 0.799 - 0.439 = +0.360\ V$$

Now write the first reaction as the sum of two half-reactions.

oxid: $V^{2+} \longrightarrow V^{3+} + e^- \qquad E^\circ_{ox} = -E^\circ_{red} = ?$

red: $VO^{2+} + 2\ H^+ + e^- \longrightarrow V^{3+} + H_2O \qquad E^\circ_{red} = +0.360\ V$

net: $V^{2+} + VO^{2+} + 2\ H^+ \longrightarrow 2\ V^{3+} + H_2O \qquad E^\circ_{cell} = +0.616\ V$

$$E^\circ_{cell} = 0.360\ V - E^\circ_{red} = 0.616\ V \qquad E^\circ_{red} = 0.360 - 0.616 = -0.256\ V$$

The standard electrode potential for the reduction process, $V^{3+} + e^- \longrightarrow V^{2+}$ is -0.256 V.

Predicting oxidation-reduction reactions

19-14. (a) *oxid:* $Sn(s) \longrightarrow Sn^{2+}(aq) + 2\,e^-$ $E^\circ_{ox} = -(-0.136) = +0.136$ V

red: $Zn^{2+}(aq) + 2\,e^- \longrightarrow Zn(s)$ $E^\circ_{red} = -0.763$ V

net: $Sn(s) + Zn^{2+}(aq) \longrightarrow Sn^{2+}(aq) + Zn(s)$ $E^\circ_{cell} = -0.627$

The reaction *does not* occur spontaneously as written.

(b) *oxid:* $2\,I^-(aq) \longrightarrow I_2(s) + 2\,e^-$ $E^\circ_{ox} = -(+0.54) = -0.54$ V

red: $2\,Fe^{3+}(aq) + 2\,e^- \longrightarrow 2\,Fe^{2+}(aq)$ $E^\circ_{red} = +0.771$ V

net: $2\,Fe^{3+}(aq) + 2\,I^-(aq) \longrightarrow 2\,Fe^{2+}(aq) + I_2(s)$ $E^\circ_{cell} = +0.23$ V

The reaction *does* occur as written.

(c) *oxid:* $6\,H_2O \longrightarrow 3\,O_2(g) + 12\,H^+ + 12\,e^-$ $E^\circ_{ox} = -(+1.229) = -1.229$ V

red: $4\,NO_3^-(aq) + 16\,H^+ + 12\,e^- \longrightarrow 4\,NO(g) + 8\,H_2O$ $E^\circ_{red} = +0.96$ V

net: $4\,NO_3^-(aq) + 4\,H^+ \longrightarrow 3\,O_2(g) + 4\,NO(g) + 2\,H_2O$ $E^\circ_{cell} = -0.27$ V

The reaction *does not* occur spontaneously as written.

(d) *oxid:* $2\,Cl^-(aq) + 4\,OH^- \longrightarrow 2\,ClO^-(aq) + 2\,H_2O + 4\,e^-$ $E^\circ_{ox} = -(+0.89)$ V

red: $O_2(g) + 2\,H_2O + 4\,e^- \longrightarrow 4\,OH^-(aq)$ $E^\circ_{red} = +0.401$ V

net: $O_2(g) + 2\,Cl^-(aq) \longrightarrow 2\,ClO^-(aq)$ $E^\circ_{cell} = -0.49$ V

The reaction *does not* occur spontaneously as written.

(e) *oxid:* $H_2O_2(aq) \longrightarrow O_2(g) + 2\,H^+ + 2\,e^-$ $E^\circ_{ox} = -(+0.682) = -0.682$ V

red: $H_2O_2(aq) + 2\,H^+ + 2\,e^- \longrightarrow 2\,H_2O$ $E^\circ_{red} = +1.77$ V

net: $2\,H_2O_2(aq) \longrightarrow 2\,H_2O + O_2(g)$ $E^\circ_{cell} = +1.09$ V

The reaction *does* occur as written.

19-15. In each of the following cases an equation is written to correspond to the proposed reaction. If $E^\circ_{cell} > 0$, the reaction does occur spontaneously as written.

(a) *oxid:* $Mg(s) \longrightarrow Mg^{2+}(aq) + 2\,e^-$ $E^\circ_{ox} = -(-2.37) = +2.37$ V

red: $Sn^{2+}(aq) + 2\,e^- \longrightarrow Sn(s)$ $E^\circ_{red} = -0.136$ V

net: $Mg(s) + Sn^{2+}(aq) \longrightarrow Mg^{2+}(aq) + Sn(s)$ $E^\circ_{cell} = 2.23$ V

The reaction *does* occur as written.

(b) *oxid:* $Pb(s) \longrightarrow Pb^{2+}(aq) + 2\,e^-$ $E^\circ_{ox} = -(-0.126) = +0.126$ V

red: $2\,H^+(aq) + 2\,e^- \longrightarrow H_2(g)$ $E^\circ_{red} = 0.000$ V

net: $Pb(s) + 2\,H^+(aq) \longrightarrow Pb^{2+}(aq) + H_2(g)$ $E^\circ_{cell} = +0.126$ V

Lead metal *will* dissolve in HCl(aq).

(c) *oxid:* $2\ Fe^{2+}(aq) \longrightarrow 2\ Fe^{3+}(aq) + 2\ e^-$ $\quad E^\circ_{ox} = -(+0.771) = -0.771$ V

red: $SO_4^{2-}(aq) + 4\ H^+ + 2\ e^- \longrightarrow H_2SO_3(aq) + H_2O$ $\quad E^\circ_{red} = +0.17$ V

net: $2\ Fe^{2+} + SO_4^{2-} + 4\ H^+ \longrightarrow 2\ Fe^{3+} + H_2SO_3 + H_2O$ $\quad E^\circ_{cell} = -0.60$ V

SO_4^{2-} *will not* oxidize Fe^{2+} to Fe^{3+} in acidic solution.

(d) *oxid:* $2\ Fe^{2+}(aq) \longrightarrow 2\ Fe^{3+} + 2\ e^-$ $\quad E^\circ_{ox} = -(+0.771) = -0.771$ V

red: $SO_4^{2-}(aq) + H_2O + 2\ e^- \longrightarrow SO_3^{2-}(aq) + 2\ OH^-(aq)$ $\quad E^\circ_{red} = -0.93$ V

net: $2\ Fe^{2+} + SO_4^{2-} + H_2O \longrightarrow 2\ Fe^{3+} + SO_3^{2-} + 2\ OH^-$ $\quad E^\circ_{cell} = -1.70$ V

SO_4^{2-} *will not* oxidize Fe^{2+} to Fe^{3+} in basic solution.

(e) *oxid:* $2\ I^-(aq) \longrightarrow I_2 + 2\ e^-$ $\quad E^\circ_{ox} = -(0.54) = -0.54$ V

red: $Cl_2(g) + 2\ e^- \longrightarrow 2\ Cl^-(aq)$ $\quad E^\circ_{red} = +1.360$ V

net: $Cl_2(g) + 2\ I^-(aq) \longrightarrow I_2 + 2\ Cl^-(aq)$ $\quad E^\circ_{cell} = +0.82$ V

$Cl_2(aq)$ *will* displace I^- from aqueous solution.

19-16. A reduction that can occur in aqueous solution, and which does occur more readily than the reduction of Mg^{2+}, is: $2\ H_2O + 2\ e^- \longrightarrow H_2(g) + 2\ OH^-$. Or, considered in another way, the favored reaction below is the one with the most positive value of E°_{cell}.

(1) $2\ Na(s) + Mg^{2+}(aq) \longrightarrow Mg(s) + 2\ Na^+(aq)$ $\quad E^\circ_{cell} = +0.34$ V

(2) $2\ Na(s) + 2\ H_2O \longrightarrow 2\ Na^+(aq) + 2\ OH^-(aq) + H_2(g)$ $\quad E^\circ_{cell} = +1.89$ V

19-17. (a) To dissolve in HCl(aq), Cu(s) would have to liberate $H_2(g)$. This is a reaction with $E^\circ_{cell} < 0$. It is *nonspontaneous*.

$Cu(s) + 2\ H^+(aq) \longrightarrow Cu^{2+}(aq) + H_2(g)$ $\quad E^\circ_{cell} = -0.34$ V

(b) The reduction half-reaction when Cu(s) is dissolved in $HNO_3(aq)$ is not the reduction of $H^+(aq)$ to $H_2(g)$, but the reduction of $NO_3^-(aq)$ to NO(g). The resulting oxidation-reduction has $E^\circ_{cell} > 0$. It is spontaneous.

oxid: $3\left\{Cu(s) \longrightarrow Cu^{2+}(aq) + 2\ e^-\right\}$ $\quad E^\circ_{ox} = -(+0.34) = -0.34$ V

red: $2\left\{NO_3^-(aq) + 4\ H^+ + 3\ e^- \longrightarrow 2\ H_2O + NO(g)\right\}$ $\quad E^\circ_{red} = +0.96$ V

net: $3\ Cu(s) + 2\ NO_3^- + 8\ H^+ \longrightarrow 3\ Cu^{2+} + 4\ H_2O + 2\ NO(g)$ $\quad E^\circ_{cell} = +0.62$ V

19-18. (a) If the strip of copper metal is weighed before and after the reaction, its mass is found to remain unchanged. Copper does not dissolve in HCl(aq).

(b) The reaction is $Zn(s) + 2\ H^+(aq) \longrightarrow Zn^{2-}(aq) + H_2(g)$.

(c) Electrons lost in the oxidation of zinc [$Zn(s) \longrightarrow Zn^{2+}(aq) + 2\ e^-$] are conducted to the copper metal, where hydrogen gas is evolved [$2\ H^+(aq) + 2\ e^- \longrightarrow H_2(g)$].

19-19. (a) No reaction would occur since neither copper nor silver can displace H_2 from an acid solution.

(b) Both metals can dissolve in $HNO_3(aq)$. The oxidizing agent is nitrate ion. Oxides of nitrogen (NO, NO_2), but no hydrogen, are produced.

$$3\,Cu(s) + 8\,H^+ + 2\,NO_3^- \longrightarrow 3\,Cu^{2+}(aq) + 4\,H_2O + 2\,NO(g) \qquad E^\circ_{cell} = +0.62\ V$$

$$3\,Ag(s) + 4\,H^+ + NO_3^- \longrightarrow 3\,Ag^+(aq) + 2\,H_2O + NO(g) \qquad E^\circ_{cell} = +0.16\ V$$

We should expect the dissolving of Cu to proceed more readily. Electrons from the copper are transferred to the Ag, where the reduction of NO_3^- occurs.

Voltaic (galvanic) cells

19-20. (anode) —electron flow→ (cathode)

(a) $Cu(s)\ |\ Cu^{2+}(aq)\ ||\ Fe^{2+}(aq),\ Fe^{3+}(aq)\ |\ Pt(s)$

oxid: $Cu(s) \longrightarrow Cu^{2+}(aq) + 2\,e^- \qquad E^\circ_{ox} = -0.337\ V$

red: $2\,\{Fe^{3+}(aq) + e^- \longrightarrow Fe^{2+}(aq)\} \qquad E^\circ_{red} = +0.771\ V$

net: $Cu(s) + 2\,Fe^{3+}(aq) \longrightarrow Cu^{2+}(aq) + 2\,Fe^{2+}(aq) \qquad E^\circ_{cell} = +0.434\ V$

(anode) —electron flow→ (cathode)

(b) $Pt\ |\ Sn^{2+}(aq),\ Sn^{4+}(aq)\ ||\ Cr^{3+}(aq),\ Cr_2O_7^{2-}(aq)\ |\ Pt$

oxid: $3\,\{Sn^{2+}(aq) \longrightarrow Sn^{4+}(aq) + 2\,e^-\} \qquad E^\circ_{ox} = -0.15\ V$

red: $Cr_2O_7^{2-}(aq) + 14\,H^+ + 6\,e^- \longrightarrow 2\,Cr^{3+}(aq) + 7\,H_2O \qquad E^\circ_{red} = +1.33\ V$

net: $3\,Sn^{2+} + Cr_2O_7^{2-} + 14\,H^+ \longrightarrow 3\,Sn^{4+} + 2\,Cr^{3+} + 7\,H_2O \qquad E^\circ_{cell} = 1.18\ V$

(anode) —electron flow→ (cathode)

(c) $Pt\ |\ O_2(g)\ |\ H_2O,\ H^+\ ||\ Cl^-(aq)\ |\ Cl_2(g)\ |\ Pt$

oxid: $2\,H_2O \longrightarrow O_2(g) + 4\,H^+ + 4\,e^- \qquad E^\circ_{ox} = -1.229\ V$

red: $2\,\{Cl_2(g) + 2\,e^- \longrightarrow 2\,Cl^-(aq)\} \qquad E^\circ_{red} = +1.360\ V$

net: $2\,Cl_2(g) + 2\,H_2O \longrightarrow 4\,H^+ + 4\,Cl^- + O_2(g) \qquad E^\circ_{cell} = +0.131\ V$

19-21. (a) *oxid:* $Sn(s) \longrightarrow Sn^{2+} + 2\,e^- \qquad E^\circ_{ox} = +0.136\ V$

red: $Zn^{2+} + 2\,e^- \longrightarrow Zn(s) \qquad E^\circ_{red} = -0.763\ V$

net: $Sn(s) + Zn^{2+} \longrightarrow Sn^{2+} + Zn(s) \qquad E^\circ_{cell} = -0.627\ V$

The cell does not function as a voltaic cell in the manner in which it is written because $E^\circ_{cell} < 0$.

(b) *oxid:* $H_2O_2(aq) \longrightarrow O_2(g) + 2\,H^+ + 2\,e^- \qquad E^\circ_{ox} = -0.682\ V$

red: $2\,\{Ag^+ + e^- \longrightarrow Ag(s)\} \qquad E^\circ_{red} = +0.799\ V$

net: $H_2O_2(aq) + 2\,Ag^+ \longrightarrow 2\,Ag(s) + 2\,H^+ + O_2(g) \qquad E^\circ_{cell} = +0.117\ V$

This cell does function as a voltaic cell.

(c) *oxid:* $2\ H_2O \longrightarrow O_2(g) + 4\ H^+ - 4\ e^-$ $E^\circ_{ox} = -1.229$ V

red: $2\ Cu^{2+} + 2\ e^- \longrightarrow Cu(s)$ $E^\circ_{red} = +0.337$ V

net: $2\ Cu^{2+} + 2\ H_2O \longrightarrow 2\ Cu(s) + O_2(g) + 4\ H^+$ $E^\circ_{cell} = -0.892$ V

This cell does not function as a voltaic cell in the manner in which it is written.

19-22. (a) The result we wish to achieve here is:

oxid: $Fe(s) \longrightarrow Fe^{2+} + 2\ e^-$ $E^\circ_{ox} = +0.440$ V

red: $Cl_2(g) + 2\ e^- \longrightarrow 2\ Cl^-$ $E^\circ_{red} = +1.360$ V

net: $Fe(s) + Cl_2(g) \longrightarrow Fe^{2+} + 2\ Cl^-$ $E^\circ_{cell} = 1.800$ V

The cell in which the reaction occurs is: $Fe(s)\ |\ Fe^{2+}(aq)\ ||\ Cl^-(aq)\ |\ Cl_2(g)\ |\ Pt(s)$

(b) If Zn^{2+} is to be reduced to Zn(s), for which $E^\circ_{red} = -0.763$ V, we must select an oxidation couple for which $E^\circ_{ox} > +0.763$ V. For example:

oxid: $Mg(s) \longrightarrow Mg^{2+}(aq) + 2\ e^-$ $E^\circ_{ox} = +2.37$ V

red: $Zn^{2+}(aq) + 2\ e^- \longrightarrow Zn(s)$ $E^\circ_{red} = -0.763$ V

net: $Mg(s) + Zn^{2+}(aq) \longrightarrow Mg^{2+}(aq) + Zn(s)$ $E^\circ_{cell} = +1.61$ V

$Mg(s)\ |\ Mg^{2+}(aq)\ ||\ Zn^{2+}(aq)\ |\ Zn(s)$

(c) The required half-reactions are:

oxid: $Cu^+(aq) \longrightarrow Cu^{2+}(aq) + e^-$

red: $Cu^+(aq) + e^- \longrightarrow Cu(s)$

net: $2\ Cu^+(aq) \longrightarrow Cu^{2+}(aq) + Cu(s)$

$Pt\ |\ Cu^+(aq),\ Cu^{2+}(aq)\ ||\ Cu^+(aq)\ |\ Cu(s)$

Note that whereas the cathode can be made of Cu(s), the anode cannot. Cu(s) is not involved in the oxidation half-reaction.

Concentration dependence of E_{cell}--the Nernst equation

19-23. (*19.5*) $$E_{cell} = E^\circ_{cell} - \frac{0.0592}{n} \log \frac{[Cu^{2+}]}{[Ag^+]^2}$$

By writing half-equations we see that $E^\circ_{cell} = 0.462$ *V* and n = 2.

oxid: $Cu(s) \longrightarrow Cu^{2+} + 2\ e^-$ $E^\circ_{ox} = -0.337$ *V*

red: $2\ Ag^+ + e^- \longrightarrow Ag(s)$ $E^\circ_{red} = +0.799$ *V*

net: $Cu(s) + 2\ Ag^+ \longrightarrow Cu^{2+} + 2\ Ag(s)$ $E^\circ_{cell} = +0.462$ *V*

$$E_{cell} = 0.462 - \frac{0.0592}{2} \log \frac{[Cu^{2+}]}{[Ag^+]^2}$$

(*19.25*) $E_{cell} = 2.00 - \frac{0.0592}{6} \log \frac{[Al^{3+}]^2}{[Cu^{2+}]^3}$

(*19.52*) $E_{cell} = 0.74 - \frac{0.0592}{5} \log \frac{[Fe^{3+}]^5[Mn^{2+}]}{[Fe^{2+}]^5[MnO_4^-][H^+]^8}$

The values of E°_{ox} and E°_{red} can be obtained from Table 19-2.

$E^\circ_{cell} = E^\circ_{ox} + E^\circ_{red} = -0.771\ V + 1.51\ V = +0.74\ V$

19-24. *oxid:* $2\{Mn^{2+} + 2\ H_2O \longrightarrow MnO_2(s) + 4\ H^+ + 2\ e^-\}$ $E^\circ_{ox} = -1.23\ V$

red: $O_2(g) + 4\ H^+ + 4\ e^- \longrightarrow 2\ H_2O$ $E^\circ_{red} = +1.229\ V$

net: $2\ Mn^{2+} + O_2(g) + 2\ H_2O \longrightarrow 2\ MnO_2(s) + 4\ H^+$ $E^\circ_{cell} \simeq 0.00\ V$

The reaction will be essentially at equilibrium if all reactants and products are in their standard states.

(a) $[H^+] = 10$ M. Increasing $[H^+]$ above its standard state value favors the reverse of the reaction shown.

(b) $[H^+] = 1.0$ M. This is the condition under which the reaction is essentially in a state of equilibrium, with all reactants and products in their standard states and $E_{cell} = E^\circ_{cell} \simeq 0$.

(c) $[H^+] = 0.10$ M. This condition, according to Le Chatelier's principle, should favor the forward reaction.

(d) pH = 9.50; $[H_3O^+] = 3.2 \times 10^{-10}$. Following the reasoning in part (c), this condition should very much favor the forward reaction.

19-25. *oxid:* $3\{2\ Cl^- \longrightarrow Cl_2(g) + 2\ e^-\}$ $E^\circ_{ox} = -1.36\ V$

red: $Cr_2O_7^{2-} + 14\ H^+ + 6\ e^- \longrightarrow 2\ Cr^{3+} + 7\ H_2O$ $E^\circ_{red} = +1.33\ V$

net: $Cr_2O_7^{2-} + 6\ Cl^- + 14\ H^+ \longrightarrow 2\ Cr^{3+} + 3\ Cl_2(g) + 7\ H_2O$ $E^\circ_{cell} = -0.03\ V$

Because $E^\circ_{cell} < 0$, the reaction is not spontaneous if all reactants and products are in their standard states. The reason that this reaction can be used as a laboratory preparation of $Cl_2(g)$ is that as the gas escapes (especially if the reaction mixture is heated) the forward reaction must proceed to replace the lost $Cl_2(g)$. The reaction never reaches a condition of equilibrium.

19-26. (a) The power of an oxidizing agent is pH dependent for every reduction half-reaction that involves H^+. Of the species listed, this includes $O_2(g)$, $MnO_4^-(aq)$ and $H_2O_2(aq)$.

(b) The oxidizing power is independent of pH if H^+ does not appear in the reduction half-reaction at all. This is the case with $Cl_2(g)$ and $F_2(g)$.

(c) If the reduction half-equation has H^+ appearing on the left side, the power of the oxidizing agent increases in acidic solution. This is the case with the following:

$O_2(g) + 4\ H^+(aq) + 4\ e^- \longrightarrow 2\ H_2O$

$MnO_4^-(aq) + 8\ H^+(aq) + 5\ e^- \longrightarrow Mn^{2+}(aq) + 4\ H_2O$

$H_2O_2(aq) + 2\ H^+(aq) + 2\ e^- \longrightarrow 2\ H_2O$

In order for the oxidizing agent to be more powerful in basic solution, the reduction half-reaction would have to have H^+ appearing on the right side of the half-equation. This is a situation that we would not frequently expect to encounter.

19-27. The reaction of interest in this exercise is:

$$Zn(s) + Cu^{2+}(aq) \longrightarrow Cu(s) + Zn^{2+}(aq) \qquad E^\circ_{cell} = 1.10\ V$$

The dependence of the cell potential on ion concentrations is given by the Nernst equation.

$$E_{cell} = 1.10 - \frac{0.0592}{2} \log \frac{[Zn^{2+}]}{[Cu^{2+}]}$$

(a) If $[Zn^{2+}] = 1.0$ M, the smallest concentration of Cu^{2+} for which the reaction is still spontaneous is obtained by solving the expression:

$$0.00 = 1.10 - \frac{0.0592}{2} \log \frac{1}{[Cu^{2+}]} \qquad -1.10 = \frac{0.0592}{2} \log [Cu^{2+}]$$

$$\log [Cu^{2+}] = \frac{-2 \times 1.10}{0.0592} = -37.16 \qquad [Cu^{2+}] = 7 \times 10^{-38}$$

(b) The concentration of Cu^{2+} calculated in part (a) is immeasurably small. The displacement of copper metal from an aqueous solution of copper ion by zinc metal is a reaction that goes to completion.

19-28. The spontaneous cell reaction is the sum of these two half-reactions:

oxid: $H_2(g, 1\ atm) \longrightarrow 2\ H^+(\text{in } 1.0\ M\ KOH) + 2\ e^-$

red: $2\ H^+(\approx 1.0\ M) + 2\ e^- \longrightarrow H_2(g, 1\ atm)$

net: $2\ H^+(\approx 1.0\ M) \longrightarrow 2\ H^+(\text{in } 1.0\ M\ KOH)$

$$E_{cell} = E^\circ_{cell} - \frac{0.0592}{2} \log \frac{[H^+]^2}{(1.0)^2} = 0.00 - 0.0592 \log [H^+]$$

(a) In 1.0 M KOH, $[OH^-] = 1.0$ and $[H^+] = 1.0 \times 10^{-14}$

$$E_{cell} = -0.0592 \log (1 \times 10^{-14}) = 14 \times 0.0592 = +0.83\ V$$

(b) The value of E° (see Table 19-2) for the reduction half-reaction, $2\ H_2O + 2\ e^- \longrightarrow H_2(g) + 2\ OH^-$, is -0.828 V. This is for the case where $[OH^-] = 1$ M, $[H^+] = 10^{-14}$ M and $P_{H_2} = 1$ atm. The calculation in (a) was for the oxidation of $H_2(g)$ in this same solution; the value obtained was simply the negative of the standard electrode potential.

19-29. Substitution of 1.0 M NH_3 for 1.0 M KOH in exercise 19-28 means that the cell reaction is: $2\ H^+(\approx 1.0\ M) \longrightarrow 2\ H^+(\text{in } 1.0\ M\ NH_3)$. The Nernst expression for the cell reaction remains unchanged.

$$E_{cell} = E^\circ_{cell} - \frac{0.0592}{2} \log \frac{[H^+]^2}{(1.0)^2} = 0.00 - 0.0592 \log [H^+]$$

(a) Since $[H^+]$ in 1.0 M NH_3 is *larger* than in 1.0 M KOH, E_{cell} is *lower*.

(b) To determine the value of E_{cell} requires first a calculation of $[H^+]$ in 1.0 M NH_3.

$$\frac{[NH_4^+][OH^-]}{[NH_3]} = \frac{[OH^-]^2}{1.0} = 1.8 \times 10^{-5} \qquad [OH^-]^2 = 1.8 \times 10^{-5}$$

$$[OH^-] = 4.24 \times 10^{-3} \qquad [H^+] = \frac{1.0 \times 10^{-14}}{4.24 \times 10^{-3}} = 2.4 \times 10^{-12}$$

$$E_{cell} = -0.0592 \cdot \log 2.4 \times 10^{-12} = -0.0592 \times (-11.6) = 0.69\ V$$

19-30. *oxid:* $Ag(s) \longrightarrow Ag^+(\text{satd. } Ag_2SO_4(aq)) + e^-$

red: $Ag^+(0.10\ M) + e^- \longrightarrow Ag(s)$

net: $Ag^+(0.10\ M) \longrightarrow Ag^+(\text{satd. } Ag_2SO_4(aq))$

$K_{sp}(Ag_2SO_4) = [Ag^+]^2[SO_4^{2-}] = 1.4 \times 10^{-5}$

let $x = [SO_4^{2-}]$ and $2x = [Ag^+]$ $\qquad (2x)^2(x) = 4x^3 = 1.4 \times 10^{-5}$

$x = 1.5 \times 10^{-2}$ $\qquad [Ag^+] = 2x = 3.0 \times 10^{-2}\ M$

net: $Ag^+(0.10\ M) \longrightarrow Ag^+(0.030\ M)$

$$E_{cell} = E°_{cell} - \frac{0.0592}{n}\log\frac{0.030}{0.10} = 0.00 - \frac{0.0592}{1}\log 0.30 = 0.031\ V$$

19-31. *oxid:* $Ag(s) \longrightarrow Ag^+(\text{satd. } AgI(aq)) + e^-$

red: $Ag^+(\text{satd. AgCl, } x\ M\ Cl^-) + e^- \longrightarrow Ag(s)$

net: $Ag^+(\text{satd. AgCl, } x\ M\ Cl^-) \longrightarrow Ag^+(\text{satd. } AgI(aq))$

$K_{sp}(AgI) = [Ag^+][I^-] = [Ag^+]^2 = 8.5 \times 10^{-17}$ $\qquad [Ag^+] = 9.2 \times 10^{-9}\ M$

$$E_{cell} = E°_{cell} - \frac{0.0592}{1}\log\frac{9.2 \times 10^{-9}}{[Ag^+]}$$ ⟵ This is $[Ag^+]$ in saturated AgCl, x M Cl^-

$0.050 = 0.00 - 0.0592\ (\log 9.2 \times 10^{-9} - \log [Ag^+])$

$0.050 = -0.0592 \times (-8.04) + 0.0592 \log [Ag^+]$

$\log [Ag^+] = \dfrac{0.050 - 0.476}{0.0592} = -7.20$ $\qquad [Ag^+] = 6.3 \times 10^{-8}$

$K_{sp}(AgCl) = [Ag^+][Cl^-] = (6.3 \times 10^{-8})[Cl^-] = 1.6 \times 10^{-10}$

$[Cl^-] = 2.5 \times 10^{-3}\ M$

$\Delta\bar{G}°$, $E°_{cell}$, and K

19-32. (a) *oxid:* $2\{Al(s) \longrightarrow Al^{3+} + 3\ e^-\}$ $\qquad E°_{ox} = +1.66\ V$

red: $3\{Zn^{2+} + 2\ e^- \longrightarrow Zn(s)\}$ $\qquad E°_{red} = -0.763\ V$

net: $2\ Al(s) + 3\ Zn^{2+} \longrightarrow 2\ Al^{3+} + 3\ Zn(s)$ $\qquad E°_{cell} = 0.90\ V$

$\Delta\bar{G}° = -n\mathcal{F}E°_{cell} = -6 \times 96{,}500\ C/mol \times 0.90\ V = -5.2 \times 10^5\ J/mol = -520\ kJ/mol$

(b) *oxid:* $5\{Pb^{2+} + 2\ H_2O \longrightarrow PbO_2(s) + 4\ H^+ + 2\ e^-\}$ $\qquad E°_{ox} = -1.455\ V$

red: $2\{MnO_4^- + 8\ H^+ + 5\ e^- \longrightarrow Mn^{2+} + 4\ H_2O\}$ $\qquad E°_{red} = +1.51\ V$

net: $5\ Pb^{2+} + 2\ MnO_4^- + 2\ H_2O \longrightarrow 5\ PbO_2(s) + 2\ Mn^{2+} + 4\ H^+$ $\qquad E°_{cell} = 0.05\ V$

$\Delta\bar{G}° = -n\mathcal{F}E°_{cell} = -10 \times 96{,}500\ C/mol \times 0.05\ V = -4.8 \times 10^4\ J/mol = -48\ kJ/mol$

(c) *oxid:* $2\ Cl^- \longrightarrow Cl_2(g) + 2\ e^-$ $\qquad E^\circ_{ox} = -1.36$ V

red: $MnO_2(s) + 4\ H^+ + 2\ e^- \longrightarrow Mn^{2-} + 2\ H_2O$ $\qquad E^\circ_{red} = +1.33$ V

net: $MnO_2(s) + 4\ H^+ + 2\ Cl^- \longrightarrow Mn^{2+} + 2\ H_2O + Cl_2(g)$ $\qquad E^\circ_{cell} = -0.03$ V

$\Delta\bar{G}^\circ = -n\mathcal{F}E^\circ_{cell} = -2 \times 96{,}500\ \text{C/mol} \times (-0.03)\text{V} = +5790\ \text{J/mol} = +5.79\ \text{kJ/mol}$

19-33. $\Delta\bar{G}^\circ = -2.303 \cdot RT \cdot \log K = -5.2 \times 10^5$ J/mol

$$\log K = \frac{-5.2 \times 10^5\ \text{J/mol}}{-2.303 \times 8.314\ \text{J mol}^{-1}\ \text{K}^{-1} \times 298\ \text{K}} = 91.1 \qquad K = 1.3 \times 10^{91}$$

	2 Al(s) +	$3\ Zn^{2+}$	$\rightleftharpoons$	$2\ Al^{3+}$	+ 3 Zn(s)
initial:		1.0 M		--	
changes:		$-(1.0 - x)$M		$+2/3(1.0 - x)$M	
equil:		x M		$2/3(1.0 - x)$M	
assume $x << 1.0$:		x M		0.67 M	

$$K = \frac{[Al^{3+}]^2}{[Zn^{2+}]^3} = \frac{(0.67)^2}{x^3} = 1.2 \times 10^{91} \qquad x^3 = 3.7 \times 10^{-92} \qquad x = [Zn^{2+}] = 3.3 \times 10^{-31}\text{M}$$

The displacement of Zn^{2+} by Al(s) goes to completion.

19-34. *oxid:* $Fe(s) \longrightarrow Fe^{2+} + 2\ e^-$ $\qquad E^\circ_{ox} = +0.440$ V

red: $2\ \{Cr^{3+} + e^- \longrightarrow Cr^{2+}\}$ $\qquad E^\circ_{red} = -0.407$ V

net: $Fe(s) + 2\ Cr^{3+} \longrightarrow Fe^{2+} + 2\ Cr^{2+}$ $\qquad E^\circ_{cell} = +0.033$ V

$\Delta\bar{G}^\circ = -n\mathcal{F}E^\circ_{cell} = -2.303\ RT \log K$

$$\log K = \frac{n\mathcal{F}E^\circ_{cell}}{2.303\ RT} = \frac{2 \times 96{,}500\ \text{C/mol} \times 0.033\ \text{V}}{2.303 \times 8.314\ \text{J mol}^{-1}\ \text{K}^{-1} \times 298} = 1.12 \qquad K = 13$$

	Fe(s) +	$2\ Cr^{3+}$	$\rightleftharpoons$	Fe^{2+}	+	$2\ Cr^{2-}$
initial:		1.00 M		--		
changes:		$-2x$ M		$+x$ M		$+2x$ M
equil:		$(1.00 - 2x)$M		x M		$2x$ M

$$K = \frac{[Fe^{2+}][Cr^{2+}]^2}{[Cr^{3+}]^2} = \frac{x\ (2x)^2}{(1.00 - 2x)^2} = 13$$

We are seeking a value of x that will make the above expression equal to 13. Note that x must be less than 0.50 (which corresponds to $[Cr^{3+}] = 1.00 - 2x = 0$).

Try $x = 0.40$: $\dfrac{0.40(0.80)^2}{(1.00 - 0.80)^2} = 6.4 < 13$ $\qquad$ Try $x = 0.41$: $\dfrac{0.41(0.82)^2}{(1.00 - 0.82)^2} = 8.5 < 13$

Try $x = 0.42$: $\dfrac{0.42(0.84)^2}{(1.00 - 0.84)^2} = 11.6 < 13$ $\qquad$ Try $x = 0.43$: $\dfrac{0.43(0.86)^2}{(1.00 - 0.86)^2} = 16.2 > 13$

Our result is $x = [Fe^{2+}] = 0.42$ M

Batteries and fuel cells

19-35. *Anode (oxid)* $Cd(s) + 2\ OH^-(aq) \longrightarrow Cd(OH)_2(s) + 2\ e^-$

Cathode (red) $2\{Ni(OH)_3(s) + e^- \longrightarrow Ni(OH)_2(s) + OH^-(aq)\}$

Discharge reaction $Cd(s) + 2\ Ni(OH)_3(s) \longrightarrow Cd(OH)_2(s) + 2\ Ni(OH)_2(s)$

19-36. *Anode (oxid)* $CH_4(g) + 4\ O^{2-} \longrightarrow CO_2(g) + 2\ H_2O(g) + 8\ e^-$

Cathode (red) $2\{O_2(g) + 4\ e^- \longrightarrow 2\ O^{2-}\}$

Net reaction $CH_4(g) + 2\ O_2(g) \longrightarrow CO_2(g) + 2\ H_2O(g)$

Electrochemical mechanism of corrosion

19-37. In a galvanic cell electrons lost at the anode in an **oxidation** half-reaction are conveyed through an external electrical circuit to the cathode, where a reduction half-reaction occurs. In a corroding metal an oxidation half-reaction occurs in one region (the anodic reaction) and electrons are transferred to another region, where a reduction half-reaction occurs (the cathodic reaction). The two processes are quite similar. The essential difference is that the galvanic cell reaction is a desirable one that produces useful work whereas the corrosion reaction is undesirable and does no useful work.

19-38. (a) Oxidation would continue to occur at the exposed ends of the iron nail, yielding a blue precipitate. The cathodic (reduction) half-reaction would occur on the copper wire. The wire would develop a pink color, signaling the presence of OH^-.

(b) The zinc metal would oxidize (yielding a precipitate of zinc ferricyanide). The reduction half-reaction would occur on the iron nail, detectable by the characteristic color of phenolphthalein in a basic medium. No corrosion of the iron would occur; no precipitate would appear on the iron.

19-39. The combination of the transmission pipe and the inert electrode functions as an electrolysis cell. The inert electrode is made to be the anode (positive electrode). Whatever oxidation half-reaction can occur does so on this electrode. The pipe is made the cathode (negative electrode). Here a reduction half-reaction occurs, but this does not affect the metal. (A metal corrodes by oxidation, not reduction.)

Electrolysis reactions

19-40. In an electrolysis reaction we generally expect that whatever combination of oxidation and reduction half-reactions can proceed with the smallest applied potential difference will occur. In the electrolysis of $MgCl_2$ the anode (oxidation) reaction is the same whether in concentrated aqueous solution or in the pure molten salt. But the reduction of water in aqueous solutions proceeds more readily than that of Mg^{2+}.

Aqueous soln. $Mg^{2+} + 2\ Cl^- + 2\ H_2O \longrightarrow Mg^{2+} + 2\ OH^- + H_2(g) + Cl_2(g)$

$E^\circ_{cell} = -2.19\ V$

Molten state $Mg^{2+} + 2\ Cl^- \longrightarrow Mg(l) + Cl_2(g)$ $E^\circ_{cell} = -3.73\ V$

19-41. (a) *$CuCl_2(aq)$* Anode: $2\ Cl^- \longrightarrow Cl_2(g) + 2\ e^-$

Cathode: $Cu^{2+} + 2\ e^- \longrightarrow Cu(s)$

(b) *HCl(aq)* Anode: $2\ Cl^- \longrightarrow Cl_2(g) + 2\ e^-$

Cathode: $2\ H^+ + 2\ e^- \longrightarrow H_2(g)$

(c) $H_2SO_4(aq)$ Anode: $2\ H_2O \longrightarrow O_2(g) + 4\ H^+ - 4\ e^-$

Cathode: $2\ H^+ + 2\ e^- \longrightarrow H_2(g)$

(d) $BaCl_2(l)$ Anode: $2\ Cl^- \longrightarrow Cl_2(g) + 2\ e^-$

Cathode: $Ba^{2+} + 2\ e^- \longrightarrow Ba(l)$

(e) $KI(aq)$ Anode: $2\ I^- \longrightarrow I_2 + 2\ e^-$

Cathode: $2\ H_2O + 2\ e^- \longrightarrow 2\ OH^- + H_2(g)$

(f) $KOH(aq)$ Anode: $2\ H_2O \longrightarrow O_2(g) + 4\ H^+ + 4\ e^-$

Cathode: $2\ H_2O + 2\ e^- \longrightarrow H_2(g) + 2\ OH^-$

19-42. (a) The gases produced by overcharging a lead storage battery are $O_2(g)$ and $H_2(g)$.

(b) *Anode (oxid)* $2\ H_2O \longrightarrow O_2(g) + 4\ H^+ + 4\ e^-$

Cathode (red) $2\{2\ H^+ + 2\ e^- \longrightarrow H_2(g)\}$

Net reaction $2\ H_2O \longrightarrow O_2(g) + 2\ H_2(g)$

Faraday's laws of electrolysis

19-43. $\text{no. C} = 0.600\ h \times \frac{1.20\ C}{s} \times \frac{60\ min}{1\ h} \times \frac{60\ s}{1\ min} = 2.59 \times 10^3\ C$

(a) $\text{no. g Cu} = 2.59 \times 10^3\ C \times \frac{1\ mol\ e}{96,500\ C} \times \frac{1\ mol\ Cu}{2\ mol\ e} \times \frac{63.5\ g\ Cu}{1\ mol\ Cu} = 0.852\ g\ Cu$

(b) $\text{no. g Ag} = 2.59 \times 10^3\ C \times \frac{1\ mol\ e}{96,500\ C} \times \frac{1\ mol\ Ag}{1\ mol\ e} \times \frac{107.9\ g\ Ag}{1\ mol\ Ag} = 2.90\ g\ Ag$

(c) $\text{no. g Fe} = 2.59 \times 10^3\ C \times \frac{1\ mol\ e}{96,500\ C} \times \frac{1\ mol\ Fe}{2\ mol\ e} \times \frac{55.85\ g\ Fe}{1\ mol\ Fe} = 0.749\ g\ Fe$

(d) $\text{no. g Al} = 2.59 \times 10^3\ C \times \frac{1\ mol\ e}{96,500\ C} \times \frac{1\ mol\ Al}{3\ mol\ e} \times \frac{26.98\ g\ Al}{1\ mol\ Al} = 0.241\ g\ Al$

19-44. The electrodeposition can be described by the half-equation: $Cu^{2+} + 2\ e^- \longrightarrow Cu(s)$. The critical step in the set-up below is to recognize that a current of 2.20 A represents a flow of electrical charge of 2.20 C/s.

$$\text{no. min} = 0.500\ L \times \frac{0.100\ mol\ CuSO_4}{1\ L} \times \frac{1\ mol\ Cu^{2+}}{1\ mol\ CuSO_4} \times \frac{2\ mol\ e^-}{1\ mol\ Cu^{2+}} \times \frac{96,500\ C}{1\ mol\ e^-} \times \frac{1\ s}{2.20\ C} \times \frac{1\ min}{60\ s} = 73.1\ min$$

19-45. The oxidation half-reaction, in which $O_2(g)$ is produced, is $2\ H_2O \longrightarrow O_2(g) + 4\ H^+ + 4\ e^-$. Four moles of electrons are transferred for every mole of $O_2(g)$ produced.

(a) This calculation is performed as if the water solution being electrolyzed had no vapor pressure. The $O_2(g)$ is assumed to be dry.

$\text{no. C} = 0.283\ h \times \frac{60\ min}{1\ hr} \times \frac{60\ s}{1\ min} \times \frac{2.50\ C}{1\ s} = 2.55 \times 10^3\ C$

$\text{no. mol } O_2 = 2.55 \times 10^3\ C \times \frac{1\ mol\ e^-}{96,500\ C} \times \frac{1\ mol\ O_2}{4\ mol\ e^-} = 6.61 \times 10^{-3}\ mol\ O_2$

$PV = nRT; \quad V = nRT/P$

$$V = \frac{6.61 \times 10^{-3}\ mol \times 0.0821\ L\ atm\ mol^{-1}\ K^{-1} \times 298\ K}{(740/760)\ atm} = 0.166\ L\ (166\ cm^3)$$

(b) When the gas produced is saturated with water vapor, the partial pressure of $O_2(g)$ is $P_{bar} - P_{H_2O} = 740 - 23.8 = 716$ mmHg. The calculation of part (a) can be repeated with a simple substitution of 716 mmHg for 740 mmHg as the pressure of the gas, or, according to Boyle's law, the 166 ml of dry gas would expand by the factor, 740/716, if it were saturated with water vapor.

$$V = 166\ cm^3 \times \frac{740\ mmHg}{716\ mmHg} = 172\ cm^3\ O_2(g)$$

19-46. The electrodeposition reaction on which the following calculations are made is: $Ag^+ + e^- \longrightarrow Ag(s)$. In part (b) the definition of an ampere is used: 1 A = 1 C/s.

(a) $$\text{no. C} = 2.08\ g\ Ag \times \frac{1\ mol\ Ag}{108\ g\ Ag} \times \frac{1\ mol\ e^-}{1\ mol\ Ag} \times \frac{96{,}500\ C}{1\ mol\ e^-} = 1.86 \times 10^3\ C$$

(b) $$\text{no. A} = \frac{1.86 \times 10^3\ C}{14\ min \times \frac{60\ s}{1\ min}} = 2.21\ C/s = 2.21\ A$$

Stoichiometry of oxidation-reduction reactions

19-47. (a) equiv wt of $(NH_4)_2S_2O_8$ = 1/2 f wt = 1/2(228) = 114 g $(NH_4)_2SO_4$/equiv

(b) equiv wt of HNO_3 = 1/4 mol wt = 1/4(63.0) = 15.8 g HNO_3/equiv

(c) equiv wt of CO_2 = 1/8 mol wt = 1/8(44.0) = 5.5 g CO_2/equiv

(d) equiv wt of $KBrO_3$ = 1/6 f wt = 1/6(167.0) = 27.8 g $KBrO_3$/equiv

(e) equiv wt of KNO_3 = 1/8 f wt = 1/8(101.1) = 12.6 g KNO_3/equiv

19-48. $$\text{no. mol } Cr_2O_7^{2-} = 36.10\ ml \times \frac{1\ L}{1000\ ml} \times \frac{0.0410\ mol\ K_2Cr_2O_7}{1\ L} \times \frac{1\ mol\ Cr_2O_7^{2-}}{1\ mol\ K_2Cr_2O_7} = 1.48 \times 10^{-3}\ mol\ Cr_2O_7^{2-}$$

$$\text{no. g Fe} = 1.48 \times 10^{-3}\ mol\ Cr_2O_7^{2-} \times \frac{6\ mol\ Fe^{2+}}{1\ mol\ Cr_2O_7^{2-}} \times \frac{1\ mol\ Fe}{1\ mol\ Fe^{2+}} \times \frac{55.85\ g\ Fe}{1\ mol\ Fe} = 0.496\ g\ Fe$$

$$\%\ Fe = \frac{0.496\ g\ Fe}{0.8500\ g\ iron\ ore} \times 100 = 58.4\%$$

19-49. **(a)** The equation for this reaction is that given for Exercise 48.

$$\text{no. mol } K_2Cr_2O_7 = 0.2050\ g\ sample \times \frac{99.72\ g\ FeSO_4}{100.0\ sample} \times \frac{1\ mol\ FeSO_4}{151.9\ g\ FeSO_4} \times \frac{1\ mol\ Fe^{2+}}{1\ mol\ FeSO_4}$$

$$\times \frac{1\ mol\ Cr_2O_7^{2-}}{6\ mol\ Fe^{2+}} \times \frac{1\ mol\ K_2Cr_2O_7}{1\ mol\ Cr_2O_7^{2-}} = 2.243 \times 10^{-4}\ mol\ K_2Cr_2O_7$$

$$\text{molarity of } K_2Cr_2O_7(aq) = \frac{2.243 \times 10^{-4}\ mol\ K_2Cr_2O_7}{0.04010\ L} = 5.594 \times 10^{-3}\ M$$

(b) The equation on which the calculation in part (a) is based involves the transfer of 6 mol of electrons, that is, 6 equiv of Fe^{2+} and 6 equiv of $Cr_2O_7^{2-}$.

$$\text{normality of } K_2Cr_2O_7(aq) = 6 \times \text{molarity} = 6 \times 5.594 \times 10^{-3} = 3.356 \times 10^{-2}\ N$$

19-50. The $KMnO_4(aq)$ in Example 19-11 is 0.1070 N for a reaction involving the transfer of 5 mol of electrons. Its molarity is 1/5(0.1070) = 0.02140 M. In the reaction of MnO_4^- and $S_2O_3^{2-}$,

oxid: $3\{S_2O_3^{2-} + 5\ H_2O \longrightarrow 2\ SO_4^{2-} + 10\ H^+ + 8\ e^-\}$

red: $8\{MnO_4^- + 4\ H^+ + 3\ e^- \longrightarrow MnO_2(s) + 2\ H_2O\}$

net: $3\ S_2O_3^{2-} + 8\ MnO_4^- + 2\ H^+ \longrightarrow 6\ SO_4^{2-} + 8\ MnO_2(s) + H_2O$

The equivalent of MnO_4^- is based on a gain of 3 electrons.

normality = 3 x molarity = 3 x 0.02140 = 0.06420 N

equiv wt $Na_2S_2O_3$ = 1/8 f wt = 1/8(158.10) = 19.76 g $Na_2S_2O_3$/equiv

$$\text{no. mequiv } KMnO_4 = 0.0525\text{ g } Na_2S_2O_3 \times \frac{1\text{ equiv } Na_2S_2O_3}{19.76\text{ g } Na_2S_2O_3} \times \frac{1\text{ equiv } KMnO_4}{\text{equiv } Na_2S_2O_3} \times \frac{1000\text{ mequiv } KMnO_4}{1\text{ equiv } KMnO_4}$$

$$= 2.66\text{ mequiv } KMnO_4$$

$$\text{no. ml } KMnO_4(aq) = 2.66\text{ mequiv } KMnO_4 \times \frac{1\text{ ml } KMnO_4(aq)}{0.06420\text{ mequiv } KMnO_4} = 41.4\text{ ml}$$

Self-test Questions

1. (*d*) This reaction involves the oxidation of Cu to Cu^{2+} by H_2SO_4. H_2SO_4 is reduced to $SO_2(g)$. H_2SO_4 is the oxidizing agent.

2. (*c*) The oxidation state of Np decreases from +5 in NpO_2^+ to +4 in Np^{4+}. This is a reduction process.

3. (*b*) The reaction in question is nonspontaneous. This reaction cannot be made to produce electricity but it can be carried out in an electrolysis cell.

4. (*b*) For this reaction, the Nernst equation is $E_{cell} = E°_{cell} - \frac{0.0592}{2}\log\frac{[Zn^{2+}]}{[Pb^{2+}]}$. Since $[Zn^{2+}] = [Pb^{2+}]$, $\log [Zn^{2+}]/[Pb^{2+}] = \log 1 = 0$. $E_{cell} = E°_{cell} = +0.66$ V.

5. (*c*) Because $E°_{cell} > 0$, we should expect a spontaneous reaction in the forward direction. However, because of the small magnitude of $E°_{cell}$ (+0.03 V), we should not expect the reaction to go to completion.

6. (*a*) The reduction of Al^{3+} to Al requires 3 mol of electrons per mol Al (27.0 g). To deposit 4.5 g Al (0.167 mol) requires 3 x 0.167 = 0.50 mol electrons. In turn 0.50 mol electrons will produce 0.25 mol (5.6 L) $H_2(g)$: $2\ H^+(aq) + 2\ e^- \longrightarrow H_2(g)$.

7. *oxid:* $3\{PbO(s) + 2\ OH^- \longrightarrow PbO_2(s) + H_2O + 2\ e^-\}$

   red: $2\{MnO_4^- + 2\ H_2O + 3\ e^- \longrightarrow MnO_2(s) + 4\ OH^-\}$

   net: $3\ PbO(s) + 2\ MnO_4^- + H_2O \longrightarrow 3\ PbO_2(s) + 2\ MnO_2(s) + 2\ OH^-$

8. *oxid:* $3\{Zn(s) \longrightarrow Zn^{2+} + 2\ e^-\}$ $\quad E°_{ox} = +0.763$ V

   red: $2\{NO_3^- + 4\ H^+ + 3\ e^- \longrightarrow NO(g) + 2\ H_2O\}$ $\quad E°_{red} = +0.96$ V

   net: $3\ Zn(s) + 2\ NO_3^- + 8\ H^+ \longrightarrow 3\ Zn^{2+} + 2\ NO(g) + 4\ H_2O$ $\quad E°_{cell} = 1.72$ V (anode) (cathode)

$Zn(s) \mid Zn^{2+}(aq) \parallel H^+(aq),\ NO_3^-(aq) \mid NO(g) \mid Pt(s)$

9. *oxid:* $H_2(g, 1\text{ atm}) \longrightarrow 2\,H^+(x\text{ M}) + 2\,e^-$

red: $2\,H^+(0.10\text{ M}) + 2\,e^- \longrightarrow H_2(g, 1\text{ atm})$

net: $2\,H^+(0.10\text{ M}) \longrightarrow 2\,H^+(x\text{ M})$

$$E_{cell} = E^\circ_{cell} - \frac{0.0592}{2}\log\frac{x^2}{(0.10)^2} = 0.00 - \frac{0.0592}{2} \times 2 \times \log\frac{x}{0.10} = +0.108$$

$$\log x - \log 0.10 = \frac{0.108}{-0.0592} = -1.82 \qquad \log x = -1.82 + \log 0.10 = -1.82 - 1.00 = -2.82$$

$$pH = -\log[H^+] = -\log x = -(-2.82) = 2.82$$

10. Determine K from the value given for E°_{cell}.

$$\Delta \bar{G}^\circ = -2.303 \cdot RT \cdot \log K = -n\mathfrak{F}E^\circ_{cell}$$

$$\log K = \frac{n\mathfrak{F}E^\circ_{cell}}{2.303 \cdot RT} = \frac{2 \times 96{,}500\text{ C/mol} \times (-0.005)\text{V}}{2.303 \times 8.314\text{ J mol}^{-1}\text{ K}^{-1}\ 298\text{ K}} = -0.169$$

K = 0.678 Based on the initial concentrations given, $Q = \frac{[Cu^{2+}]^2[Sn^{2+}]}{[Cu^+]^2[Sn^{4+}]} = 1.00 > 0.678.$

The reverse reaction must occur.

	$2\,Cu^{2+}$	+ Sn^{4+}	$\rightleftharpoons$ $2\,Cu^{2+}$	+ Sn^{2+}
initial:	1.00 M	1.00 M	1.00 M	1.00 M
changes:	$+2x$ M	$+x$ M	$-2x$ M	$-x$ M
equil:	$(1.00 + 2x)$M	$(1.00 + x)$M	$(1.00 - 2x)$M	$(1.00 - x)$M

$$K = \frac{[Cu^{2+}]^2[Sn^{2+}]}{[Cu^+]^2[Sn^{4+}]} = \frac{(1.00 - 2x)^2(1.00 - x)}{(1.00 + 2x)^2(1.00 + x)} = 0.678$$

Use a method of successive approximations:

Try $x = 0.10$: $\frac{(1.00 - 0.20)^2(1.00 - 0.10)}{(1.00 + 0.20)^2(1.00 + 0.10)} = 0.36 < 0.678$

Try $x = 0.010$: $\frac{(1.00 - 0.020)^2(1.00 - 0.010)}{(1.00 + 0.020)^2(1.00 + 0.010)} = 0.905 > 0.678$

Try $x = 0.050$: $\frac{(1.00 - 0.10)^2(1.00 - 0.050)}{(1.00 + 0.10)^2(1.00 + 0.050)} = 0.606 < 0.678$

Try $x = 0.040$: $\frac{(1.00 - 0.080)^2(1.00 - 0.040)}{(1.00 + 0.080)^2(1.00 + 0.040)} = 0.670 \simeq 0.678$

Equilibrium concentrations: $[Cu^+] = 1.08$ M; $[Sn^{4+}] = 1.04$ M; $[Cu^{2+}] = 0.92$ M; $[Sn^{2+}] = 0.96$ M.

Chapter 20

The Chemistry of Selected Representative Elements

Group IA and IIA elements

20-1. (a) $Ca(s) + Cl_2(g) \longrightarrow CaCl_2(s)$

(b) $K(s) + O_2(g) \longrightarrow KO_2(s)$

(c) $Ba(s) + 2\ H_2O \longrightarrow Ba^{2+} + 2\ OH^- + H_2(g)$

(d) $CaO(s) + H_2O \longrightarrow Ca(OH)_2(s)$

(e) $Mg_3N_2(s) + 6\ H_2O \longrightarrow 3\ Mg(OH)_2(s) + 2\ NH_3(g)$

20-2. *Oxidation* $2\ H^- \longrightarrow H_2(g) + 2\ e^-$

Reduction $2\ H_2O + 2\ e^- \longrightarrow 2\ OH^- + H_2(g)$

Net $2\ H^- + 2\ H_2O \longrightarrow 2\ OH^- + 2\ H_2(g)$

or $H^- + H_2O \longrightarrow OH^- + H_2(g)$

20-3. $Be + 2\ Na^+ + 2\ OH^- \longrightarrow 2\ Na^+ + BeO_2^{2-} + H_2(g)$

20-4. (a) The simplest way to determine whether the compound can be pure MgO is to **calculate** the expected mass of MgO that would be obtained from 0.200 g Mg.

$$\text{no. g MgO} = 0.200\ \text{g Mg} \times \frac{1\ \text{mol Mg}}{24.3\ \text{g Mg}} \times \frac{1\ \text{mol MgO}}{1\ \text{mol Mg}} \times \frac{40.3\ \text{g MgO}}{1\ \text{mol MgO}} = 0.332\ \text{g MgO}$$

The amount of product actually obtained is only 0.305 g. This suggests that the product contains a substance with a higher percentage of Mg than MgO.

(b) A probable substance that is present is magnesium nitride--Mg_3N_2. (Note that this compound has 72.2% Mg compared to 60.3% in MgO.)

(c) Add water to the solid material. If $NH_3(g)$ is evolved (detectable by its odor), the presence of Mg_3N_2 can be inferred. $Mg_3N_2 + 6\ H_2O \longrightarrow 3\ Mg(OH)_2 + 2\ NH_3(g)$.

20-5. First determine the amount of $H_2(g)$ required to fill the balloon.

$$PV = nRT; \quad n = \frac{PV}{RT} = \frac{(755/760)\text{atm} \times 200\ \text{L}}{0.0821\ \text{L atm mol}^{-1}\ \text{K}^{-1} \times 291\ \text{K}} = 8.32\ \text{mol}\ H_2(g)$$

The hydrogen is produced by the reaction, $CaH_2 + 2\ H_2O \longrightarrow Ca(OH)_2 + 2\ H_2(g)$

$$\text{no. g } CaH_2 = 8.32\ \text{mol}\ H_2 \times \frac{1\ \text{mol}\ CaH_2}{2\ \text{mol}\ H_2} \times \frac{42.1\ \text{g}\ CaH_2}{1\ \text{mol}\ CaH_2} = 175\ \text{g}\ CaH_2$$

20-6. The reduction half-reaction is $2\ H_2O + 2\ e^- \longrightarrow 2\ OH^- + H_2(g)$. First, we calculate the number of moles of OH^- produced.

$$\text{no. mol } OH^- = 123\ \text{s} \times \frac{1.40\ \text{C}}{1\ \text{s}} \times \frac{1\ \text{mol e}^-}{96{,}500\ \text{C}} \times \frac{2\ \text{mol OH}^-}{2\ \text{mol e}^-} = 1.78 \times 10^{-3}\ \text{mol OH}^-$$

Next we determine $[OH^-]$ in the solution.

$$[OH^-] = \frac{1.78 \times 10^{-3} \text{ mol } OH^-}{0.500 \text{ L}} = 3.56 \times 10^{-3} \text{ M}$$

$pOH = -\log 3.56 \times 10^{-3} = 2.45$ $\qquad$ $pH = 14.00 - 2.45 = 11.55$

Boron and aluminum

20-7. (a) An electron-deficient compound has one or more atoms with an incomplete octet of electrons, as is the case with B in BF_3. The compound is expected to act in such a way as to acquire additional electrons (a Lewis acid).

(b) A dimer is a molecule made up of two simpler molecules. For example, the monomer molecules NO_2 can join to form dimers, N_2O_4.

(c) A Lewis acid is a substance able to accept electrons from another substance to which it forms a bond. Usually this means that some atom in the Lewis acid has an empty orbital available for receiving electrons.

(d) An adduct is a product of the reaction of a Lewis acid and a Lewis base. The acid and base are joined by a coordinate covalent bond, as in $F_3B{:}NH_3$.

20-8. The oxidizing and reducing agents can be identified most simply by the changes in oxidation state indicated in the equation.

$$\overset{0}{2\,Al(s)} + 12\,H^+ + 3\,\overset{+6}{S}O_4^{2-} \longrightarrow 2\,\overset{+3}{Al}{}^{3+} + 6\,H_2O + 3\,\overset{+4}{S}O_2(g)$$

$Al(s)$ is oxidized to Al^{3+}; it is the reducing agent. SO_4^{2-} is reduced to $SO_2(g)$; it is the oxidizing agent.

20-9.

oxid: $AlH_4^- \longrightarrow Al^{3+} + 2\,H_2(g) + 4\,e^-$

red: $2\{2\,H_2O + 2\,e^- \longrightarrow OH^- + H_2(g)\}$

net: $AlH_4^- + 4\,H_2O \longrightarrow Al^{3+} + 4\,OH^- + 4\,H_2(g)$

or $AlH_4^- + 4\,H_2O \longrightarrow Al(OH)_3(s) + OH^- + 4\,H_2(g)$

or $AlH_4^- + 4\,H_2O \longrightarrow [Al(OH)_4]^- + 4\,H_2(g)$

20-10. (a) $2\,Al + Fe_2O_3 \longrightarrow 2\,Fe + Al_2O_3$

$\Delta H° = \Delta\overline{H}_f°(Al_2O_3) - \Delta\overline{H}_f°(Fe_2O_3) = -1670 - (-824) = -846$ kJ

For one mole of iron, $\Delta\overline{H}° = -846/2 = -423$ kJ/mol Fe

(b) $4\,Al + 3\,MnO_2 \longrightarrow 3\,Mn + 2\,Al_2O_3$

$\Delta H° = 2\,\Delta\overline{H}_f°(Al_2O_3) - 3\,\Delta\overline{H}_f°(MnO_2) = 2 \times (-1670) - 3 \times (-519) = -1783$ kJ

For one mole of Mn, $\Delta\overline{H}° = -1783/3 = -594$ kJ/mol Mn

(c) $2\,Al + 3\,MgO \longrightarrow 3\,Mg + Al_2O_3$

$\Delta H° = \Delta\overline{H}_f°(Al_2O_3) - 3\,\Delta\overline{H}_f°(MgO) = -1670 - 3 \times (-602) = 136$ kJ

For one mole of Mg, $\Delta\overline{H}° = 136/3 = +45$ kJ/mol Mg. This reaction is endothermic; ΔH is positive.

20-11. Let us assume that the melting point and boiling point of an interhalogen compound are intermediate to the values of the pure halogens.

	Cl_2	<	BrCl	<	Br_2		Br_2	<	IBr	<	I_2
mp.	-101	ca.	-54		- 7.2°C	mp.	- 7.2	ca.	53		+114°C
bp.	- 34	ca.	+12		+58.8°C	bp.	+58.8	ca.	122		+184.4°C

The correct values obtained from a handbook are: BrCl (mp. = -54°C, bp. = ca. 5°C) and IBr (mp. = 42°C, bp. = 116-119°C).

The principle employed here is that the strength of intermolecular forces (of the London type) is a function of the number of electrons in a species. We should not expect an exact adherence to this principle, however, because BrCl and IBr have some polar character and Cl_2, Br_2, and I_2 do not.

20-12. The more direct approach is to calculate E°_{cell} for each of the following reactions. Because $E^\circ_{cell} > 0$ for the first reaction, this one occurs spontaneously; the others do not.

$Cl_2 + 2\ I^- \longrightarrow 2\ Cl^- + I_2$ $\quad E^\circ_{cell} = +1.36 - 0.54 = +0.82$ V

$I_2 + 2\ Br^- \longrightarrow 2\ I^- + Br_2$ $\quad E^\circ_{cell} = +0.54 - 1.065 = -0.52$ V

$Br_2 + 2\ Cl^- \longrightarrow 2\ Br^- + Cl_2$ $\quad E^\circ_{cell} = +1.065 - 1.36 = -0.30$ V

A principle that can be derived from the results of the above calculations is that a given halogen element will displace from solution any halide ions *below* it in Group VIIA of the periodic table. Thus, Cl_2 will displace I^-, but I_2 will not displace Cl^-.

20-13. $ClO^- + H_2O + 2\ e^- \longrightarrow Cl^- + 2\ OH^-$

20-14. The following reaction is displaced to the right in alkaline solution (a solution containing a high $[OH^-]$) and should occur spontaneously.

$3\ Cl_2(g) + 3\ H_2O \longrightarrow 5\ Cl^- + ClO_3^- + 6\ H^+$ $\quad E^\circ_{cell} = -0.11$ V

Another method of arriving at this same conclusion is to write the Nernst expression for the reaction, substitute $[H^+] \simeq 10^{-14}$ and unit activities for all other terms, and calculate E_{cell}. The value obtained is positive.

$$E_{cell} = -0.11 - \frac{0.0592}{5}\log [H^+]^6 = (-0.11) - \frac{6 \times 0.0592 \times \log(10^{-14})}{5} = -0.11 + \frac{6 \times 14 \times 0.0592}{5}$$

$$= +0.88 \text{ V}$$

20-15. (a) $2\ HClO + 2\ H^+ + 2\ e^- \longrightarrow Cl_2 + 2\ H_2O$ $\quad \Delta G^\circ = -2 \cdot \mathfrak{F} \cdot (1.62)$

$Cl_2 + 2\ e^- \longrightarrow 2\ Cl^-$ $\quad \Delta G^\circ = -2 \cdot \mathfrak{F} \cdot (1.36)$

$2\ HClO + 2\ H^+ + 4\ e^- \longrightarrow 2\ Cl^- + 2\ H_2O$ $\quad \Delta G^\circ = -4 \cdot \mathfrak{F} \cdot (E^\circ)$

$-4 \cdot \mathfrak{F} \cdot (E^\circ) = -2 \cdot \mathfrak{F} \cdot (1.62 + 1.36)$ $\quad E^\circ = (1.62 + 1.36)/2 = +1.49$ V

(b) Use the result of part (a) in writing the reduction half-equation below:

oxid: $HClO + H_2O \longrightarrow HClO_2 + 2\ H^+ + 2\ e^-$ $\quad E^\circ_{ox} = -(1.63)$ V

red: $HClO + H^+ + 2\ e^- \longrightarrow Cl^- + H_2O$ $\quad E^\circ_{red} = +1.49$ V

net: $2\ HClO \longrightarrow HClO_2 + H^+ + Cl^-$ $\quad E^\circ_{cell} = -0.14$ V

This reaction *will not* occur spontaneously as written.

20-16. (a) When HClO acts as an oxidizing agent it is reduced. Select the following reduction half-reaction from Figure 20-6:

$$2\ HClO + 2\ H^+ + 2\ e^- \longrightarrow Cl_2(g) + 2\ H_2O \qquad E^\circ_{red} = +1.62\ V$$

Combine this with an oxidation half-reaction such that E_{cell} for the overall reaction will be positive, for example,

$$Fe^{2+} \longrightarrow Fe^{3+} + e^- \qquad E^\circ_{ox} = -(0.771)\ V$$

The net reaction and its cell potential are:

$$2\ HClO + 2\ Fe^{2+} + 2\ H^+ \longrightarrow 2\ Fe^{3+} + Cl_2(g) + 2\ H_2O \qquad E^\circ_{cell} = +0.85\ V$$

(b) Here we select an oxidation half-reaction involving HClO and an appropriate reduction half-reaction from Table 19-2.

oxid: $HClO + H_2O \longrightarrow HClO_2 + 2\ H^+ + 2\ e^- \qquad E^\circ_{ox} = -(1.63)\ V$

red: $H_2O_2 + 2\ H^+ + 2\ e^- \longrightarrow 2\ H_2O \qquad E^\circ_{red} = +1.77\ V$

net: $HClO + H_2O_2 \longrightarrow HClO_2 + H_2O \qquad E^\circ_{cell} = +0.14\ V$

(c) $HClO + Na^+ + OH^- \longrightarrow Na^+ + OCl^- + H_2O$

20-17. (a) Because 5 mol of gaseous reactants produce 4 mol of gaseous products in the reaction below, the forward reaction is favored by maintaing a small volume at a high pressure.

$$4\ HCl(g) + O_2(g) \longrightarrow 2\ H_2O(g) + 2\ Cl_2(g)$$

(b) To determine the effect of temperature on equilibrium in the above reaction requires calculating the heat of reaction from tabulated enthalpies of formation (Appendix D).

$$\Delta\overline{H}^\circ = 2\ \Delta\overline{H}^\circ_f[H_2O(g)] - 4\ \Delta\overline{H}^\circ_f[HCl(g)] = 2(-241.84) - 4(-92.30) = -114.48\ kJ/mol$$

The forward reaction is exothermic; it is favored at low temperatures.

20-18. For the IO_3^-/I^- couple,

oxid: $3\{H_2SO_3 + H_2O \longrightarrow SO_4^{2-} + 4\ H^+ + 2\ e^-\} \qquad E^\circ_{ox} = -0.17\ V$

red: $IO_3^- + 6\ H^+ + 6\ e^- \longrightarrow I^- + 3\ H_2O \qquad E^\circ_{red} = ?$

net: $3\ H_2SO_3 + IO_3^- \longrightarrow 3\ SO_4^{2-} + I^- + 6\ H^+ \qquad E^\circ_{cell} = E^\circ_{ox} + E^\circ_{red} = 0.92\ V$

$$E^\circ_{red} = 0.92 - (-0.17) = +1.09\ V$$

For the HIO/I_2 couple,

oxid: $2\ I^- \longrightarrow I_2(s) + 2\ e^- \qquad E^\circ_{ox} = -0.54\ V$

red: $2\ HIO + 2\ H^+ + 2\ e^- \longrightarrow I_2(s) + 2\ H_2O \qquad E^\circ_{red} = ?$

net: $HIO + H^+ + I^- \longrightarrow I_2 + H_2O \qquad E^\circ_{cell} = E^\circ_{ox} + E^\circ_{red} = 0.91\ V$

$$E^\circ_{red} = 0.91 - (-0.54) = +1.45\ V$$

For the IO_3^-/HIO couple,

$$IO_3^- + 5\ H^+ + 4\ e^- \longrightarrow HIO + 2\ H_2O \qquad \Delta\overline{G}^\circ = -n\mathcal{F}E^\circ = -4\mathcal{F}E^\circ$$

$$2\,HIO + 2\,H^+ + 2\,e^- \longrightarrow I_2 + 2\,H_2O \qquad \Delta\bar{G}^\circ = -2 \times \mathcal{F} \times (1.45)$$

$$I_2 + 2\,e^- \longrightarrow 2\,I^- \qquad \Delta\bar{G}^\circ = -2 \times \mathcal{F} \times (0.54)$$

Rewrite these equations as follows:

$$IO_3^- + 5\,H^+ + 4\,e^- \longrightarrow \cancel{HIO} + 2\,H_2O \qquad \Delta\bar{G}^\circ = -4\mathcal{F}E^\circ$$

$$\cancel{HIO} + H^+ + e^- \longrightarrow \cancel{1/2\,I_2} + H_2O \qquad \Delta\bar{G}^\circ = -\mathcal{F} \times (1.45)$$

$$\cancel{1/2\,I_2} + e^- \longrightarrow I^- \qquad \Delta\bar{G}^\circ = -\mathcal{F} \times (0.54)$$

$$IO_3^- + 6\,H^+ + 6\,e^- \longrightarrow I^- + 3\,H_2O \qquad \Delta\bar{G}^\circ = -\mathcal{F}\{4\,E^\circ + 1.45 + 0.54\}$$

Also, $\Delta\bar{G}^\circ = -6 \times \mathcal{F} \times (1.09)$ $\qquad -6 \times \mathcal{F} \times (1.09) = -\mathcal{F}\{4\,E^\circ + 1.45 + 0.54\}$

$$E^\circ = \frac{(6 \times 1.09) - 1.45 - 0.54}{4} = 1.14\ V$$

Oxygen

20-19. (a) Lewis structures of H_2S and H_2O are quite similar. It is the existence of intermolecular hydrogen bonding among H_2O molecules that allows water to persist as a liquid at higher temperatures than is possible for hydrogen sulfide, which does not engage in hydrogen bonding.

(b) Although alternate structures are possible for ozone, each structure has all electrons paired, for example,

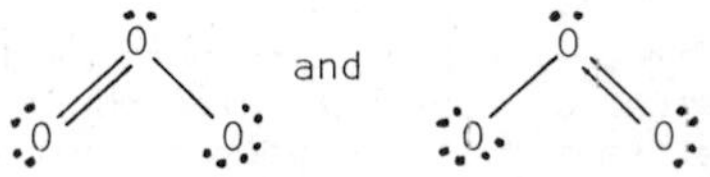

(c) The O—O bond in O_2, as indicated through molecular orbital theory, is essentially a double bond. In O_3, as suggested in part (b), the bond is intermediate between a single and a double bond. In H_2O_2 the bond is essentially a single bond.

$$H-\ddot{\underset{..}{O}}-\ddot{\underset{..}{O}}-H$$

We should expect the bond lengths to be in the order: $O_2 < O_3 < H_2O_2$

20-20. (a) *oxid:* $O_2^{2-} \longrightarrow O_2(g) + 2\,e^-$

red: $O_2^{2-} + 2\,H_2O + 2\,e^- \longrightarrow 4\,OH^-$

net: $2\,O_2^{2-} + 2\,H_2O \longrightarrow O_2(g) + 4\,OH^-$

(b) *oxid:* $3\,\{O_2^- \longrightarrow O_2(g) + e^-\}$

red: $O_2^- + 2\,H_2O + 3\,e^- \longrightarrow 4\,OH^-$

net: $4\,O_2^- + 2\,H_2O \longrightarrow 3\,O_2(g) + 4\,OH^-$

20-21. *oxid:* $H_2O_2 \longrightarrow O_2(g) + 2\,H^+ + 2\,e^-$

red: $H_2O_2 + 2\,H^+ + 2\,e^- \longrightarrow 2\,H_2O$

net: $2\,H_2O_2 \longrightarrow 2\,H_2O + O_2(g)$

20-22. In Na_2O_2(aq): $O_2^{2-} + H_2O \rightleftharpoons HO_2^- + OH^-$

$$K_h = \frac{K_w}{K_a \text{ (for } H_2O_2)} = \frac{1.0 \times 10^{-14}}{2 \times 10^{-12}} = 5 \times 10^{-3}$$

This is a large value for a hydrolysis constant, suggesting that hydrolysis of O_2^{2-} to produce OH^- proceeds to a considerable extent. Na_2O_2(aq) is basic.

20-23. (a) *oxid:* $2 I^- \longrightarrow I_2 + 2 e^-$

   red: $O_3(g) + 2 H^+ + 2 e^- \longrightarrow O_2(g) + H_2O$

   net: $O_3(g) + 2 H^+ + 2 I^- \longrightarrow H_2O + I_2 + O_2(g)$

   (b) *oxid:* $S + 4 H_2O \longrightarrow SO_4^{2-} + 8 H^+ + 6 e^-$

   red: $3 \left\{ O_3(g) + 2 H^+ + 2 e^- \longrightarrow O_2(g) + H_2O \right\}$

   net: $S + 3 O_3(g) + H_2O \longrightarrow 2 H^+ + SO_4^{2-} + 3 O_2(g)$

   (c) *oxid:* $2 \left\{ [Fe(CN)_6]^{4-} \longrightarrow [Fe(CN)_6]^{3-} + e^- \right\}$

   red: $O_3(g) + H_2O + 2 e^- \longrightarrow O_2(g) + 2 OH^-$

   net: $2 [Fe(CN)_6]^{4-} + O_3(g) + H_2O \longrightarrow 2 [Fe(CN)_6]^{3-} + O_2(g) + 2 OH^-$

20-24. Based on this Lewis structure: we consider that *three* electron pairs must be distributed around the central O atom. (Recall that in the valence-shell electron-pair repulsion theory the O—O double bond is treated as if only one pair of electrons were involved.) The distribution should be trigonal planar--three atoms in a plane with a 120° bond angle. The measured bond angle, as we have seen, is 116.5°.

20-25. The ozone layer must be thought of as a spherical shell with a radius of about 4000 mi and a thickness of 0.3 cm. First, determine the surface area of the shell and then multiply by the thickness to obtain the approximate volume of O_3(g). The remainder of the calculation follows easily.

$$A = 4\pi r^2 = 4\pi \times \left\{ 4000 \text{ mi} \times \frac{5280 \text{ ft}}{1 \text{ mi}} \times \frac{12 \text{ in.}}{1 \text{ ft}} \times \frac{1 \text{ m}}{39.37 \text{ in.}} \times \frac{100 \text{ cm}}{1 \text{ m}} \right\}^2 = 5.2 \times 10^{18} \text{ cm}^2$$

$$V = 5.2 \times 10^{18} \text{ cm}^2 \times 0.3 \text{ cm} = 1.6 \times 10^{18} \text{ cm}^3$$

$$\text{no. mol } O_3(g) = 1.6 \times 10^{18} \text{ cm}^3 \times \frac{1 \text{ L}}{1000 \text{ cm}^3} \times \frac{1 \text{ mol } O_3}{22.4 \text{ L}} = 7 \times 10^{13} \text{ mol } O_3$$

$$\text{no. molecules } O_3(g) = 7 \times 10^{13} \text{ mol } O_3 \times \frac{6.02 \times 10^{23} \text{ molecules } O_3}{1 \text{ mol } O_3} = 4 \times 10^{37} \text{ molecules } O_3$$

Sulfur

20-26. In each of the following species the oxidation state of O is -2 and the total of all the oxidation numbers must be zero. Thus, the oxidation state of the sulfur in each species is:

SO_2, +4; SO_3, +6; SO_4, +8; S_2O, +1; S_2O_3, +3; S_2O_7, +7.

20-27. (a) In comparing the structures of H_2O_2 and S_2Cl_2, the S—S bond is analogous to the O—O bond. The Cl atoms bonded to the S atom are limited to forming one covalent bond, just as are the H atoms in H_2O_2.

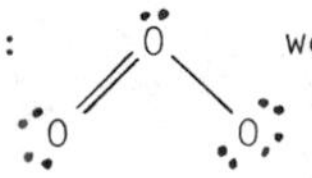

The Lewis structures are:

H—Ö—Ö—H and :C̈l—S̈—S̈—C̈l:

The geometric structure of H_2O_2 is pictured in Figure 20-8, and that of S_2Cl_2 is similar.

(b) The structures of both SO_2 and SO_3 are based on the distribution of three electron pairs. They both have bond angles of about 120°, and, of course, the electronegativity difference between S and O is the same in each. However, because the structure of SO_3 is symmetrical whereas that of SO_2 is not, SO_3 is nonpolar and SO_2 is polar.

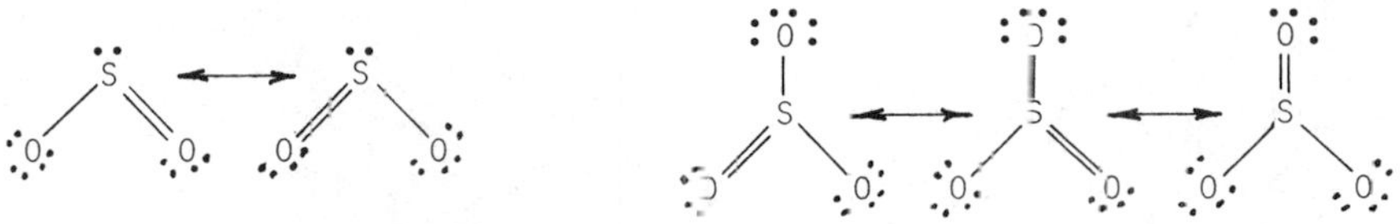

(c) We should expect a paramagnetic, diatomic molecule of sulfur to be similar to that of oxygen.

:Ö:Ö: and :S̈:S̈:

20-28. Although sulfide ion in aqueous solution can be oxidized fairly readily by atmospheric oxygen, when the sulfide ion is part of a very insoluble compound (such as HgS and CuS) it is less easily oxidized. When sulfur exists in a sulfate compound, it is in its highest naturally occurring oxidation state. As a result, sulfates are stable. Sulfites do not occur naturally because they are rather easily oxidized to sulfates.

20-29. (a) $4\ FeS(s) + 7\ O_2(g) \longrightarrow 2\ Fe_2O_3(s) + 4\ SO_2(g)$

(b) $Zn(s) + 4\ H^+ + SO_4^{2-} \longrightarrow Zn^{2+} + 2\ H_2O + SO_2(g)$

(c) $HSO_4^-(aq) + OH^-(aq) \longrightarrow H_2O + SO_4^{2-}(aq)$

(d) $HS^- + H_2O \longrightarrow H_2S + OH^-$ Also, to a slight extent: $HS^- + H_2O \longrightarrow H_3O^+ + S^{2-}$

(e) $3\ FeS(s) + 8\ H^+ + 2\ NO_3^- \longrightarrow 3\ Fe^{2+} + 4\ H_2O + 2\ NO(g) + 3\ S(s)$

(f) $PbS(s) + H^+ + Cl^- \longrightarrow$ no reaction. [K_{sp} for PbS is too small for it to dissolve in a nonoxidizing acid (see Table 20-7).]

20-30. One must compare not the values of K_{sp} but the actual molar solubilities to determine which is the least soluble of the two sulfides. If we let x equal the solubility in moles per liter of HgS and y, that of Bi_2S_3, we obtain the following expressions:

HgS

$$[Hg^{2+}][S^{2-}] = K_{sp}$$
$$(x)(x) = 3 \times 10^{-52}$$
$$x \simeq 2 \times 10^{-26}$$

Bi_2S_3

$$[Bi^{3+}]^2[S^{2-}]^3 = K_{sp}$$
$$(2y)^2(3y)^3 = 1 \times 10^{-96}$$
$$4y^2 \times 27y^3 = 1 \times 10^{-96}$$
$$108y^5 = 1 \times 10^{-96}$$
$$y \simeq 2 \times 10^{-20}$$

20-31. The sodium sulfite in acidic solution reduces permanganate ion to manganese(II) ion and is itself oxidized to sulfate ion.

$$5\ SO_3^{2-} + 2\ MnO_4^- + 6\ H^+ \longrightarrow 5\ SO_4^{2-} + 2\ Mn^{2+} + 3\ H_2O$$

$$\text{no. g } Na_2SO_3 = 0.02650 \text{ L} \times \frac{0.0510 \text{ mol } MnO_4^-}{1 \text{ L}} \times \frac{5 \text{ mol } SO_3^{2-}}{2 \text{ mol } MnO_4^-} \times \frac{1 \text{ mol } Na_2SO_3}{1 \text{ mol } SO_3^{2-}} \times \frac{126 \text{ g } Na_2SO_3}{1 \text{ mol } Na_2SO_3}$$

$$= 0.426 \text{ g } Na_2SO_3$$

20-32. Refer to equations (20.21) and (20.46).

$$\text{no. g Cu} = 0.01124 \text{ L} \times \frac{0.1000 \text{ mol } S_2O_3^{2-}}{1 \text{ L}} \times \frac{1 \text{ mol } I_2}{2 \text{ mol } S_2O_3^{2-}} \times \frac{2 \text{ mol } Cu^{2+}}{1 \text{ mol } I_2} \times \frac{1 \text{ mol Cu}}{1 \text{ mol } Cu^{2+}} \times \frac{63.55 \text{ g Cu}}{1 \text{ mol Cu}}$$

$$= 7.143 \times 10^{-2} \text{ g Cu}$$

$$\% \text{ Cu} = \frac{7.143 \times 10^{-2} \text{ g Cu}}{1.100 \text{ g sample}} \times 100 = 6.49\%$$

Nitrogen

20-33. (a) $2\ NO_2(g) \rightleftharpoons N_2O_4(g)$

(b) $2\ HNO_3 \longrightarrow N_2O_5 + H_2O$

(c) $NH_3 + H_2SO_4 \longrightarrow NH_4^+ + HSO_4^-$ and $NH_3 + HSO_4^- \longrightarrow NH_4^+ + SO_4^{2-}$

(d) $Ag(s) + 2\ H^+ + NO_3^- \longrightarrow Ag^+ + H_2O + NO_2(g)$

(e) $(CH_3)_2N_2H_2 + 4\ O_2(g) \longrightarrow 2\ CO_2(g) + 4\ H_2O(g) + N_2(g)$

20-34. (a) $NH_2OH + H_2O \rightleftharpoons NH_3OH^+ + OH^-$ $\qquad K_b = 9.1 \times 10^{-9}$

Let $[NH_3OH^+] = [OH^-] = x$ $\qquad [NH_2OH] = 0.025 - x \simeq 0.025$ M

$$\frac{[NH_3OH^+][OH^-]}{[NH_2OH]} = \frac{x^2}{0.025} = 9.1 \times 10^{-9} \qquad x^2 = 2.28 \times 10^{-10} \qquad x = 1.51 \times 10^{-5}$$

$$[H_3O^+] = \frac{1.00 \times 10^{-14}}{1.51 \times 10^{-5}} = 6.62 \times 10^{-10}$$

$$pH = -\log [H_3O^+] = -\log 6.62 \times 10^{-10} = -[0.82 - 10] = 9.18$$

(b) $NH_3OH^+ + H_2O \rightleftharpoons NH_2OH + H_3O^+ \quad K_h = \dfrac{1.0 \times 10^{-14}}{9.1 \times 10^{-9}} = 1.1 \times 10^{-6}$

Let $x = [NH_2OH] = [H_3O^+]$ $\qquad \dfrac{[NH_2OH][H_3O^+]}{[NH_3OH^+]} = \dfrac{x^2}{0.015} = 1.1 \times 10^{-6}$

$x = [H_3O^+] = 1.3 \times 10^{-4}$ $\qquad pH = -\log (1.3 \times 10^{-4}) = 3.89$

20-35. Listed below are the oxidation states of the N atom in the nitrogen-containing species shown in Figure 20-12.

NO_3^-, +5; NO_2, +4; $HNO_2(NO_2^-)$, +3; NO, +2; N_2O, +1; N_2, 0; $NH_3OH^+(NH_2OH)$, -1;

$N_2H_5^+(N_2H_4)$, -2; $NH_4^+(NH_3)$, -3.

20-36. (a) $NH_3OH^+ \; + \; 2\,H^+ \; + \; 2\,e^- \longrightarrow NH_4^+ \; + \; H_2O$

(b) This calculation requires a combination of two half-reactions in the manner illustrated in Example 20-2.

$$2\,NH_3OH^+ \; + \; H^+ \; + \; 2\,e^- \longrightarrow \cancel{N_2H_5^+} \; + \; 2\,H_2O \qquad \Delta\bar{G}° = -2\mathcal{F}(1.46)$$

$$\cancel{N_2H_5^+} \; + \; 3\,H^+ \; + \; 2\,e^- \longrightarrow 2\,NH_4^+ \qquad \Delta\bar{G}° = -2\mathcal{F}(1.24)$$

$$2\,NH_3OH^+ \; + \; 4\,H^+ \; + \; 4\,e^- \longrightarrow 2\,NH_4^+ \; + \; 2\,H_2O \qquad \Delta\bar{G}° = -4\mathcal{F}E° = -2\mathcal{F}[1.46 + 1.24]$$

$$E° = \frac{-2\mathcal{F}(2.70)}{-4\mathcal{F}} = +1.35\ V$$

(c)

$$2\left\{Fe^{2+} \longrightarrow Fe^{3+} \; + \; e^-\right\} \qquad E°_{ox} = -(0.771)\ V$$

$$NH_3OH^+ \; + \; 2\,H^+ \; + \; 2\,e^- \longrightarrow NH_4^+ \; + \; H_2O \qquad E°_{red} = +1.35\ V$$

$$NH_3OH^+ \; + \; 2\,Fe^{2+} \; + \; 2\,H^+ \longrightarrow NH_4^+ \; + \; 2\,Fe^{3+} \; + \; H_2O \qquad E°_{cell} = +0.58\ V$$

This reaction *will* occur as written.

20-37. Use data from Appendix D, together with the value given for $\Delta\bar{H}_f°[N_2H_4(l)]$, to determine $\Delta\bar{H}°$ for the reaction.

$$N_2H_4(l) \; + \; O_2(g) \longrightarrow N_2(g) \; + \; 2\,H_2O(l)$$

$$\Delta\bar{H}° = 2\left\{\Delta\bar{H}_f°[H_2O(l)]\right\} - \Delta\bar{H}_f°[N_2H_4(l)] = 2 \times (-285.85) - (50.63) = -622.33\ kJ/mol$$

20-38. The balanced equation for the reaction in which nitrate ion is reduced to ammonia is written first.

oxid: $4\left\{Zn(s) \; + \; 4\,OH^- \longrightarrow Zn(OH)_4^{2-} \; + \; 2\,e^-\right\}$

red: $NO_3^- \; + \; 6\,H_2O \; + \; 8\,e^- \longrightarrow NH_3(g) \; + \; 9\,OH^-$

net: $4\,Zn(s) \; + \; NO_3^- \; + \; 7\,OH^- \; + \; 6\,H_2O \longrightarrow 4\,Zn(OH)_4^{2-} \; + \; NH_3(g)$

Determine the total number of moles of H_3O^+ in 50.00 ml of 0.1500 M HCl.

$$\text{no. mol } H_3O^+ \text{ available} = 0.0500\ L \times \frac{0.1500\ mol\ HCl}{1\ L} \times \frac{1\ mol\ H_3O^+}{1\ mol\ HCl} = 7.500 \times 10^{-3}\ mol\ H_3O^+$$

Determine the total number of moles of H_3O^+ left unreacted. (This is what is titrated by the NaOH.)

$$\text{no. mol } H_3O^+ \text{ unreacted} = 0.03210\ L \times \frac{0.1000\ mol\ NaOH}{1\ L} \times \frac{1\ mol\ OH^-}{1\ mol\ NaOH} \times \frac{1\ mol\ H_3O^+}{1\ mol\ OH^-} = 3.210 \times 10^{-3}\ mol\ H_3O^+$$

The number of moles of ammonia gas produced and H_3O^+ consumed are given by the following difference:

$$(7.500 \times 10^{-3}) - (3.210 \times 10^{-3}) = 4.290 \times 10^{-3}\ mol$$

Finally, we return to the balanced equation for the main reaction.

$$\text{no. mol } NO_3^- = 4.290 \times 10^{-3}\ mol\ NH_3 \times \frac{1\ mol\ NO_3^-}{1\ mol\ NH_3} = 4.290 \times 10^{-3}\ mol\ NO_3^-$$

$$[NO_3^-] = \frac{4.290 \times 10^{-3}\ mol\ NO_3^-}{0.02500\ L} = 0.1716\ M$$

Phosphorus

20-39. In order to reduce the number of conversion factors, the idea of a kilomole is used in the set up below. This idea was introduced and used in several of the exercises in Chapter 4.

$$\text{no. kg rock} = 100 \text{ kg P} \times \frac{1 \text{ kmol P}}{30.97 \text{ kg P}} \times \frac{1 \text{ kmol } P_4}{4 \text{ kmol P}} \times \frac{2 \text{ kmol } Ca_3(PO_4)_2}{1 \text{ kmol } P_4} \times \frac{310 \text{ kg } Ca_3(PO_4)_2}{1 \text{ kmol } Ca_3(PO_4)_2}$$

$$\times \frac{100 \text{ kg rock}}{58.0 \text{ kg } Ca_3(PO_4)_2} = 863 \text{ kg rock}$$

20-40. (a) This hydrolysis reaction occurs to a considerable extent in aqueous solution because of the very small value of K_{a_3} for the dissociation of H_3PO_4.

$$PO_4^{3-} + H_2O \rightleftharpoons HPO_4^{2-} + OH^- \qquad K_h = K_w/K_{a_3}, \text{ where } K_{a_3} = 4.8 \times 10^{-13}$$

(b) At the first equivalence point of phosphoric acid, the salt produced is NaH_2PO_4. Further dissociation of $H_2PO_4^-$ is more significant than its hydrolysis, which means that solutions containing this ion are acidic.

$$H_2PO_4^- + H_2O \rightleftharpoons H_3O^+ + HPO_4^{2-}$$

20-41. Only H atoms that are bonded to O atoms are ionizable in a ternary acid. Since H_3PO_2 is monoprotic, its molecules must have one H atom bonded to an O atom and two H atoms bonded directly to the P atom. The following structure is consistent with these facts.

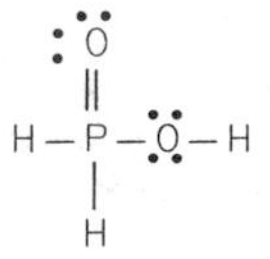

20-42. (a) calcium metaphosphate = $Ca(PO_3)_2$

(b) potassium pyrophosphate = $K_4P_2O_7$

(c) $NaSbO_2$ = sodium metaantimonite

(d) $NaBiO_3$ = sodium metabismuthate

(e) sodium orthobismuthate = Na_3BiO_4

Silicon

20-43. The composition of mica is expressed in Table 20-12 as $KAl_2(AlSi_3O_{10})(OH)_2$

If we assign the usual oxidation states of +1 for K and H, +3 for Al, +4 for Si, and -2 for O, we see that the total of all the oxidation numbers is zero, as expected for a neutral formula unit.

$$(+1) + 2\cdot(+3) + (+3) + 3\cdot(+4) + 10\cdot(-2) + 2\cdot(-2) + 2\cdot(+1)$$
$$= +1 \quad +6 \quad +3 \quad +12 \quad -20 \quad -4 \quad +2 = 0$$

20-44. (a)

$$\underset{\text{(orthosilicic acid)}}{Si(OH)_4} + 4\ NaOH \longrightarrow \underset{\text{(sodium orthosilicate)}}{Na_4SiO_4} + 4\ H_2O$$

The meta acid results from the elimination of one molecule of water from the ortho acid.

$$Si(OH)_4 \xrightarrow{-H_2O} \underset{\text{(metasilicic acid)}}{H_2SiO_3} + 2\ NaOH \longrightarrow \underset{\text{(sodium metasilicate)}}{Na_2SiO_3} + 2\ H_2O$$

(b) The pyro acid is obtained by eliminating one molecule of water from two molecules of the ortho acid.

$$Si(OH)_4 + Si(OH)_4 \xrightarrow{-H_2O} H_6Si_2O_7 \xrightarrow{6\ OH^-} 6\ H_2O + Si_2O_7^{6-}$$
$$\text{(pyrosilicic acid)} \qquad \text{(pyrosilicate anion)}$$

20-45. (a)

$$H_3C-\underset{\underset{CH_3}{|}}{\overset{\overset{CH_3}{|}}{Si}}-Cl + H_2O \longrightarrow H_3C-\underset{\underset{CH_3}{|}}{\overset{\overset{CH_3}{|}}{Si}}-OH + HCl$$

$$H_3C-\underset{\underset{CH_3}{|}}{\overset{\overset{CH_3}{|}}{Si}}-OH + HO-\underset{\underset{CH_3}{|}}{\overset{\overset{CH_3}{|}}{Si}}-CH_3 \longrightarrow H_3C-\underset{\underset{CH_3}{|}}{\overset{\overset{CH_3}{|}}{Si}}-O-\underset{\underset{CH_3}{|}}{\overset{\overset{CH_3}{|}}{Si}}-CH_3$$

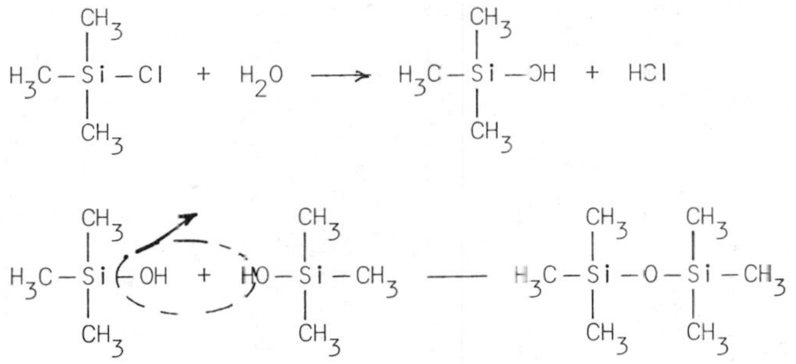

(b) A silicone polymer does not form. At best two of the $(CH_3)_3SiOH$ molecules (monomers) join to form a dimer. The chains cannot grow longer than two units in length.

(c) $CH_3SiCl_3 + 3\ H_2O \longrightarrow H_3C-Si(OH)_3 + 3\ HCl$

A silicone polymer can be produced from $CH_3Si(OH)_3$ because each monomer unit is able to link up with three other units in a three-dimensional structure.

Self-test Questions

1. (b) The displacement of Br_2 from a solution of Br^- is an oxidation process. The oxidizing agent employed must be a stronger one than Br_2. $Cl_2(aq)$ meets this requirement, but not $I_2(aq)$ nor $I_3^-(aq)$. $Cl^-(aq)$ can act as a reducing agent but not as an oxidizing agent.

2. (a) $BeCl_2$ has considerable covalent bond character. The other compounds--KF, CsI, and NaCl--are all strongly ionic.

3. (b) To act as an oxidizing agent, a substance must contain an element that can undergo a decrease in oxidation state. If the element is already present in its lowest possible oxidation state, e.g., Cl^-, it can act as a reducing agent but not as an oxidizing agent.

4. (d) SO_2 and CO_2 are both acidic oxides (forming H_2SO_3 and H_2CO_3 when they react with water). K_2O is a basic oxide (producing KOH). Al_2O_3 is the amphoteric oxide (yielding Al^{3+} in acidic solutions and AlO_2^- or $Al(OH)_4^-$ in basic solution).

5. (c) HgS is the most insoluble of all metal sulfides. In order to dissolve HgS, it is necessary to oxidize S^{2-} to S (the function of HNO_3) and complex Hg^{2+} as $HgCl_4^{2-}$ (the function of HCl). HgS will only dissolve in aqua regia--a mixture of HNO_3 and HCl.

6. (a) In the electrolysis of NaCl(l), the oxidation process is $2\ Cl^- \longrightarrow Cl_2(g) + 2\ e^-$. The reduction process is $Na^+ + e^- \longrightarrow Na(l)$. In NaCl(aq) the reduction process is $2\ H_2O + 2\ e^- \longrightarrow 2\ OH^- + H_2(g)$. Thus, in the electrolysis of NaCl(aq) two gases are produced--$H_2(g)$ and $Cl_2(g)$.

(b) H_3BO_3 is an extremely weak acid. Only the first H atom is ionizable to any extent. To cause the ionization of the second and third H atoms would require an NaOH(aq) of an impossibly high concentration. As a result, only the first H atom of H_3BO_3 can be removed by NaOH(aq) and only one end point is observed.

(c) I_2 reacts with $I^-(aq)$ to form $I_3^-(aq)$. This makes I_2 more soluble in a solution containing a high concentration of I^- [such as KI(aq)] than in pure water.

(d) Certain metals that will not dissolve in mineral acids which contain H^+ as the only oxidizing agent will dissolve in an acid containing a stronger oxidizing agent, such as NO_3^- or SO_4^{2-}.

(e) We might suspect that the ClO^- will oxidize NH_3, producing poisonous $Cl_2(g)$ as a product.

oxid: $2\ NH_3 + 6\ OH^- \longrightarrow N_2(g) + 6\ H_2O + 6\ e^-$

red: $3\{2\ ClO^- + 2\ H_2O + 2\ e^- \longrightarrow Cl_2(g) + 4\ OH^-\}$

net: $2\ NH_3 + 6\ ClO^- \longrightarrow N_2(g) + 3\ Cl_2(g) + 6\ OH^-$

7. (a) Mg_3N_2 (b) calcium hydroxide (c) rubdium superoxide

(d) chlorite ion (e) $HBrO_3$ (f) $S_2O_3^{2-}$

(g) Si_3H_8 (h) calcium metasilicate (i) magnesium pyrophosphate

(j) $Ca(H_2PO_4)_2$

8. (a) $MgCl_2(l) \xrightarrow{\text{electrolysis}} Mg(l) + Cl_2(g)$

(b) $BaCO_3(s) \xrightarrow{\text{heat}} BaO(s) + CO_2(g)$

(c) $CaO(s) + H_2O \longrightarrow Ca(OH)_2(s)$

(d) $2\ Al(s) + 3\ Cu^{2+}(aq) \longrightarrow 2\ Al^{3+}(aq) + 3\ Cu(s)$

(e) *oxid:* $5\{HSO_3^- + H_2O \longrightarrow SO_4^{2-} + 3\ H^+ + 2\ e^-\}$

red: $2\ IO_3^- + 12\ H^+ + 10\ e^- \longrightarrow I_2 + 6\ H_2O$

net: $2\ IO_3^- + 5\ HSO_3^- \longrightarrow I_2 + 5\ SO_4^{2-} + 3\ H^+ + H_2O$

(f) *oxid:* $H_2O_2 \longrightarrow O_2(g) + 2\ H^+ + 2\ e^-$

red: $Cl_2(g) + 2\ e^- \longrightarrow 2\ Cl^-$

net: $H_2O_2 + Cl_2(g) \longrightarrow O_2(g) + 2\ H^+ + 2\ Cl^-$

(g) *oxid:* $3\{ZnS(s) \longrightarrow Zn^{2+} + S(s) + 2\ e^-\}$

red: $2\{NO_3^- + 4\ H^+ + 3\ e^- \longrightarrow NO(g) + 2\ H_2O\}$

net: $3\ ZnS(s) + 8\ H^+ + 2\ NO_3^- \longrightarrow 3\ Zn^{2+} + 3\ S(s) + 2\ NO(g) + 4\ H_2O$

(h) *oxid:* $4\{NH_3(g) + H_2O \longrightarrow NO(g) + 5\ H^+ + 5\ e^-\}$

red: $5\{O_2(g) + 4\ H^+ + 4\ e^- \longrightarrow 2\ H_2O\}$

net: $4\ NH_3(g) + 5\ O_2(g) \longrightarrow 4\ NO(g) + 6\ H_2O$

9. The great value of I_2(aq) and I^-(aq) in analytical chemistry stems from the fact that I_2 can oxidize $S_2O_3^{2-}$ (thiosulfate ion) to $S_4O_6^{2-}$ (tetrathionate ion) and that I_2 can be detected even in trace amounts by starch indicator (yielding a deep blue complex). Titrations of oxidizing agents can be carried out, for example, by allowing the oxidizing agent to react with an excess of I^-(aq), producing I_2. The I_2 is then titrated with $S_2O_3^{2-}$(aq) in the presence of starch.

10.

$$H_2SeO_3 + 4\,H^+ + 4\,e^- \longrightarrow Se + 3\,H_2O \qquad \Delta G° = -4\mathcal{F} \times (0.74)V$$

$$Se + 2\,H^+ + 2\,e^- \longrightarrow H_2Se \qquad \Delta G° = -2\mathcal{F} \times (-0.35)V$$

$$H_2SeO_3 + 6\,H^+ + 6\,e^- \longrightarrow H_2Se + 3\,H_2O \qquad \Delta G° = \{-4\mathcal{F}(0.74) + 2\mathcal{F}(0.35)\}\ V$$

$$\Delta G° = -n\mathcal{F}E°$$

$$E° = \frac{-\Delta G°}{n\mathcal{F}} = \frac{-\{-4\mathcal{F}(0.74) + 2\mathcal{F}(0.35)\}\ V}{6\mathcal{F}} = \frac{2.96 - 0.70}{6} = 0.33\ V$$

Chapter 21

The Chemistry of Transition Elements

Properties of the transition elements

21-1. Transition metal atoms or their ions have partially filled *d* or *f* orbitals of an inner electronic shell. In representative element atoms and ions, *d* and *f* orbitals are either vacant or filled, but not partially filled.

21-2. Transition metal atoms display variable oxidation states. Representative metal atoms, such as those in group IIA, display a fixed oxidation state. Group IIA metal atoms and ions are diamagnetic. Group IA metal atoms are paramagnetic but their ions are diamagnetic. Most transition metal atoms and ions are paramagnetic. Most transition metal ions are colored; representative metal ions are not. Representative metal ions form few complexes, whereas transition metal ions form many.

21-3. In a series of transition elements, additional electrons go into an inner electron shell whereas the number of electrons in the outer shell tends to remain constant. Thus, the outershell electrons experience an essentially unvarying force of attraction. Atomic sizes change very little in a transition series. The atomic radius decreases from the alkali metal atom of group IA to the alkaline earth metal atom of group IIA and successively throughout a period of elements, as described on page 180 of the text.

21-4. The ionization of the first electron from a zinc atom requires that the stable "18 + 2" electron configuration be disrupted. Also, the electron to be lost is one of a pair. The energy requirement for this first electron is comparatively high. The second electron lost by a zinc atom is an unpaired 4*s* electron. The third electron would have to be extracted from the closed 3*d* subshell. This requires a high expenditure of energy. For copper, the first electron lost is an unpaired 4*s* electron. This is ionized more easily than the first electron of zinc. The second electron of the copper atom to be ionized must come from a closed 3*d* subshell. The energy requirement for this is higher than for the ionization of the second electron from a zinc atom. The third electron to be ionized from a copper atom is an unpaired 3*d* electron from a subshell that has already been disrupted.

21-5. Because its 3*d* subshell is closed, the zinc atom has less opportunity to form metallic bonds than do the transition metal atoms with *d*-orbital vacancies. The melting point of a metal is closely related to the number and strength of the bonds in the solid metal.

21-6. The Roman numerals of the B-group elements, with some exceptions, correspond to the maximum oxidation states in which the elements can commonly occur in their compounds. Thus, the maximum oxidation state for chromium is +6 and for manganese, +7. Exceptions occur in group IB, where copper commonly occurs in the oxidation state +2 and gold, +3.

21-7. (a) The "*d*-block" elements are all of the elements whose electron configurations are characterized by the filling of *d* orbitals. These are the elements in the central portion of the periodic table, from IIIB to IIB.

(b) The iron triad is the set of three similar elements in group VIII of the periodic table--Fe, Co, Ni.

(c) Atomic radii change very little in a regular transition series. In an inner transition series the *f* electrons of an inner electronic shell are not particularly effective in shielding the outer-shell electrons from the attractive force of the nucleus. As a result, an actual decrease in atomic radius with atomic number occurs in the lanthanoid series. This is called the lanthanoid contraction.

(d) Ferromagnetism is a phenomenon associated with Fe, Co, Ni and certain alloys. In ferromagnetism ordinary paramagnetic species are aligned into larger regions called domains, and the domains themselves become aligned in a magnetic field. As a result, an object with aligned magnetic domains is left permanently magnetized.

(e) A metal carbonyl is a compound between a metal (in particular a transition metal) and molecules of CO, such as $Ni(CO)_4$.

Chemistry of chromium and chromium compounds

21-8. The two half-reactions must be combined in the manner first illustrated in Example 20-2.

$$\text{~~Cr}^{2+}\text{(aq)~~} + 2\,e^- \longrightarrow Cr(s) \qquad \Delta G° = -n\mathcal{F}E° = +2\mathcal{F}(0.91)$$

$$Cr^{3+}(aq) + e^- \longrightarrow \text{~~Cr}^{2+}\text{(aq)~~} \qquad \Delta G° = -n\mathcal{F}E° = +\mathcal{F}(0.41)$$

$$Cr^{3+}(aq) + 3\,e^- \longrightarrow Cr(s) \qquad \Delta G° = -n\mathcal{F}E° = -3\mathcal{F}E° = 2.23\,\mathcal{F}$$

$E° = -2.23/3 = -0.74$ V

21-9. (a) In the nonoxidizing acid, HCl, we would expect Cr simply to displace H^+, yielding Cr^{2+} and $H_2(g)$.

$$Cr(s) + 2\,H^+(aq) + 2\,Cl^-(aq) \longrightarrow Cr^{2+}(aq) + 2\,Cl^-(aq) + H_2(g)$$

(b) In the oxidizing acid, H_2SO_4, the expected products are Cr^{3+} and $SO_2(g)$, but not $H_2(g)$.

$$2\,Cr(s) + 12\,H^+ + 3\,SO_4^{2-} \longrightarrow 2\,Cr^{3+} + 6\,H_2O + 3\,SO_2(g)$$

21-10. (a) Acidification of Na_2CrO_4 produces $Na_2Cr_2O_7$.

$$2\,CrO_4^{2-}(aq) + 2\,H^+(aq) \longrightarrow Cr_2O_7^{2-}(aq) + H_2O$$

(b) The key step involves reduction of Cr(VI) to Cr(III).

$$2\,CrO_4^{2-} + 16\,H^+ + 6\,Cl^- \longrightarrow 2\,Cr^{3+} + 8\,H_2O + 3\,Cl_2(g)$$

$$Cr^{3+} + 3\,OH^- \longrightarrow Cr(OH)_3(s) \qquad 2\,Cr(OH)_3(s) \xrightarrow{\Delta} Cr_2O_3(s) + 3\,H_2O$$

(c) The product of the first reaction in part (b) is $CrCl_3(aq)$. The solid can be obtained by evaporating the solution to dryness.

(d) If either $Cr(OH)_3(s)$ or $Cr_2O_3(s)$ from part (b) is dissolved in excess NaOH(aq), the product is $NaCrO_2(aq)$.

21-11. In acidic solution CrO_4^{2-} is converted to $Cr_2O_7^{2-}$, which has a large value of $E°_{red}$, +1.33 V. In basic solution, where CrO_4^{2-} predominates, the reduction potential to Cr^{3+} or $Cr(OH)_3$ is only -0.13 V. Thus, CrO_4^{2-} is not a particularly good oxidizing agent. However, since many metals form insoluble chromates, CrO_4^{2-} is used as a precipitating agent.

21-12. The chrome plating bath contains chromium in the oxidation state +6 ($Cr_2O_7^{2-}$). The electrolytic reduction is Cr(VI) + 6 e^- ⟶ Cr.

$$\text{no. C required} = \left(35.5\text{ cm}^2 \times 0.0010\text{ mm} \times \frac{1\text{ cm}}{10\text{ mm}}\right) \times \frac{7.14\text{ g Cr}}{1.00\text{ cm}^3} \times \frac{1\text{ mol Cr}}{52.00\text{ g Cr}} \times \frac{6\text{ mol e}^-}{1\text{ mol Cr}} \times \frac{96{,}500\text{ C}}{1\text{ mol e}^-} = 282\text{ C}$$

$$\text{no. s} = 282\text{ C} \times \frac{1\text{ s}}{5.0\text{ C}} = 56\text{ s}$$

Chromate-dichromate equilibrium

21-13. Use equation (21.25) to complete the calculations in parts (a) and (b).

(a) At pH = 5.0, $[H_3O^+] = 1.0 \times 10^{-5}$.

$$\frac{[Cr_2O_7^{2-}]}{[CrO_4^{2-}]^2} = 3.2 \times 10^{14}\,[H_3O^+]^2 = 3.2 \times 10^{14} \times (1.0 \times 10^{-5})^2 = 3.2 \times 10^4$$

For example, if $[CrO_4^{2-}] = 0.01$ M, $[Cr_2O_7^{2-}] = 3.2$ M.

(b) At pH = 9.3, $[H_3O^+] = 5.0 \times 10^{-10}$.

$$\frac{[Cr_2O_7^{2-}]}{[CrO_4^{2-}]^2} = 3.2 \times 10^{14}\,[H_3O^+]^2 = 3.2 \times 10^{14} \times (5.0 \times 10^{-10})^2 = 8.0 \times 10^{-5}$$

For example, if $[CrO_4^{2-}] = 1.0$ M, $[Cr_2O_7^{2-}] = 8.0 \times 10^{-5}$ M.

21-14. According to the text, the equilibrium between CrO_4^{2-} and $Cr_2O_7^{2-}$ can be thought of in terms of the following two reactions:

$$2\,H^+ + 2\,CrO_4^{2-} \rightleftharpoons \cancel{2\,HCrO_4^-} \qquad K = (1/3.2 \times 10^{-7})^2$$

$$\cancel{2\,HCrO_4^-} \rightleftharpoons Cr_2O_7^{2-} + H_2O \qquad K = ?$$

$$2\,H^+ + 2\,CrO_4^{2-} \rightleftharpoons Cr_2O_7^{2-} + H_2O \qquad K = 3.2 \times 10^{14}$$

But also, K for the net reaction, (3.2×10^{-14}) is equal to the product of the other K values, that is, $3.2 \times 10^{14} = K \times \frac{1}{(3.2 \times 10^{-7})^2}$ $\qquad K = 33$

21-15. First use equation (18.10) to determine $[H_3O^+]$ in the acetic acid-ammonium acetate buffer.

$$pH = 4.76 + \log\frac{[C_2H_3O_2^-]}{[HC_2H_3O_2]} = 4.76 + \log\frac{1.0}{1.0} = 4.76 \qquad [H_3O^+] = 1.74 \times 10^{-5}\text{ M}$$

Now use equation (21.25) to calculate $[CrO_4^{2-}]$ in a buffer solution with $[H_3O^+] = 1.74 \times 10^{-5}$ M.

$$\frac{[Cr_2O_7^{2-}]}{[CrO_4^{2-}]^2} = 3.2 \times 10^{14} \times (1.74 \times 10^{-5})^2 = 9.7 \times 10^4$$

Since the ratio $[Cr_2O_7^{2-}]/[CrO_4^{2-}]^2$ is so large--9.7×10^4--it is safe to assume that most of the chromium remains as $Cr_2O_7^{2-}$ at this pH. That is, assume that $[Cr_2O_7^{2-}] = 1.0 \times 10^{-3}$ M and that

$$[CrO_4^{2-}]^2 = \frac{[Cr_2O_7^{2-}]}{9.7 \times 10^4} = \frac{1.0 \times 10^{-3}}{9.7 \times 10^4} = 1.0 \times 10^{-8} \qquad [CrO_4^{2-}] = 1.0 \times 10^{-4}\text{ M}$$

Only the solubility product constant of $BaCrO_4$ is exceeded.

$$[Ba^{2+}][CrO_4^{2-}] = (0.10)(1.0 \times 10^{-4}) = 1.0 \times 10^{-5} > 1.2 \times 10^{-10}$$

$$[Sr^{2+}][CrO_4^{2-}] = (0.10)(1.0 \times 10^{-4}) = 1.0 \times 10^{-5} < 2.2 \times 10^{-5}$$

$$[Ca^{2+}][CrO_4^{2-}] = (0.10)(1.0 \times 10^{-4}) = 1.0 \times 10^{-5} < 7.1 \times 10^{-4}$$

The separation of Ba^{2+} from Sr^{2+} and Ca^{2+} does occur under the stated conditions.

The iron triad

21-16. Differences in the electron configurations of Fe, Co, and Ni are limited to the $3d$ subshell (that is, $3d^6$, $3d^7$ and $3d^8$, respectively). Each atom has two electrons in the $4s$ subshell. The atomic sizes are very similar and the way in which the electron configurations become altered through ionization and compound formation are also similar. As a result, these three elements resemble one another in physical and chemical properties.

21-17. Paramagnetism requires simply that unpaired electrons be present in individual atoms, ions or molecules. Ferromagnetism requires that, in addition to being paramagnetic, ions cluster into magnetic domains. When these domains are oriented in a magnetic field, an object displays ferromagnetism. Magnetic domains can only be produced by species having ionic radii corresponding to those of iron, cobalt, and nickel.

21-18. The reduction half-reaction is $O_2 + 4\ H^+ + 4\ e^- \longrightarrow 2\ H_2O$ $\quad E° = -1.229$ V.

We should expect Fe^{2+} to be oxidized to Fe^{3+}, as suggested by the half-reaction:

$Fe^{2+} \longrightarrow Fe^{3+} + e^-$ $\quad E°_{ox} = -(0.771)$ V [from Table 19-2]. But we should not expect Co^{2+} to be oxidized to Co^{3+}: $Co^{2+} \longrightarrow Co^{3+} + e^-$ $\quad E°_{ox} = -(1.82)$ V [from page 540].

For the reason stated on page 540 of the text, we should expect Ni^{2+} to behave in a similar manner to Co^{2+}. We should not expect it to be oxidized to Ni^{3+} by $O_2(g)$ in acidic solution.

21-19. The blue precipitate is formed by the reaction of Fe^{2+} with $[Fe(CN)_6]^{3-}$ following oxidation of the iron nail to Fe^{2+}. That is, $Fe(s) \longrightarrow Fe^{2+}(aq) + 2\ e^-$ is followed by reactions (21.35) and (21.34).

The pink color is assumed by phenolphthalein in a basic solution. Hydroxide ion is produced in the reduction half-reaction of the corrosion.

$O_2 + 2\ H_2O + 4\ e^- \longrightarrow 4\ OH^-$

Carbonyls

21-20. (a) Mo has an atomic number of 42. To bring the total number of electrons in its carbonyl to that of the noble gas at the end of the fifth period, Xe (Z = 54), requires that 12 electrons or 6 electron pairs be made available through CO molecules. This means six CO molecules and a carbonyl with the formula $Mo(CO)_6$ and an octahedral structure.

(b) Five pairs of electrons brought to the carbonyl structure by CO molecules produces a noble gas electron configuration, that of Rn (Z = 86). The formula is $Os(CO)_5$ and the structure is trigonal bipyramidal.

(c) Rhenium carbonyl must form a binuclear carbonyl. The basic unit, $Re(CO)_5$, requires an extra electron from a second unit to produce the electron configuration of Rn (Z = 86). The formula of the carbonyl is $Re_2(CO)_{10}$.

21-21. Nickel and iron carbonyls are $Ni(CO)_4$ and $Fe(CO)_5$, respectively, whereas cobalt forms a *binuclear* carbonyl, $Co_2(CO)_8$. Because the binuclear carbonyl has a considerably higher molecular weight than the other two, we should expect it to exist as a solid at a higher temperature than would be the case for the others.

21-22. The total number of electrons associated with the V atom in $V(CO)_6$ is 35. We might expect this covalent carbonyl molecule to acquire one extra electron, say from a sodium atom. The result is a compound consisting of the ions Na^+ and $[V(CO)_6]^-$.

Oxidation-reduction

21-23. (a) $Cr_2O_7^{2-} + 14\ H^+ + 6\ e^- \longrightarrow 2\ Cr^{3+} + 7\ H_2O$

(b) $Cr^{2+}(aq) \longrightarrow Cr^{3+}(aq) + e^-$

(c) $Fe(OH)_3(s) + 5\ OH^- \longrightarrow FeO_4^{2-} + 4\ H_2O + 3\ e^-$

(d) $[Ag(CN)_2]^- + e^- \longrightarrow Ag(s) + 2\ CN^-$

21-24. (a) *oxid:* $2\ \{Fe_2S_3(s) + 6\ OH^- \longrightarrow 2\ Fe(OH)_3(s) + 3\ S(s) + 6\ e^-\}$

red: $3\ \{O_2(g) + 2\ H_2O + 4\ e^- \longrightarrow 4\ OH^-\}$

net: $2\ Fe_2S_3(s) + 6\ H_2O + 3\ O_2(g) \longrightarrow 4\ Fe(OH)_3(s) + 6\ S(s)$

(b) *oxid:* $4\ \{Ag(s) + 2\ CN^- \longrightarrow [Ag(CN)_2]^- + e^-\}$

red: $O_2(g) + 2\ H_2O + 4\ e^- \longrightarrow 4\ OH^-$

net: $4\ Ag(s) + 8\ CN^- + O_2(g) + 2\ H_2O \longrightarrow 4\ [Ag(CN)_2]^- + 4\ OH^-$

(c) *oxid:* $2\ \{Mn^{2+} + 4\ H_2O \longrightarrow MnO_4^- + 8\ H^+ + 5\ e^-\}$

red: $5\ \{S_2O_8^{2-} + 2\ e^- \longrightarrow 2\ SO_4^{2-}\}$

net: $2\ Mn^{2+} + 5\ S_2O_8^{2-} + 8\ H_2O \longrightarrow 2\ MnO_4^- + 10\ SO_4^{2-} + 16\ H^+$

21-25. $Cr_2O_7^{2-} + 3\ Zn(s) + 14\ H^+ \longrightarrow 2\ Cr^{3+} + 7\ H_2O + 3\ Zn^{2+}$
(orange) ... (green)

$2\ Cr^{3+} + Zn(s) \longrightarrow 2\ Cr^{2+} + Zn^{2+}$
(green) ... (blue)

$4\ Cr^{2+} + O_2 + 4\ H^+ \longrightarrow 4\ Cr^{3+} + 2\ H_2O$
(blue) ... (green)

21-26. Use the method of Example 20-2 as follows:

$MnO_4^- + 4\ H^+ + 3\ e^- \longrightarrow \cancel{MnO_2(s)} + 2\ H_2O \qquad \Delta\bar{G}° = -3\mathcal{F}(1.70)$

$\cancel{MnO_2(s)} + 4\ H^+ + 2\ e^- \longrightarrow Mn^{2+} + 2\ H_2O \qquad \Delta\bar{G}° = -2\mathcal{F}(1.23)$

$MnO_4^- + 8\ H^+ + 5\ e^- \longrightarrow Mn^{2+} + 4\ H_2O \qquad \Delta\bar{G}° = -5\mathcal{F}E°_{red}$

$-5\mathcal{F}E°_{red} = -3\mathcal{F}(1.70) - 2\mathcal{F}(1.23) \qquad E°_{red} = \frac{(3 \times 1.70) + (2 \times 1.23)}{5} = 1.51\ V$

Qualitative analysis

21-27. (a) Water: NaOH is soluble and $Fe(OH)_3$ is not.

(b) $NH_3(aq)$: Ni^{2+} forms a complex ion; Fe^{3+} does not (see Figure 21-5).

(c) NaOH(aq): Cr_2O_3 is amphoteric; $Fe(OH)_3$ is not.

(d) HCl(aq): MnS is one of the more soluble metal sulfides. Although not soluble in water, it will dissolve in a dilute acid. PbS can only be dissolved in an oxidizing acid such as HNO_3 (recall Table 20-7).

21-28. (a) $FeS(s) + 2\ H^+ \longrightarrow Fe^{2+} + H_2S(g)$

(b) $CoS + 4\ H^+ + 2\ NO_3^- + 4\ Cl^- \longrightarrow [CoCl_4]^{2-} + S + 2\ H_2O + 2\ NO_2(g)$

(c) $2\ Cr^{3+} + 3\ H_2O_2 + 10\ OH^- \longrightarrow 2\ CrO_4^{2-} + 8\ H_2O$

(d) $Ni(OH)_2(s) + 6\ NH_3(aq) \longrightarrow [Ni(NH_3)_6]^{2+}(aq) + 2\ OH^-(aq)$

(e) $Fe^{2+} + K_3[Fe(CN)_6] \longrightarrow$ Turnbull's blue

(f) $MnO_2(s) + 4\ H^+ + 2\ Cl^- \longrightarrow Mn^{2+} + 2\ H_2O + Cl_2(g)$

21-29. (a) In the absence of NH_4Cl, the hydroxide ion concentration would be great enough that $Mg(OH)_2$ would precipitate with the ammonium sulfide group.

(b) Without the addition of H_2O_2, Cr^{3+} would not be oxidized to CrO_4^{2-} nor would cobalt be oxidized to the oxidation state +3 [in $Co(OH)_3$].

(c) The hydroxides of Fe, Co, and Ni would all precipitate if NaOH were used as the reagent instead of NH_3. The desired separation of Co^{3+} and Ni^{3+} from Fe^{3+} through the formation of ammine complex ions would not occur.

(d) Dissolving of CoS and NiS would occur along with MnS; a separation of Co^{2+}, Ni^{2+} and Mn^{2+} would not be achieved.

(e) Traces of Fe^{3+} would fail to be complexed and would interfere with the test for cobalt if NaF were omitted from the reagent in step 7.

21-30. Dissolve the sample in HCl(aq). The expected ions that would appear in solution are Fe^{2+} and some combination of Mn^{2+}, Ni^{2+} and Cr^{3+}. Treat this solution with NaOH and H_2O_2. If chromium is present, a yellow color (CrO_4^{2-}) appears in solution. The precipitate that forms is $Fe(OH)_3$ and either $Ni(OH)_2$ or MnO_2 or a mixture of the two. Treat the precipitate with HCl(aq). Dissolving should be complete. Now add NH_3(aq). The precipitate that forms is $Fe(OH)_3$. The filtrate contains Mn^{2+}, $[Ni(NH_3)_6]^{2+}$, both or neither. Add HCl and H_2S. If precipitation occurs, the precipitate is NiS. Add a strong oxidizing agent, such as $(NH_4)_2S_2O_8$, to the remaining solution. If Mn^{2+} is present it will be oxidized to the strongly colored purple MnO_4^-.

Quantitative analysis

21-31. (a) Formula of nickel dimethylglyoximate: $NiC_8H_{14}N_4O_4$

(b) $$\text{no. g Ni} = 0.259\ \text{g NiC}_8\text{H}_{14}\text{N}_4\text{O}_4 \times \frac{1\ \text{mol Ni}}{289\ \text{g NiC}_8\text{H}_{14}\text{N}_4\text{O}_4} \times \frac{58.71\ \text{g Ni}}{1\ \text{mol Ni}} = 0.0526\ \text{g Ni}$$

$$\%\ \text{Ni} = \frac{0.0526\ \text{g Ni}}{1.502\ \text{g steel}} \times 100 = 3.50\%$$

21-32. $$\text{no. mol H}_2\text{C}_2\text{O}_4\ \text{available} = 1.651\ \text{g H}_2\text{C}_2\text{O}_4 \cdot 2\ \text{H}_2\text{O} \times \frac{1\ \text{mol H}_2\text{C}_2\text{O}_4}{126.0\ \text{g H}_2\text{C}_2\text{O}_4 \cdot 2\ \text{H}_2\text{O}} = 0.01310\ \text{mol H}_2\text{C}_2\text{O}_4$$

$$\text{no. mol H}_2\text{C}_2\text{O}_4\ \text{reacting with MnO}_4^- = 0.03006\ \text{L} \times \frac{0.1000\ \text{mol MnO}_4^-}{\text{L}} \times \frac{5\ \text{mol H}_2\text{C}_2\text{O}_4}{2\ \text{mol MnO}_4^-} = 0.007515\ \text{mol H}_2\text{C}_2\text{O}_4$$

$$\text{no. mol H}_2\text{C}_2\text{O}_4\ \text{reacting with MnO}_2 = 0.01310 - 0.00752 = 0.00558\ \text{mol H}_2\text{C}_2\text{O}_4$$

$$\text{no. mol } MnO_2 = 0.00558 \text{ mol } H_2C_2O_4 \times \frac{1 \text{ mol } MnO_2}{1 \text{ mol } H_2C_2O_4} = 0.00558 \text{ mol } MnO_2$$

$$\% \; MnO_2 = \frac{0.00558 \text{ mol } MnO_2 \times \dfrac{86.9 \text{ g } MnO_2}{1 \text{ mol } MnO_2}}{0.589 \text{ g ore}} \times 100 = 82.3\%$$

Self-test Questions

1. (*c*) Strong metallic bonding in the transition elements leads to high melting points. The ionization energies, though not as low as for IA and IIA metals, are not particularly high. Most of the transition elements are more metallic than hydrogen and have negative standard reduction potentials. In general, the transition elements do have a variety of oxidation states.

2. (*d*) The electron configurations of Cr and Fe are $[Ar]3d^5 4s^1$ and $[Ar]3d^6 4s^2$, respectively. In Cr^{2+} there are four unpaired electrons; in Fe^{3+} there are five. Cu has the electron configuration $[Ar]3d^{10}4s^1$ and Cu^{2+}, $[Ar]3d^9$; Cu^{2+} is paramagnetic. Only Zn^{2+}, with the electron configuration $[Ar]3d^{10}$ is diamagnetic.

3. (*a*) The maximum oxidation state of Ti, a member of group IVB is +4. Ti is not expected to display an oxidation state of +6; the other elements listed do.

4. (*b*) $Cl_2(g)$ is produced from HCl(aq) through an oxidation half-reaction; this requires an oxidizing agent. Of the substances listed, only MnO_2 is a strong oxidizing agent.

5. (*a*) Write an equation for the disproportionation reaction.

oxid: $2\{MnO_4^{2-} \longrightarrow MnO_4^- + e^-\}$

red: $MnO_4^{2-} + 4\,H^+ + 2\,e^- \longrightarrow MnO_2(s) + 2\,H_2O$

net: $3\,MnO_4^{2-} + 4\,H^+ \longrightarrow 2\,MnO_4^- + MnO_2(s) + 2\,H_2O$

From the net equation we see that the forward reaction--the disproportionation reaction is favored by high $[H^+]$.

6. The ionization energy, I_1, is lowest for Rb because it is the largest of the atoms, is in group IA, and the electron to be lost is $5s^1$. Next comes another element in group IA, but having somewhat smaller atoms, K. The Ca atom, in group IIA, is smaller than K and has a higher first ionization energy. Smallest of all is the Zn atom and, correspondingly, its I_1 is largest.

7. With a limited amount of OH^-, both Mg^{2+} and Cr^{3+} yield hydroxide precipitates.

$Mg^{2+} + 2\,OH^- \longrightarrow Mg(OH)_2(s)$ and $Cr^{3+} + 3\,OH^- \longrightarrow Cr(OH)_3(s)$

With an excess of NaOH, the $Cr(OH)_3(s)$ would redissolve whereas the $Mg(OH)_2(s)$ would not. This is simply a case of $Cr(OH)_3$ being an amphoteric hydroxide whereas $Mg(OH)_2$ has only basic properties.

Mg^{2+} + excess $OH^- \longrightarrow Mg(OH)_2(s)$ and Cr^{3+} + excess $OH^- \longrightarrow CrO_2^-$

8. The concentration of CrO_4^{2-} in equilibrium with $Cr_2O_7^{2-}$, even in acidic solution, is sufficiently high that K_{sp} for $PbCrO_4$ is exceeded.

$Cr_2O_7^{2-}$ (orange) $+ H_2O \rightleftharpoons 2\,CrO_4^{2-}$ (yellow) $+ 2\,H^+$

$Pb^{2+} + CrO_4^{2-}$ (yellow) $\longrightarrow PbCrO_4(s)$ (yellow)

9. (a) $ZnSO_4$ will dissolve in all three reagents. The $Zn(OH)_2$ that might first precipitate from NaOH(aq) would redissolve to form zincate ion, ZnO_2^{2-}. $Zn(OH)_2$ is amphoteric.

(b) $Ni(OH)_2$ is insoluble in water, but soluble in HCl(aq). Because it is not amphoteric, $Ni(OH)_2$ will not dissolve in NaOH(aq).

(c) $AgNO_3$ is soluble in water but not in NaOH, where a hydroxide precipitate would form, nor in HCl, from which the chloride would deposit as a precipitate.

(d) FeS is soluble in HCl(aq) [recall Table 20-7], but not in water nor in NaOH(aq).

0. The formation of a precipitate with NaOH(aq) and H_2O_2 establishes that Fe^{3+} and/or Ni^{2+} is present. That the solution obtained is colorless suggests that Cr^{3+} is absent (that is, no yellow CrO_4^{2-} is formed). Zn^{2+} may or may not be present. That the precipitate [$Fe(OH_3)$ and/or $Ni(OH)_2$] redissolves in HCl(aq) but does *not* reform upon addition of NH_3(aq), establishes that the initial precipitate was $Ni(OH)_2$ only. (If Fe^{3+} had been present it would have reprecipitated as $Fe(OH)_3$ in the presence of NH_3(aq); Ni^{2+} remains in solution as the complex ion $[Ni(NH_3)_6]^{2+}$.) Ions present: Ni^{2+}; ions absent: Cr^{3+}, Fe^{3+}; further tests needed: Zn^{2+}.

Chapter 22

Complex Ions and Coordination Compounds

Definitions and terminology

22-1. (a) Ligands are the species (usually neutral molecules or anions) that are attached to a central metal ion in a complex ion.

(b) The coordination number refers to the number of points in the coordination sphere of a metal ion at which attachment of ligands can occur.

(c) A unidentate ligand is one that is attached to a central metal ion at one point only. A multidentate ligand can be attached to the metal ion at two or more points simultaneously.

(d) An aquo complex is a complex ion that has water molecules as ligands.

22-2. (a) A complex ion with square planar geometry can be pictured as one in which the central metal ion is situated at the center of a square and a ligand at each corner.

(b) A metal ion that employs d^2sp^3 hybrid orbitals to attach ligands has a coordination number of six and an octahedral structure, such as $[Co(NH_3)_6]^{3+}$.

(c) Consider, for example, an octahedral complex with two ligands of one type (X) and the remaining ligands of another type (Y). Species with differing properties (isomers) may result, depending on how these ligands are attached to the central metal ion. If the two (X) are along the same edge of the structure, one isomer (*cis*) results. If they are on opposite sides, that is, not joined by an edge, a different isomer (*trans*) is obtained.

22-3. A chelate complex involves multidentate ligands. These attach themselves to the central metal ion at more than one point and produce rings of atoms. Ordinary complex ions usually involve unidentate ligands; attachment occurs at a single point.

Nomenclature

22-4. (a) $[Ni(NH_3)_6]^{2+}$: The coordination number is 6. Because the ligands are neutral mclecules, the oxidation state of the Ni must be the same as the charge on the ion, +2.

(b) $[AlF_6]^{3-}$: The coordination number is 6. The ligands each carry a charge of -1. To account for a total ionic charge of -3, the oxidation state of Al must be +3.

(c) $[Cu(CN)_4]^{3-}$: The coordination number is 4. The oxidation state of the copper is +1.

(d) $[Cr(NH_3)_3Br_3]$: The coordination number is 6. This is a neutral complex. Because each Br^- carries a charge of -1, the oxidation state of Cr must be +3.

(e) $[Fe(C_2O_4)_3]^{3-}$: Oxalate ion, $C_2O_4^{\ 2-}$, is a bidentate ligand. Three oxalate ions attach themselves to the central metal ion at a total of six points; the coordination number is 6. Since the oxalate ions carry a charge of -2, we conclude that the iron must be in an oxidation state of +3.

22-5. The seven rules listed in Section 22-4 are applied in establishing the following names:

(a) $[Ag(NH_3)_2]^+$: diamminesilver(I) ion

(b) $[Fe(H_2O)_6]^{3+}$: hexaaquoiron(III) ion

(c) $[CuCl_4]^{2-}$: tetrachlorocuprate(II) ion

(d) $[Pt(en)_2]^{2+}$: bis(ethylenediamine)platinum(II) ion

(e) $[Co(NH_3)_4(NO_2)Cl]^+$: nitrochlorotetraamminecobalt(III) ion

22-6. (a) $[Co(NH_3)_5Br]SO_4$: bromopentaamminecobalt(III) sulfate

(b) $[Co(NH_3)_5SO_4]Br$: sulfatopentaamminecobalt(III) bromide

(c) $[Cr(NH_3)_6][Co(CN)_6]$: hexaamminechromium(III) hexacyanocobaltate(III)

(d) $Na_3[Co(NO_2)_6]$: sodium hexanitrocobaltate(III)

(e) $[Co(en)_3]Cl_3$: tris(ethylenediamine)cobalt(III) chloride

22-7. (a) Dicyanosilver(I) ion: $[Ag(CN)_2]^-$

(b) Tetrachlorodiamminenickelate(II) ion: $[Ni(NH_3)_2Cl_4]^{2-}$

(c) Hexachloroplatinate(IV) ion: $[PtCl_6]^{2-}$

(d) Sodium tetrachlorocuprate(II): $Na_2[CuCl_4]$

(e) Potassium hexacyanoferrate(II): $K_4[Fe(CN)_6]$

(f) Bis(ethylenediamine)copper(II) ion: $[Cu(en)_2]^{2+}$

(g) Dihydroxotetraaquoaluminum(III) chloride: $[Al(H_2O)_4(OH)_2]Cl$

(h) Chlorobis(ethylenediamine)amminechromium(III) sulfate: $[Cr(en)_2(NH_3)Cl]SO_4$

Bonding and structure of complex ions

20-8. We might expect a linear structure for the complex ion $[Au(CN)_2]^-$ simply because there are only two ligands in the structure. This expectation is corroborated through a consideration of electron configurations. That of Au^+ is $[Xe]4f^{14}5d^{10}$. The orbitals of the sixth electronic shell that are involved in complex ion formation are the $6s$ and $6p$, hybridized into a pair of sp orbitals. The angle between the sp orbitals is 180°, corresponding to a linear structure.

20-9. (a) $[Ni(CN)_4]^{2-}$: [Ar] 3d: [↓↑|↓↑|↓↑|↓↑] dsp^2: [••|••|••|••] 4p: [ ] (••) represents electrons donated by CN^- ions.

Structure: square planar, similar to that shown for $[Cu(NH_3)_4]^{2+}$ in Figure 22-1.

(b) All the electons shown in the structure in part (a) are paired. We should expect the complex ion to be *diamagnetic*.

20-10. To account for the tetrahedral structure, the bonding scheme in the complex ion must involve sp^3 hybridization. This scheme requires that the complex ion possess *five* unpaired electrons.

$[FeCl_4]^-$: [Ar] 3d: [↓|↓|↓|↓|↓] $4sp^3$: [••|••|••|••] (••) represents electrons donated by Cl^- ions.

22-11. The complex ion $[Co(NH_3)_6]^{2+}$, like $[Co(NH_3)_6]^{3+}$, has an octahedral structure, but in contrast to $[Co(NH_3)_6]^{3+}$ it has unpaired electrons. An orbital scheme that is consistent with these facts is

$[Co(NH_3)_6]^{2+}$: [Ar] 3*d* [↓↑ | ↓↑ | ↓ | ↓ | ↓] sp^3d^2 [•• | •• | •• | •• | •• | ••] (••) represents electrons donated by NH_3 molecules.

Note further that sp^3d^2 hybridization is involved, rather than d^2sp^3 as in $[Co(NH_3)_6]^{3+}$.

22-12. (a) $[Fe(en)Cl_4]^-$

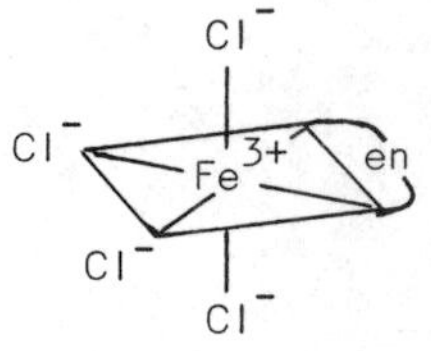

(b) $[Fe(en)(ox)Cl_2]^-$

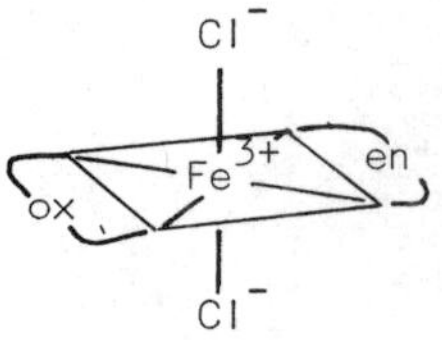

or

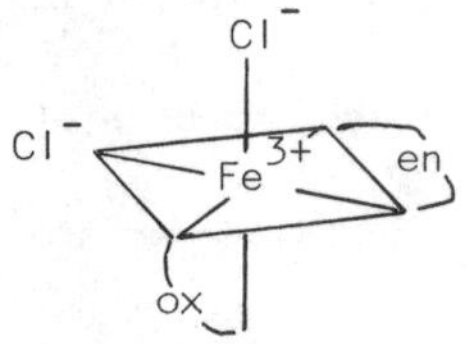

(c) $[Fe(ox)_3]^{3-}$

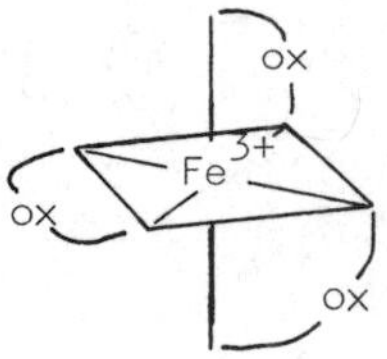

22-13. (a) $[Pt(en)_2]^{2+}$

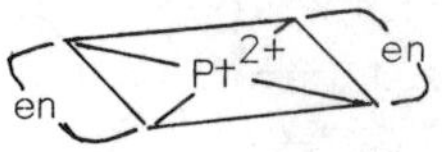

(b) $[Cr(dien)_2]^{3+}$. Each dien attaches at three of the six points in the coordination sphere (see Table 22-3).

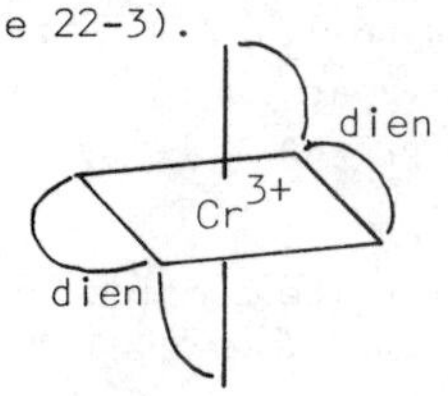

(c) $[Fe(EDTA)]^{2-}$. The EDTA attaches to all six points in the coordination sphere (see Table 22-3).

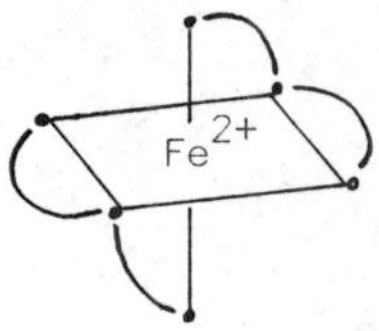

22-14.

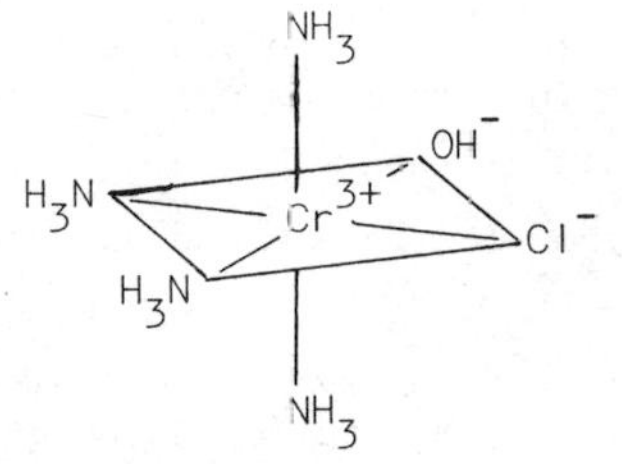

22-15. Each of the complex ions has an octahedral structure. The requirement in each case is to discover in how many different ways the ligands can be substituted into the structure. ($X = H_2O$; $Y = NH_3$)

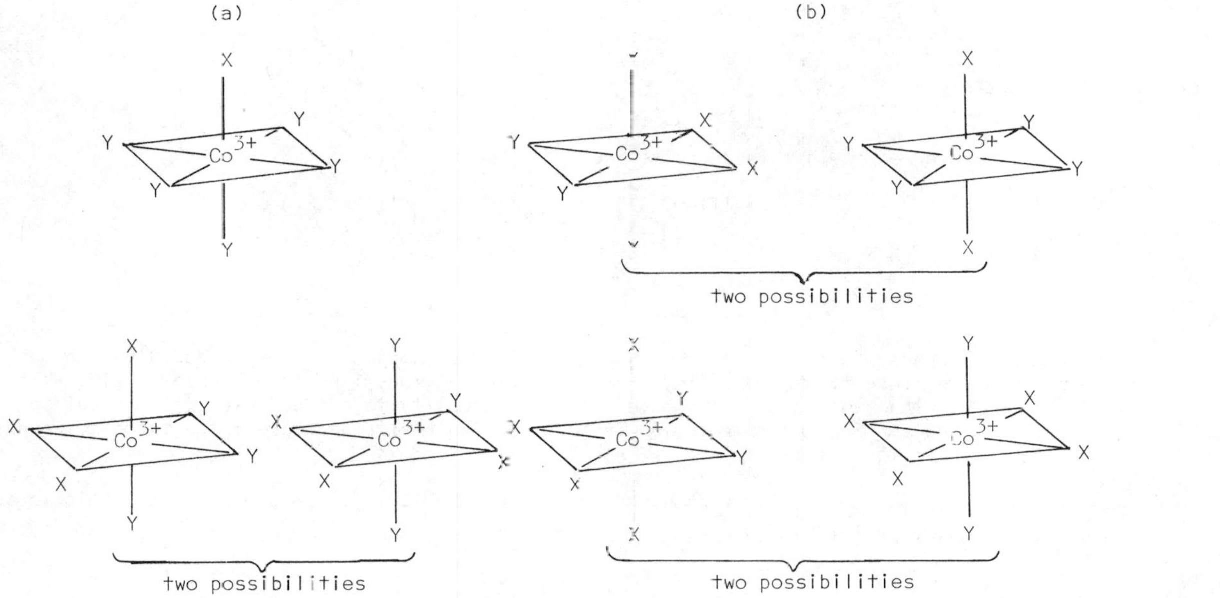

22-16. (a) *Cis-trans* isomerism does not exist in complex ions with a tetrahedral structure because all positions that ligands occupy are equivalent.

(b) There are two basic orientations that a pair of ligands may have with respect to one another in a square planar structure, either along the same edge or at opposite corners of the square. For this reason, square planar complexes do exhibit *cis-trans* isomerism.

(c) The two positions that ligands may occupy in a linear complex ion are identical. Whether the two ligands are the same or different, there is still only one possibility for each complex ion.

22-17. $[Co(en)_3]^{3+}$ *cis*-dichlorobis(ethylenediamine)cobalt(III) ion

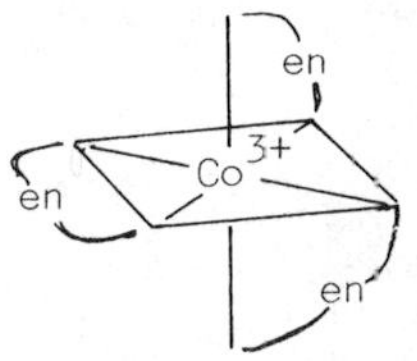

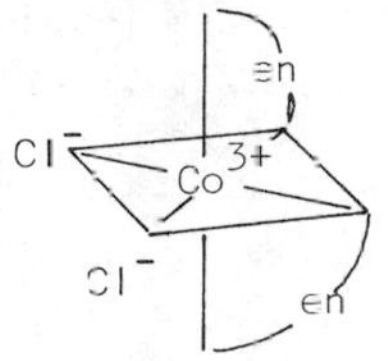

22-18. (a) The metal ions Zn^{2+} and Cu^{2+} can be interchanged. That is, the isomers are:

$[Zn(NH_3)_4][CuCl_4]$ and $[Cu(NH_3)_4][ZnCl_4]$

This is an example of coordination isomerism.

(b) As indicated in the marginal note on page 558, the thiocyanate ion can be linked to a central metal ion either through the S atom or the N atom. This is an example of linkage isomerism.

(c) All the positions in the coordination sphere available to the Cl^- ion are equivalent. There is no isomerism.

(d) Here the structure is square planar with Cl^- ligands at three of the available positions and pyridine (py) at the fourth. All four positions at which the py may be found are equivalent. There is no isomerism.

(e) In this octahedral complex the three NH_3 (and also the three OH^-) may be found either at the corners of one face or along a perimeter of the octahedron. This leads to two isomers of the *cis-trans* type.

Electrical conductivity

22-19. The compounds referred to in this exercise are

(I)	(II)	(III)
$[Co(NH_3)_6]Cl_3$	$[Co(NH_3)_5Cl]Cl_2$	$[Co(NH_3)_4Cl_2]Cl$
4 ions per formula unit	3 ions per formula unit	2 ions per formula unit

Each of the compounds has the same formula weight, but the numbers of ions produced by a given mass of compound are different. For example, there are twice as many ions in a sample of (I) as in a sample of (III) of the same mass. We should expect the ability to conduct electric current to increase as the number of ions in solution increases. The best conductor of the three compounds is (I) and the poorest is (III).

22-20. The compound referred to here is the neutral complex $[Co(NH_3)_3Cl_3]$. We should expect this to be the poorest conductor of the four compounds; in fact it is a nonconductor.

Crystal field theory

22-21. The ion Fe^{2+} has a 3*d* configuration with 6 electrons. Because all of the complex ions in question are octahedral, the *d*-level splitting takes the form shown below. H_2O is a weak-field ligand and CN^- is a strong-field ligand.

$[Fe(H_2O)_6]^{3+}$
paramagnetic

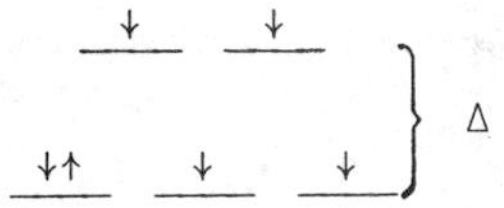

$[Fe(CN)_6]^{4-}$
diamagnetic

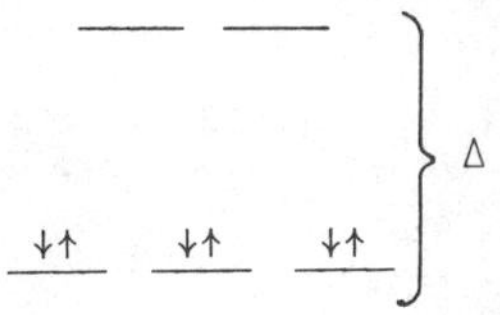

22-22. Both ions have an octahedral structure and the *d*-level splitting shown below. Ethylenediamine is a strong-field ligand and Cl^- is a weak-field ligand.

(a) Weak field

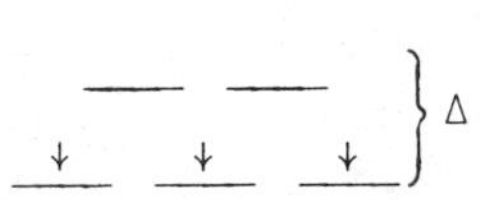

$[MoCl_6]^{3-}$
paramagnetic

(b) Strong field

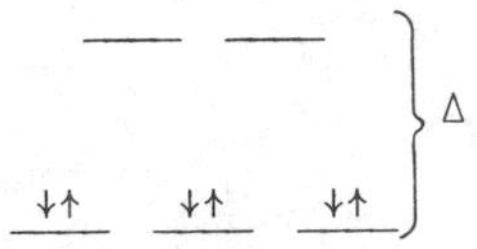

$[Co(en)_3]^{3+}$
diamagnetic

22-23. The *d*-level splitting in octahedral complexes of Cr^{2+} and the placement of the *four* 3*d* electrons follows the pattern indicated below and corresponds to the observations stated in the exercise.

Weak field *Strong field*

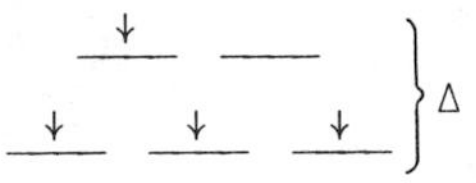

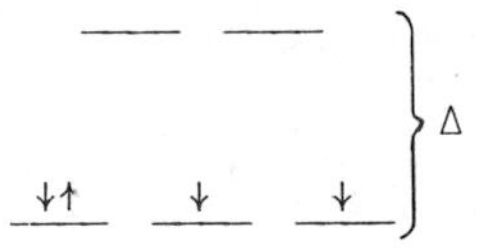

22-24. The situation with Cr^{3+} corresponding to that of Cr^{2+} in the preceding exercise is

Weak field *Strong field*

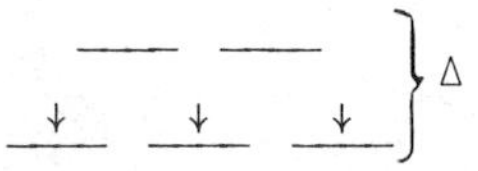

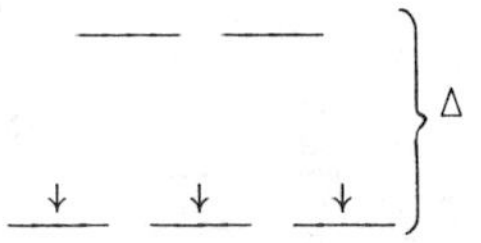

Because Cr^{3+} has *three* 3*d* electrons, all of them remain unpaired, whether in a weak-field or a strong-field complex.

22-25. CN^- is a strong-field ligand and H_2O is weak; *d*-level splitting is greater in cyano complexes than in aquo complexes. To produce an electronic transition from the lower to higher energy levels in the cyano complexes generally requires an absorption of more energy than is the case for aquo complexes. The highest energy content of the visible colors is associated with blue light. Absorption of blue light means that yellow is the color of the transmitted light. Many solutions of cyano complexes are yellow. In contrast, the absorption of red or yellow light, which have lower energies than blue light, results in solutions that are green and blue, respectively.

22-26. In the ion $[FeCl_4]^-$ iron exists as Fe^{3+}. Its electron configuration is $1s^2 2s^2 2p^6 3s^2 3p^6 3d^5$. For a tetrahedral complex the *d* level splitting is

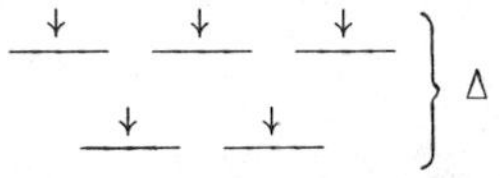

Because Cl^- is a weak-field ligand, we should expect the crystal field splitting, Δ, to be small and for all five electrons to be unpaired. In Exercise 10 we also concluded that there would be five unpaired electrons (based on valence bond theory).

Complex ion equilibria

22-27. (a) $Mg(OH)_2(s) + NH_3(aq) \longrightarrow$ no reaction

$Zn(OH)_2(s) + 4\ NH_3(aq) \longrightarrow [Zn(NH_3)_4]^{2+}(aq) + 2\ OH^-(aq)$

(b) $Cu^{2+} + \cancel{SO_4^{2-}} + \cancel{2\ Na^+} + 2\ OH^- \longrightarrow Cu(OH)_2(s) + \cancel{2\ Na^+} + \cancel{SO_4^{2-}}$

$Cu(OH)_2(s) + 4\ NH_3(aq) \longrightarrow [Cu(NH_3)_4]^{2+} + 2\ OH^-$

$[Cu(NH_3)_4]^{2+} + 4\ H_3O^+ \longrightarrow [Cu(H_2O)_4]^{2+} + 4\ NH_4^+$

(Cu^{2+} exists primarily as the light blue aquo complex, $[Cu(H_2O)_4]^{2+}$.)

(c) $CuCl_2(s) + \cancel{2\ H^+} + 2\ Cl^- \longrightarrow [CuCl_4]^{2-} + \cancel{2\ H^+}$
yellow

$$[CuCl_4]^{2-} + 4\ H_2O \longrightarrow [Cu(H_2O)_4]^{2+} + 4\ Cl^-$$

yellow — blue

The equilibrium mixture of the yellow and blue complex ions accounts for the green color of the solution. With a large excess of water, equilibrium is shifted far to the right and the solution color becomes bale blue.

22-28. *In $HNO_3(aq)$:* $PbCl_2(s) \rightleftharpoons Pb^{2+}(aq) + 2\ Cl^-(aq)$

$$Pb^{2+}(aq) + Cl^-(aq) + H^+(aq) + NO_3^-(aq) \longrightarrow \text{no reaction}$$

Therefore, the solubility of $PbCl_2(s)$ is unaffected by $HNO_3(aq)$.

In HCl(aq): $PbCl_2(s) \rightleftharpoons Pb^{2+}(aq) + 2\ Cl^-(aq)$

$$Pb^{2+}(aq) + \underset{\substack{\text{large excess}\\ \text{from HCl(aq)}}}{3\ Cl^-(aq)} \rightleftharpoons PbCl_3^-$$

$PbCl_2(s)$ is rendered more soluble in HCl(aq) because of the formation of chloro complex ions, such as $PbCl_3^-$.

22-29. The concentration of silver ion in the $AgNO_3$–NH_3 solution of Example 22-7 was calculated to be $[Ag^+] = 1.0 \times 10^{-8}$ M. The maximum $[I^-]$ that could be accomodated in this solution before AgI(s) would precipitate is calculated in a familiar way.

$$[Ag^+][I^-] = K_{sp} = 8.5 \times 10^{-17} \qquad [I^-] = \frac{8.5 \times 10^{-17}}{1.0 \times 10^{-8}} = 8.5 \times 10^{-9}$$

In terms of a quantity of KI, this means

$$\text{no. g KI} = 1.00\ \text{L soln.} \times \frac{8.5 \times 10^{-9}\ \text{mol I}^-}{1\ \text{L soln.}} \times \frac{1\ \text{mol KI}}{1\ \text{mol I}^-} \times \frac{166\ \text{g KI}}{1\ \text{mol KI}} = 1.4 \times 10^{-6}\ \text{g KI}$$

22-30. Proceed in three steps: (a) Calculate $[Pb^{2+}]$ in the solution; (b) calculate $[I^-]$ that would result by the addition of KI indicated; (c) determine if the solubility product constant of $PbI_2(s)$ is exceeded.

$$\text{(a)}\quad K_f = \frac{[[PbCl_3]^-]}{[Pb^{2+}][Cl^-]^3} = \frac{1.0 \times 10^{-1}}{[Pb^{2+}](1.5)^3} = 2.4 \times 10^1 \qquad [Pb^{2+}] = \frac{1.0 \times 10^{-1}}{(1.5)^3 \times 2.4 \times 10^1} = 1.2 \times 10^{-3}\ \text{M}$$

$$\text{(b)}\quad [I^-] = \frac{0.020\ \text{g KI} \times \frac{1\ \text{mol KI}}{166\ \text{g KI}} \times \frac{1\ \text{mol I}^-}{1\ \text{mol KI}}}{0.400\ \text{L}} = 3.0 \times 10^{-4}\ \text{M}$$

$$\text{(c)}\quad [Pb^{2+}][I^-]^2 = (1.2 \times 10^{-3})(3.0 \times 10^{-4})^2 = 1.1 \times 10^{-10} < K_{sp} = 7.1 \times 10^{-9}$$

Precipitation of PbI_2 *will not* occur.

22-31. If a solution is to have $[Cl^-] = 0.410$ M, the maximum concentration of Ag^+ that can be maintained without precipitating AgCl is

$$[Ag^+] = \frac{K_{sp}}{[Cl^-]} = \frac{1.6 \times 10^{-10}}{0.410} = 3.9 \times 10^{-10}\ \text{M}$$

Now, we calculate $[CN^-]$ necessary to maintain this $[Ag^+]$ in a solution that has a total concentration of silver of 2.5 M (that is, $[[Ag(CN)_2]^-] = 2.5$ M).

$$K_f = \frac{[[Ag(CN)_2]^-]}{[Ag^+][CN^-]^2} = \frac{2.5}{3.9 \times 10^{-10}\ [CN^-]^2} = 5.6 \times 10^{18}$$

$$[CN^-]^2 = \frac{2.5}{3.9 \times 10^{-10} \times 5.6 \times 10^{18}} = 1.14 \times 10^{-9} \qquad [CN^-] = 3.4 \times 10^{-5}\ M$$

(Of course, the *total* concentration of CN^- in solution is 5.0 M. Both the silver and cyanide occur predominantly as the complex ion $[Ag(CN)_2]^-$, not as free ions.)

22-32. Let us proceed in three steps: (a) Calculate $[Cu^{2+}]$ from K_f for $[Cu(NH_3)_2]^{2+}$; (b) calculate $[OH^-]$ in a solution containing NH_3 and the common ion, NH_4^+; (c) determine whether the solubility product constant of $Cu(OH)_2$ is exceeded.

(a) $$K_f = \frac{[[Cu(NH_3)_4]^{2+}]}{[Cu^{2+}][NH_3]^4} = \frac{0.15}{[Cu^{2+}] \times (0.10)^4} = 2.1 \times 10^{14}$$

$$[Cu^{2+}] = \frac{0.15}{2.1 \times 10^{14} \times (0.10)^4} = 7.1 \times 10^{-12}$$

(b) $$K_b = \frac{[NH_4^+][OH^-]}{[NH_3]} = \frac{0.10 \times [OH^-]}{0.10} = 1.74 \times 10^{-5}$$

(c) $[Cu^{2+}][OH^-]^2 = 7.1 \times 10^{-12} \times (1.74 \times 10^{-5})^2 = 2.1 \times 10^{-21} < K_{sp} = 1.6 \times 10^{-19}$

Precipitation of $Cu(OH)_2$ *will not* occur.

22-33. Two equilibrium constant expressions must be satisfied simultaneously.

$$[Ag^+][Cl^-] = K_{sp} = 1.6 \times 10^{-10} \qquad \frac{[[Ag(NH_3)_2]^+]}{[Ag^+][NH_3]^2} = K_f = 1.6 \times 10^7$$

The dissolving of AgCl(s) in NH_3(aq) is represented by the equation below, from which it can be seen that the *total* molar concentration of silver in solution (call this x) is equal to $[Cl^-]$.

$$\underset{x \text{ mol/L}}{AgCl(s)} + 2\ NH_3(aq) \longrightarrow [Ag(NH_3)_2]^+ + \underset{x \text{ mol/L}}{Cl^-}$$

If $[Cl^-] = x$, then $[Ag^+] = K_{sp}/x$. Also, since $[Cl^-] = [Ag^+] + [[Ag(NH_3)_2]^+]$, we may write that $[[Ag(NH_3)_2]^+] = [Cl^-] - [Ag^+] = x - [Ag^+]$. However, we can safely assume that practically all the silver in solution exists as the ammine complex. This means that $[[Ag(NH_3)_2]^+] = x$. We may now solve the following equation for x.

$$\frac{[[Ag(NH_3)_2]^+]}{[Ag^+][NH_3]^2} = \frac{x}{(K_{sp}/x)(0.10)^2} = K_f$$

$$x^2 = K_f \times K_{sp} \times (0.10)^2 = 1.6 \times 10^{-7} \times 1.6 \times 10^{-10} \times (0.10)^2 = 2.56 \times 10^{-5}$$

$$x = \text{no. mol AgCl/L} = 5.1 \times 10^{-3}$$

$$\text{no. g AgCl} = 0.250\ L \times \frac{5.1 \times 10^{-3}\ \text{mol AgCl}}{1\ L} \times \frac{143\ \text{g AgCl}}{1\ \text{mol AgCl}} = 0.18\ \text{g AgCl}$$

Applications

22-34. (a) Iron(III) chloride hexahydrate: $FeCl_3 \cdot 6H_2O$

(b) Cobalt(II) hexachloroplatinate(IV) hexahydrate: $Co[PtCl_6] \cdot 6\ H_2O$

22-35. (a) $[Cr(H_2O)_5OH]^{2+} + H_2O \rightleftharpoons [Cr(H_2O)_4(OH)_2]^+ + H_3O^+$

(b) $[Cr(H_2O)_5OH]^{2+} + H_3O^+ \longrightarrow [Cr(H_2O)_6]^{3+} + H_2O$

22-36. Since the NH_3—NH_4Cl solution is alkaline, reduction of H_2O_2 produces OH^-.

oxid: $2\ \{Co^{2+}(aq) + 6\ NH_3(aq) \longrightarrow [Co(NH_3)_6]^{3+} + e^-\}$

red: $H_2O_2 + 2\ e^- \longrightarrow 2\ OH^-$

net: $2\ Co^{2+} + H_2O_2 + 12\ NH_3 \longrightarrow 2\ [Co(NH_3)_6]^{3+} + 2\ OH^-$

22-37. AgCl(s) is moderately soluble in NH_3(aq), but AgBr(s), which is widely used in photographic film, is only slightly soluble. To dissolve AgBr requires a solution in which a complex ion of silver is formed that is more stable than $[Ag(NH_3)_2]^+$. $[Ag(S_2O_3)_2]^{3-}$ is such a complex ion. This accounts for the choice of $Na_2S_2O_3$(aq) as a photographic fixer.

22-38. In each of the following calculations the first step is to write a reduction half-equation. Because two electrons must be gained per copper atom deposited in reduction (a), only one half the mass of copper is produced in (a) as in (b).

(a) $[Cu(H_2O)_4]^{2+} + 2\ e^- \longrightarrow Cu(s) + 4\ H_2O$

$$\text{no. g Cu} = 0.333\ \text{h} \times \frac{60\ \text{min}}{1\ \text{h}} \times \frac{60\ \text{s}}{1\ \text{min}} \times \frac{1.50\ \text{C}}{1\ \text{s}} \times \frac{1\ \text{mol e}^-}{96{,}500\ \text{C}} \times \frac{1\ \text{mol Cu}}{2\ \text{mol e}^-} \times \frac{63.55\ \text{g Cu}}{1\ \text{mol Cu}} = 0.592\ \text{g Cu}$$

(b) $[Cu(CN)_3]^{2-} + e^- \longrightarrow Cu(s) + 3\ CN^-$

$$\text{no. g Cu} = 0.333\ \text{h} \times \frac{60\ \text{min}}{1\ \text{h}} \times \frac{60\ \text{s}}{1\ \text{min}} \times \frac{1.50\ \text{C}}{1\ \text{s}} \times \frac{1\ \text{mol e}^-}{96{,}500\ \text{C}} \times \frac{1\ \text{mol Cu}}{1\ \text{mol e}^-} \times \frac{63.55\ \text{g Cu}}{1\ \text{mol Cu}} = 1.18\ \text{g Cu}$$

22-39. This calculation is based on equation (22.38), which provides a conversion factor in the set up below.

$$\text{no. g NaCN} = 1000\ \text{kg ore} \times \frac{1000\ \text{g ore}}{1\ \text{kg ore}} \times \frac{0.005\ \text{g Au}}{100\ \text{g ore}} \times \frac{1\ \text{mol Au}}{197\ \text{g Au}} \times \frac{8\ \text{mol CN}^-}{4\ \text{mol Au}} \times \frac{1\ \text{mol NaCN}}{1\ \text{mol CN}^-}$$

$$\times \frac{49.0\ \text{g NaCN}}{1\ \text{mol NaCN}} = 25\ \text{g NaCN}$$

Very little NaCN is actually required to complex the gold, only 25 g. However, in order to promote the complete conversion of Au^+ to $[Au(CN)_2]^-$ a large excess of CN^- is necessary.

Self-test Questions

1. (*c*) Each CN^- ion carries a charge of -1, as does I^-. The total charge associated with the ligands is -5. The net charge on the complex ion is -3. This leaves a charge on the Ni of +2--its oxidation state.

2. (*d*) Dien has three points of attachment as a ligand. This, together with three Cl^- ions, yields a coordination number of six.

3. (*b*) There can be no isomerism in the linear complex ion $[Ag(NH_3)_2]^+$. Neither can there be in the ion $[Co(NH_3)_5Cl]^{3+}$; all positions at which the Cl^- might be attached are equivalent. In $[Pt(en)Cl_2]$ the two points of attachment of the en must be along the same side of the square (*cis*); the two Cl^- ions must also be *cis*. In the complex ion $[Co(NH_3)_5NO_2]^{2+}$ attachment of the NO_2^- may be either through an N atom (nitro) or through an O atom (nitrito); thus, isomerism is involved.

4. (*c*) The only one of the species that can ionize as an acid is $[Al(H_2O)_6]^{3+}$. For example, $[Al(H_2O)_6]^{3+} + H_2O \rightleftharpoons [Al(H_2O)_5OH]^{2+} + H_3O^+$.

5. (*b*) The soluble compound will be that which can produce a stable ammine complex ion. Ba^{2+} does not, nor do Mg^{2+} or Si^{4+}. However, the complex ion $[Cu(NH_3)_4]^{2+}$ is quite stable (has a high value of K_f).

6. (*a*) The electron configuration of Cr^{2+} is $[Ar]3d^4$. NH_3 is a strong field ligand, leading to the result

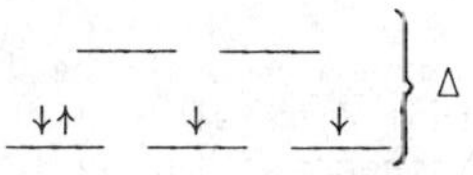

7.

(a)

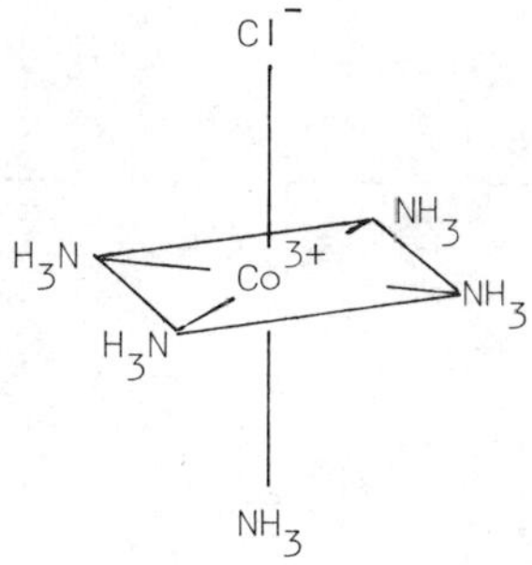

(b)

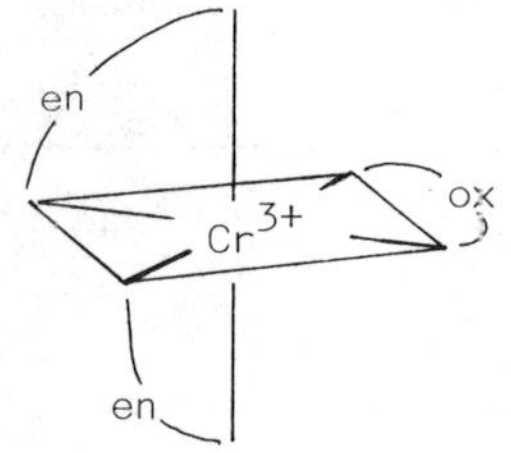

(c)

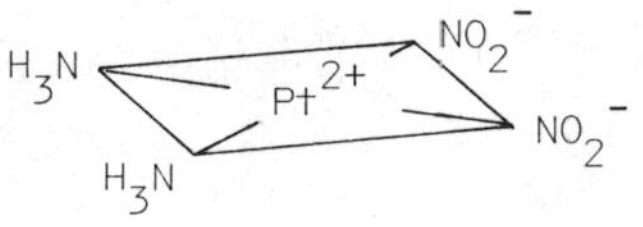

(d)

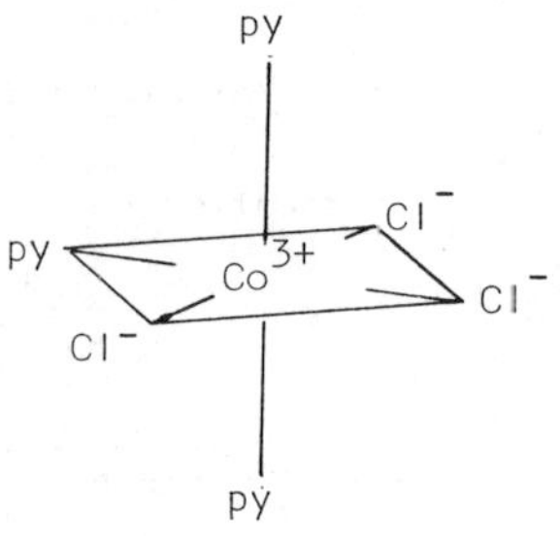

8. (a) Al^{3+} does not form an ammine complex. $Al(OH)_3(s) + NH_3(aq) \longrightarrow$ no reaction. However, Al^{3+} does form soluble aquo and hydroxo complexes.

$$Al(OH)_3(s) + OH^-(aq) + 2\ H_2O \longrightarrow [Al(H_2O)_2(OH)_4]^- \quad (\text{or } AlO_2^-)$$

This reaction will only occur at high concentrations of OH^-. These concentrations cannot be achieved in $NH_3(aq)$--a weak base--but they can in NaOH(aq)--a strong base.

(b) Zn^{2+} forms a stable ammine complex $Zn(NH_3)_4{}^{2+}$. $ZnCO_3(s)$ must produce a high enough $[Zn^{2+}]$ for this reaction to proceed far in the forward direction. Thus, $ZnCO_3$ is soluble in $NH_3(aq)$.

$$ZnCO_3(s) \rightleftharpoons Zn^{2+}(aq) + CO_3{}^{2-}(aq) \qquad Zn^{2+} + 4\ NH_3 \rightleftharpoons [Zn(NH^3)_4]^{2+}$$

ZnS must produce a far lower $[Zn^{2+}]$ at equilibrium because of a smaller value of K_{sp}. Little ZnS dissolves before equilibrium is established.

The difference in the solubilities of $ZnCO_3$ and ZnS in $NH_3(aq)$ is much like the differences in the solubilities AgCl and AgI in $NH_3(aq)$ described in the text.

(c) The half-reaction, $Co^{3+} + e^- \longrightarrow Co^{2+}$, has a large positive $E°_{red}$, sufficiently large to cause the oxidation of H_2O to $O_2(g)$. In the presence of $NH_3(aq)$, the very stable complex ion $[Co(NH_3)_6]^{3+}$ is formed. In this aqueous solution, $[Co^{3+}]$ is very small, and the reduction potential for the half-reaction, $Co^{3+} + e^- \longrightarrow Co^{2+}$, is lowered to the point where spontaneous oxidation of water no longer occurs.

9. Ligands attached to a transition metal ion produce a splitting of the *d* energy level of the ion. The magnitude of this splitting (Δ) corresponds roughly to the energy content of visible light. When white light is passed through a solution of the complex ion, that component of the light with energy equal to Δ is absorbed. The transmitted light is of a complementary color to the component that is absorbed.

10. Combine equilibrium data into a single expression to describe the dissolving of a copper compound with complex ion formation. Calculate the molar solubility from this expression.

CuS: $CuS(s) \rightleftharpoons Cu^{2+}(aq) + S^{2-}(aq) \qquad K_{sp} = 6.3 \times 10^{-36}$

$Cu^{2+}(aq) + 4\ NH_3(aq) \rightleftharpoons [Cu(NH_3)_4]^{2+} \qquad K_f = 2.1 \times 10^{14}$

$CuS(s) + 4\ NH_3(aq) \rightleftharpoons [Cu(NH_3)_4]^{2+}(aq) + S^{2-}(aq) \qquad K = K_{sp} \times K_f = 1.3 \times 10^{-21}$

$$\frac{[Cu(NH_3)_4{}^{2+}][S^{2-}]}{[NH_3]^4} = 1.3 \times 10^{-21}$$

molar solubility $= [Cu(NH_3)_4{}^{2+}] = [S^{2-}]$

Assume $[NH_3] \simeq 1.0$ M $\qquad \dfrac{[S^{2-}]^2}{(1.0)^4} = 1.3 \times 10^{-21} \qquad$ molar solubility $\simeq 3.6 \times 10^{-11}$ M

$CuS(s)$ is essentially insoluble in $NH_3(aq)$.

$CuCO_3$: The net equation here will be $CuCO_3(s) + 4\ NH_3(aq) \rightleftharpoons [Cu(NH_3)_4]^{2+} + CO_3{}^{2-}$

$K = K_{sp} \times K_f = 2.9 \times 10^4$

$$\frac{[Cu(NH_3)_4{}^{2+}][CO_3{}^{2-}]}{[NH_3]^4} = \frac{[CO_3{}^{2-}]^2}{(1.0)^4} = 2.9 \times 10^4 \qquad [CO_3{}^{2-}] = 1.7 \times 10^2\ M$$

$CuCO_3(s)$ is highly soluble in $NH_3(aq)$.

Chapter 23

Nuclear Chemistry

Definitions and terminology

23-1. (a) The neutron-to-proton ratio is the number of neutrons in the nucleus of an atom divided by the number of protons. Only when the ratio n:p falls within certain limits is the nucleus stable. If these limits are exceeded, the nucleus either cannot exist at all or it is radioactive.

(b) A nucleon is one of two fundamental nuclear particles, a proton or a neutron.

(c) The mass-energy relationship is the expression, $E = mc^2$, which indicates the quantity of energy that is liberated when a given quantity of mass is destroyed.

(d) Background radiation refers to a constant presence of radioactivity from natural sources, like cosmic rays and emanations from rocks containing radioactive elements (such as uranium and thorium).

(e) A radioactive decay series describes a sequence of nuclear disintegrations in which one radioactive nucleus (a parent) gives rise to another (a daughter), which gives rise to still another (a daughter), and so on, until eventually a stable nucleus is formed.

(f) A nuclear accelerator is a device used to accelerate charged particles, increasing their energies to the point where these particles can penetrate atomic nuclei and produce nuclear reactions.

23-2. (a) A naturally occurring radioisotope is a radioactive species which, though sometimes rare, can be found in natural sources. An artificial radioisotope cannot be found in natural sources; it can only be produced by bombarding stable atomic nuclei with appropriate particles, that is, by a nuclear reaction.

(b) An electron is the basic unit of negative electric charge found in all atoms. A positron is a particle that is produced as a result of certain nuclear reactions. It has the same mass as an electron and the same magnitude charge, but *positive*. A positron is a positive electron, so to speak.

(c) Primary ionization refers to the loss of electrons by atoms (and the consequent production of ions) as a result of a direct impact by radiation, such as α, β, and γ rays. Energetic electrons ionized from atoms by primary ionization may themselves strike atoms and dislodge additional electrons; this is the process of secondary ionization.

(d) The transuranium elements are those having an atomic number greater than uranium ($Z > 92$). The actin**oids** are a group of 14 elements with electron configurations featuring the filling of the $5f$ subshell. The transactinoids are the elements following the actinoids. They have $Z > 103$.

(e) Nuclear fission is a process in which a heavy nucleus disintegrates into smaller nuclei and some free neutrons. Energy is released in the process. Nuclear fusion is a process in which small nuclei coalesce into a larger nucleus. Again, the destruction of a small quantity of matter is accompanied by the release of energy.

23-3. (a) The symbol α designates an alpha particle.

(b) Gamma rays are represented by the symbol γ.

(c) The half-life of a radioisotope is designated by the symbol $t_{1/2}$. This is the time required for one half of the nuclei in a radioactive sample to disintegrate.

(d) The disintegration of a radioactive sample is a first-order process. The rate constant for this process, known as the radioactive decay constant, is denoted by the symbol λ. The decay constant is related to the half-life through the familiar equation: $\lambda = 0.693\ t_{1/2}$.

(e) A β^+ particle is a positron--a positive electron.

23-4. (a) ${}^{4}_{2}He$ represents an alpha particle, α.

(b) A beta particle, an electron, can be represented either as β^- or ${}^{0}_{-1}e$.

(c) A neutron has the symbol ${}^{1}_{0}n$.

(d) The symbol ${}^{1}_{1}H$ stands for a proton.

(e) The symbol ${}^{0}_{+1}e$ represents a unit of positive electric charge with the same mass as an electron--a positron. At times the positron is also represented as β^+.

(f) Tritium is a nuclide of hydrogen with mass number 3, that is, ${}^{3}_{1}H$.

Radioactive processes

23-5. (a) ${}^{234}_{94}Pu \longrightarrow {}^{230}_{92}U + {}^{4}_{2}He$

(b) ${}^{248}_{97}Bk \longrightarrow {}^{248}_{98}Cf + {}^{0}_{-1}e$

(c) ${}^{196}Pb \xrightarrow{E.C.} {}^{196}Tl \xrightarrow{E.C.} {}^{196}Hg$

(d) ${}^{214}_{82}Pb \longrightarrow {}^{214}_{84}Po + 2\,{}^{0}_{-1}e$

(e) ${}^{226}_{88}Ra \longrightarrow {}^{214}_{82}Pb + 3\,{}^{4}_{2}He$

(f) ${}^{69}_{33}As \longrightarrow {}^{69}_{32}Ge + {}^{0}_{+1}e$

23-6. (a) ${}^{35}_{16}S \longrightarrow {}^{35}_{17}Cl + {}^{0}_{-1}e$

(b) ${}^{14}_{8}O \longrightarrow {}^{14}_{7}N + {}^{0}_{+1}e$

(c) ${}^{235}_{92}U \longrightarrow {}^{231}_{90}Th + {}^{4}_{2}He$

(d) ${}^{214}_{83}Bi \longrightarrow {}^{214}_{84}Po + {}^{0}_{-1}e$

23-7. All naturally occurring radioisotopes of high atomic number have n:p ratios greater than allowable for stable nuclei. Conversion of neutrons to protons within their nuclei and the emission of β^- particles is a means by which these ratios can be lowered. Some artificially produced radioisotopes have n:p ratios above and some below the range for stable nuclei. Thus, some of the nuclei emit β^- and some β^+ particles.

Radioactive decay series

23-8.

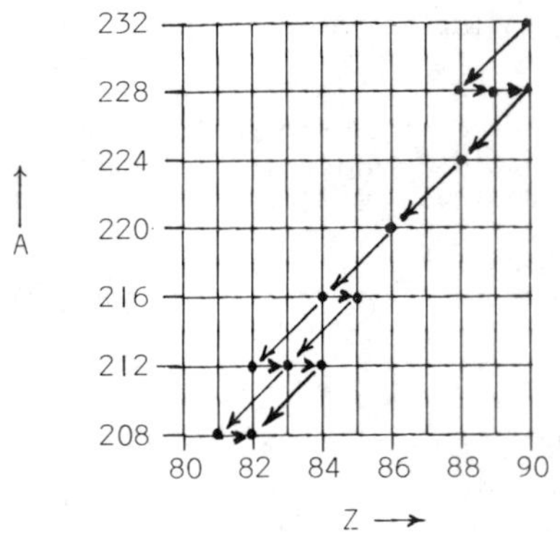

23-9. Start with the first member of the series: ${}^{238}_{92}U$.

$A = 4n + 2 = 238; \quad 4n = 236; \quad n = 59$

Now note that the only mass numbers that appear in Figure 23-3 are 238, 234, 230, and so on. Since n is an integer when the "4n + 2" formula is applied to A = 238, it must also be an integer as A is decreased four units at a time. All members of the U-238 decay series follow the "4n + 2" formula.

Nuclear reactions

23-10. (a) ${}^{7}_{3}\text{Li} + {}^{1}_{1}\text{H} \longrightarrow {}^{8}_{4}\text{Be} + \gamma$ (b) ${}^{33}_{16}\text{S} + {}^{1}_{0}\text{n} \longrightarrow {}^{33}_{15}\text{P} + {}^{1}_{1}\text{H}$

(c) ${}^{239}_{94}\text{Pu} + {}^{4}_{2}\text{He} \longrightarrow {}^{242}_{96}\text{Cm} + {}^{1}_{0}\text{n}$ (d) ${}^{238}_{92}\text{U} + {}^{4}_{2}\text{He} \longrightarrow {}^{239}_{94}\text{Pu} + 3\,{}^{1}_{0}\text{n}$

23-11. (a) ${}^{23}_{11}\text{Na} + {}^{2}_{1}\text{H} \longrightarrow {}^{24}_{11}\text{Na} + {}^{1}_{1}\text{H}$ (b) ${}^{59}_{27}\text{Co} + {}^{1}_{0}\text{n} \longrightarrow {}^{56}_{25}\text{Mn} + {}^{4}_{2}\text{He}$

(c) ${}^{238}_{92}\text{U} + {}^{2}_{1}\text{H} \longrightarrow {}^{240}_{94}\text{Pu} + {}^{0}_{-1}\text{e}$ (d) ${}^{246}_{96}\text{Cm} + {}^{13}_{6}\text{C} \longrightarrow {}^{254}_{102}\text{No} + 5\,{}^{1}_{0}\text{n}$

(e) ${}^{238}_{92}\text{U} + {}^{14}_{7}\text{N} \longrightarrow {}^{246}_{99}\text{Es} + 6\,{}^{1}_{0}\text{n}$

23-12. ${}^{238}_{92}\text{U} \longrightarrow {}^{234}_{90}\text{Th} + {}^{4}_{2}\text{He}$; ${}^{234}_{90}\text{Th} \longrightarrow {}^{234}_{91}\text{Pa} + {}^{0}_{-1}\text{e}$; ${}^{234}_{91}\text{Pa} \longrightarrow {}^{234}_{92}\text{U} + {}^{0}_{-1}\text{e}$;

${}^{234}_{92}\text{U} \longrightarrow {}^{230}_{90}\text{Th} + {}^{4}_{2}\text{He}$; ${}^{230}_{90}\text{Th} \longrightarrow {}^{226}_{88}\text{Ra} + {}^{4}_{2}\text{He}$; ${}^{226}_{88}\text{Ra} \longrightarrow {}^{222}_{86}\text{Rn} + {}^{4}_{2}\text{He}$;

${}^{222}_{86}\text{Rn} \longrightarrow {}^{218}_{84}\text{Po} + {}^{4}_{2}\text{He}$; {(a) ${}^{218}_{84}\text{Po} \longrightarrow {}^{214}_{82}\text{Pb} + {}^{4}_{2}\text{He}$; ${}^{214}_{82}\text{Pb} \longrightarrow {}^{214}_{83}\text{Bi} + {}^{0}_{-1}\text{e}$

or (b) ${}^{218}_{84}\text{Po} \longrightarrow {}^{218}_{85}\text{At} + {}^{0}_{-1}\text{e}$; ${}^{218}_{85}\text{At} \longrightarrow {}^{214}_{83}\text{Bi} + {}^{4}_{2}\text{He}$} {(a) ${}^{214}_{83}\text{Bi} \longrightarrow {}^{210}_{81}\text{Tl} + {}^{4}_{2}\text{He}$;

${}^{210}_{81}\text{Tl} \longrightarrow {}^{210}_{82}\text{Pb} + {}^{0}_{-1}\text{e}$ *or* (b) ${}^{214}_{83}\text{Bi} \longrightarrow {}^{214}_{84}\text{Po} + {}^{0}_{-1}\text{e}$; ${}^{214}_{84}\text{Po} \longrightarrow {}^{210}_{82}\text{Pb} + {}^{4}_{2}\text{He}$}

${}^{210}_{82}\text{Pb} \longrightarrow {}^{210}_{83}\text{Bi} + {}^{0}_{-1}\text{e}$; {(a) ${}^{210}_{83}\text{Bi} \longrightarrow {}^{206}_{81}\text{Tl} + {}^{4}_{2}\text{He}$; ${}^{206}_{81}\text{Tl} \longrightarrow {}^{206}_{82}\text{Pb} + {}^{0}_{-1}\text{e}$

or (b) ${}^{210}_{83}\text{Bi} \longrightarrow {}^{210}_{84}\text{Po} + {}^{0}_{-1}\text{e}$; ${}^{210}_{84}\text{Pb} \longrightarrow {}^{206}_{82}\text{Pb} + {}^{4}_{2}\text{He}$}

Rate of radioactive decay

23-13. Since the disintegration rate is proportional to the number of atoms in a radioactive sample, simply substitute 1000 for N_0 and the activity at some later time, t, for N_t in equation (23.18). First, however, it is necessary to determine λ from the half-life, through equation (23.19).

$$\lambda = \frac{0.693}{t_{1/2}} = \frac{0.693}{87.9\text{ day}} = 7.88 \times 10^{-3}\text{ d}^{-1}$$

(a) $\log N_t - \log N_0 = \dfrac{-\lambda t}{2.303}$ $\qquad \log 125 - \log 1000 = 2.097 - 3.000 = \dfrac{-7.88 \times 10^{-3}\text{ day}^{-1} \times t}{2.303}$

$$t = \frac{2.303 \times (2.097 - 3.000)}{-7.88 \times 10^{-3}}\text{ d} = 264\text{ d}$$

(b) $\log 100 - \log 1000 = \dfrac{-7.88 \times 10^{-3}\text{ day}^{-1} \times t}{2.303}$

$$t = \frac{2.303 \times (2.000 - 3.000)}{-7.88 \times 10^{-3}}\text{ d} = 292\text{ d}$$

(c) $\log 50 - \log 1000 = \frac{-7.88 \times 10^{-3} \text{ day}^{-1} \times t}{2.303}$

$$t = \frac{2.303 \times (1.699 - 3.000)}{-7.88 \times 10^{-3}} \text{ d} = 380 \text{ d}$$

23-14. The equation required here is (23.17): rate of decay = λN. The rate of decay is given. The value of λ is obtained from the half-life; however, this must be expressed in the unit min^{-1}.

$$\lambda = \frac{0.693}{t_{1/2}} = \frac{0.693}{5.2 \text{ y}} \times \frac{1 \text{ y}}{365 \text{ d}} \times \frac{1 \text{ d}}{24 \text{ h}} \times \frac{1 \text{ h}}{60 \text{ min}} = 2.5 \times 10^{-7} \text{ min}^{-1}$$

$$N = \frac{\text{rate of decay}}{\lambda} = \frac{240 \text{ atom min}^{-1}}{2.5 \times 10^{-7} \text{ min}^{-1}} = 9.6 \times 10^{8} \text{ atoms}$$

23-15. Use the method of Exercise 13 with $N_0 \propto 240$ and $N_t \propto 100$. For λ, substitute $(0.693/5.2) \text{ y}^{-1}$.

$$\log 100 - \log 240 = \frac{-\lambda t}{2.303} = \frac{-(0.693/5.2) \text{ y}^{-1} \times t}{2.303}$$

$$t = \frac{5.2 \times 2.303 \times (2.000 - 2.380)}{-0.693} \text{ y} = 6.6 \text{ y}$$

23-16. Again, the situation is similar to those encountered in preceding exercises. The key in this case is that the initial number of atoms is 1000 times greater than at the limit of detection. For example, take $N_0 = 1000$ and $N_t = 1$. For λ substitute $(0.693/14.2) \text{ day}^{-1}$.

$$\log 1 - \log 1000 = \frac{-\lambda t}{2.303} = \frac{-(0.693/14.2) \text{ day}^{-1} \times t}{2.303}$$

$$t = \frac{14.2 \times 2.303 \times (0.000 - 3.000)}{-0.693} \text{ day} = 142 \text{ day}$$

23-17. The simplest approach is to use equation (23.18) with two representative data points, say $t = 0$, 1000 cpm and $t = 100$ h, 452 cpm. Note that as in previous cases the decay rate is proportional to the number of atoms in a radioactive sample. This means that we can take $N_0 = 1000$ and $N_t = 452$, with $t = 100$ h.

$$\log N_t - \log N_0 = \log 452 - \log 1000 = \frac{-\lambda t}{2.303} = \frac{-\lambda \times 100 \text{ h}}{2.303}$$

$$\lambda = \frac{2.303 \times (3.000 - 2.655)}{100 \text{ h}} = 7.95 \times 10^{-3} \text{ h}^{-1}$$

$$t_{1/2} = \frac{0.693}{\lambda} = \frac{0.693}{7.95 \times 10^{-3}} \text{ h} = 87.2 \text{ h} = 3.63 \text{ d}$$

This result may be checked by (a) substituting other pairs of data points into equation (23.18), (b) plotting N_t versus time and estimating the time required for N_t to decrease to one half of some former value, or (d) plotting $\log N_t$ versus t and determining λ from the slope of this plot.

23-18. First convert the half-life from the unit, y, to the unit, s. Then use equation (23.19) to convert half-life to decay constant, λ. This is followed by a straightforward application of equation (23.17) to determine the number of atoms of Ra-226 required to produce the measured activity--1 millicurie = 3.7×10^{7} dis s^{-1}. Finally, conversion from number of atoms to mass follows in a familiar fashion.

$$t_{1/2} = 1602 \text{ y} \times \frac{365 \text{ d}}{1 \text{ y}} \times \frac{24 \text{ h}}{1 \text{ d}} \times \frac{60 \text{ min}}{1 \text{ h}} \times \frac{60 \text{ s}}{1 \text{ min}} = 5.05 \times 10^{10} \text{ s}$$

$$\lambda = \frac{0.693}{t_{1/2}} = \frac{0.693}{5.05 \times 10^{10} \text{ s}} = 1.37 \times 10^{-11} \text{ s}^{-1}$$

Rate of decay = λN; $N = \dfrac{\text{rate of decay}}{\lambda} = \dfrac{3.7 \times 10^{7} \text{ atom s}^{-1}}{1.37 \times 10^{-11} \text{ s}^{-1}} = 2.7 \times 10^{18}$ atoms

no. g Ra-226 = 2.7×10^{18} atoms Ra-226 $\times \dfrac{226 \text{ g Ra-226}}{6.02 \times 10^{23} \text{ atoms Ra-226}} = 1.0 \times 10^{-3}$ g Ra-226

23-19. Consider starting with 1 mol ^{232}Th and calculate the amount remaining after 4.5×10^{9} y. Then determine the amount of ^{208}Pb that must have been formed. Convert these amounts to a gram basis and establish the mass ratio.

$$\lambda = \frac{0.693}{t_{1/2}} = \frac{0.693}{1.39 \times 10^{10} \text{ y}} = 4.99 \times 10^{-11} \text{ y}^{-1}$$

$$\log \frac{N_t}{N_0} = \log \frac{N_t}{1.00} = \frac{-(4.99 \times 10^{-11} \text{ y}^{-1}) \times (4.5 \times 10^{9} \text{ y})}{2.303} = -0.0975$$

$$\frac{N_t}{1.00} = 0.799 \qquad N_t = 0.799 \text{ mol } ^{232}\text{Th remaining}$$

no. mol ^{208}Pb produced = 1.000 − 0.799 = 0.201 mol ^{208}Pb.

$$\text{mass ratio} = \frac{0.201 \text{ mol} \times \dfrac{208 \text{ g Pb}}{1 \text{ mol}}}{0.799 \text{ mol} \times \dfrac{232 \text{ g Th}}{1 \text{ mol}}} = \frac{41.8 \text{ g } ^{208}\text{Pb}}{185 \text{ g } ^{232}\text{Th}} = 0.226 \text{ g } ^{208}\text{Pb}/1.00 \text{ g } ^{232}\text{Th}$$

23-20. This problem is simplified if we note that the initial nuclide (^{87}Rb) and the final nuclide (^{87}Sr) have the same mass numbers (i.e., the same atomic weights). In this case the mass ratio (0.004:1.00) and the mol ratio are identical. If we start with 1.00 mol of ^{87}Rb, disintegration proceeds to the point where 0.004 mol ^{87}Sr has formed and 0.996 mol ^{87}Rb remains. That is, we can use N_0 = 1.00 mol and N_t = 0.996 mol.

$$\lambda = \frac{0.693}{t_{1/2}} = \frac{0.693}{5 \times 10^{11} \text{ y}} = 1.4 \times 10^{-12} \text{ y}^{-1}$$

$$\log \frac{N_t}{N_0} = \log \frac{0.996}{1.00} = -1.74 \times 10^{-3} = \frac{-(1.4 \times 10^{-12} \text{ y}^{-1}) \times t}{2.303}$$

$$t = \frac{2.303 \times 1.74 \times 10^{-3}}{1.4 \times 10^{-12}} = 3 \times 10^{9} \text{ y}$$

Radiocarbon dating

23-21. Use the method of Example 23-4 with $N_0 \propto 15/\lambda$ and $N_t \propto 12/\lambda$.

$$\log N - \log N_0 = \frac{-\lambda t}{2.303}$$

$$\log (12/\lambda) - \log (15/\lambda) = \frac{-1.21 \times 10^{-4} \text{ y}^{-1} \times t}{2.303}$$

$$\log 12 - \cancel{\log \lambda} - \log 15 + \cancel{\log \lambda} = -5.25 \times 10^{-5} \text{ y}^{-1} \times t$$

$$1.079 - 1.176 = -5.25 \times 10^{-5} \text{ y}^{-1} \times t$$

$$t = \frac{1.079 - 1.176}{-5.25 \times 10^{-5}} = \frac{-0.097}{-5.25 \times 10^{-5}} = 1.8 \times 10^{3} \text{ y}$$

The sample in question is less than 2000 years old. It can not have been an artifact of the ancient Egyptians.

23-22. Use the same basic equation as in Exercise 21 but substitute $N_t \propto 0.03/\lambda$.

$$\log(0.03/\lambda) - \log(15/\lambda) = \frac{-1.21 \times 10^{-4}\ y^{-1} \times t}{2.303}$$

$$-1.523 - 1.176 = -2.699 = -5.25 \times 10^{-5}\ y^{-1} \times t$$

$$t = 2.699/5.25 \times 10^{-5} = 5 \times 10^{4}\ y$$

23-23. The assumption of a constant rate of production of C-14 in the atmosphere may be invalidated in the future because of the possible large amounts of C-14 that were produced in the 1950's and early 1960's as a result of the atmospheric testing of nuclear weapons. The failure of this assumption might be particularly significant in tests made generations from now on objects that were in equilibrium with C-14 during the period mentioned.

Energetics of nuclear reactions

23-24. (a) The relationship we are asked to establish is $1\ \text{MeV} = 1.602 \times 10^{-13}$ J. This can be done most simply by using the definition of an electron volt and certain conversion factors.

$$1\ \text{MeV} = 1 \times 10^{6}\ \text{eV} \times \frac{1.602 \times 10^{-19}\ \text{V C}}{1\ \text{eV}} \times \frac{1\ \text{J}}{1\ \text{V C}} = 1.602 \times 10^{-13}\ \text{J}$$

(b) For this calculation we need to use data from Table 2-1 and the Einstein relationship, $E = mc^2$.

$$E = 1.000\ \text{amu} \times \frac{1.673 \times 10^{-27}\ \text{kg}}{1.0073\ \text{amu}} \times (2.998 \times 10^{8})^2\ \text{m}^2\ \text{s}^{-2} \times \frac{1\ \text{J}}{1\ \text{kg m}^2\ \text{s}^{-2}} \times \frac{1\ \text{MeV}}{1.602 \times 10^{-13}\ \text{J}}$$

$$= 931.8\ \text{MeV}$$

23-25. Determine the sum of the masses of the fundamental particles in an atom of Ne-20. The difference between this sum and the measured nuclidic mass is the quantity of mass that is converted to nuclear binding energy.

10p = 10 × 1.0073 amu	=	10.073 amu
10n = 10 × 1.0087	=	10.087
10e = 10 × 0.00055	=	0.006
calculated mass	=	20.166 amu
measured mass	=	19.992 amu
mass defect	=	0.174 amu

$$\text{Total nuclear binding energy} = 0.174\ \text{amu} \times \frac{931.2\ \text{MeV}}{1\ \text{amu}} = 162\ \text{MeV}$$

Binding energy per nucleon = 162 MeV/20 = 8.10 MeV

23-26. First determine the mass change in the nuclear reaction and then convert this to energy.

Mass Change = 13.00335 + 1.00783 − 10.01294 − 4.00260 = −0.00436 amu

$$\text{Energy (release)} = -0.00436\ \text{amu} \times \frac{931.2\ \text{MeV}}{1\ \text{amu}} = -4.06\ \text{MeV}$$

23-27. This exercise is similar to Exercise 26.

Mass Change = 4.00260 + 3.01604 − 6.01513 − 1.008665 = −0.005155 amu

$$\text{Energy (release)} = -0.005155\ \text{amu} \times \frac{931.2\ \text{MeV}}{1\ \text{amu}} = -4.80\ \text{MeV}$$

Nuclear stability

23-28. (a) $^{20}_{10}Ne$: For nuclides of low atomic number the most stable nuclei are expected to be those that have equal numbers of protons and neutrons.

(b) $^{18}_{8}O$: A nuclide in which the number of protons and number of neutrons are both even is generally more stable than a nuclide in which one number is odd and the other even (or both numbers are odd).

(c) $^{7}_{3}Li$: A nuclide in which the number of protons and the number of neutrons are both odd is generally less stable than one in which one or both of these quantities is even.

23-29. β^- emission results in neutrons being converted to protons and β^+, in protons being converted to neutrons. Thus, β^- emission is expected for a nuclide with a high n:p ratio and β^+ for one with a low n:p ratio.

(a) β^- emission: $^{33}_{15}P$; β^+ emission: $^{29}_{15}P$ (b) β^- emission: $^{134}_{53}I$; β^+ emission: $^{120}_{53}I$

23-30. If the rounded off atomic weight corresponds to a nuclide having a number of protons and number of neutrons both even or one even and one odd, that nuclide is likely to exist naturally. Such is the case with $^{39}_{19}K$, $^{85}_{37}Rb$, and $^{88}_{38}Sr$. If the result of the rounding off is an odd number both of protons and neutrons, the nuclide is expected to be radioactive and not to occur naturally. Such is the case with $^{36}_{17}Cl$ and $^{64}_{29}Cu$.

23-31. A doubly magic nuclide is one having a magic number both for protons and neutrons. Thus $^{40}_{20}Ca$ is a doubly magic nuclide. Another would be an atom with 82 p and 126 n, that is, $^{208}_{82}Pb$.

Fission and fusion

23-32. (a) A nuclear burner is the type of nuclear reactor in use today. The isotope U-235 is separated from uranium ore. This isotope is the basic nuclear fuel which undergoes fission into lighter fragments and releases energy in the reactor.

(b) In a breeder nuclear reactor energetic neutrons convert U-238, the principal isotope of uranium, to Np-239 and Pu-239. The isotope Pu-239 undergoes fission and releases energy in the reactor. The basic principle of a breeder reactor, then, is that an abundant non-fissionable nuclide, U-238, is converted to a fissionable nuclide, Pu-239.

(c) Thermonuclear reactors, which do not exist presently, are conceived on the principle of nuclear fusion, not fission. For example, in one design deuterium and tritium atoms would be fused into hellium atoms. This a process which is accompanied by a loss of mass, compensated for by the release of an equivalent quantity of energy.

23-33. In both fission and fusion, the new nuclei that are produced have a higher binding energy per nucleon than the nuclei from which they are formed. An inspection of Figure 23-6 suggests, however, that in the fusion of light nuclei this increase is two or three-fold per nucleon, whereas for the fission process it is only about 10%. We should expect the energy release to be greater with fusion than with fission.

23-34. $$\text{no. m ton coal} = 1.00 \text{ kg U-235} \times \frac{1000 \text{ g U-235}}{1.00 \text{ kg U-235}} \times \frac{8.20 \times 10^7 \text{ kJ}}{1.00 \text{ g U-235}} \times \frac{1.00 \text{ g C}}{32.8 \text{ kJ}} \times \frac{1.00 \text{ kg C}}{1000 \text{ g C}} \times \frac{1 \text{ m ton C}}{1000 \text{ kg C}}$$

$$\times \frac{100 \text{ m ton coal}}{85 \text{ m ton C}} = 2.94 \times 10^3 \text{ m ton coal}$$

Effect of radiation on matter

23-35. The rad is based simply on the quantity of energy deposited in matter (1×10^{-2} J/kg). The rem takes into account the fact that the biolcgical damage depends both on the energy deposited and the kind of radiation involved.

23-36. Gamma rays have a lower ionizing power than α and β rays and they penetrate matter much more readily. In a cloud chamber a particle is detected through the trail of ions that it leaves behind. If very few ions are formed, the opportunity to detect radiation is limited. In a Geiger-Muller counter, on the other hand, even a single ionizing event gives rise to a pulse of electric current, which can be counted. This fact makes the G-M tube a more sensitive detector, especially for γ rays, than a cloud chamber.

23-37. There are at least two basic difficulties in establishing the effects of low dosages of radiation. If this is to be done by inference from observations made at high dosage levels, where the effects are easily measured, extrapolation of data must be made over a very long interval. Such long extrapolations are usually not reliable. If the effects of low radiation levels are to be made by direct measurement, the problem is that these effects become apparent only after many years. Experiments conducted over very long pericds of time are difficult to perform. In both cases heavy reliance must be made on sophisticated statistical tests.

23-38. ^{90}Sr is a particularly hazardous radioactive material for several reasons. Of foremost concern is that if this material is taken into the body (ingested) it tends to follow the metabolic pathways of calcium, an element closely related to strontium. This means that Sr-90 tends to deposit in the bones if it is ingested. A particularly pernicious source of Sr-90 during the period in which atmospheric nuclear tests were being performed was in cow's milk. Another cause for concern about Sr-90 is that its half-life is of such a magnitude (28 y) that it tends to persist in the environment for a long time (say 1000 y) before its radioactivity drops to a safe level.

Application of radioisotopes

23-39. The hydrogen isotope, tritium, $^{3}_{1}H$, is radioactive. If a trace quantity of tritium is introduced with the $H_2(g)$ in an ammonia synthesis plant, radioactivity will appear wherever the leak occurs in the hydrogen supply line. The radioactivity can be detected with a Geiger-Mueller tube or other suitable radiation detector.

23-40. If an attempt is made to determine trace amounts of materials by precipitation, extremely small quantities of precipitate are obtained, perhaps too small even to be detected on an analytical balance. If titration is used instead, small volumes of very dilute solutions must be employed. The sources of error are again numerous. Neutron activation analysis is an ideal method because radioactivity can be detected in minute amounts.

23-41. When radioactive NaCl is added to an aquecus solution it dissociates. In this respect the radioactive material is no different from ordinary nonradioactive NaCl. When $NaNO_3$ is later recrystallized from the $NaNO_3$-NaCl solution, Na-23 and Na-24 ions appear in the precipitated material in the same ratio as they appeared in solution. Thus, even though radioactivity was introduced only through the NaCl, it will appear in the recrystallized $NaNO_3$.

23-42. Once a hydrogen ion attaches itself to the N atom of NH_3 through a coordinate covalent bond to form NH_4^+, that H atom becomes indistinguishable from the other three. In particular, when a proton is later donated by NH_4^+ to OH^- to produce $NH_3(g)$ and H_2O, the donated H^+ will be a tritium atom in some cases and not in others; the process is random. Thus, some of the H_2O molecules formed will be radioactive and some will not; and some of the NH_3 molecules will be radioactive and some will not. Our conclusion must be that the original radioactivity of the HCl appears both in the H_2O and the $NH_3(g)$.

Self-test Questions

1\. (*c*) Beta rays are negatively charged particles (electrons). Neutrons are neutral particles and x rays and γ rays are forms of electromagnetic radiation.

2\. (*b*) A one unit increase in atomic number results from the process $n \longrightarrow p + e^-$, that is, β^- emission. Electron capture results in a decrease of one unit in atomic number and α emission, two units. The emission of γ rays does not affect the atomic number.

3\. (*d*) The combination most likely to lead to radioactivity is an odd number of protons and an odd number of neutrons. This condition is found in ^{108}Ag--47 protons and 61 neutrons.

4\. (*c*) Here we look for the combination of an even number of protons and an even number of neutrons. Au and Br have odd numbers of protons (odd atomic numbers). All isotopes of Ra are radioactive. Cd (with atomic number 48) is the only possible answer.

5\. (*a*) Positron emission occurs when the n:p ratio is too low. The most likely of the isotopes to decay by positron emission is the one with the smallest number of neutrons--^{59}Cu.

6\. (*c*) Recall the general shape of Figure 23-6 which plots binding energy per nucleon against atomic number. It has a maximum value at about $Z = 26$--iron.

7\. (a) $^{230}_{90}Th \longrightarrow ^{226}_{88}Ra + ^{4}_{2}He$ (b) $^{54}_{27}Co \longrightarrow ^{54}_{26}Fe + ^{0}_{+1}e$

(c) $^{232}_{90}Th + ^{4}_{2}He \longrightarrow ^{232}_{92}U + 4\,^{1}_{0}n$

8\. From the half-life we determine the radioactive decay constant.

$$\lambda = \frac{0.693}{t_{1/2}} = \frac{0.693}{1.7 \times 10^7\ y} = 4.1 \times 10^{-8}\ y^{-1}$$

The disintegration rate is given by the expression: decay rate = λN. To use this expression we must express N as the number of ^{129}I atoms.

$$\text{decay rate} = 1.00\ mg\ ^{129}I \times \frac{1.00\ g\ ^{129}I}{1000\ mg\ ^{129}I} \times \frac{1\ mol\ ^{129}I}{129\ g\ ^{129}I} \times \frac{6.02 \times 10^{23}\ ^{129}I\ atoms}{1\ mol\ ^{129}I} \times \frac{4.1 \times 10^{-8}}{y}$$

$$\times \frac{1\ y}{365\ d} \times \frac{1\ d}{24\ h} \times \frac{1\ h}{60\ min} \times \frac{1\ min}{60\ sec} = 6.1 \times 10^3\ dis/s$$

9\. The radioactive decay constant $\lambda = 0.693/t_{1/2} = 0.693/11.4\ d = 6.08 \times 10^{-2}\ d^{-1}$. Since the decay rate is proportional to the number of atoms, when the decay rate has decreased to 1% of its original value, $N_t = 0.010\ N_0$.

$$\log \frac{N_t}{N_0} = \log \frac{0.010\ N_0}{N_0} = \log 0.010 = -2.00 = \frac{-(6.08 \times 10^{-2})\ d^{-1} \times t}{2.303}$$

$$t = \frac{2.303 \times 2.00}{6.08 \times 10^{-2}\ d^{-1}} = 75.8\ d$$

10\. (a) Radioactive isotopes with extremely short half-lives are completely disintegrated before having a chance to do much damage. Those with very long half-lives persist for a long time but their rates of decay are so low as to be of little harm. Isotopes with intermediate half-lives have both a high level of activity and a fairly long persistence in the environment. This makes them potentially quite hazardous.

(b) Gamma emitters are generally hazardous even at long distances because γ rays are so highly penetrating through matter. Alpha emitters, on the other hand, because of the low penetrating power of α rays are generally not very harmful at a distance. They can be extremely hazardous when ingested (taken internally) because this puts them very close to biological tissue. (Recall that α particles have a very high ionizing power.)

(c) Argon is produced from radioactive potassium (^{40}K) and has thus accumulated in the atmosphere as ^{40}K has undergone radioactive decay over several billion years.

(d) Although Fr is an alkali metal and resembles them, it does not occur mixed with them. It is only encountered as one of the transient products in a radioactive decay series. Thus it is likely to be found mixed, in trace quantities, with other radioactive elements rather than with the nonradioactive alkali metals.

(e) To bring positively charged nuclei in close enough proximity to promote nuclear fusion requires that very large repulsive forces be overcome. For this to occur the nuclei must have high thermal energies, which in turn requires extremely high temperatures.

Chapter 24

Organic Chemistry

Definitions and terminology

24-1. (a) An organic compound is one containing carbon in combination with hydrogen and often other elements, such as nitrogen and/or oxygen.

(b) An alkane hydrocarbon is a carbon-hydrogen compound in which all C-C and C-H bonds are single covalent bonds. Each carbon atom in an alkane molecule is bonded simultaneously to four other atoms.

(c) An aromatic hydrocarbon is a carbon-hydrogen compound whose carbon atoms are joined into ring-like structures. The basic structural unit is a hexagonal ring with each carbon atom joined to two other carbon atoms and a third atom which may be carbon or hydrogen. The bonds within the rings possess some multiple bond character.

24-2. (a) Aliphatic molecules have straight or branched chain carbon skeletons. Alicyclic molecules feature carbon atoms joined into a ring. An alicyclic molecule can be thought of as resulting from the elimination of an H atom from each end of an aliphatic chain, followed by ring closure.

(b) An aliphatic compound has a carbon atom skeleton that is either a straight or branched chain. In an aromatic compound the carbon atom skeleton consists of a hexagonal ring of carbon atoms or of two or more rings fused together. The ring system possesses multiple bond character.

(c) Paraffins and olefins are both aliphatics, that is, the carbon atom skeletons are straight or branched chains. The paraffins (alkanes), however, contain only single bonds between carbon atoms whereas the olefins (alkenes) have some double bonds.

(d) An alkane is a hydrocarbon molecule with a formula, C_nH_{2n+2}. An alkyl group has one less hydrogen atom than the corresponding alkane molecule. It is not a stable species, but it can be bonded to another atom or group to form a molecule. For example,

CH_3CH_3	CH_3CH_2-	CH_3CH_2Cl
ethane	ethyl	ethyl chloride

(e) A normal molecule or group has all carbon atoms in a straight chain. An *iso* group has a branched chain.

$CH_3CH_2CH_2CH_2-$

n-butyl

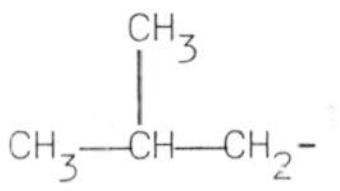

isobutyl

(f) Primary, secondary and tertiary are terms used to indicate the placement of a substituent group on a hydrocarbon chain. If the group *X* is attached to the end of a chain the compound is referred to as primary. If the carbon atom to which the group *X* is attached is bonded to two other carbon atoms, the compound is called secondary; and if the carbon atom to which *X* is attached is bonded to three other carbon atoms, the compound is tertiary.

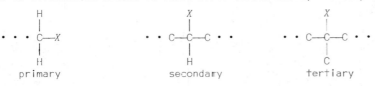

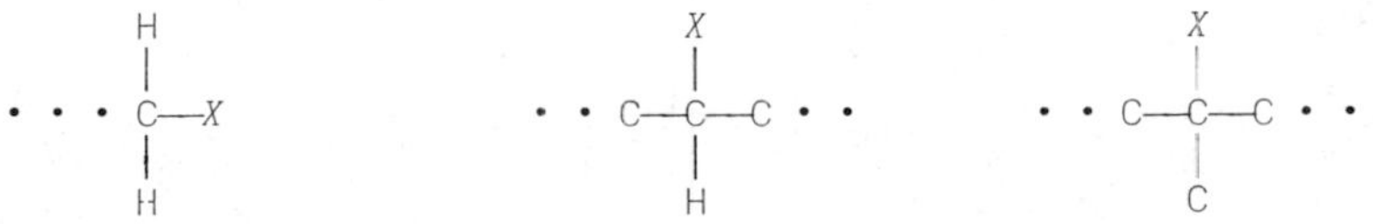

primary secondary tertiary

(g) Axial and equatorial refer to the placement of substituent groups on the chair conformation of the cyclohexane ring structure (see Figure 24-4). Equatorial groups extend outward from the ring, and axial groups are directed above and below the ring.

24-3. (a) A condensed formula indicates both the total number of atoms of all types in a molecule and the manner in which these atoms are bonded together (that is, single or multiple bonds, straight or branched chains, and so on). The condensed formula of 2,3-dimethylbutane is $CH(CH_3)_2CH(CH_3)_2$ and stands for the structure:

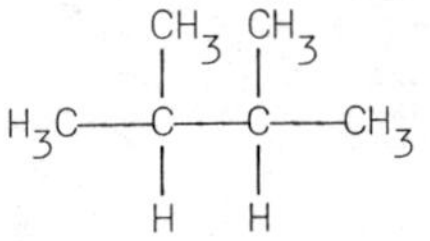

(b) Compounds in a homologous series differ from one another by some constant unit in their formulas. Each succeeding member of the alkane series of hydrocarbons has an additional $-CH_2$ unit, for example, *n*-butane is $CH_3CH_2CH_2CH_3$ and *n*-pentane is $CH_3CH_2CH_2CH_2CH_3$.

(c) An olefin is an alkene hydrocarbon. The molecule contains a double bond between carbon atoms, as in propene, $CH_3CH{=}CH_2$.

(d) A free radical is a grouping of atoms that may participate in chemical reactions but that cannot be isolated as a stable substance. One example is the methyl radical, $\cdot CH_3$, which participates in chain reactions such as (24.5).

(e) The positions on a benzene ring with respect to the location of a substituent group *X* are denoted as ortho, meta, and para.

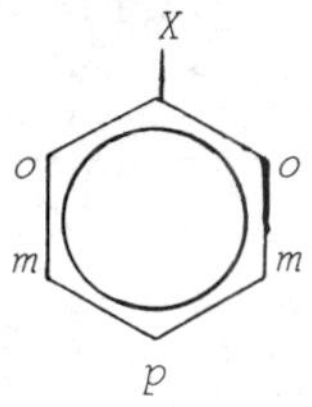

When additional substituents *Y* are added to the ring by appropriate chemical reactions, the group *X* tends to direct the *Y* groups to preferred positions on the ring. If these positions are *o*- and *p*-, the substituent *X* is said to be an ortho-para director (for example, -OH). If the preferred position for the second group *Y* is a meta position, *X* is said to be a meta director (for example, $-NO_2$).

Organic structures

24-4. (a) 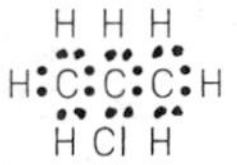 (b) 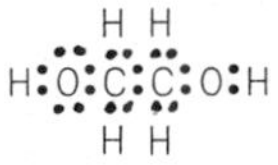 (c) 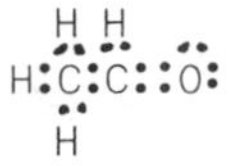

24-5. (a) 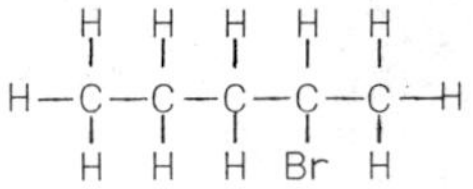 (b) 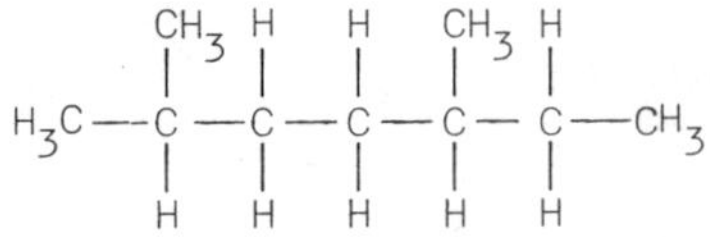

(c) 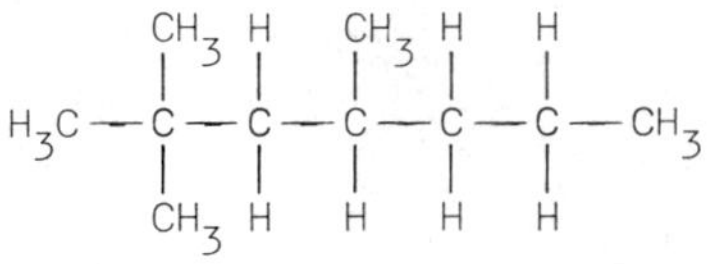 (d) 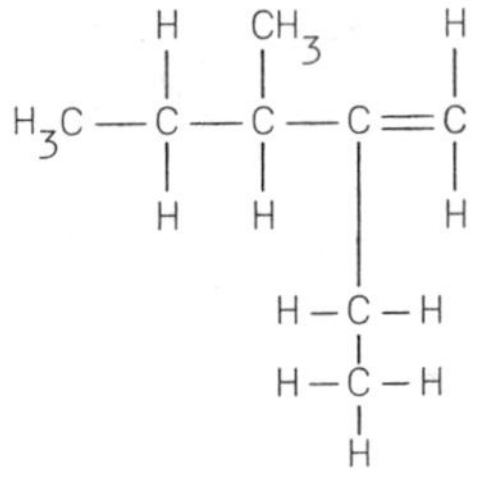

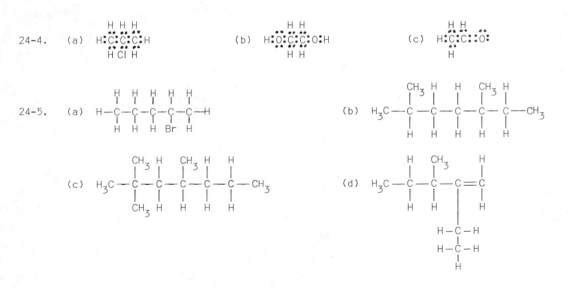

24-6. All C-H bonds involve the overlap, $(2sp^3, 1s)$ unless otherwise indicated.

(a)

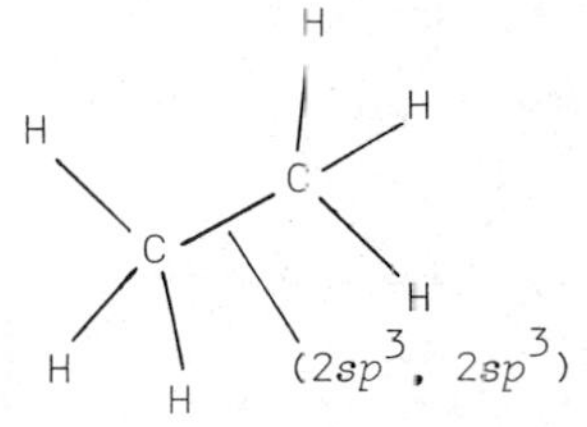

(b)

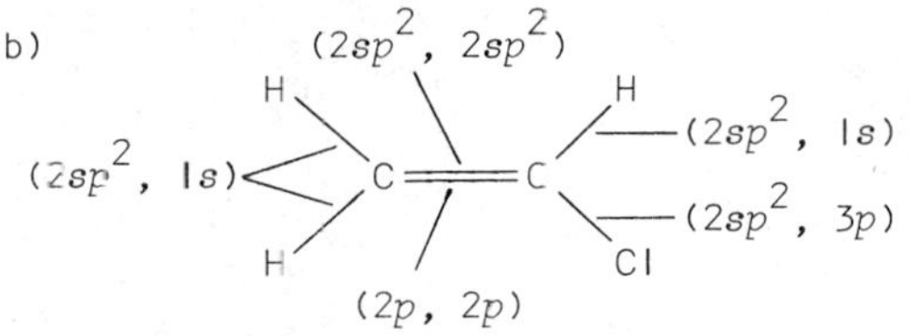

(c)

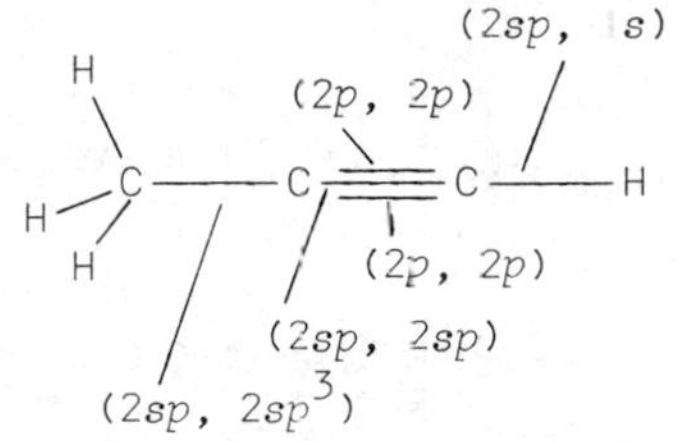

(d)

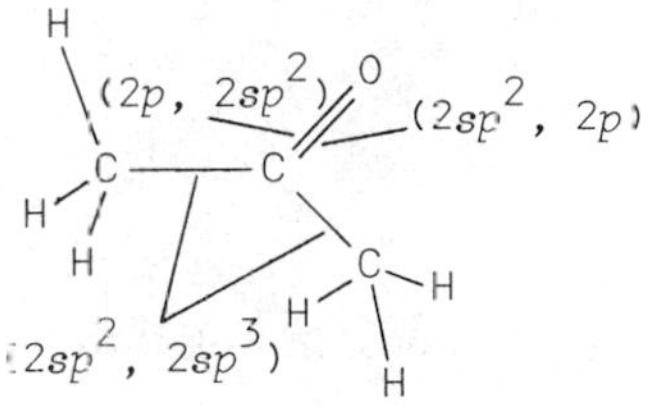

(e)

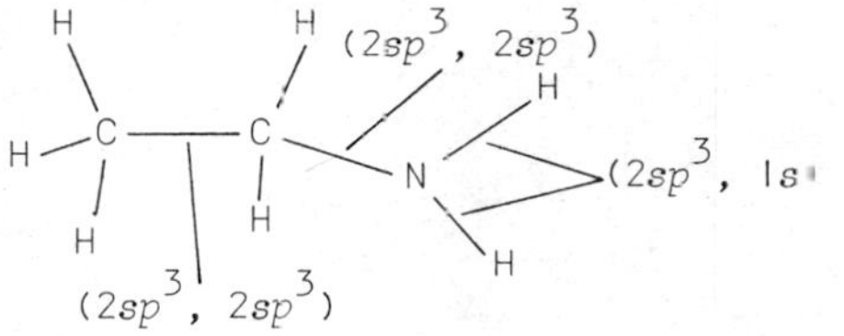

Isomers

24-7. (a) The compounds have different formulas, C_4H_{10} and C_4H_8. They cannot be isomers.

(b) The compounds have the same formula, C_9H_{20}. They are skeletal isomers.

(c) The structures shown are *identical*. This is a single compound, not isomers.

(d) Again, the structures are *identical* (rotate either structure by 180° to obtain the other).

(e) The two structures are *identical*. There is no isomerism.

(f) The different positions on the benzene ring indicate ortho-para isomerism.

24-8. Skeletal isomers differ in the basic carbon atom framework of their molecules, such as straight and branched chains. Positional isomers differ in the placement of substituent groups on the carbon atom framework. Isomers that exist because of restricted rotation about a double bond are called geometric isomers.

(a) positional; (b) skeletal; (c) positional; (d) positional (ortho and metal);
(e) geometric.

24-9. (a) There are three isomers of pentane. Only the carbon-atom skeletons are shown below:

```
                        C              C
                        |              |
(1) C-C-C-C-C   (2) C-C-C-C    (3) C-C-C
                                       |
                                       C
```

(b) There are nine isomers of heptane; their carbon-atom skeltons are as follows.

```
                              C               C
                              |               |
(1) C-C-C-C-C-C-C   (2) C-C-C-C-C-C   (3) C-C-C-C-C-C
```

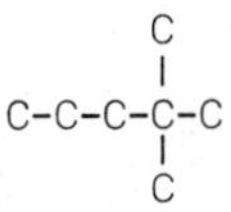

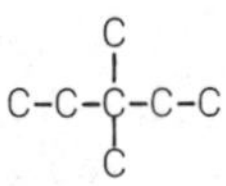

```
                C                          C                        C C
                |                          |                        | |
(4)  C-C-C-C-C             (5)  C-C-C-C-C              (6)  C-C-C-C-C
                |                          |
                C                          C
                                                                      C
                                                                      |
       C    C                           C C                           C
       |    |                           | |                           |
(7)  C-C-C-C-C             (8)  C-C-C-C                (9)  C-C-C-C-C
                                        |
                                        C
```

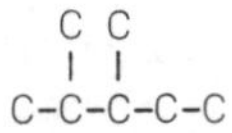

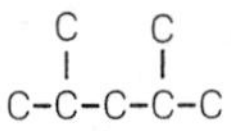

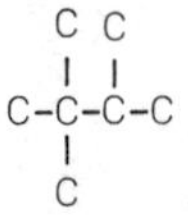

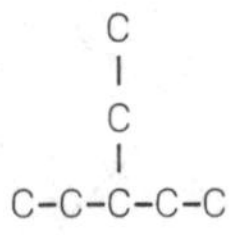

24-10. Draw the five skeletal structures of C_6H_{14} established in Example 24-1 and determine the number of possibilities of substituting a single Cl atom into each of these.

```
                                               Cl                 Cl
                                               |                  |
(1)  C-C-C-C-C-C  leads to  Cl-C-C-C-C-C-C;  C-C-C-C-C-C;  and  C-C-C-C-C-C   (three)

       C                          C        C          C          C          C
       |                          |        |          |          |          |
(2)  C-C-C-C-C  leads to  Cl-C-C-C-C-C;  C-C-C-C-C;  C-C-C-C-C;  C-C-C-C-C;  C-C-C-C-C-Cl  (five)
                                           |            |            |
                                           Cl           Cl           Cl

         C                          C        C          C          C-Cl
         |                          |        |          |          |
(3)  C-C-C-C-C  leads to  Cl-C-C-C-C-C;  C-C-C-C-C;  C-C-C-C-C;  C-C-C-C-C  (four)
                                           |            |
                                           Cl           Cl

       C C                      C C      C C
       | |                      | |      | |
(4)  C-C-C-C  leads to  Cl-C-C -C-C;  C-C-C-C  (two)
                                       |
                                       Cl

         C                          C       Cl C        C
         |                          |       |  |        |
(5)  C-C-C-C  leads to  Cl-C-C-C-C;  C-C-C-C;  C-C-C-C-Cl  (three)
         |                          |          |          |
         C                          C          C          C
```

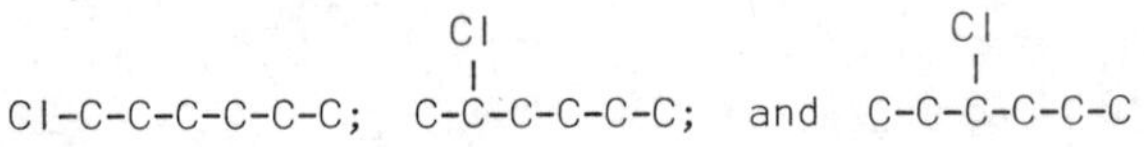

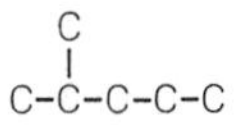

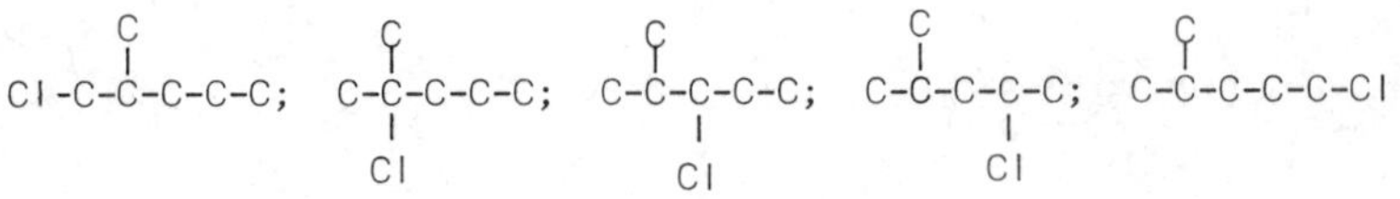

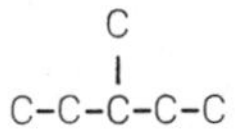

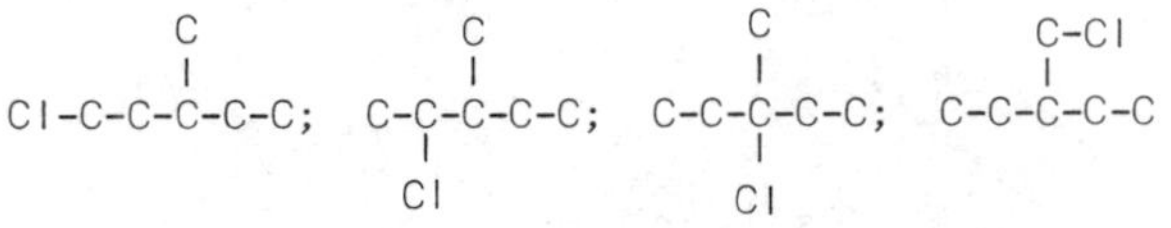

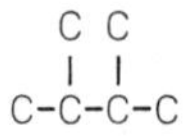

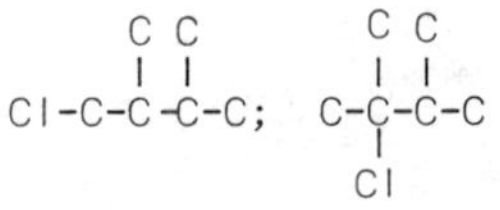

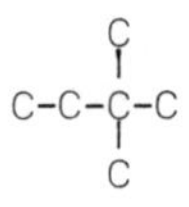

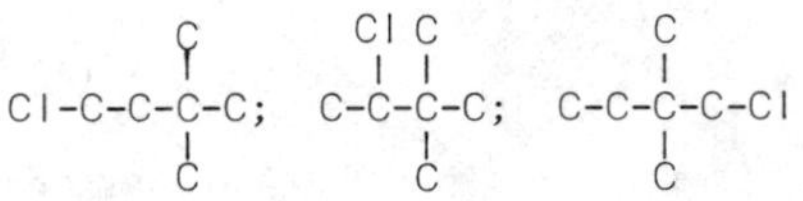

Functional groups

24-11. (a) halide (bromide); (b) carboxylic acid; (c) aldehyde; (d) ether; (e) ketone; (f) amine; (g) phenyl; (h) ester.

24-12. (a) Both carbonyl and carboxyl groups are based on the unit $R-\overset{O}{\overset{\|}{C}}-R$ 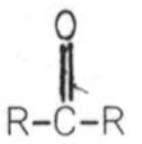 but in a carboxylic acid one R group is replaced by OH. (In an aldehyde one R group is replaced by an H atom.)

(b) An amide has the $-NH_2$ group attached to a carbonyl group, that is:

```
  O
  ||
R-C-NH2
```

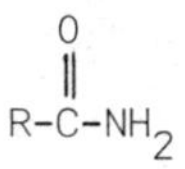

When the $-NH_2$ group is attached directly to an organic residue R, the compound is an amine, $R-NH_2$.

(c) A carboxylic acid has the functional group -COOH, that is, R-COOH. Elimination of a water molecule from two acid molecules leads to an acid anhydride.

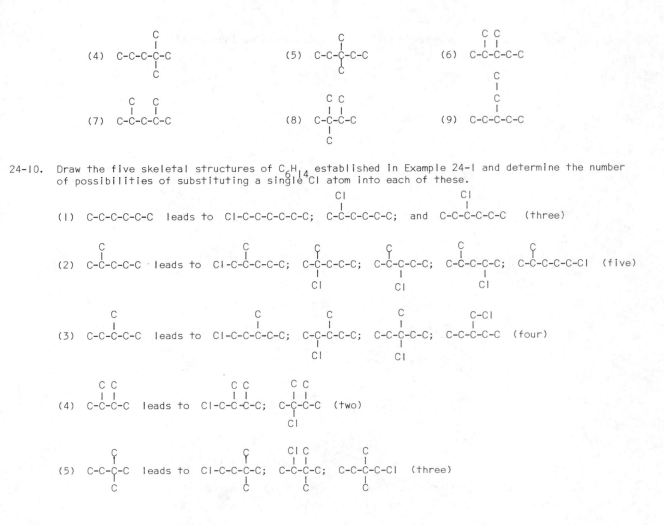

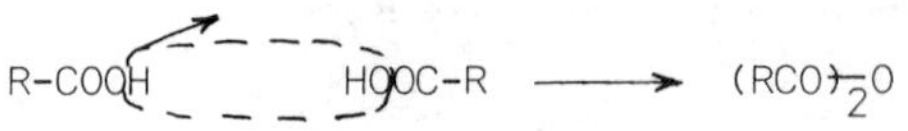

(d) Both aldehydes and ketones contain the carbonyl group, $>C=O$. If the two groups attached to the carbonyl are organic residues, R, the compound is a ketone; if one is an R group and the other an H atom, the molecule is an aldehyde.

24-13. (a) $R-NO_2$, where R is $-CH_3$, $-CH_2CH_3$, $-CH_2CH_2CH_3$, $-CH(CH_3)_2$, and so on.

(b) $R-NH_2$. R groups might be  or 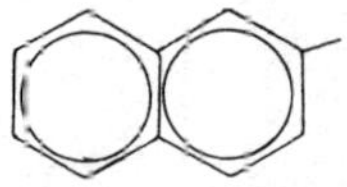 or 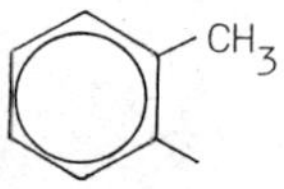 and so on.

(c) A chlorophenol has one or more Cl atoms on the ring structure of a phenol, such as

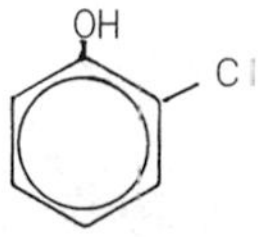

(d) An aliphatic diol has two OH groups as substituents on a straight or branched chain hydrocarbon, such as

$$\underset{\displaystyle \;\;\;\;\;\mid \atop \;\;\;\;\;OH}{H_3CCHCH_2OH}$$

(e) An unsaturated aliphatic alcohol is a straight or branched chain hydrocarbon that contains one or more multiple bonds and an OH group as a substituent on the chain, such as

$H_3CCH{=}CHCH_2OH$

(f) An alicyclic ketone has the carbonyl group incorporated into a saturated ring hydrocarbon, such as cyclohexanone.

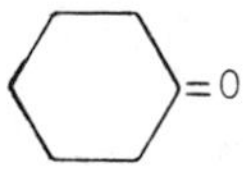

(g) A halogenated alkane has one or more halogen atoms X (X = F, Cl, Br or I) substituted on an alkane hydrocarbon chain, such as

$H_3CCCl_2CH_2CH_3$

(h) An aromatic dicarboxylic acid has two carboxyl groups as substituents on an aromatic hydrocarbon.

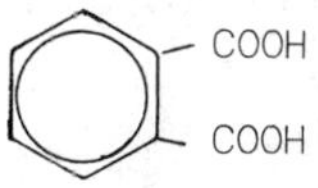

Nomenclature and formulas

24-14. (a) 2,2-dimethylbutane; (b) 2-methyl-1-propene (or simply methylpropene); (c) methylcyclopropane; (d) 4-methyl-2-pentyne; (e) 2-ethyl-3-methyl pentane; (f) 3,4-dimethyl-2- *n*-propyl-1-pentene

24-15. (a) $H_3C-\overset{\displaystyle CH_3}{\underset{\displaystyle H}{C}}-CH_2-CH_3$

(b) 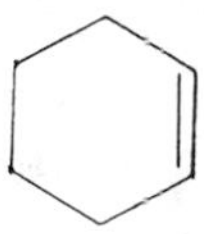

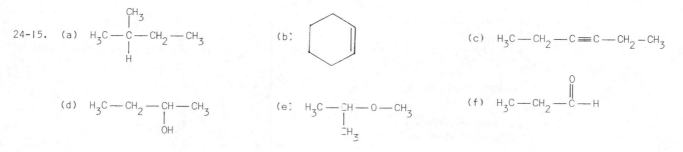

(c) $H_3C-CH_2-C{\equiv}C-CH_2-CH_3$

(d) $H_3C-CH_2-\underset{\displaystyle OH}{CH}-CH_3$

(e) $H_3C-\underset{\displaystyle CH_3}{CH}-O-CH_3$

(f) $H_3C-CH_2-\overset{\displaystyle O}{\overset{\|}{C}}-H$

(g)
$$H_3C - \overset{\overset{\displaystyle Cl}{|}}{\underset{\underset{\displaystyle CH_3}{|}}{C}} - CH_3$$

(h)
$$H_3C - CH_2 - \overset{\overset{\displaystyle CH_3}{|}}{N} - CH_2 - CH_3$$

(i)
$$H_3C - \overset{\overset{}{\underset{\underset{\displaystyle CH_3}{|}}{CH}}}{} - \overset{\overset{\displaystyle O}{\|}}{C} - OH$$

(j)
$$H_3C - \overset{\overset{}{\underset{\underset{\displaystyle CH_3}{|}}{CH}}}{} - CH_2 - O - \overset{\overset{\displaystyle O}{\|}}{C} - CH_2 - CH_3$$

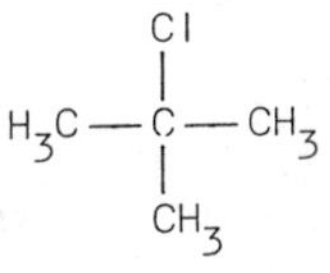

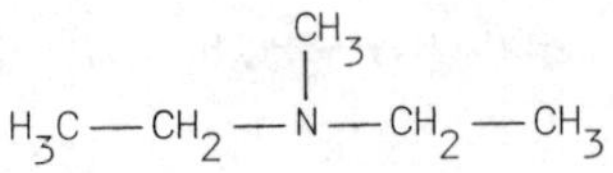

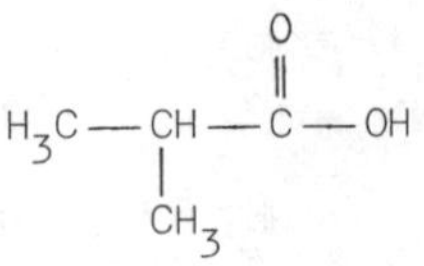

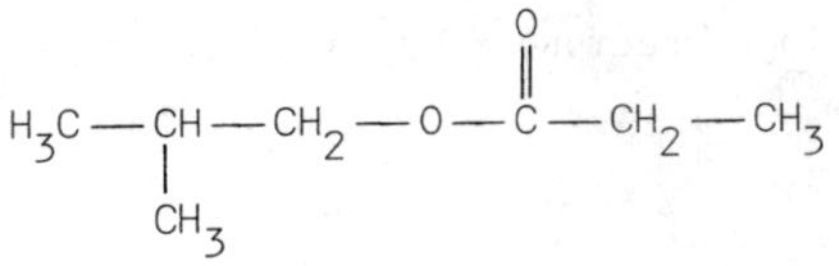

24-16. (a) No. The double bond in pentene could be located either at the first or second carbon atom. The compound must be named in such a way as to distinguish between these two possibilities, that is, either 1-pentene or 2-pentene.

(b) Yes. The carbonyl group must be either at the second or third position in the four-carbon chain of butane, but these two positions are identical.

(c) No. The alcohol could be primary, secondary, or tertiary butyl alcohol.

(d) No. Even if it were understood that the $-NH_2$ group is attached to the benzene ring and not directly to the N atom (that is, not N-methylaniline), there are still three possibilities for the $-CH_3$ group with respect to $-NH_2$--ortho, meta, and para.

(e) Yes. All positions on the cyclopentane ring where a methyl group might be substituted are equivalent.

24-17. (a) No. The double bond at the number "3" carbon atom is really at "2" (counting from the other end of the chain).

$$H_3C - CH = CH - CH_2 - CH_3 \qquad \text{2-pentene}$$

(b) No. There are two double bonds, but more than one way in which these double bonds may be placed in the molecule, for example

$$H_2C = CH - CH = CH - CH_3 \quad \text{or} \quad H_2C = CH - CH_2 - CH = CH_2$$

(c) No. A ketone must have an organic residue R on either side of the carbonyl group. If the carbonyl group is at the first position on the chain, the compound is an aldehyde.

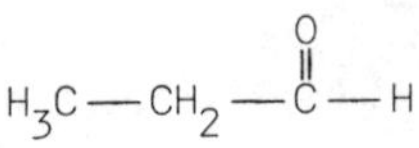

$$H_3C - CH_2 - \overset{\overset{\displaystyle O}{\|}}{C} - H \quad \text{propanal;} \qquad H_3C - \overset{\overset{\displaystyle O}{\|}}{C} - CH_3 \quad \text{propanone}$$

(d) No. The bromine atom can be either on the first or second carbon atom, that is, 1-bromopropane or 2-bromopropane.

(e) No. The compound in question is *m*-dichlorobenzene. If numbers are to be used in its name they should be the lowest numbers possible, 1,3-dichlorobenzene.

(f) No. The compound in question is the following:

$$H_3C - C \equiv C - \overset{\overset{\displaystyle CH_3}{|}}{CH} - CH_3$$

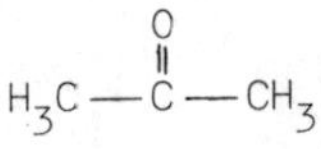

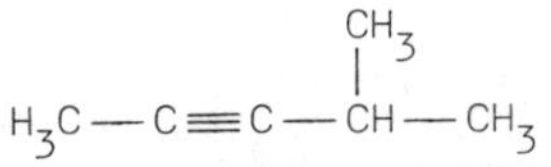

It should be named so that the triple bond appears at the lowest number possible, 4-methyl-2-pentyne.

(g) No. The compound suggested by the name given is

$$H_3C - \overset{\overset{}{\underset{\underset{\displaystyle CH_3}{|}}{CH}}}{} - CH_2 - \overset{\overset{}{\underset{\underset{\underset{\underset{\underset{\displaystyle CH_3}{|}}{CH_2}}{|}}{CH_2}}{|}}{CH}}{} - CH_2 - CH_2 - CH_2 - CH_3$$

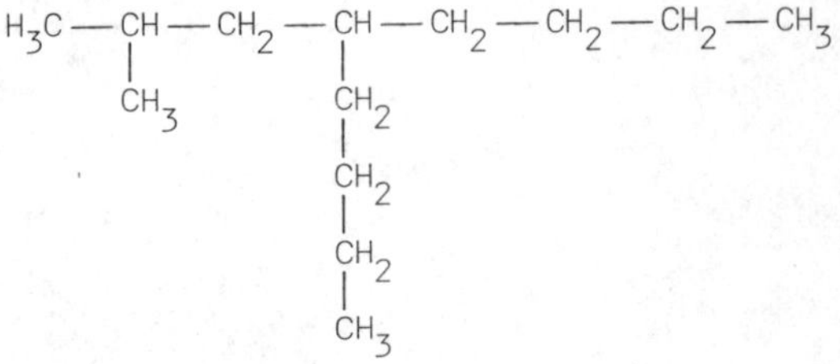

It should be named 5-isobutylnonane.
(The carbon chain is *nine* atoms long.)

(h)   No.   The compound indicated is

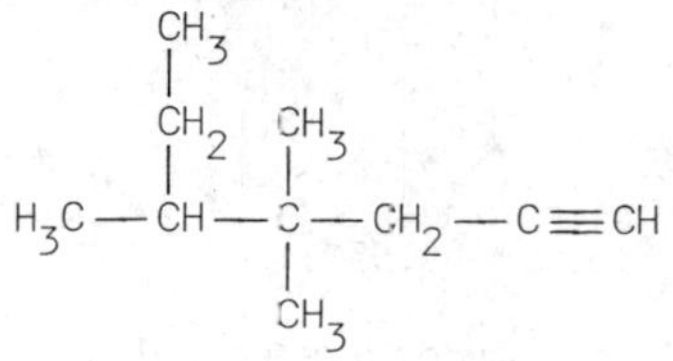

The name should be based on a *seven* carbon chain.
The correct name is 4,4,5 trimethyl-1-heptyne.

(i)   Correct.

(j)   Correct.

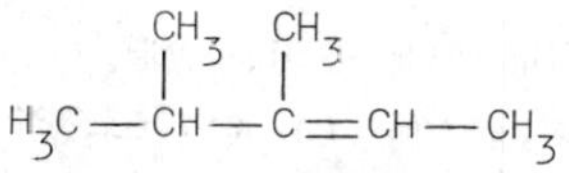

24-18.   (a) $CH_3CH(OH)CH_3$

(b) $Pb(C_2H_5)_4$

(c) $CH_2{=}C(CH_3)CH{=}CH_2$

(d) $(CH_3)_3CCH_2CH(CH_3)_2$

(e)

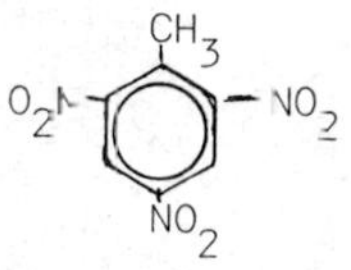

(f)

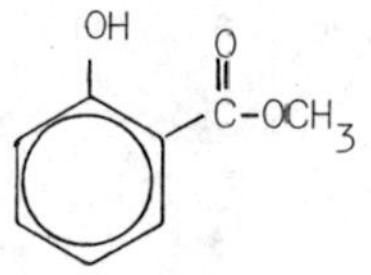

(g)   ⬡—$CH_2CH(NH_2)CH_3$

(h) $(CH_3)_2CH(C_5H_{31})$

(i) $(CH_3)_2C{=}CH(CH_2)_2C(CH_3){=}CH(CH_2)_2C(C{-}_3){=}CHCH_2OH$

Experimental determination of formulas

24-19.   Recall the methods used in Chapter 3. That is, determine the number of moles of C in the hydrocarbon from the given mass of CO_2 and the number of moles of H from the mass of H_2O. An empirical formula can be written directly at this point.

$$\text{no. mol C} = 0.577 \text{ g } CO_2 \times \frac{1 \text{ mol C}}{44.0 \text{ g } CO_2} = 0.0131 \text{ mol C}$$

$$\text{no. mol H} = 0.236 \text{ g } H_2O \times \frac{2 \text{ mol H}}{18.0 \text{ g } H_2O} = 0.0262 \text{ mol H}$$

Empirical formula: $C_{0.0131}H_{0.0262} = CH_2$

Molecular formula (based on a molecular weight of 56): C_4H_8

Alkanes

24-20.   Isobutane has a more compact structure than *n*-butane and a lower boiling point.

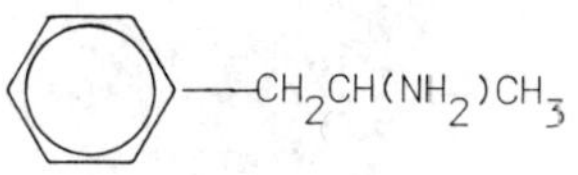

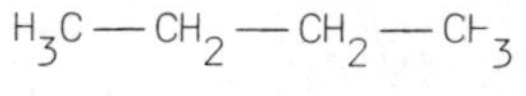

$H_3C{-}CH_2{-}CH_2{-}CH_3$

n-butane (b. pt. -0.5°C)

$H_3C{-}CH(CH_3){-}CH_3$

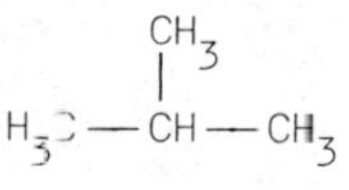

isobutane (b. pt. -11.7°C)

The relative boiling points of the pentane isomers also reflect the compactness of the molecular structures.

$$H_3C-CH_2-CH_2-CH_2-CH_3$$

n-pentane (b. pt. 36.1°C)

$$H_3C-\underset{\underset{CH_3}{|}}{CH}-CH_2-CH_3$$

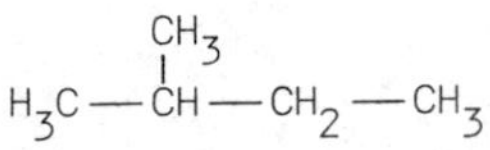

isopentane
(b. pt. 27.9°C)

$$H_3C-\underset{\underset{CH_3}{|}}{\overset{\overset{CH_3}{|}}{C}}-CH_3$$

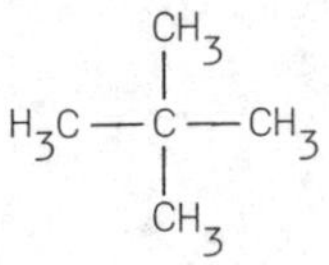

neopentane
(b. pt. 9.5°C)

There are five hexane isomers whose boiling points decrease in the order listed below.

$$H_3C-CH_2-CH_2-CH_2-CH_2-CH_3$$
n-hexane (b. pt. 68.7°C)

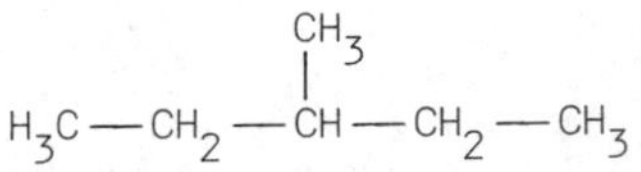

$$H_3C-CH_2-\underset{\underset{CH_3}{|}}{CH}-CH_2-CH_3$$
3-methylpentane (b. pt. 63.3°C)

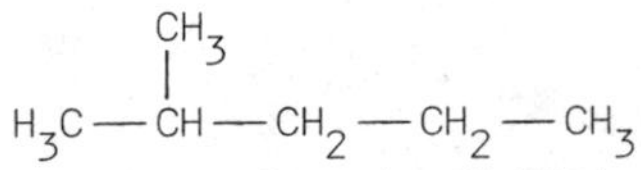

$$H_3C-\underset{\underset{CH_3}{|}}{CH}-CH_2-CH_2-CH_3$$
isohexane (b. pt. 60.3°C)

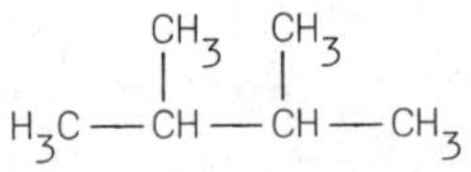

$$H_3C-\underset{\underset{CH_3}{|}}{CH}-\underset{\underset{CH_3}{|}}{CH}-CH_3$$
2,3-dimethylbutane (b. pt. 58.0°C)

$$H_3C-\underset{\underset{CH_3}{|}}{\overset{\overset{CH_3}{|}}{C}}-CH_2-CH_3$$

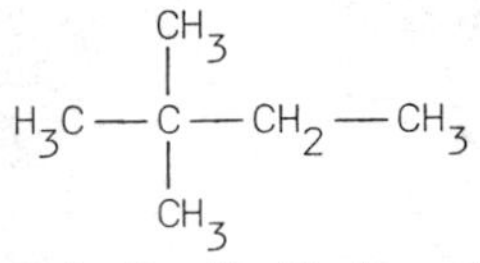

2,2-dimethylbutane (b. pt. 49.7°C)

24-21. The most stable conformation of t-butylcyclohexane is the chair form with the t-butyl group substituting for a hydrogen atom in an equatorial position (that is, extending outward from the ring).

24-22. (a) If the alkane hydrocarbon has a molecular weight of 44, it must have the formula C_3H_8. The structure is $H_3C-CH_2-CH_3$ and the monochlorination products are $H_3C-CH_2-CH-Cl$ and $H_3C-CHCl-CH_3$.

(b) The molecular weight of 58 corresponds to the alkane C_4H_{10}. The structure can be either n-butane or isobutane; each would form two monobromides.

$$H_3C-CH_2-CH_2-CH_3 \quad \text{or} \quad H_3C-\underset{\underset{CH_3}{|}}{CH}-CH_3$$

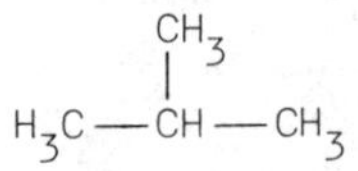

24-23. (a) $CH_3CH_2CH=CH_2 + H_2 \longrightarrow CH_3CH_2CH_2CH_3$
n-butane

(b) $2\ H_3CCH_2CH_2Br + 2\ Na \longrightarrow H_3CCH_2CH_2-CH_2CH_2CH_3 + 2\ NaBr$
n-hexane

(c) $H_3CCH_2CH_2COONa + NaOH \longrightarrow H_3CCH_2CH_3 + Na_2CO_3$
n-propane

(d) $H_3CCH_2CH_3 + Cl_2 \xrightarrow{h\nu} H_3CCH_2CH_2Cl + H_3CCHClCH_3$
1-chloropropane   2-chloropropane

24-24. One possibility for the chain termination reaction is the combination of two methyl radicals to form a molecule of ethane. Ethane molecules so formed may themselves undergo chlorination to ethyl chloride, C_2H_5Cl.

Alkenes

24-25. Only one position is available for the double bond in ethene and propene. In butene two non-equivalent positions are available for the double bond. The position of this double bond must be indicated in the name used.

$H_2C{=}CHCH_2CH_3$ — 1-butene $H_3CCH{=}CHCH_3$ — 2-butene

24-26. Alkenes and alicyclic hydrocarbons both can be thought of as resulting from the elimination of two hydrogen atoms and the formation of an additional carbon-to-carbon bond. In alkenes these hydrogen atoms come from *adjacent* carbon atoms, and the introduction of a new bond leads to a *double* bond between the carbon atoms. In alicyclic hydrocarbons the hydrogen atoms are derived from *opposite* ends of an alkane chain. A new carbon-to-carbon *single* bond is formed and the chain is converted to a ring.

24-27. (a) $H_2C{=}CHCH_3 + H_2 \xrightarrow{Pt,\Delta} H_3C-CH_2-CH_3$

(b) $H_3C-CH(OH)-CH_2-CH_3 \xrightarrow[H_2SO_4]{\Delta} H_2C{=}CH-CH_2-CH_3 + H_3C-CH{=}CH-CH_3 + H_2O$ 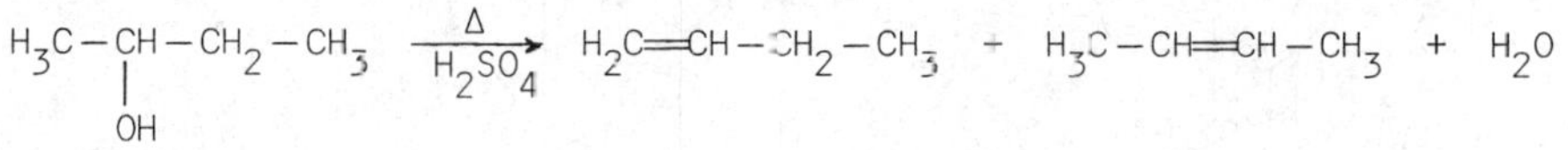

(c) 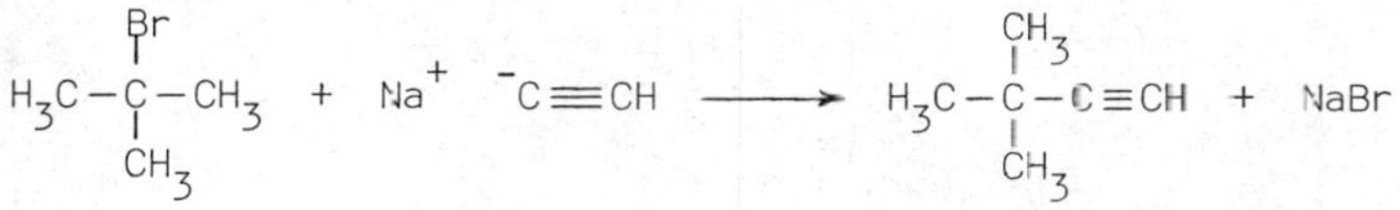 24-28. (a) 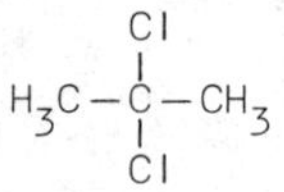(b) 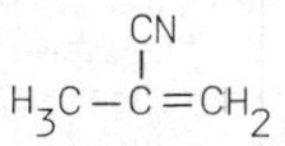(c) 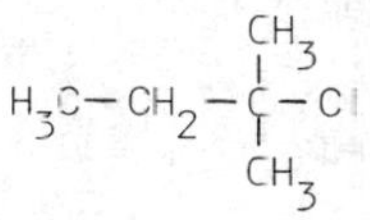(d) 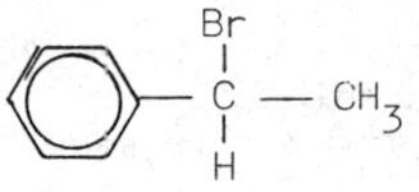 *Aromatic compounds*

24-29. (a) 2-methylaniline (or o-methylaniline); (b) 1,3-dinitrobenzene (or m-dinitrobenzene); (c) 4-aminobiphenyl

(d) 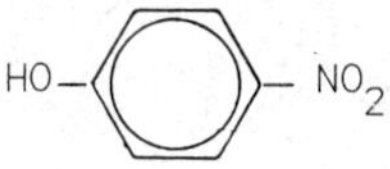(e) 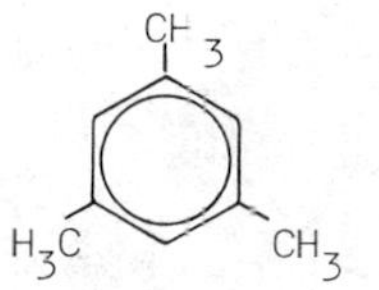(f) 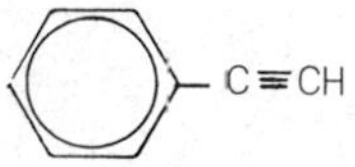(g) 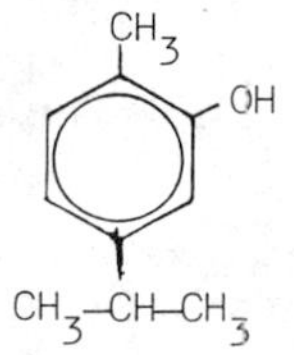 24-30.

(a) 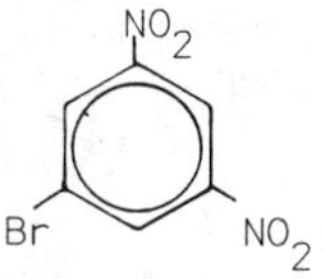(b) 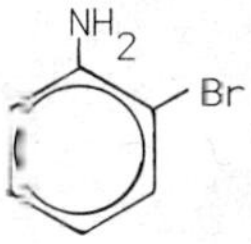 and 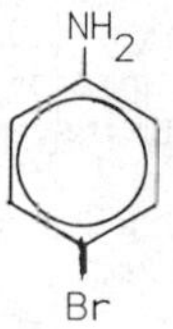(c) 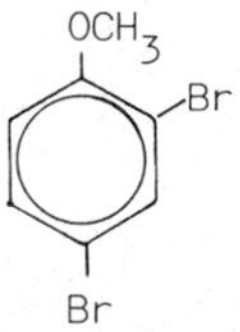 24-31. If the outcome of the substitution were determined by the -CHO group, the result should be 3-methoxy-5-nitrobenzaldehyde.

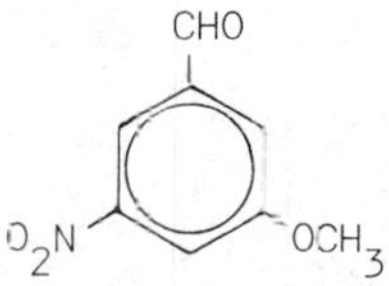

The fact that this compound is not produced suggests that the ortho-para director is stronger than the meta director. The expected isomers are

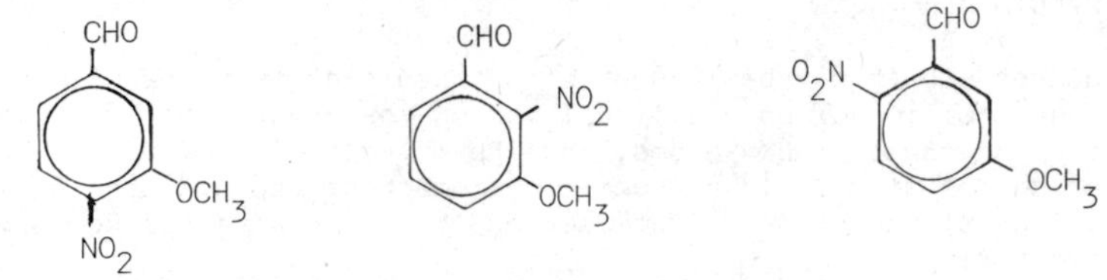

24-32. (a)

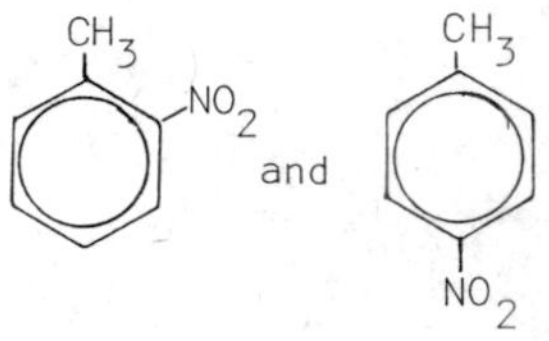

(b)

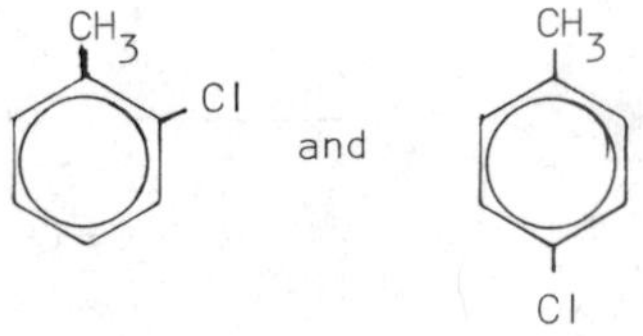

(c)

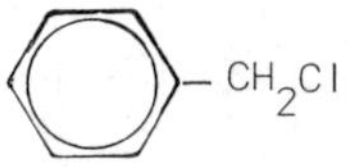

24-33. Cyclohexatriene is an unsaturated alicyclic hydrocarbon with localized double bonds between alternate pairs of carbon atoms. Benzene, although it has the same empirical formula, is a different substance. It is an aromatic compounds, with the three pairs of electrons associated with its double bonds delocalized and spread out over the ring structure (recall Figure 10-20).

24-34. Replace the molecular orbital representation by Kekulé structures.

There are 10 electrons associated with the five double bonds in the Kekule structures. Thus the two circles in the molecular orbital representation must represent a total of 10 electrons in the π bonding system of $C_{10}H_8$.

Organic reactions

24-35. (a) The substitution of another group for an H atom on an alkane molecule is an aliphatic substitution reaction, such as reaction (24.5).

(b) In an aromatic substitution reaction a hydrogen atom(s) on a benzene ring or a condensed ring system is (are) replaced by another group. Four examples are given in Figure 24-6.

(c) In an addition reaction, such as those involving alkenes and alkynes, a small molecule dissociates and the fragments are added to the carbon atoms at the site of a multiple bond [see equation (24.17)].

(d) Atoms or small groups from adjacent carbon atoms are removed and joined into a small molecule in an elimination reaction. A double bond is produced between the carbon atoms where the elimination occurs. Examples are given in equations (24.7) and (24.8).

24-36. (a) $CH_3CH_2CH_2CH_2CH_2OH \xrightarrow[H^+]{Cr_2O_7^{2-}} H_3C-CH_2-CH_2-CH_2-\overset{\overset{O}{\|}}{C}-OH$

(b) $CH_3CH_2CH_2COOH + HOCH_2CH_3 \xrightarrow[H^+]{\Delta} H_3C-CH_2-CH_2-\overset{\overset{O}{\|}}{C}-O-CH_2-CH_3$

(c)

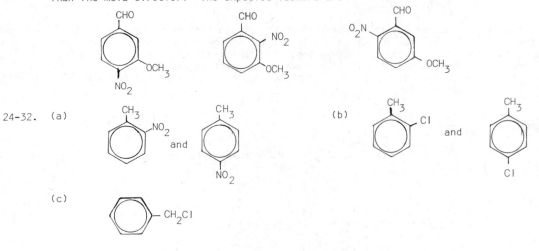

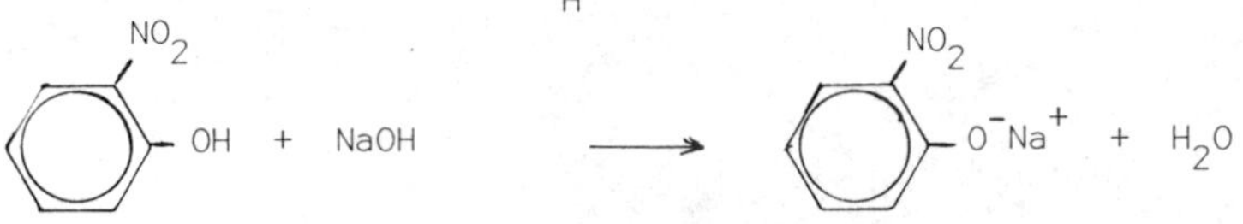

(d) $CH_3CH_2C(CH_3)=CH_2 \xrightarrow[H_2SO_4]{H_2O} H_3C-CH_2-\overset{\overset{\displaystyle CH_3}{|}}{\underset{\underset{\displaystyle OH}{|}}{C}}-CH_3$

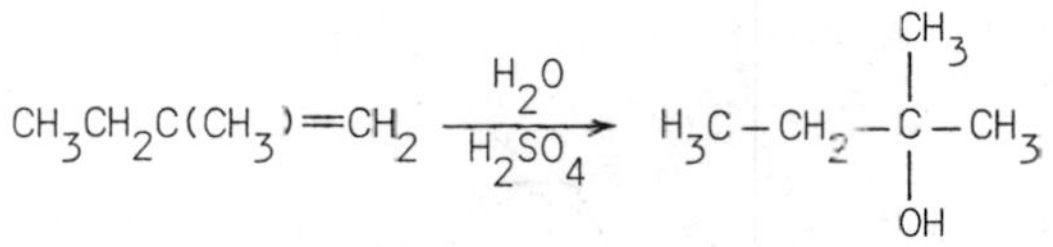

24-37. (a) *oxid:* $2\{Fe \longrightarrow Fe^{3+} + 3\ e^-\}$

red: $-NO_2 + 7\ H^+ + 6\ e^- \longrightarrow$ $-NH_3^+ + 2\ H_2O$

net: $-NO_2 + 2\ Fe + 7\ H^+ \longrightarrow$ $-NH_3^+ + 2\ Fe^{3+} + 2\ H_2O$

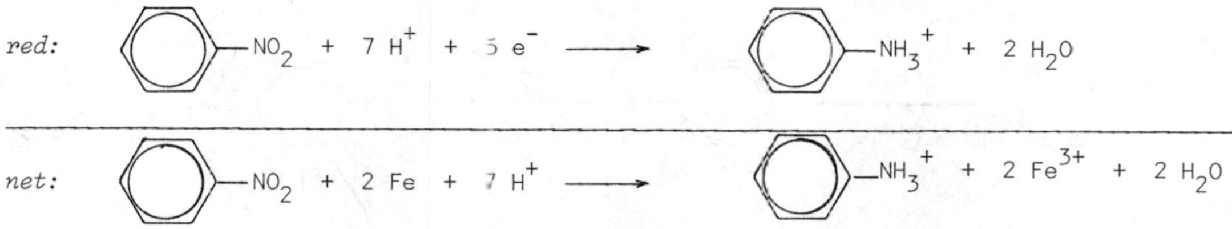

(b) *oxid:* $3\{CH_3CH=CH_2 + 2\ OH^- \longrightarrow CH_3CHCHCH_2OH + 2\ e^-\}$

red: $2\{MnO_4^- + 2\ H_2O + 3\ e^- \longrightarrow MnO_2 + 4\ OH^-\}$

net: $3\ CH_3CH=CH_2 + 2\ MnO_4^- + 4\ H_2O \longrightarrow 3\ CH_3CHOHCH_2OH + 2\ MnO_2 + 2\ OH^-$

(c) *oxid:* $C_6H_{12}O_2 \longrightarrow C_6H_{10}O_2 + 2\ H^+ + 2\ e^-$

red: $Pb(C_2H_3O_2)_4 + 2\ e^- \longrightarrow Pb(C_2H_3O_2)_2 + 2\ C_2H_3O_2^-$

net: $C_6H_{12}O_2 + Pb(C_2H_3O_2)_4 \longrightarrow C_6H_{10}O_2 + Pb(C_2H_3O_2)_2 + 2\ HC_2H_3O_2$

(d) *oxid:* $H_3C-$$-CH_3 + 4\ H_2O \longrightarrow HOOC-$$-COOH + 12\ H^+ + 12\ e^-$

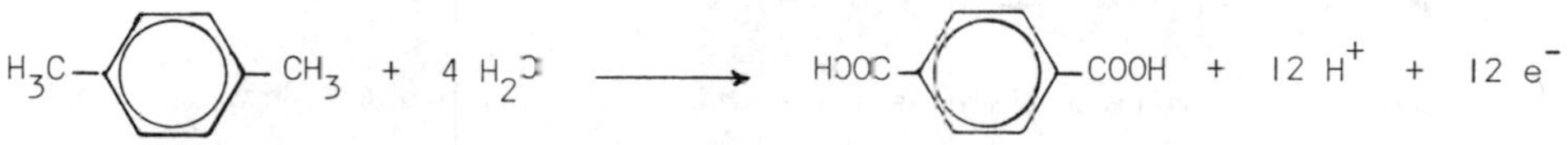

red: $2\{Cr_2O_7^{2-} + 14\ H^+ + 6\ e^- \longrightarrow 2\ Cr^{3+} + 7\ H_2O\}$

$H_3C-$$-CH_3 + 16\ H^+ + 2\ Cr_2O_7^{2-} \longrightarrow HOOC-$$-COOH + 4\ Cr^{3+} + 10\ H_2O$

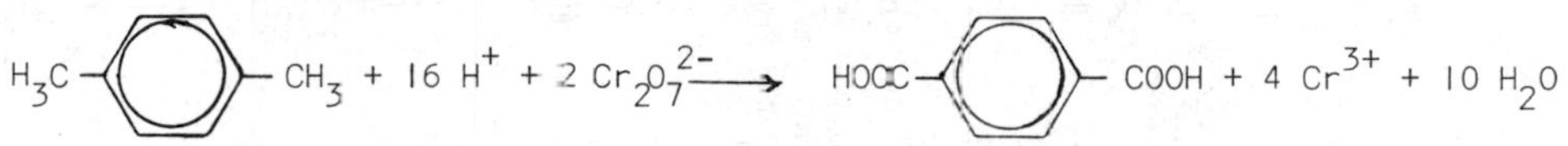

24-38. First write a balanced equation for this oxidation-reduction reaction.

3 $-CHO + 2\ KMnO_4 + KOH \longrightarrow 3$ $-CO_2K + 2\ MnO_2 + 2\ H_2O$

$\downarrow 3\ H^+$

3 $-COOH$

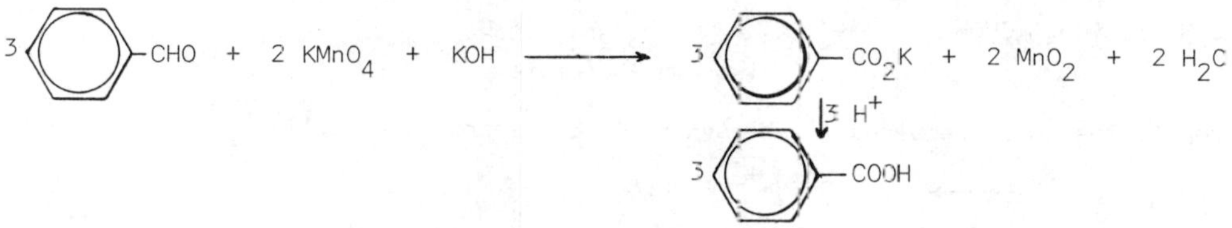

Next, determine the limiting reagent.

no. mol benzaldehyde $= 10.6\ g \times \dfrac{1\ mol}{106\ g} = 0.10$ mol benzaldehyde

no. mol $KMnO_4 = 5.9\ g \times \dfrac{1\ mol}{158\ g} = 0.037$ mol $KMnO_4$

All of the $KMnO_4$ is consumed; it is the limiting reagent.

no. g benzoic acid $= 0.037$ mol $KMnO_4 \times \dfrac{3\ mol\ benzoic\ acid}{2\ mol\ KMnO_4} \times \dfrac{122\ g\ benzoic\ acid}{1\ mol\ benzoic\ acid} = 6.8$ g benzoic acid

% Yield $= \dfrac{6.1\ g\ actual}{6.8\ g\ theoretical} \times 100 = 90\%$

24-39. (a)

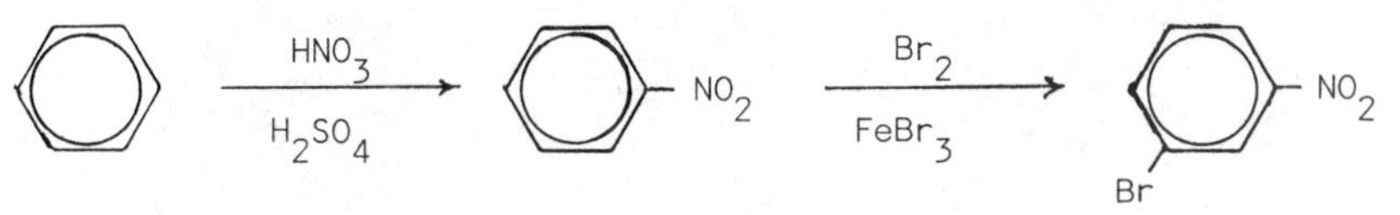

(b)

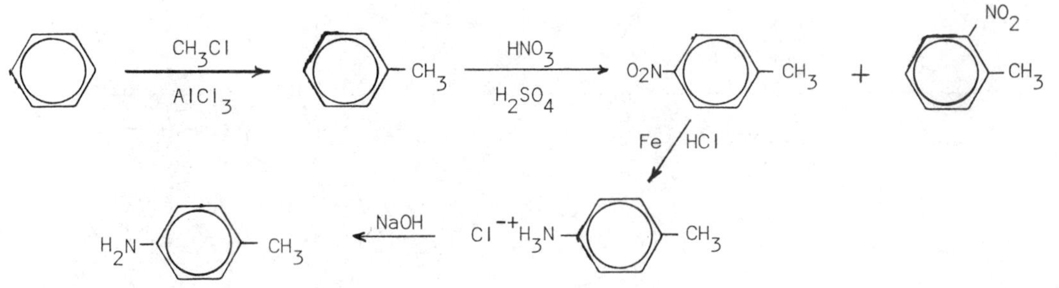

24-40. (a) $HC\equiv CH \xrightarrow[H_2]{Pt} H_2C=CH_2 \xrightarrow[H_2SO_4]{H_2O} CH_3CH_2OH$ $\qquad CH_3CH_2OH \xrightarrow[H^+]{Cr_2O_7^{2-}} CH_3CHO$

(b) $HC\equiv CH \xrightarrow{Br_2} CHBr=CHBr \xrightarrow{Br_2} CHBr_2CHBr_2$

(c) $HC\equiv CH \xrightarrow[H_2]{Pt} H_2C=CH_2 \xrightarrow[H_2SO_4]{H_2O} CH_3CH_2OH$ $\qquad CH_3CH_2OH \xrightarrow[H^+]{K_2Cr_2O_7} CH_3CO_2H$

$$CH_3COOH + NH_3 \longrightarrow CH_3COO^- + NH_4^+$$

Decompose ammonium acetate as in reactions (24.42) and (24.43).

(d) Prepare isopropyl alcohol by the following series of reactions:

$HC\equiv CH \xrightarrow{NaNH_2} HC\equiv C^-Na^+ + NH_3$ $\qquad HC\equiv C^-Na^+ + CH_3Cl \longrightarrow CH_3C\equiv CH + NaCl$

$$CH_3C\equiv CH \xrightarrow{Pt/H_2} CH_3CH=CH_2 \xrightarrow[H_2SO_4]{H_2O} CH_3CHOHCH_3$$

Prepare acetic acid as in part (c) and allow it to react with isopropyl alcohol.

$$CH_3CO_2H + (CH_3)_2CHOH \longrightarrow \underset{\text{isopropyl acetate}}{CH_3CO_2CH(CH_3)_2} + H_2O$$

To prepare the CH_3Cl required in the synthesis of isopropyl alcohol,

$$CH_3CO_2H + NaOH \longrightarrow CH_3CO_2^-Na^+ + H_2O$$

$CH_3CO_2^-Na^+ + NaOH \xrightarrow{\Delta} Na_2CO_3 + CH_4$ $\qquad CH_4 + Cl_2 \longrightarrow CH_3Cl + HCl$

Self-test Questions

1. (*b*) The formula C_7H_{14} (a) describes *all* the heptane isomers, not isoheptane uniquely. The formula $CH_3(CH_2)_5CH_3$ (c) is that of *normal* heptane, the straight-chain isomer. Although the compound $C_6H_5CH_3$ (d) has seven carbon atoms, it is not an alkane. It is the aromatic hydrocarbon toluene (note the presence of the C_6H_5 group). Compound (b) has seven carbon atoms, the formula C_7H_{14},

and the necessary chain branching implied by the term "iso."

$$CH_3-\underset{\underset{\displaystyle CH_3}{|}}{C}HCH_2CH_2CH_2CH_3$$

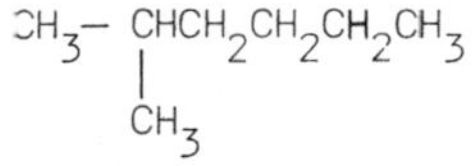

2. (d) Propane, C_3H_8, has no isomers and butane, C_4H_{10}, has two.

$$CH_3CH_2CH_2CH_3 \quad \text{and} \quad (CH_3)_3CH$$

Benzene, C_6H_6, may be thought of as a resonance hybrid of two contributing forms but these are not isomers because they cannot be isolated.

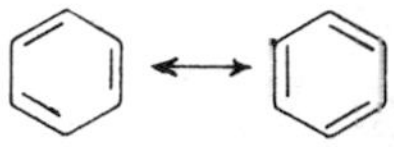

C_5H_{12} (pentane) must be the compound with three isomers:

$$CH_3(CH_2)_3CH_3 \quad \text{and} \quad (CH_3)_2CHCH_2CH_3 \quad \text{and} \quad C(CH_3)_4 .$$

3. (b) The compound C_4H_{10} (a) is butane. Cyclobutane is obtained from it by the elimination of two H atoms and conversion of the straight chain to a ring. Cyclobutane is C_4H_8. 2-Butene (b) has the formula C_4H_8 and, therefore, the same C:H ratio as cyclobutane. 2-Butyne (c) has the formula C_4H_6. The C:H ratio in benzene, C_6H_6, is 1:1, not 1:2 as in cyclobutane.

4. (a) The distinct forms of 1,2-dichloroethylene are

      cis   *trans*

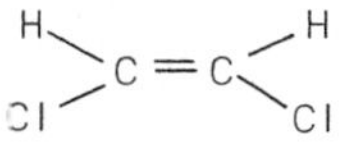

In 1,1-dichloroethylene (b), since both Cl atoms are on the same C atom, there is no isomerism. That is, the following structures are identical.

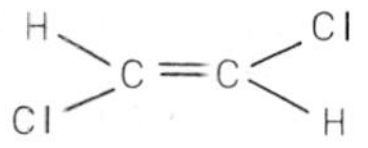

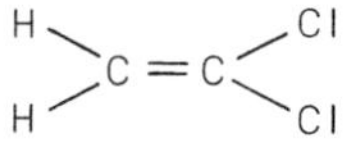

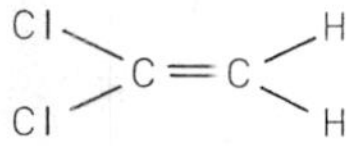

(Flip one over and the other is obtained.)

Cis-trans isomerism does not occur in saturated hydrocarbons. There is essentially free rotation about the C — C single bond in $ClCH_2CH_2Cl$ (c). In 1,1,2,2-tetrachloroethylene, $Cl_2C=CCl_2$ (d), all Cl atoms are equivalent and again there is no isomerism.

5. (c) Look for a chain of four carbon atoms with appropriate substituents on the chain. Eliminate (a) because it is only a three-carbon chain. Eliminate (b) because it does not have OH on the first carbon atom. Compound (c) has OH on the first carbon, Cl on the second and $-CH_3$ on the third. Compound (d) has the Cl and $-CH_3$ interchanged.

6. (d) The name of this compound can be based either or the $-CH_3$ group (toluene) or the $-NH_2$ group (aniline), but the groups are in meta positions to one another. This eliminates (a) and (b). Compound (c) is eliminated since it does not have an $-NH_2$ group. (Also the name m-methylbenzene is meaningless. The methyl group would be meta to what?) If we use a ring numbering system, starting with $-NH_2$ at the number one C atom, the name is 3-methylaniline.

7. (b) Aniline (a) is a weak base. Phenol (c) is a very weak acid, and acetaldehyde has no significant acidic properties. Benzoic acid (b) is a common carboxylic acid--a weak acid.

8. (c) Oxidation of 2-propanol would produce dimethyl ketone. Oxidation of 1-butanol would produce the aldehyde $CH_3CH_2CH_2CHO$. Oxidation of 2-butanol produces methyl ethyl ketone. A carbonyl group cannot be present on a *t*-butyl group (five bonds to C).

9.　(a)　dichlorodifluoromethane:

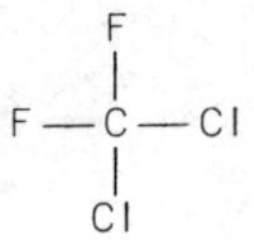

$$F\overset{\overset{\textstyle F}{|}}{\underset{\underset{\textstyle Cl}{|}}{C}}Cl$$

　　(b)　*p*-bromophenol:　Br——⟨◯⟩——OH

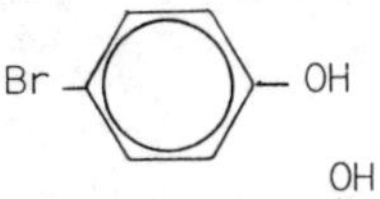

　　(c)　3-hydroxy-2-butanone:　$H_3C—\overset{\overset{\textstyle OH}{|}}{CH}—\overset{\overset{\textstyle O}{||}}{C}—CH_3$

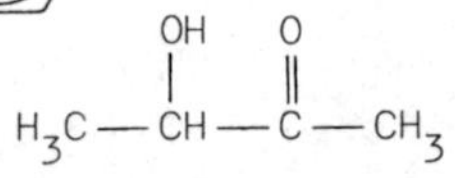

10.　The following structures simply represent the carbon-atom chain and the placement of C atoms on the chain.　H atoms have been omitted.

C—C—C—C—C—Br
1-bromopentane

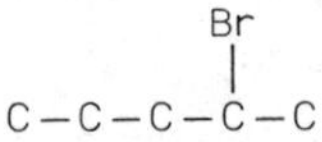

$$C—C—C—\overset{\overset{\textstyle Br}{|}}{C}—C$$
2-bromopentane

$$C—C—\overset{\overset{\textstyle Br}{|}}{C}—C—C$$
3-bromopentane

$$C—\overset{\overset{\textstyle C}{|}}{C}—C—C—Br$$
1-bromo-3-methylbutane

$$C—\overset{\overset{\textstyle C}{|}}{C}—\overset{\overset{\textstyle Br}{|}}{C}—C$$
2-bromo-3-methylbutane

$$C—\overset{\overset{\textstyle C}{|}}{\underset{\underset{\textstyle Br}{|}}{C}}—C—C$$
2-bromo-2-methylbutane

$$Br—C—\overset{\overset{\textstyle C}{|}}{C}—C—C$$
1-bromo-2-methylbutane

$$C—\overset{\overset{\textstyle C}{|}}{\underset{\underset{\textstyle C}{|}}{C}}—C—Br$$
1-bromo-2,2-dimethylpropane

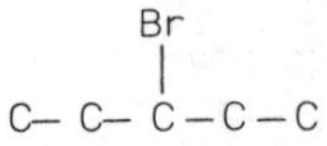

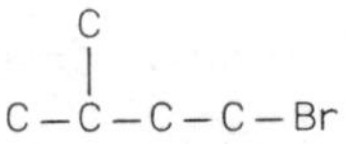

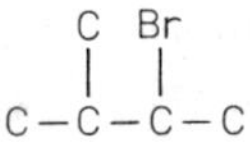

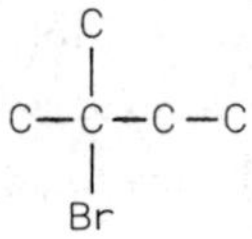

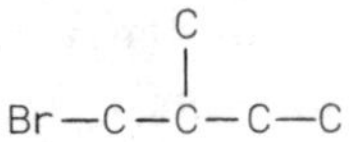

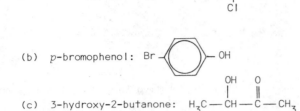

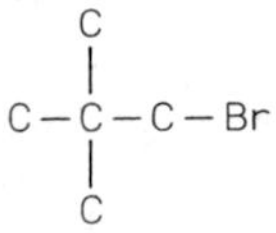

Chapter 25

Chemistry of the Living State

Structure and composition of the cell

25-1. First determine the cell volume and then the volume of water in the cell.

$$V = \pi r^2 h = \pi \left\{0.5\ \mu m \times \frac{1 \times 10^{-4}\ cm}{1\ \mu m}\right\}^2 \times \left\{2\ \mu m \times \frac{1 \times 10^{-4}\ cm}{1\ \mu m}\right\} = 1.57 \times 10^{-12}\ cm^3$$

Volume of cell water = $0.80 \times 1.57 \times 10^{-12}\ cm^3 = 1.3 \times 10^{-12}\ cm^3$

(a) $pH = -\log [H_3O^+] = 6.4 \qquad [H_3O^+] = 4.0 \times 10^{-7}$

$$\text{no. } H^+ \text{ ions} = 1.3 \times 10^{-12}\ cm^3 \times \frac{1\ L}{1000\ cm^3} \times \frac{4.0 \times 10^{-7}\ mol\ H^+}{1\ L} \times \frac{6.02 \times 10^{23}\ H^+\ ions}{1\ mol\ H^+} \approx 300$$

(b) $$\text{no. } K^+ \text{ ions} = 1.3 \times 10^{-12}\ cm^3 \times \frac{1\ L}{1000\ cm^3} \times \frac{1.5 \times 10^{-4}\ mol\ K^+}{1\ L} \times \frac{6.02 \times 10^{23}\ K^+\ ions}{1\ mol\ K^+}$$

$= 1 \times 10^5\ K^+$ ions

25-2. $$\text{Volume of a ribosome} = \frac{4}{3}\pi r^3 = \frac{4}{3}\pi \left\{9\ nm \times \frac{1 \times 10^{-7}\ cm}{1\ nm}\right\}^3 = 3.05 \times 10^{-18}\ cm^3$$

$$\text{\% Volume occupied by ribosomes} = \frac{1.5 \times 10^4\ \text{ribosomes} \times \dfrac{3.05 \times 10^{-18}\ cm^3}{1\ \text{ribosome}}}{1.57 \times 10^{-12}\ cm^3} \times 100 = 3\%$$

25-3. $$\text{no. lipid molecules} = (0.02 \times 2 \times 10^{-12})\text{g lipid} \times \frac{1\ \text{mol lipid}}{700\ \text{g lipid}} \times \frac{6.02 \times 10^{23}\ \text{lipid molecules}}{1\ \text{mol lipid}}$$

$= 3 \times 10^7$ lipid molecules

25-4. $$\text{no. protein molecules} = (0.15 \times 0.90 \times 2 \times 10^{-12})\text{g protein} \times \frac{1\ \text{mol protein}}{3 \times 10^4\ \text{g protein}}$$

$$\times \frac{6.02 \times 10^{23}\ \text{protein molecules}}{1\ \text{mol protein}} = 5 \times 10^6\ \text{protein molecules}$$

25-5. $$\text{Hypothetical length} = \frac{4.5 \times 10^6\ \text{units}}{1\ \text{molecule}} \times \frac{450\ pm}{1\ \text{unit}} \times \frac{1 \times 10^{-12}\ m}{1\ pm} \times \frac{1\ \mu m}{1 \times 10^{-6}\ m} = 2 \times 10^3\ \mu m$$

This length is many times greater than the length of the cell itself. This fact suggests that the DNA molecule must be coiled and folded to be maintained within the cell nucleus.

Lipids

25-6. (a) A lipid is a cell constituent that is soluble in nonpolar solvents.

(b) A triglyceride is an ester of glycerol with three, long-chain monocarboxylic acids (fatty acids).

(c) In a simple glyceride all three fatty acid molecules esterified with glycerol are of the same type, e.g., tristearin.

(d) In a mixed glyceride at least two and often all three fatty acid molecules esterified with glycerol are different.

(e) A fatty acid is a long-chain (C_{12} - C_{18}) monocarboxylic acid.

(f) A soap is a metal salt of a fatty acid. The metal ion is usually Na^+ or K^+ and the fatty acid is derived from a triglyceride by hydrolysis in alkaline solution.

25-7. (a) A lipid is any cell constituent that is soluble in a nonpolar solvent. A fat is a type of lipid; it is a triglyceride in which the fatty acid residues (R groups) are mostly saturated.

(b) Fats and oils are both triglycerides and differ only in the composition of their fatty acid groups. In fats these are mostly saturated, and in oils there is unsaturation (carbon-to-carbon double bonds) in most of the fatty acid groups.

(c) A fat is an ester of the trihydric alcohol, glycerol. A wax is an ester of a fatty acid with a long-chain *monohydric* alcohol.

(d) Butter is a lipid derived from natural sources (milk) in which saturated fatty acids predominate. Margarine is a synthetic, butter-like material that is derived from oils by hydrogenation. Thus, in the manufacture of margarine unsaturated fatty acids are converted to saturated fatty acids.

25-8. Simple and mixed glycerides have only nonpolar components (long-chain fatty acid residues). As a result they tend to dissolve in nonpolar solvents, such as CCl_4, but not in a polar solvent like water. Phospholipids have a polar portion of the molecule (the phosphate ester group) as well as nonpolar portions. As a result their water solubility is greater than that of simple and mixed glycerides.

25-9. (a)

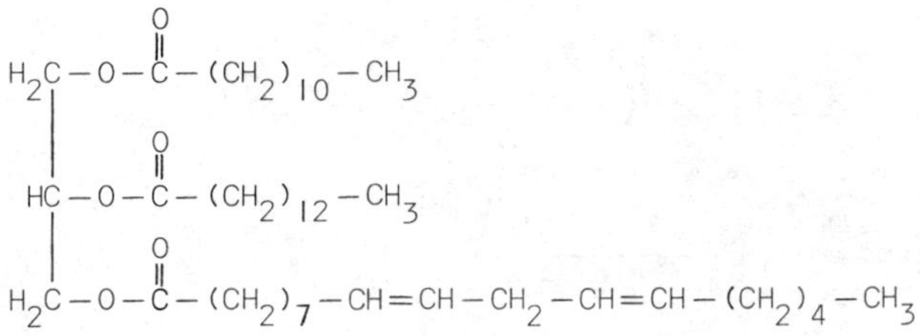

$$H_2C-O-\overset{\overset{O}{\|}}{C}-(CH_2)_{10}-CH_3$$
$$HC-O-\overset{\overset{O}{\|}}{C}-(CH_2)_{12}-CH_3$$
$$H_2C-O-\overset{\overset{O}{\|}}{C}-(CH_2)_{7}-CH=CH-CH_2-CH=CH-(CH_2)_4-CH_3$$

(b)

$$H_2C-O-\overset{\overset{O}{\|}}{C}-(CH_2)_{10}-CH_3$$
$$HC-O-\overset{\overset{O}{\|}}{C}-(CH_2)_{10}-CH_3$$
$$H_2C-O-\overset{\overset{O}{\|}}{C}-(CH_2)_{10}-CH_3$$

(c) $$K^+ \ ^-O-\overset{\overset{O}{\|}}{C}-(CH_2)_{14}-CH_3$$

(d) $$H_3C-(CH_2)_{15}-O-\overset{\overset{O}{\|}}{C}-(CH_2)_{7}-CH=CH-CH_2-CH=CH-(CH_2)_4-CH_3$$

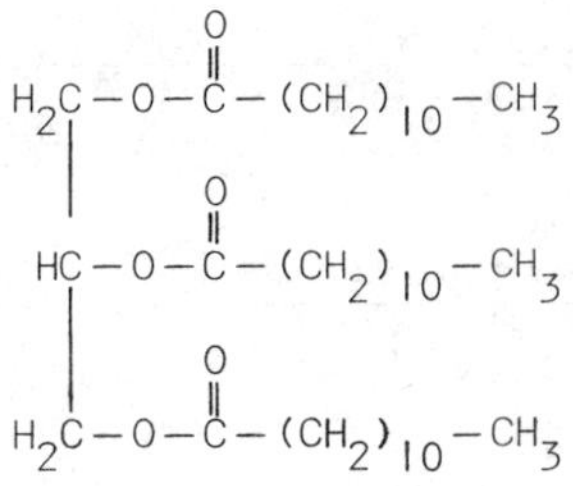

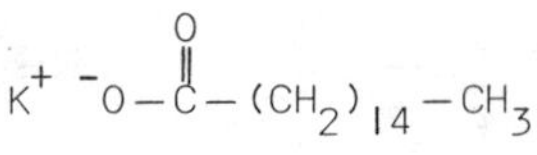

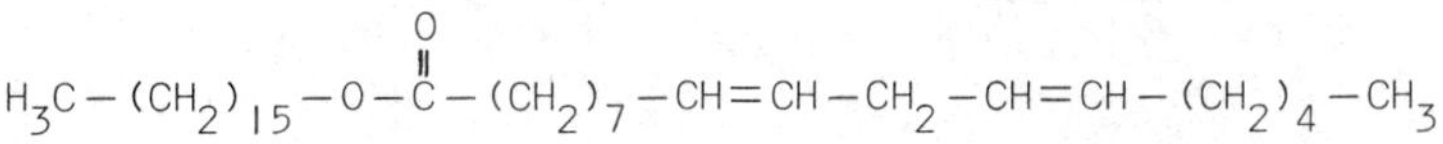

25-10. (a) glyceryl laurooleostearate; (b) glyceryl trilinoleate; (c) sodium myristate

25-11. Start with the structure of the triglyceride. This is necessary to determine its molecular weight. Three moles of KOH are required per mole of glyceride for the saponification. Express the quantity of KOH consumed as mg KOH per gram of glyceride. The saponification value is 216.

$$H_2C-OOC-C_{11}H_{23}$$
$$HC-OOC-C_{15}H_{31} \qquad \text{molecular weight} = 779$$
$$H_2C-OOC-C_{17}H_{35}$$

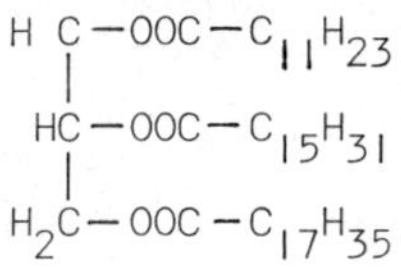

$$\text{no. mg KOH} = 1.00 \text{ g glyceride} \times \frac{1 \text{ mol glyceride}}{779 \text{ g glyceride}} \times \frac{3 \text{ mol KOH}}{1 \text{ mol glyceride}} \times \frac{56.1 \text{ g KOH}}{1 \text{ mol KOH}} \times \frac{1000 \text{ mg KOH}}{1 \text{ g KOH}} = 216$$

25-12. The glyceride has all three acid residues the same (it is a simple glyceride). Moreover, the fatty acid residues must be unsaturated, otherwise there would be no iodine number. Finally, the fatty acid must be listed in Table 23-2. All of the possible triglycerides have a molecular weight of about 880.

The four possibilities derived from Table 23-2 all have about the same saponification value but their iodine numbers would be different because of the different degrees of unsaturation in the fatty acids. Triolein would require three moles of iodine per mole of glyceride; trilinolein would require six; and trilinolenin and trieleostearin would require nine. As shown below, the experimentally determined iodine number leads to 6 mol I_2 per mole of glyceride. The glyceride is trilinolein.

$$\frac{\text{no. mol } I_2}{\text{mol glyceride}} = \frac{174 \text{ g } I_2}{100 \text{ g glyceride}} \times \frac{880 \text{ g glyceride}}{1 \text{ mol glyceride}} \times \frac{1 \text{ mol } I_2}{254 \text{ g } I_2} = 6.0$$

25-13. Polyunsaturated acids have more than one double bond per fatty acid chain. Stearic acid is a saturated fatty acid, but eleostearic acid is polyunsaturated. Safflower oil is recommended in dietary programs because it has a much higher proportion of linoleic acid groups in its triglycerides than do most edible oils; it is polyunsaturated.

25-14. The saponification value of a glyceride is related to its molecular weight but not to its degree of unsaturation. The higher the iodine number of a lipid the more unsaturated its fatty acid components and the more desirable it is as a food. The "best" of the lipids listed in Table 25-3 from this standpoint is safflower oil.

Carbohydrates

25-15. (a) A monosaccharide is a simple sugar, for example, glucose. It is a polyhydroxy aldehyde or ketone.

(b) A disaccharide is formed by the joining together (through acetal formation) of two monosaccharide units. Sucrose is a common disaccharide.

(c) An oligosaccharide is a molecule formed by the linking of from two to ten monosaccharide units.

(d) A polysaccharide is formed by the joining together of a large number of monosaccharide units (more than ten). Starch and cellulose are polysaccharides.

(e) Sugar is a term used to denote any monosaccharide or an oligosaccharide.

(f) Glycose is a term used to refer to any carbohydrate, whether a sugar or a polysaccharide.

(g) An aldose is a polyhydroxy aldehyde.

(h) A ketose is a polyhydroxy ketone.

(i) A pentose is a five carbon atom chain (or ring) monosaccharide. It may be either a polyhydroxy aldehyde or a polyhydroxy ketone. Ribose and deoxyribose are examples considered in this chapter.

(j) A hexose is a six carbon atom chain (or ring) monosaccharide. Glucose is a hexose.

25-16. (a) A dextrorotatory compound rotates the plane of polarized light to the right.

(b) A levorotatory compound rotates the plane of polarized light to the left.

(c) A racemic mixture contains equal proportions of the dextrorotatory and levorotatory isomers of an optically active compound. As a result, the racemic mixture does not rotate the plane of polarized light at all. The racemic mixture is denoted as *dl*.

(d) Diastereomers are isomers of a compound that are optically active but are not mirror images.

(e) The symbol (+) is used to indicate a dextrorotatory isomer.

(f) The symbol (-) represents a levorotatory isomer.

(g) The designation D (meaning small capital d) refers to a particular configuration in space of the groups attached to an asymmetric carbon atom. This configuration is described on page 634 of the textbook.

(h) The symbol l, like (-), represents a levorotatory isomer.

(i) The symbol d, as does (+), designates a dextrorotatory isomer.

25-17. The D configuration of glucose is shown in the text to be (+). The L configuration must be (-), that is, levorotatory.

```
        CHO
         |
  HO — C — H
         |
   H —— C — OH
         |
  HO — C — H
         |
  HO — C — H
         |
        CH₂OH
```

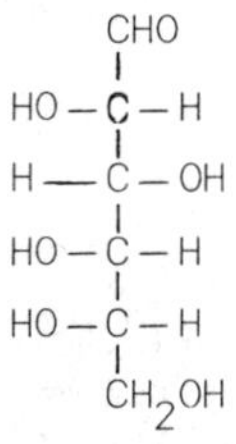

25-18. The structure of D-(—)-arabinose, the enantiomer of L-(+)-arabinose, is shown below.

```
        CHO
         |
  HO — C — H
         |
   H — C — OH
         |
   H — C — OH
         |
        CH₂OH
```

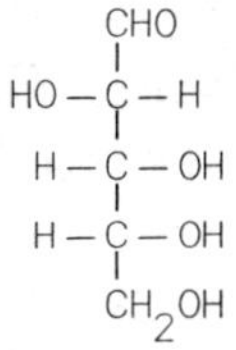

D-(—)-arabinose

One diastereomer of L-(+)-arabinose is

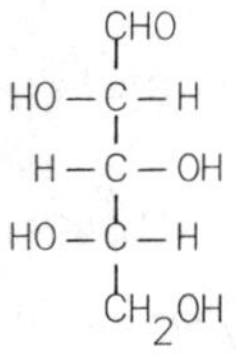

```
        CHO
         |
  HO — C — H
         |
   H — C — OH
         |
  HO — C — H
         |
        CH₂OH         and there are several others.
```

25-19. The α and β forms of glucose are diastereomers. The magnitudes of their rotation of plane polarized light are different, and they are both dextrorotatory. If they were enantiomers the magnitudes would be the same and the directions would be opposite, that is one + and one -. The α and β structures are not mirror images (see Figure 25-6).

25-20. Let the fraction of the α form be x and that of the β form, $1 - x$.

$112x + 18.7(1 - x) = 52.7$

$112x + 18.7 - 18.7x = 52.7$

$93.3x = 34; \quad x = 0.36; \quad 1 - x = 0.64$

36% α; 64% β

25-21. The monosaccharide fructose (and the monosaccharide glucose as well) is in equilibrium with the straight chain form of the sugar. This is the form that can undergo reaction with Cu^{2+}. In sucrose both monosaccharide units are tied up (glucose as an acetal and fructose as a ketal). No straight chain form exists and so no reduction of Cu^{2+} is possible.

Amino acids, polypeptides, and proteins

25-22. (a) An alpha amino acid is a carboxylic acid that has an amino group ($-NH_2$) attached to the first carbon atom beyond the carboxyl group. By this definition both of the following are α-amino acids.

H_2NCH_2COOH
(glycine)

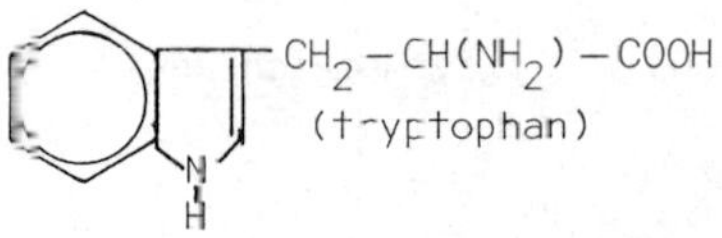

$CH_2-CH(NH_2)-COOH$
(tryptophan)

(b) A zwitterion is a dipolar ion (an ion with both a positive and negative charge center) formed by the transfer of a proton from the carboxyl to the amino group of an α-amino acid. The zwitterion of glycine is depicted below.

$$H-\underset{\underset{+}{\overset{|}{NH_3}}}{\overset{}{C}}-\overset{\overset{O}{\parallel}}{C}-O^-$$

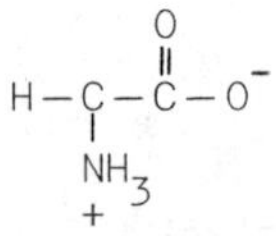

(c) The isoelectric point of an amino acid is the pH at which the acid exists primarily as the zwitterion. Under these conditions the amino acid unit has no net electrical charge and does not migrate in an electric field.

(d) A peptide bond joins two amino acid units through the elimination of water; the H atom originates from the $-NH_2$ group of one amino acid and the OH from the carboxyl group of the other.

peptide bond

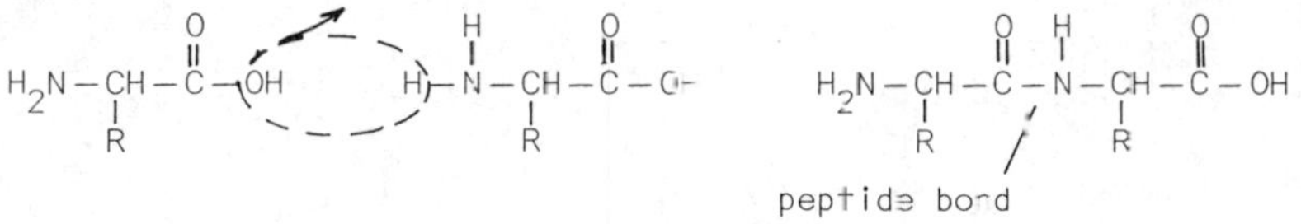

(e) A polypeptide is a chain of several α-amino acids joined by peptide bonds.

(f) If the number of α-amino acid units in a polypeptide exceeds about 50-75, the polypeptide is usually called a protein.

(g) In a polypeptide chain the last amino acid unit at one end of the chain has a free $-NH_2$ group. This is called the N-terminal amino acid. (The other end of the chain has a free carboxyl group and is called C-terminal.)

(h) In many proteins the polypeptide chains are coiled, with bonding between successive turns of the coil occurring through hydrogen bonds. The alpha helix is the right-handed spiral structure characteristic of many polypeptide chains (see Figure 25-12).

(i) Denaturation refers to any process by which the secondary, tertiary, and/or quaternary structures of proteins are disrupted. Usually this means a process in which hydrogen bonds, salt (ionic) linkages, or disulfide bonds are broken--by heating, addition of heavy metal ions, treatment with acids and bases, and so forth.

25-23. (a) 1.0 M HCl:

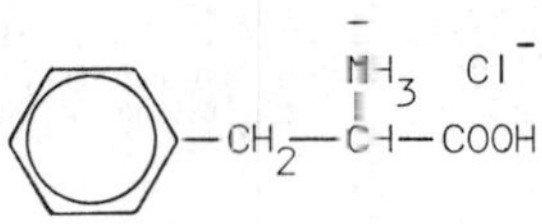

$$-CH_2-\underset{\overset{|}{NH_3}}{\overset{}{C}H}-COOH \quad Cl^-$$

(b) 1.0 M NaOH:

$$-CH_2-\underset{\overset{|}{NH_2}}{\overset{}{C}H}-COO^- \quad Na^+$$

(c) pH = 5.5:

$$-CH_2-\underset{\overset{|}{NH_3}}{\overset{}{C}H}-COO^-$$

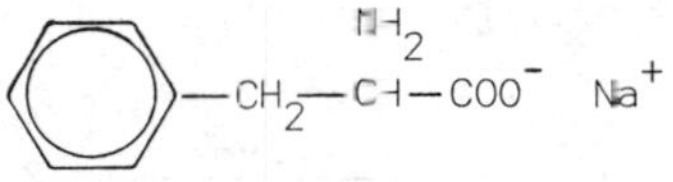

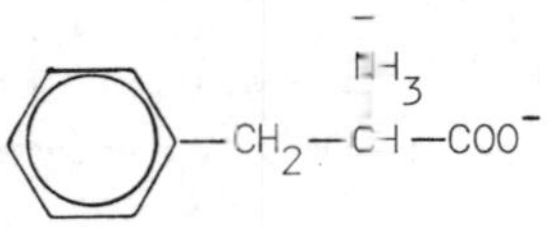

25-24. In a buffer solution with pH = 6.3, amino acids that carry a negative charge (pI < 6.3) migrate to the anode (positive electrode). Those with a positive charge (pI > 6.3) migrate to the cathode. Those with a pI = 6.3 do not migrate at all.

Lysine, cathode; proline, no migration; glutamic acid, anode.

25-25. (a) 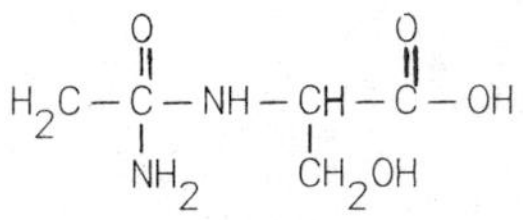 glycylmethionine

(b) 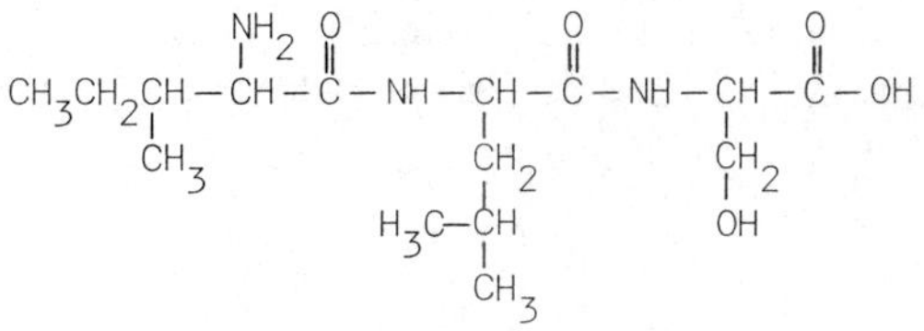 isoleucylleucylserine

(c) The six possibilities are Ala-Ser-Lys; Ala-Lys-Ser; Ser-Lys Ala; Ser-Ala-Lys; Lys-Ala-Ser; Lys-Ser-Ala.

(d) The six possibilities are Ser-Ser-Ala-Ala; Ser-Ala-Ser-Ala; Ser-Ala-Ala-Ser; Ala-Ala-Ser-Ser; Ala-Ser-Ala-Ser; Ala-Ser-Ser-Ala.

25-26. (a) 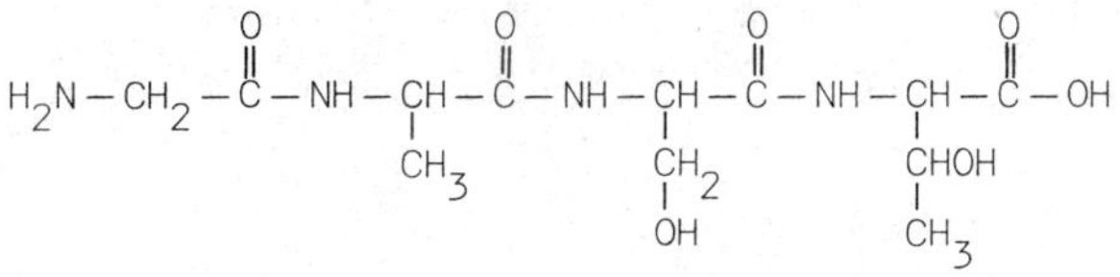

(b) glycylalanylserylthreonine

25-27. (a) Proceed as in Example 25-5. Arrange the fragments as follows:

```
                  Ser - Gly - Val
                              Val - Thr
            Ala - Ser
                              Val - Thr - Leu
                        Gly - Val - Thr
_______________________________________________
Sequence:   Ala - Ser - Gly - Val - Thr - Leu
```

(b) alanylserylglycylvalylthreonylleucine

25-28. The primary structure of a protein refers to the sequence of amino acid units in the polypeptide chain. The bonds involved are amide bonds (-CO-NH-). The secondary structure of a protein describes the actual structure of the polypeptide chain, that is, whether a spiral, a pleated sheet, or simply random coiling. The bonds responsible for secondary structure are hydrogen bonds between the groups >NH and O=C< . Tertiary structure refers to additional structure beyond the secondary, for example the folding and intertwining of a helical coil (as depicted in Figure 25-15). Several different types of linkages lead to this tertiary structure (illustrated through Figure 25-14). In cases where the protein consists of more than a single polypeptide chain, an additional structural feature is the relationship of these chains to one another. This is callec the quaternary structure of the protein (see Figure 25-16, for example). If the protein consists of a single polypeptide chain, it has no quaternary structure.

25-29. If it is assumed that there is a single Ag^+ associated with each enzyme molecule (one active site per molecule), the molecular weight of the protein is simply the mass of enzyme required to bind one mole of Ag^+.

$$\text{no. g enzyme} = 1 \text{ mol } Ag^+ \times \frac{1.0 \text{ mg enzyme}}{0.346 \times 10^{-6} \text{ mol } Ag^+} \times \frac{1 \text{ g enzyme}}{1000 \text{ mg enzyme}} = 2.9 \times 10^3$$

The value obtained is a minimum molecular weight. For example, if we had assumed two active sites per molecule, the molecular weight would have been the mass of enzyme required to bind two moles of Ag^+--twice the value determined above.

25-30. The origin of sickle-cell anemia is in the substitution of valine for glutamic acid at one site in two of the four polypeptide chains in a hemoglobin molecule. That is, there is a very slight difference in the primary structures of normal hemoglobin and sickle-cell hemoglobin. Since this change in molecular structure produces a diseased condition, it is appropriate to refer to the disease as a "molecular disease".

Biochemical reactivity

25-31. (a) A metabolite is a chemical substance involved in a metabolic process.

(b) Anabolism is a metabolic process in which substances are synthesized from smaller molecules.

(c) Catabolism refers to the degradation of large into smaller molecules in a metabolic process.

(d) An endergonic biochemical reaction is one that is accompanied by an increase in free energy.

(e) ADP is the symbol for adenosine diphosphate, an intermediate in metabolic processes.

(f) ATP is the symbol for adenosine triphosphate, also an intermediate in metabolism. The addition of inorganic phosphate and absorption of energy converts ADP to ATP. Thus, ATP is a molecule in which metabolic energy is stored.

25-32. If we assume that 33.5 kJ of energy is stored for every mole of ADP that is converted to ATP, the total quantity of energy stored is 15 x 33.5 = 502 kJ, of a possible 837 kJ.

$$\% \text{ efficiency} = \frac{502 \text{ kJ}}{837 \text{ kJ}} \times 100 = 60\%$$

25-33. Use equation (15.15), $\Delta\bar{G}° = -2.303 \cdot RT \cdot \log K$.

$$\log K = \frac{-13.8 \times 10^3 \text{ J/mol}}{-2.303 \times 8.314 \text{ J mol}^{-1} \text{ K}^{-1} \times 298 \text{ K}} = 2.42 \qquad K = 2.6 \times 10^2$$

25-34. An enzyme is a protein. Any process that denatures a protein (disrupts secondary, tertiary and/or quarternary structures) would be expected seriously to inhibit or even to destroy enzyme action. The linkages responsible for higher level structure in proteins (hydrogen bonds and salt linkages, for example) are altered as the pH of the environment of the enzyme changes.

Nucleic acids

25-35. The two types of nucleic acid are ribonucleic acid (RNA) and deoxyribonucleic acid (DNA). Their principal constituents are listed below.

DNA: deoxyribose; the purine bases adenine and guanine; the pyrimidine bases thymine and cytosine; phosphate groups.

RNA: ribose; the purine bases adenine and guanine; the pyrimidine bases cytosine and uracil; phosphate groups.

25-36. The chain pictured is RNA. This can be inferred in two ways: (a) ribose sugar groups and (b) uracil as a constituent rather than thymine. The chain components are the ribose sugar units, linked by phosphate groups and, as bases, adenine, uracil, guanine, and cytosine (from top to bottom).

25-37. The text comments on the manner in which DNA replication occurs and on how the synthesis of proteins is directed by DNA. From this standpoint it would certainly appear that DNA is the basic chemical substance of the living state. Given further, the shape of the molecule--long, coiled, and thread-like--the term "thread of life" seems quite appropriate.

25-38. (a) DNA serves as the template upon which a molecule of messenger RNA (mRNA) is synthesized. The sequence of amino acids in a protein can be traced back ultimately to the sequence of bases on a DNA strand.

(b) mRNA is the molecule that carries the genetic information of DNA into the cell cytoplasm where protein synthesis occurs. This information is coded in the form of the sequence of bases on the mRNA strand.

(c) tRNA is a smaller RNA molecule, formed in the cytoplasm, that carries an amino acid unit to the site on a ribosome where protein synthesis occurs. The tRNA can interact with the mRNA and transfer its amino acid to the protein chain only if the anti-codon of the tRNA matches the codon of the mRNA.

25-39. The ribosome attaches at the site of protein synthesis only the tRNA molecule carrying the amino acid unit called for by the mRNA code. In this sense, the ribosome must "read" the code to make the proper selection of tRNA.

25-40. We must make use of the genetic code in Table 25-5 to determine the amino acids involved and their sequence.

Code (mRNA)	ACC CAU CCC UUG GCG AGU GGU AUG UAA
Amino Acids	Thr His Pro Leu Ala Ser Gly Met (nonsense)

The polypeptide chain is Thr-His-Pro-Leu-Ala-Ser-Gly-Met.

25-41. Here we must work in the reverse fashion from Exercise 40. That is, given the amino acid sequence in the polypeptide we must determine a corresponding code on the mRNA; but since there is more than one codon for some amino acids, several codes are possible. We will write only one. The next step is to determine the sequence of bases on DNA that is complementary to the code on the mRNA. This requires using the scheme for hydrogen bonding presented in Figure 25-22.

amino acid sequence	Ser-Gly-Val-Ala
possible mRNA code	UCU GGU GUU GCU
DNA base sequence	AGA CCA CAA CGA

25-42. The triplet TCG on one DNA strand is complementary to the triplet AGC on the opposite strand. Hydrogen bonding between the two strands is represented below.

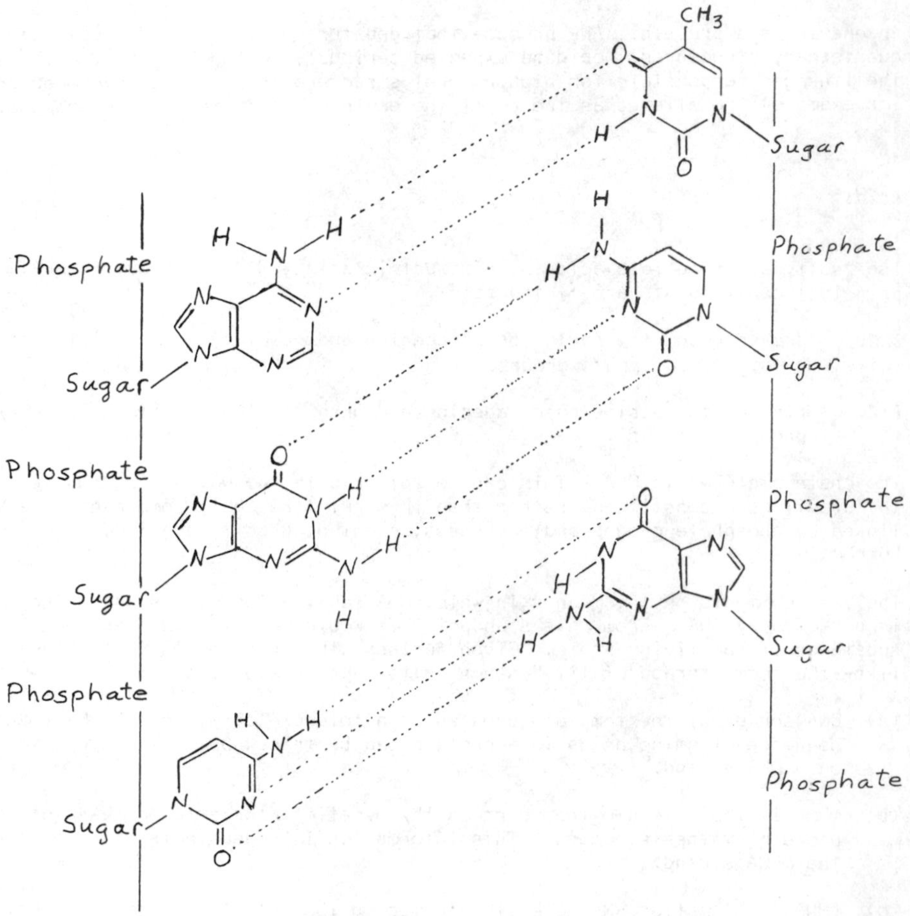

Self-test Questions

1. (*b*) From the name that is given we see that the substance is a triglyceride. Thus it must be either a fat or an oil. If a 17-carbon chain is saturated it would correspond to the group $-C_{17}H_{35}$ (based on the hydrocarbon C_nH_{2n+2} or $C_{17}H_{36}$). The group in this case is $-C_{17}H_{31}$. It contains two double bonds and is therefore unsaturated (loss of two H atoms per double bond). The substance is an oil.

2. (*c*) The hydrocarbon group $-C_{17}H_{35}$ is saturated and $-C_{17}H_{33}$ is unsaturated (one double bond). The two triglycerides would differ by only 5 H atoms or 5 units in a molecular weight of about 900. Saponification values, which depend only on molecular weight, would be almost the same for the two triglycerides. On the other hand, only the triglyceride with unsaturation would have an iodine number.

3. (*d*) The *d* isomer rotates the plane of polarized light in one direction, and the *l* isomer, to the same extent in the opposite direction. As a result, the racemic mixture would not rotate the plane of polarized light at all.

4. (*d*) Egg white is a protein. Coagulation of a protein is a denaturation process. Hydrolysis of a protein refers to breaking down the polypeptide chain into amino acids. Saponification refers to the hydrolysis of a triglyceride in alkaline solution.

5. (*a*) Glucose is a metabolite and releases energy as it is broken down into H_2O and CO_2. This energy is stored by the conversion of ADP to ATP.

6. (*c*) Purine bases, phosphate groups, and pentose sugars are all constituents of nucleic acids. Glycerol is a fundamental constituent of all triglycerides.

7.

$$\begin{array}{lcccccc}
CH_2OOC(CH_2)_{14}CH_3 & & & & CH_2OH & & \\
| & & & & & & \\
CHOOC(CH_2)_{14}CH_3 & + & 3\ NaOH & \longrightarrow & CHOH & + & 3\ CH_3(CH_2)_{14}COONa \\
| & & & & & & \\
CH_2OOC(CH_2)_{14}CH_3 & & & & CH_2OH & & \text{soap}
\end{array}$$

(MW = 807)

$$\text{no. g soap} = 125\ \text{g triglyc.} \times \frac{1\ \text{mol triglyc.}}{807\ \text{g triglyc.}} \times \frac{3\ \text{mol soap}}{1\ \text{mol triglyc.}} \times \frac{278\ \text{g soap}}{1\ \text{mol soap}} = 129\ \text{g soap}$$

8.

		Val	Phe	
	Cys	Val	Phe	
Gly	Cys			
			Phe	Tyr

Sequence: Gly - Cys - Val - Phe - Tyr

9. Enzymes are proteins that catalyze biochemical reactions in regions of the protein molecule called active sites. If the active sites are blocked by a foreign substance, such as a metal ion, the enzyme loses its catalytic activity. If structural changes occur in the protein, this can distort the active sites, leading to a loss of catalytic activity. Such structural changes occur when a protein is subjected to increased temperatures or to changes in pH outside of a fairly narrow range. A precise match must exist between the structure of the substrate and the active site on an enzyme (lock-and-key model). The enzyme is very specific in the reaction it catalyzes.

10. The primary structure of a protein refers to the amino acid sequence in the polypeptide chain. Secondary structure describes the shape of the chain, e.g., whether coiled into a helix or arranged into a pleated sheet. The ternary structure of a protein describes its overall three-dimensional shape, such as the folding and compression of a helical chain into a globular or spherical form.

Chapter 26

Natural Resources, the Environment, and Synthetic Materials

Occurrence of the elements

26-1. *N:* This element occurs mostly in the free state (N_2 in the atmosphere). This is expected because of the unusually strong N≡N bond.

Br: Because it is an active nonmetal we should expect bromine to occur exclusively in combined form, mostly as bromides, and much of it in solution (seawater and natural brines).

Ag: Silver is less active a metal than hydrogen so we should expect to encounter some of it in the free state, but not to the exclusion of such combined forms as the sulfide or chloride.

Rn: Radon is a nonreactive noble gas. It is not found in abundance in the earth's crust but what little there is will be found in the free state.

Ga: This metal is similar to, but not quite as reactive as, aluminum. We should expect to encounter it only in chemical combination, for example, as the oxide.

Fr: Francium is an extremely rare element, formed only by the radioactive decay of other elements. Because it is an alkali metal, however, we should expect it to be encountered in its ionic form, Fr^+.

26-2. Elements or compounds found in the atmosphere or in seawater are in solution, that is, their distribution is fairly uniform. Whether extraction of an element from these sources is economically feasible is largely a matter of whether the percent abundance is sufficiently great. The solid crust of the earth is heterogeneous. Economic feasibility of producing an element from its naturally occurring combined forms in the solid crust of the earth depends on the existence of localized deposits of relatively high concentrations of the element, that is, as ores.

The atmosphere

26-3. $$\text{no. L air} = 1.77 \times 10^7 \text{ ton } O_2 \times \frac{2000 \text{ lb } O_2}{1 \text{ ton } O_2} \times \frac{454 \text{ g } O_2}{1 \text{ lb } O_2} \times \frac{1 \text{ mol } O_2}{32.0 \text{ g } O_2} \times \frac{22.4 \text{ L } O_2 \text{ (STP)}}{1 \text{ mol } O_2} \times \frac{100 \text{ L air (STP)}}{21 \text{ L } O_2 \text{ (STP)}}$$

$$= 5.4 \times 10^{13} \text{ L air (STP)}$$

26-4. This exercise is similar to the preceding one except that the gas extracted from air is a different one. Also, since the gas in question (Ar) is not at STP, the ideal gas equation must be used.

$$n = \frac{PV}{RT} = \frac{149 \text{ atm} \times 55 \text{ L}}{0.0821 \text{ L atm mol}^{-1} \text{ K}^{-1} \times 298 \text{ K}} = 335 \text{ mol Ar}$$

$$\text{no. L air} = 335 \text{ mol Ar} \times \frac{22.4 \text{ L Ar (STP)}}{1 \text{ mol Ar}} \times \frac{100 \text{ L air (STP)}}{0.93 \text{ L Ar (STP)}} = 7.9 \times 10^5 \text{ L air}$$

26-5. The natural gas has a ratio of He to gas of 0.3:100. In air the relative abundance is 5:1,000,000. The ratio of these two values is $0.003/5 \times 10^{-6} = 600$. Helium is 600 times more abundant in the natural gas than in air.

Atmospheric pollution

26-6. Sunlight, in particular radiation of short wavelengths and high frequencies, brings about the dissociation of NO_2 to NO and O. This is reaction (26.1) in Table 26-3; it is the first step in the smog-forming process.

26-7. Under certain conditions the bottom of the inversion layer pictured in Figure 26-5 can be at very low altitudes, including ground level. If this happens, the tops of tall buildings could be above the inversion layer, in clear, relatively unpolluted air.

26-8. (a) $\text{no. t Pb} = 75 \times 10^9 \text{ gal} \times \frac{2 \text{ ml Pb(Et)}_4}{1 \text{ gal}} \times \frac{1.65 \text{ g Pb(Et)}_4}{1 \text{ ml Pb(Et)}_4} \times \frac{207.2 \text{ g Pb}}{323.4 \text{ g Pb(Et)}_4} \times \frac{1 \text{ lb Pb}}{454 \text{ g Pb}}$

$\times \frac{1 \text{ t Pb}}{2000 \text{ lb Pb}} = 1.7 \times 10^5 \text{ t Pb}$

(b) In the setup below, NO_x represents a mixture of oxides of nitrogen.

$\text{no. t } NO_x = 75 \times 10^9 \text{ gal} \times \frac{15 \text{ mi}}{1 \text{ gal}} \times \frac{5 \text{ g } NO_x}{1 \text{ mi}} \times \frac{1 \text{ lb } NO_x}{454 \text{ g } NO_x} \times \frac{1 \text{ t } NO_x}{2000 \text{ lb } NO_x} = 6.2 \times 10^6 \text{ t } NO_x$

26-9. $\text{Increase in ppm } CO_2 = 1 \times 10^4 \times 10^9 \text{ t coal} \times \frac{0.7 \text{ ppm } CO_2}{5 \times 10^9 \text{ t coal}} = 1.4 \times 10^3 = 1400 \text{ ppm } CO_2$

26-10. $\text{no. mol } H_2S = 0.535 \text{ g PbS} \times \frac{1 \text{ mol PbS}}{239 \text{ g PbS}} \times \frac{1 \text{ mol } H_2S}{1 \text{ mol PbS}} = 2.24 \times 10^{-3} \text{ mol } H_2S$

$\text{Volume of } H_2S = V = \frac{nRT}{P} = \frac{2.24 \times 10^{-3} \text{ mol} \times 0.0821 \text{ L atm mol}^{-1} \text{ K}^{-1} \times 298 \text{ K}}{(740/760)\text{atm}} = 5.63 \times 10^{-2} \text{ L } H_2S$

$\% \ H_2S \text{, by volume} = \frac{5.63 \times 10^{-2}}{25.0} \times 100 = 0.225\% \ H_2S$

Seawater

26-11. $\text{no. t Mg} = 4 \text{ km}^3 \text{ seawater} \times \frac{(1000)^3 \text{ m}^3 \text{ seawater}}{1 \text{ km}^3 \text{ seawater}} \times \frac{(100)^3 \text{ cm}^3 \text{ seawater}}{1 \text{ m}^3 \text{ seawater}} \times \frac{1.03 \text{ g seawater}}{1.00 \text{ cm}^3 \text{ seawater}}$

$\times \frac{1 \text{ lb seawater}}{454 \text{ g seawater}} \times \frac{1 \text{ t seawater}}{2000 \text{ lb seawater}} \times \frac{1{,}272 \text{ g Mg}}{1 \text{ t seawater}} \times \frac{1 \text{ lb Mg}}{454 \text{ g Mg}} \times \frac{1 \text{ t Mg}}{2000 \text{ lb Mg}} = 5.4 \times 10^6 \text{ t Mg}$

The water environment

26-12. The milky white precipitate that first forms is $CaCO_3$, but as more $CO_2(g)$ dissolves the solution is first neutralized and then becomes slightly acidic. $CaCO_3$ is soluble in a slightly acidic solution, yielding $Ca(HCO_3)_2$.

$H_2O + CO_2(g) \longrightarrow H_2CO_3(aq)$

$H_2CO_3(aq) + Ca^{2+} + 2\ OH^- \longrightarrow CaCO_3(s) + 2\ H_2O$

$CaCO_3(s) + H_2O + CO_2(g) \longrightarrow Ca^{2+} + 2\ HCO_3^-$

26-13. (a) $\text{no. g } CaCO_3 = 1.00 \times 10^6 \text{ gal} \times \frac{3.78 \text{ L}}{1 \text{ gal}} \times \frac{1000 \text{ cm}^3}{1 \text{ L}} \times \frac{1.00 \text{ g } H_2O}{1 \text{ cm}^3} \times \frac{180 \text{ g } HCO_3^-}{10^6 \text{ g } H_2O} \times \frac{1 \text{ mol } HCO_3^-}{61.0 \text{ g } HCO_3^-}$

$\times \frac{1 \text{ mol } CaCO_3}{1 \text{ mol } HCO_3^-} \times \frac{100 \text{ g } CaCO_3}{1 \text{ mol } CaCO_3} = .12 \times 10^6 \text{ g } CaCO_3$

(b) The water softening reactions are shown below, the calcium ion associated with the water itself is in italic.

$$CaO + H_2O \longrightarrow Ca^{2+} + 2\ OH^-$$

$$\mathit{Ca}^{2+} + 2\ HCO_3^- + Ca^{2+} + 2\ OH^- \longrightarrow \mathit{CaCO_3} + CaCO_3 + 2\ H_2O$$

As these equations indicate, half the calcium ion in the precipitated $CaCO_3$ comes from the lime and half from the water itself.

26-14. (a) $2\ Na^+ + CO_3^{2-} + Ca^{2+} + SO_4^{2-} \longrightarrow CaCO_3(s) + 2\ Na^+ + SO_4^{2-}$

(b) $$\text{no. g } Na_2CO_3 = 250\ L \times \frac{1000\ cm^3}{1\ L} \times \frac{1\ g\ H_2O}{1\ cm^3} \times \frac{130\ g\ SO_4^{2-}}{10^6\ g\ H_2O} \times \frac{1\ mol\ SO_4^{2-}}{96.1\ g\ SO_4^{2-}} \times \frac{1\ mol\ Na_2CO_3}{1\ mol\ SO_4^{2-}}$$

$$\times \frac{106\ g\ Na_2CO_3}{1\ mol\ Na_2CO_3} = 35.8\ g\ Na_2CO_3$$

26-15. Base the calculation on one million grams of water. Determine the number of grams of Ca^{2+} associated with the SO_4^{2-} and with the HCO_3^-. Add these two values together to obtain the total ppm of Ca^{2+}.

$$\text{no. g } Ca^{2+} = 96\ g\ SO_4^{2-} \times \frac{1\ mol\ SO_4^{2-}}{96.1\ g\ SO_4^{2-}} \times \frac{1\ mol\ Ca^{2+}}{1\ mol\ SO_4^{2-}} \times \frac{40.1\ g\ Ca^{2+}}{1\ mol\ Ca^{2+}} = 40.1\ g\ Ca^{2+}$$

$$\text{no. g } Ca^{2+} = 183\ g\ HCO_3^- \times \frac{1\ mol\ HCO_3^-}{61.0\ g\ HCO_3^-} \times \frac{1\ mol\ Ca^{2+}}{2\ mol\ HCO_3^-} \times \frac{40.1\ g\ Ca^{2+}}{1\ mol\ Ca^{2+}} = 60.2\ g\ Ca^{2+}$$

$$\text{no. ppm} = 40.1 + 60.2 = 100.3 = 1.00 \times 10^2\ ppm\ Ca^{2+}$$

26-16. Equation (25.1) provides information from which the formula weight of the soap can be determined. Equation (26.25) indicates the relationship between the alkali and alkaline earth metal soaps.

$$\text{no. g Ca stearate} = 5.0\ L \times \frac{1000\ cm^3}{1\ L} \times \frac{1\ g\ H_2O}{1\ cm^3} \times \frac{85\ g\ Ca^{2+}}{10^6\ g\ H_2O} \times \frac{1\ mol\ Ca^{2+}}{40.1\ g\ Ca^{2+}} \times \frac{1\ mol\ Ca\ stearate}{1\ mol\ Ca^{2+}}$$

$$\times \frac{608\ g\ Ca\ stearate}{1\ mol\ Ca\ stearate} = 6.4\ g\ Ca\ stearate$$

26-17. First pass the sample of hard water through a cation exchange resin that has H^+ as its counterions.

$2\ HR + Mg^{2+} \longrightarrow MgR_2 + 2\ H^+$; $2\ HR + Ca^{2+} \longrightarrow CaR_2 + 2\ H^+$; and so on.

The sample now contains H^+ as the only cation and HCO_3^- and SO_4^{2-}, as its anions. Pass this sample through an anion exchange resin having OH^- as its counterions.

$ROH + HCO_3^- \longrightarrow RHCO_3 + OH^-$; $2\ ROH + SO_4^{2-} \longrightarrow R_2SO_4 + 2\ OH^-$

When present in the same sample, H^+ and OH^- ions combine to form water. Because all other ions were removed in the two ion exchange processes, the sample of water is deionized.

Water pollution

26-18. $$\text{no. lb Hg} = 8.5 \times 10^6 + Cl_2 \times 0.20 \times \frac{0.3\ lb\ Hg}{1 + Cl_2} = 5.1 \times 10^5\ lb\ Hg$$

26-19. Determine the total mass of P in seawater, assuming a volume of seawater of 330 million mi^3.

$$\text{no. lb P} = 330 \times 10^6\ \text{mi}^3 \times \frac{(5280)^3\ \text{ft}^3}{1\ \text{mi}^3} \times \frac{(12)^3\ \text{in.}^3}{1\ \text{ft}^3} \times \frac{(2.54)^3\ \text{cm}^3}{1\ \text{in.}^3} \times \frac{1\ \text{L}}{1000\ \text{cm}^3} \times \frac{1.06\ \text{qt}}{1\ \text{L}}$$

$$\times \frac{1\ \text{gal}}{4\ \text{qt}} \times \frac{0.6\ \text{lb CaHPO}_4}{10^6\ \text{gal}} \times \frac{31\ \text{lb P}}{136\ \text{lb CaHPO}_4} = 5 \times 10^{13}\ \text{lb P}$$

The total mass of P released to the environment from detergents in 1969 is based on a consumption of about 5 billion lb detergent, with about 40% $Na_5P_3O_{10}$ as a builder.

$$\text{no. lb P} = 5 \times 10^9\ \text{lb detergent} \times \frac{40\ \text{lb Na}_5\text{P}_3\text{O}_{10}}{100\ \text{lb detergent}} \times \frac{93\ \text{lb P}}{368\ \text{lb Na}_5\text{P}_3\text{O}_{10}} = 5 \times 10^8\ \text{lb P}$$

The quantity of P released to the environment in 1969 was about 10^{-5} of that already present in seawater. If this P derived from detergents had been uniformly distributed throughout the oceans of the world, it would have had no measurable environmental impact. Of course, this type of dispersal is impossible, and P derived from detergents can be an environmental problem.

Metallurgy

26-20. (a) $2\ PbS + 3\ O_2(g) \xrightarrow{\Delta} 2\ PbO(s) + 2\ SO_2(g)$

(b) $CdO(s) + C(s) \xrightarrow{\Delta} Cd(s) + CO(g)$

(c) $FeCO_3(s) \xrightarrow{\Delta} FeO(s) + CO_2(g)$

(d) Cu^{2+} is reduced to Cu(s) and H_2O is oxidized to $O_2(g)$

$2\ Cu^{2+} + \cancel{SO_4^{2-}} + 2\ H_2O \xrightarrow[\text{Pt electrodes}]{\text{electrolysis}} 2\ Cu(s) + \cancel{SO_4^{2-}} + 4\ H^+ + O_2(g)$

(e) $ZnO(s) + 2\ HCl(aq) \longrightarrow ZnCl_2(aq) + H_2O$

(f) $TiCl_4(g) + 4\ Na(l) \xrightarrow{\Delta} Ti(s) + 4\ NaCl(l)$

(g) $\cancel{K^+} + 2\ OH^- + Al_2O_3(s) \longrightarrow \cancel{K^+} + 2\ AlO_2^- + H_2O$

26-21. (a) $4\ CuFeS_2(s) + 13\ O_2(g) \xrightarrow{\Delta} 4\ CuO(s) + 2\ Fe_2O_3(s) + 8\ SO_2(g)$

(b) $2\ KCl(l) \xrightarrow{\text{electrolysis}} 2\ K(l) + Cl_2(g)$

(c) $Al_2O_3(s) + 6\ H^+ + \cancel{3\ SO_4^{2-}} \longrightarrow 2\ Al^{3+} + 3\ H_2O + \cancel{3\ SO_4^{2-}}$

(d) $Fe_3O_4(s) + 4\ H_2(g) \xrightarrow{\Delta} 3\ Fe(s) + 4\ H_2O(g)$

(e) $Mg^{2+} + \cancel{2\ Cl^-} + 2\ NH_3 + 2\ H_2O \longrightarrow Mg(OH)_2(s) + 2\ NH_4^+ + \cancel{2\ Cl^-}$

(f) $Si + 2\ CO \longrightarrow SiO_2 + 2\ C$; $Si + 2\ FeO \longrightarrow SiO_2 + 2\ Fe$; followed by slag-forming reactions:

$FeO + SiO_2 \longrightarrow FeSiO_3$; $MnO + SiO_2 \longrightarrow MnSiO_3$

26-22. First write a balanced equation for the roasting process.

$2\ Cu_2S + 3\ O_2(g) \xrightarrow{\Delta} 2\ Cu_2O + 2\ SO_2(g)$

Next, calculate the number of moles of $SO_2(g)$ obtained.

$$\text{no. mol } SO_2 = 3.50 \times 10^3 \text{ kg ore} \times \frac{1000 \text{ g ore}}{1 \text{ kg ore}} \times \frac{1.90 \text{ g Cu}}{100 \text{ g ore}} \times \frac{1 \text{ mol Cu}}{63.54 \text{ g Cu}} \times \frac{1 \text{ mol } Cu_2S}{2 \text{ mol Cu}}$$

$$\times \frac{2 \text{ mol } SO_2}{2 \text{ mol } Cu_2S} = 5.23 \times 10^2 \text{ mol } SO_2$$

$$V = \frac{nRT}{P} = \frac{5.23 \times 10^2 \text{ mol} \times 0.0821 \text{ L atm mol}^{-1} \text{ K}^{-1} \times 293 \text{ K}}{(740/760)\text{atm}} = 1.29 \times 10^4 \text{ L}$$

26-23. Limestone and silica combine in a 1:1 ratio in forming slag: $CaCO_3 + SiO_2 \longrightarrow CaSiO_3 + CO_2$.

$$\text{no. kg limestone} = 2.0 \times 10^3 \text{ kg ore} \times \frac{10.4 \text{ kg } SiO_2}{100 \text{ kg ore}} \times \frac{1 \text{ kmol } SiO_2}{60.1 \text{ kg } SiO_2} \times \frac{1 \text{ kmol } CaCO_3}{1 \text{ kmol } SiO_2} \times \frac{100 \text{ kg } CaCO_3}{1 \text{ kmol } CaCO_3}$$

$$\times \frac{100 \text{ kg limestone}}{97 \text{ kg } CaCO_3} = 3.6 \times 10^2 \text{ kg limestone}$$

26-24. One of the main steps in converting iron into steel involves removing impurities from the iron by oxidation and slag formation. This oxidation is achieved much more readily in a pure oxygen atmosphere, as in the basic oxygen furnace, than by using air only.

26-25. There are many ways in which one may distinguish between Aluminum 2S (99.2% Al) and Magnalium (70% Al + 30% Mg) by simple chemical tests. For example, one might calculate the volume of hydrogen gas anticipated if a sample of the metal is dissolved in HCl(aq). The volume of hydrogen obtained per gram of metal is about 9% greater for Aluminum 2S than for Magnalium.

A much simpler test is to dissolve the metal in HCl(aq), followed by neutralization with NaOH(aq) and treatment with excess NaOH(aq). If the metal is Aluminum 2S, the $Al(OH)_3$ first precipitated will redissolve, because $Al(OH)_3$ is amphoteric. [The aluminum is obtained as $AlO_2^-(aq)$.] If the alloy is Magnalium, some $Mg(OH)_2(s)$ will form and this will not redissolve; $Mg(OH)_2$ is not amphoteric.

26-26. AlO_2^- may be converted back to $Al(OH)_3(s)$ either by dilution of $AlO_2^-(aq)$ to a large volume or by adding a weak acid. In both cases the purpose is to reduce the pH of the solution to about pH = 7. Water solutions of H_2CO_3 are weakly acidic. If acidification is attempted with HCl(aq), a strong acid, the precipitated $Al(OH)_3$ redissolves and appears in solution as Al^{3+}. [Can you establish that this redissolving would occur at about pH < 3?]

26-27. The Kroll process uses magnesium as a reducing agent. If the inert atmosphere is nitrogen, magnesium reacts to some extent to form magnesium nitride, Mg_3N_2. It is for this reason that helium is used instead of nitrogen; helium is inert.

Inorganic chemical processes

26-28. Think of the $CO_2(g)$ as reacting with water to produce $H_2CO_3(aq)$, which then neutralizes the $Ca(OH)_2(aq)$. The net reaction is

$$Ca(OH)_2(aq) + CO_2(g) \longrightarrow CaCO_3(s) + H_2O$$

This same type of reaction will occur with $Ba(OH)_2$, since $BaCO_3$ is insoluble; but because K_2CO_3 is water soluble, the method will not work with KOH.

26-29. (a) The net reaction for the conversion of NaCl to $NaHCO_3$ is

$$NaCl(aq) + NH_3(g) + CO_2(g) + H_2O \longrightarrow NaHCO_3(s) + NH_4Cl(aq)$$

We must calculate the theoretical yield of $NaHCO_3(s)$ and compare it with the actual yield. Note that $NaHCO_3$ and NaCl must be involved in the same ratio as their formula weights.

$$\text{no. t } NaHCO_3 \text{ (theoretical)} = 1.00 \text{ t NaCl} \times \frac{84.0 \text{ t } NaHCO_3}{58.5 \text{ t NaCl}} = 1.44 \text{ t } NaHCO_3$$

$$\% \text{ efficiency} = \frac{1.03 \text{ t, actual}}{1.44 \text{ t, theoretical}} \times 100 = 72\%$$

(b) NH_3 is recycled in the Solvay process. Theoretically none should be consumed in an operating plant; however, a small loss of material is experienced in the recycling and must be replaced.

26-30. (a) Superheated water is water that has been heated under pressure to a temperature above its normal boiling point.

(b) To be used in the Frasch process, water must be heated (superheated) to temperatures above the normal melting point of sulfur, that is, to temperatures in excess of 119°C.

(c) Refer to Table 11-1 for vapor pressure data on water. The vapor pressure at 110°C is about 1.4 atm. We might estimate that at 120°C it is about 2 atm. This is the minimum pressure under which the water would have to be maintained.

26-31. The % P in each of the following compounds is calculated in the usual way. All that is required is the assignment of a correct formula for each name.

(a) Orthophosphoric acid: H_3PO_4 $\quad \%P = \frac{30.97 \text{ g P}}{97.99 \text{ g } H_3PO_4} \times 100 = 31.6\%$

(b) Calcium orthophosphate: $Ca_3(PO_4)_2$ $\quad \%P = \frac{2 \times 30.97 \text{ g P}}{310.2 \text{ g } Ca_3(PO_4)_2} \times 100 = 20.0\%$

(c) Fluorapatite: $3\ Ca_3(PO_4)_2 \cdot CaF_2$ $\quad \%P = \frac{6 \times 30.97 \text{ g P}}{1008.6 \text{ g cpd}} \times 100 = 18.4\%$

(d) Normal superphosphate: $3[Ca(H_2PO_4)_2 \cdot H_2O] + 7\ CaSO_4$

$$\%P = \frac{6 \times 30.97 \text{ g P}}{1709.5 \text{ g total}} \times 100 = 10.9\%$$

(e) Triple superphosphate: $10[Ca(H_2PO_4)_2 \cdot H_2O]$

$$\%P = \frac{20 \times 30.97 \text{ g P}}{2520.7 \text{ g total}} \times 100 = 24.6\%$$

26-32. From Exercise 31 it can be seen that the % P in triple superphosphate is about 2.5 times as great as in normal superphosphate. From this standpoint the term "triple superphosphate" seems to be a reasonably accurate statement.

Organic raw materials

26-33. Limestone cannot be considered as an important organic raw material, at least currently. The carbon-containing compound simplest to obtain from limestone is carbon dioxide. To convert CO_2 to organic compounds requires a reduction process, for example, reduction to carbon monoxide. Hydrocarbons and other organic compounds can be synthesized from carbon monoxide. However, no simple method exists currently for the initial reduction of CO_2 to CO. If an artificial method of conducting photosynthesis could be developed, then CO_2 could be converted to carbohydrates, as in green plants. But even in this case, the atmosphere might well be the source of CO_2, avoiding the need to decompose limestone.

26-34. Although much rubber produced currently is synthesized from organic chemicals derived from petroleum, the historic source of rubber has been from the latex of rubber trees. Thus, natural rubber is a forest product. Cellulose derived from wood pulp, a forest product, can be converted to rayon and used as a reinforcing cord in rubber tires. Even the carbon black used in tires can be obtained from forest products. The destructive distillation of wood, like that of coal, produces some gaseous products that will yield carbon black in their incomplete combustion. Only the sulfur required in the vulcanization of rubber and certain additives like zinc oxide cannot be obtained as forest products.

Polymer chemistry

26-35. In Chapter 24 we learned that an ester is formed by the condensation of a carboxylic acid and an alcohol (that is, by the elimination of a water molecule between them). Dacron is formed by the condensation of a *di*carboxylic acid with a *diol*. Thus it contains ester linkages. Because these ester linkages join large numbers of molecules, it is appropriate to call the polymer a *polyester*.

To determine the percent oxygen in Dacron, refer to the basic unit shown in Figure 26-19. It has the formula $C_{10}H_8O_4$.

$$\% \text{ O} = \frac{(4 \times 16) \text{ g O}}{192 \text{ g polymer}} \times 100 = 33.3\%$$

26-36. To form long-chain molecules every monomer must have at least two functional groups, one on each end of the molecule. Ethyl alcohol has only one functional group (-OH). It cannot participate in a polymerization reaction with dimethyl terephthalate.

26-37. The polymerization of 1,6-hexanediamine with sebacyl chloride proceeds in the following manner:

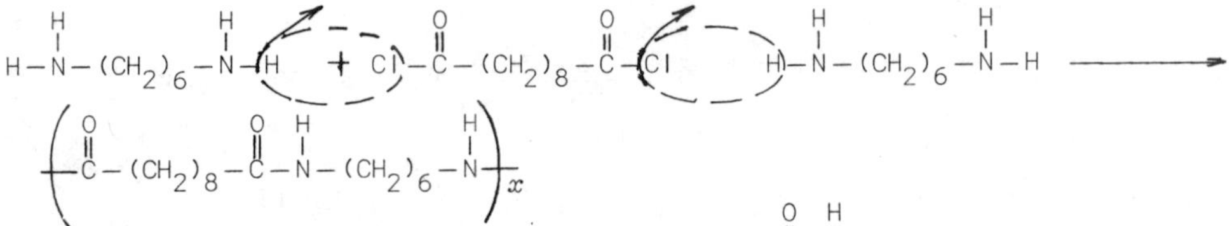

26-38. The distinctive feature of the polyamides is the $-\overset{\overset{\displaystyle O}{\|}}{C}-\overset{\overset{\displaystyle H}{|}}{N}-$ group. In naturally occurring materials we have referred to this as the peptide bond. Thus, synthetic polyamides resemble naturally occurring protein fibers, such as silk and wool.

26-39. (a)

(b)

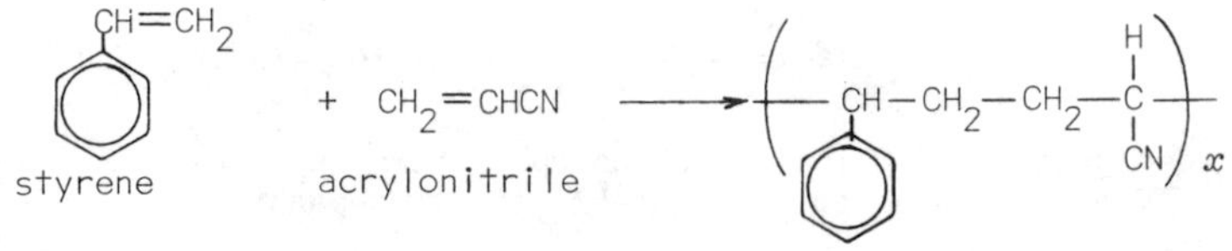

26-40. In a simple molecular substance like water, all molecules are identical (H_2O). Whatever number of these molecules is taken in one sample, any other sample with the same number of molecules has the same mass. The molecular weight--the mass in grams of one mole of molecules--is a unique quantity. Because the number of monomer units in a polymer chain is quite variable, individual polymer molecules may differ considerably in mass. Thus, the mass of a mole of these molecules must also be variable. We can only speak of this mass, this molecular weight, on a average basis.

Self-test Questions

1. (*c*) Hydrogen probably does not occur to any appreciable extent in the earth's core (comprised of Fe and Ni). In the earth's crust it occurs only to a limited extent (about 0.7% by mass; see Table 26-1). Hydrogen comprises about 11% of water, by mass, but about 75% of the mass of the universe.

2. (*a*) Aluminum is the most active of the four metals (recall Table 19-2). It should be the most difficult to produce by reduction of its ion. Therefore, it is the one that we should expect carbon not to be able to reduce.

3. (*b*) The process required in softening temporary hard water is the decomposition of HCO_3^- and the precipitation of $CaCO_3(s)$. This can be accomplished chemically by adding a base to the water

$$HCO_3^- + OH^- \longrightarrow H_2O + CO_3^{2-}$$ (followed by precipitation of $CaCO_3$). Of the species listed $CaCO_3$ is insoluble in water; NaCl and Na_2SO_4 yield aqueous solutions that are pH neutral; but CO_3^{2-} from Na_2CO_3 is strongly hydrolyzed, producing a basic solution.

4. (*b*) Limestone, $CaCO_3$, can be decomposed by heating

$$CaCO_3(s) \xrightarrow{\Delta} CaO(s) + CO_2(g)$$

The resulting CaO(s) can be treated with water to produce the base, $Ca(OH)_2$.

$$CaO(s) + H_2O \longrightarrow Ca(OH)_2(s)$$

Phosphate rock and bauxite are water insoluble. Rock salt (NaCl) produces an aqueous solution that is neutral (i.e., pH = 7).

5. (*d*) Carbonates are not used as fertilizers. Nitrogen compounds (e.g., NH_3) and phosphrus compounds (from phosphate rock) are. H_2SO_4 is used to convert phosphate rock to the more soluble superphosphate.

6. (*c*) Distillation is a physical process that permits the separation of hydrocarbon molecules, but it does not alter their basic structures. In the cracking process large molecules are broken down into smaller ones; and in alkylation, large molecules are synthesized from smaller ones. Reforming is a process in which bonds are rearranged (e.g., by converting single to double bonds) but without producing a significant change in the sizes of molecules.

7. (a) $2\ FeS(s) + 3\ O_2(g) \longrightarrow 2\ FeO(s) + 2\ SO_2(g)$

(b) $Mg(OH)_2(s) + 2\ H^+(aq) + \cancel{Cl^-(aq)} \longrightarrow Mg^{2+}(aq) + \cancel{Cl^-(aq)} + 2\ H_2O$

(c) $2\ HCO_3^-(aq) \longrightarrow H_2O + CO_2(g) + CO_3^{2-}(aq)$

$CO_3^{2-}(aq) + Ca^{2+}(aq) \longrightarrow CaCO_3(s)$

(d) $2\ NH_4Cl + Ca(OH)_2 \longrightarrow CaCl_2 + 2\ NH_3(g) + 2\ H_2O$

(e) $P_4(s) + 5\ O_2(g) \longrightarrow P_4O_{10}(s)$

$P_4O_{10}(s) + 6\ H_2O \longrightarrow 4\ H_3PO_4(l)$

8. $$\text{no. kg } F_2 = 1\ km^3 \times \frac{(1000)^3\ m^3}{1\ km^3} \times \frac{(100)^3\ cm^3}{1\ m^3} \times \frac{1.03\ g}{1\ cm^3} \times \frac{1\ lb}{453.6\ g} \times \frac{1\ t\ seawater}{2000\ lb} \times \frac{1\ g\ F^-}{1\ t\ seawater}$$

$$\times \frac{1\ g\ F_2}{1\ g\ F^-} \times \frac{1\ kg\ F_2}{1000\ g\ F_2} = 1.14 \times 10^6\ kg\ F_2$$

9. (a) A monomer is a relatively small organic molecule which, when joined to others of like kind (or in some cases another kind) yields a very large molecule called a polymer. The polymer consists of a basic structural unit (the monomer) repeated many times over.

(b) Free-radical addition polymerization and condensation polymerization are the two principal methods by which monomer units form a polymer. The free radical mechanism is a chain reaction in which the end of the polymer chain is a reactive intermediate (a free radical) that has the power to bond to another monomer unit and to convert that unit to a free radical while doing so. Thus, the chain can be perpetuated to great lengths before it is terminated.

In condensation polymerization two monomer units are linked together by eliminating a small molecule (such as H_2O) between them. If the structure of a monomer unit is such that it can link to two or more other monomers by this process, then a polymer chain can result.

(c) Chain initiation and chain termination are steps in free-radical addition polymerization. The former is the mechanism by which a chain is started and the latter, the mechanism by which the chain growth is stopped. Chain initiation in the example given in the text results from the production of free radicals in the decomposition of benzoyl perioxide (see Figure 26-20).

(d) An elastomer is a polymer that has rubber-like properties, particularly the ability to regain its shape following deformation. A fiber is a polymer that has high tensile strength along one axis. It is a thread-like polymer.

10. Air pollution control measures for automobiles must focus on a reduction of oxides of nitrogen, carbon monoxide, and unburned hydrocarbons. This can be brought about by more complete combustion and catalytic exhaust systems. Although some of the pollutants from power plants, such as oxides of nitrogen, are similar to those from automobiles, a most important pollutant from fossil-fuel power plants is sulfur dioxide. Air pollution control measures for these power plants must deal with a pollutant (SO_2) that is not a major source produced by automobiles.